ADVAN MATHEMATICS

AN APPLIED COURSE

Martin and Patricia Perkins

Unwin Hyman

Published in 1987 by Unwin Hyman Ltd
15–17 Broadwick Street
London W1V 1FP

British Library Cataloguing in Publication Data

Perkins, Martin
    Advanced mathematics: an applied course.
    1. Mathematics —— 1961–
    I. Title   II. Perkins, Patricia
    510   QA39.2

ISBN 0 7135 2820 6

Printed in Great Britain at
The Alden Press Ltd, Oxford

Preface

This is the second of two books designed to cover most Advanced Level single
subject Mathematics syllabuses. This volume provides a thorough treatment of the
Mechanics required at this level, together with chapters on probability and
elementary statistics. We hope that the inclusion of these additional topics will
enable students and teachers to plan a course of study to suit individual syllabus
requirements.

We are most grateful for permission to use questions from past G.C.E. Advanced
Level examinations. These are acknowledged as follows:
University of London University Entrance and Schools Examination
    Council (L)
The Associated Examining Board (AEB)
Joint Matriculation Board (JMB)
University of Cambridge Local Examinations Syndicate (C)
Oxford and Cambridge Schools Examination Board (O&C)
Oxford Delegacy of Local Examinations (O)
Southern Universities' Joint Board for School Examinations (SU)
Welsh Joint Education Committee (W)
We must again thank the staff of Messrs. Unwin Hyman, especially Caroline
Paines and Antonia Murphy, for both their enthusiasm and their patience. We have
also been helped and encouraged by many friends and colleagues.

M.L.P., P.P.

Contents

List of symbols

s.f.	significant figures
d.p.	decimal places
$\approx$	is approximately equal to
$<$	is less than
$\leqslant$	is less than or equal to
$>$	is greater than
$\geqslant$	is greater than or equal to
$\lvert x \rvert$	the modulus of x
$[x]$	the integral part of x
e^x, $\exp x$	exponential function of x
$\log_a x$	logarithm to the base a of x
$\ln x$	the natural logarithm of x, $\log_e x$
$\lg x$	the common logarithm of x, $\log_{10} x$
$\sin^{-1}$	inverse function of sin with range $[-\frac{1}{2}\pi, \frac{1}{2}\pi]$
$\cos^{-1}$	inverse function of cos with range $[0, \pi]$
$\tan^{-1}$	inverse function of tan with range $(-\frac{1}{2}\pi, \frac{1}{2}\pi)$
$\lim\limits_{x \to a} f(x)$	limit of $f(x)$ as x tends to a
∞	infinity
δ	small increment
$f'(x)$ or $\dfrac{dy}{dx}$	first derivative of $y = f(x)$
$f''(x)$ or $\dfrac{d^2 y}{dx^2}$	second derivative of $y = f(x)$
$\dot{x}, \dot{y}, \dot{\theta}, \ldots$	first derivative of $x, y, \theta, \ldots$ with respect to time
$\ddot{x}, \ddot{y}, \ddot{\theta}, \ldots$	second derivative of $x, y, \theta, \ldots$ with respect to time
PQ	vector represented by line segment $\overrightarrow{PQ}$
$\lvert \mathbf{PQ} \rvert$, PQ	magnitude of vector **PQ**
$\lvert \mathbf{a} \rvert$, a	magnitude of vector **a**

$\hat{\mathbf{a}}$	unit vector in the direction of $\mathbf{a}$
$\mathbf{i}, \mathbf{j}, \mathbf{k}$	unit vectors in the directions of the x-, y- and z-axes
$\mathbf{a} \cdot \mathbf{b}$	scalar product of $\mathbf{a}$ and $\mathbf{b}$
g	acceleration due to gravity (taken as 9.8 m s^{-2} unless otherwise stated)
μ	coefficient of friction
λ	angle of friction
	or modulus of elasticity
ω	angular velocity
$\varnothing$	empty set
$\mathscr{E}$	universal set
A'	complement of set A
$n(A)$	number of elements in the set A
$\cup$	union
$\cap$	intersection
$\in$	is an element of
$\mathbb{Z}$	set of integers
$\mathbb{Z}^+$	set of positive integers
$\mathbb{Q}$	set of rational numbers
$\mathbb{R}$	set of real numbers
$n!$	n factorial
$_nP_r$	number of permutations of r objects chosen from n
$_nC_r$	number of combinations of r objects chosen from n
$P(A)$	probability of event A
$P(A')$	probability that A does not occur
$P(A \cup B)$	probability of event A or event B (or both)
$P(A \cap B)$	probability of event A and event B
$P(A|B)$	probability of event A given B
$\displaystyle\sum_{r=1}^{n} f(r)$	$f(1) + f(2) + \ldots + f(n)$
$\dbinom{n}{r}$	the binomial coefficient: $_nC_r = \dfrac{n!}{r!(n-r)!}$ for $n \in \mathbb{Z}^+$, $\dfrac{n(n-1)\ldots(n-r+1)}{r!}$ for $n \in \mathbb{Q}$
$x_1, x_2, \ldots$	observations
$f_1, f_2, \ldots$	frequencies with which the observations $x_1, x_2, \ldots$ occur
$\bar{x}$	mean of observations $x_1, x_2, \ldots$
$\text{var}(x)$	variance of observations $x_1, x_2, \ldots$
s.d.	standard deviation
$X, Y, R, \ldots$	random variables
$x, y, r, \ldots$	values of the random variables $X, Y, R, \ldots$

$p(x)$	value of the probability function $P(X = x)$ of the discrete random variable X
$p_1, p_2, \ldots$	probabilities of the values $x_1, x_2, \ldots$ of the discrete random variable X
$f(x), g(x), \ldots$	value of the probability density function of the continuous random variable X
$F(x), G(x), \ldots$	value of the (cumulative) distribution function $P(X \leqslant x)$ of the continuous random variable X
$E(X), \mu$	expectation (or mean) of the random variable X
$\text{Var}(X), \sigma^2$	variance of the random variable X
$G(t)$	probability generating function for a random variable which takes the values $0, 1, 2, \ldots$
$B(n, p)$	binomial distribution, parameters n and p
$N(\mu, \sigma^2)$	normal distribution, mean μ and variance σ^2
Z	the standardised normal variable with distribution $N(0, 1)$
ϕ	probability density function for $N(0, 1)$
Φ	cumulative distribution function for $N(0, 1)$

The use of the symbols $=$ and $\approx$

In numerical work it is important to distinguish between exact values and approximate values. When giving exact answers we use the symbol $=$. For approximate results we use either the symbol $=$ (together with an appropriate phrase, such as 'by calculator', 'to 3 s.f.'), or the symbol $\approx$. The use of the symbol $\approx$ may show that a result has been obtained by an approximate method, but often indicates that a more accurate result obtained by calculator has been rounded to the given number of significant figures (or, in the case of angles, to the nearest tenth of a degree).

1 Vectors

1.1 Introduction to vectors

Some physical quantities, such as temperature, may be completely specified by a number referred to some unit of measurement, e.g. 25°C, 350°F. Such quantities, which have magnitude but which are not related to any definite direction in space, are called *scalar quantities*. Similarly, a number representing the magnitude of some physical quantity is called a *scalar*.

When measuring other quantities, such as wind velocity, it is necessary to give a direction as well as a number and a unit of measurement, e.g. 40 km/h from the north-east. These quantities, which have both magnitude and a definite direction in space, are called *vector quantities*. In general, a *vector* may be described as a number associated with a particular direction in space.

Any vector may be represented by a *directed line segment*, whose direction is that of the vector and whose length represents the magnitude of the vector.

The vector represented here is denoted by **PQ** in bold type (or PQ in manuscript). The *magnitude* or modulus of the vector is written |**PQ**| or PQ. The directed line segment joining P to Q is denoted by $\vec{PQ}$. However, since it is not usually necessary to distinguish between the line segment and the vector it represents, the notation $\vec{PQ}$ is in common use for both vector and line segment.

The magnitude of a vector is usually positive but may be zero, in which case the vector is called the *zero* or *null vector* and written **0** in bold type. The zero vector is the only vector with indeterminate direction.

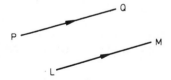

Two vectors are *equal* if they have the same magnitude and direction. Since PQ and LM are parallel and equal in length, **PQ** = **LM**.

1

A *displacement* is one of the simplest examples of a vector quantity. For instance, a car journey from a town A to a town B may be represented by a displacement vector **AB**. Its magnitude is the distance between A and B. Its direction is that of the straight line joining A to B.

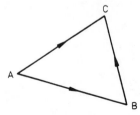

Let us suppose that a man drives from A to B and then from B to C. On another occasion he drives directly from A to C. Since the result of these two journeys is the same, we may write **AB** + **BC** = **AC**.

The displacement **AC** is the *sum* or *resultant* of the displacements **AB** and **BC**.

Consider now a journey from A to B, followed by the return journey from B to A. Since the result of these two journeys is a zero displacement, it is reasonable to write, **AB** + **BA** = **0** and **BA** = − **AB**.

All vectors represented by directed line segments may be manipulated in the same way as displacement vectors. For instance, given any three vectors **AB**, **BC** and **AC** represented by the sides of triangle ABC, we may write **AB** + **BC** = **AC**. A vector which has the same magnitude as **AB**, but the opposite direction, is denoted by **BA** or − **AB**.

Example 1 Simplify **EF** + **FG** − **HG**.

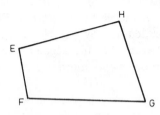

$$\mathbf{EF} + \mathbf{FG} - \mathbf{HG} = \mathbf{EG} - \mathbf{HG}$$
$$= \mathbf{EG} + \mathbf{GH}$$
$$= \mathbf{EH}.$$

It is often convenient to denote a vector by a single letter such as **a** in bold type (or $\underset{\sim}{a}$ in manuscript). Its magnitude is then written $|\mathbf{a}|$ or a.

Example 2 In the given diagram **PQ** = **a**, **RS** = **b** and **SQ** = **c**. Find expressions for **RQ**, **PS** and **PR** in terms of **a**, **b** and **c**.

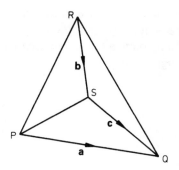

In $\triangle QRS,\quad \mathbf{RQ} = \mathbf{RS} + \mathbf{SQ} = \mathbf{b} + \mathbf{c}$
In $\triangle PQS,\quad \mathbf{PS} = \mathbf{PQ} + \mathbf{QS} = \mathbf{PQ} - \mathbf{SQ}$
$$= \mathbf{a} - \mathbf{c}$$
In $\triangle PQR,\quad \mathbf{PR} = \mathbf{PQ} + \mathbf{QR} = \mathbf{PQ} - \mathbf{RQ}$
$$= \mathbf{a} - (\mathbf{b} + \mathbf{c})$$
$$= \mathbf{a} - \mathbf{b} - \mathbf{c}.$$

More formally, *vector addition* is defined by the *triangle law*, as follows:

If two vectors **a** and **b** are represented by the sides $\overrightarrow{PQ}$ and $\overrightarrow{QR}$ of a triangle, then **a** + **b** is represented by the third side $\overrightarrow{PR}$.

In physics and mechanics it is sometimes more convenient to use the *parallelogram law* for vector addition, which states:

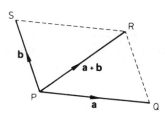

If two vectors **a** and **b** are represented by the sides $\overrightarrow{PQ}$ and $\overrightarrow{PS}$ of a parallelogram, then **a** + **b** is represented by the diagonal $\overrightarrow{PR}$. [Since the line segments $\overrightarrow{PS}$ and $\overrightarrow{QR}$ are equal in magnitude and direction, the two addition laws are equivalent.]

The *subtraction* of **b** from **a** may be defined as the addition of −**b** to **a**, i.e. $\mathbf{a} - \mathbf{b} = \mathbf{a} + (-\mathbf{b})$.

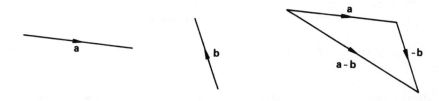

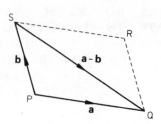

If the vectors **a** and **b** are represented by the sides $\overrightarrow{PQ}$ and $\overrightarrow{PS}$ of a parallelogram, then **a** − **b** is represented by the diagonal $\overrightarrow{SQ}$.

Exercise 1.1

1. Simplify (a) **PQ** + **QR** + **RS**,   (b) **AB** + **DE** + **CD** + **BC**,
    (c) **AC** − **BC**,   (d) **XY** + **YX**,
    (e) **MN** − **RP** − **PN**,   (f) **QT** − **QR** + **PR** − **ST**.

2. Given that *ABCDEF* is a regular hexagon, decide whether the following statements are true or false.
    (a) **BC** = **EF**,   (b) **BF** = **CE**,   (c) |**BE**| = |**CF**|,   (d) |**AB**| = |**DE**|,
    (e) **AC** and **DF** are in the same direction,   (f) **AD** is parallel to **EF**.

3. Given that *ABCDPQRS* is a cuboid lettered so that *AP*, *BQ*, *CR* and *DS* are edges, decide whether the following statements are true or false.
    (a) **PQ** = **DC**,   (b) **BR** = **PD**,   (c) |**RA**| = |**BS**|,   (d) |**PA**| = |**CR**|,
    (e) **DQ** and **AR** are in the same direction,   (f) **AQ** is parallel to **CS**.

If **a**, **b** and **c** are displacements of 1 km due east, 2 km due north and 1 km in the direction S 30° W respectively, find the magnitudes and directions of the displacements given in questions 4 to 6. (You may leave your answers in surd form.)

4. (a) 3**a**,   (b) 5**b**,   (c) −**c**,   (d) −$\frac{1}{2}$**b**.

5. (a) 2**a** + **b**,   (b) **b** + 2**a**,   (c) 2**a** − **b**,   (d) **b** − 2**a**.

6. (a) **a** + **c**,   (b) **a** + 2**c**,   (c) 2**a** + **c**,   (d) **a** − **c**.

7. The diagonals of a parallelogram *ABCD* intersect at *M*. If **AB** = **p** and **AD** = **q**, express in terms of **p** and **q** the vectors **AC**, **BD**, **AM** and **MD**.

8. In a regular hexagon *ABCDEF* **AB** = **a** and **BC** = **b**. Find expressions in terms of **a** and **b** for **DE**, **DC**, **AD** and **BD**.

9. In the pentagon *PQRST* **PQ** = **a** and **RS** = **b**. If **PT** = 2**RS** and **TS** = 2**PQ**, find expressions for **PR** and **QR** in terms of **a** and **b**.

1.2 Cartesian components and position vectors

Resolving a vector into *component vectors* means expressing it as a sum of two or more non-parallel vectors.

It is often convenient to resolve vectors into component vectors in the directions of the Cartesian coordinate axes. In three-dimensional work the third axis is the z-axis, which is constructed perpendicular to the x- and y-axes to form a *right-handed system*. This means that if we point the thumb of the right hand in the direction of the z-axis, then bend the fingers slightly, they will indicate the direction of a rotation from the x-axis to the y-axis.

Two standard ways of drawing these axes are shown below.

Any vector with magnitude 1 is called a *unit vector*. The unit vectors in the directions of the x-, y- and z-axes are denoted by **i**, **j** and **k** respectively.

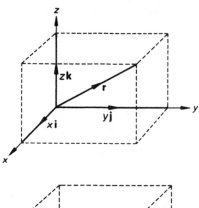

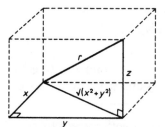

By constructing a cuboid with one diagonal representing **r** and sides parallel to the coordinate axes, we can demonstrate that there is a unique expression for any vector **r** of the form $x\mathbf{i} + y\mathbf{j} + z\mathbf{k}$. The scalars x, y and z are called the *components* of **r** in the directions of **i**, **j** and **k**, or simply the *Cartesian components* of **r**.

Since **i**, **j** and **k** are unit vectors, x, y and z are the lengths of the sides of the cuboid constructed here. Applying Pythagoras' theorem in the two right-angled triangles illustrated, we find that the magnitude of **r** is given by

$$r = \sqrt{(x^2 + y^2 + z^2)}.$$

Example 1   If $\mathbf{a} = 3\mathbf{i} + 2\mathbf{j} + 7\mathbf{k}$ and $\mathbf{b} = 2\mathbf{i} + 4\mathbf{j} - 5\mathbf{k}$, find $|\mathbf{a}|$ and $|\mathbf{a} - \mathbf{b}|$.

$|\mathbf{a}| = \sqrt{(3^2 + 2^2 + 7^2)} = \sqrt{(9 + 4 + 49)} = \sqrt{62}$

$\mathbf{a} - \mathbf{b} = (3\mathbf{i} + 2\mathbf{j} + 7\mathbf{k}) - (2\mathbf{i} + 4\mathbf{j} - 5\mathbf{k}) = \mathbf{i} - 2\mathbf{j} + 12\mathbf{k}$

$\therefore \quad |\mathbf{a} - \mathbf{b}| = \sqrt{(1^2 + \{-2\}^2 + 12^2)} = \sqrt{(1 + 4 + 144)} = \sqrt{149}.$

Since a represents the magnitude of a vector $\mathbf{a}$, the vector $\mathbf{a}/a$ has magnitude 1 and the same direction as $\mathbf{a}$. Thus the unit vector in the direction of a given vector $\mathbf{a}$ (sometimes denoted by $\hat{\mathbf{a}}$) may be expressed in the form $\mathbf{a}/a$.

Example 2   Find the unit vector in the direction of $\mathbf{a} = 2\mathbf{i} + 2\mathbf{j} - \mathbf{k}$.

$a = \sqrt{(2^2 + 2^2 + \{-1\}^2)} = \sqrt{(4+4+1)} = \sqrt{9} = 3$
$\therefore$ the unit vector in the direction of $\mathbf{a}$

$$= \tfrac{1}{3}(2\mathbf{i} + 2\mathbf{j} - \mathbf{k}) = \tfrac{2}{3}\mathbf{i} + \tfrac{2}{3}\mathbf{j} - \tfrac{1}{3}\mathbf{k}.$$

Taking a fixed point O as origin, the position of any point P can be specified by giving the vector $\mathbf{OP}$, which is then called the *position vector* of P.

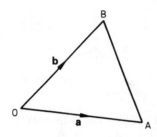

If A and B are two points with position vectors $\mathbf{a}$ and $\mathbf{b}$ respectively, then

$$\mathbf{AB} = \mathbf{AO} + \mathbf{OB} = -\mathbf{OA} + \mathbf{OB} = \mathbf{OB} - \mathbf{OA}$$
$$\therefore \quad \mathbf{AB} = \mathbf{b} - \mathbf{a}.$$

Hence the distance between the points A and B is given by $|\mathbf{b} - \mathbf{a}|$.

Consider now the mid-point M of AB.

$$\mathbf{AM} = \mathbf{MB}$$
$$\Rightarrow \mathbf{OM} - \mathbf{OA} = \mathbf{OB} - \mathbf{OM}$$
$$\Rightarrow \quad 2\mathbf{OM} = \mathbf{OA} + \mathbf{OB}$$
$$\Rightarrow \quad \mathbf{OM} = \tfrac{1}{2}(\mathbf{OA} + \mathbf{OB})$$

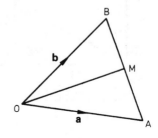

$\therefore$ | the position vector of the mid-point of AB is $\tfrac{1}{2}(\mathbf{a} + \mathbf{b})$.

When working in a Cartesian coordinate system, the point P with coordinates (x, y, z) has position vector $x\mathbf{i} + y\mathbf{j} + z\mathbf{k}$, where $\mathbf{i}$, $\mathbf{j}$ and $\mathbf{k}$ are unit vectors in the directions of the coordinate axes.

Example 3   The position vectors of points A and B with respect to an origin O are $\mathbf{a} = \mathbf{i} - 2\mathbf{j} + 7\mathbf{k}$ and $\mathbf{b} = 5\mathbf{i} + \mathbf{j} - 5\mathbf{k}$. Find (i) the distance between the origin and the point A, (ii) the distance between the points A and B, (iii) the position vector of the mid-point of AB.

(i)   the distance between the origin and the point A
$$= |\mathbf{a}| = \sqrt{(1^2 + \{-2\}^2 + 7^2)} = \sqrt{(1+4+49)} = \sqrt{54}.$$

(ii) $\mathbf{AB} = \mathbf{b} - \mathbf{a} = (5\mathbf{i} + \mathbf{j} - 5\mathbf{k}) - (\mathbf{i} - 2\mathbf{j} + 7\mathbf{k}) = 4\mathbf{i} + 3\mathbf{j} - 12\mathbf{k}$
   $\therefore$ the distance between the points A and B
   $= |\mathbf{b} - \mathbf{a}| = |4\mathbf{i} + 3\mathbf{j} - 12\mathbf{k}| = \sqrt{(16 + 9 + 144)} = 13.$

(iii) the position vector of the mid-point of AB
   $= \tfrac{1}{2}(\mathbf{a} + \mathbf{b}) = \tfrac{1}{2}(1 + 5)\mathbf{i} + \tfrac{1}{2}(-2 + 1)\mathbf{j} + \tfrac{1}{2}(7 - 5)\mathbf{k} = 3\mathbf{i} - \tfrac{1}{2}\mathbf{j} + \mathbf{k}.$

Exercise 1.2

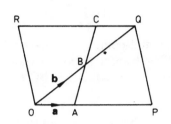

1. In the given diagram $\mathbf{OA} = \mathbf{a}$ and $\mathbf{OB} = \mathbf{b}$. The points P, Q and R are constructed so that $\mathbf{AP} = 2\mathbf{OA}$, $\mathbf{BQ} = \mathbf{OB}$ and $OPQR$ is a parallelogram. Express the following vectors as sums of component vectors in the directions of $\mathbf{a}$ and $\mathbf{b}$

(a) **OQ**,   (b) **QR**,   (c) **PR**,   (d) **AB**,   (e) **CQ**,   (f) **OC**.

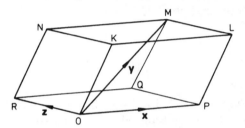

In the parallelepiped shown in the diagram $\mathbf{OP} = \mathbf{x}$, $\mathbf{OM} = \mathbf{y}$ and $\mathbf{OR} = \mathbf{z}$. In questions 2 and 3 resolve the given vectors into component vectors in the directions of of x, y and z.

2. (a) **PQ**. (b) **RQ**,   (c) **MN**,   (d) **LM**,   (e) **PR**,   (f) **RM**.

3. (a) **ON**, (b) **KM**,   (c) **OK**,   (d) **NP**,   (e) **KQ**,   (f) **LR**.

4. In quadrilateral $ABCD$, $\mathbf{AB} = 2\mathbf{i} - \mathbf{j}$, $\mathbf{BC} = 3\mathbf{i} + 4\mathbf{j}$, $\mathbf{AD} = \mathbf{i} + 5\mathbf{j}$ and M is the mid-point of CD. Express in terms of $\mathbf{i}$ and $\mathbf{j}$ the vectors
(a) **AC**,   (b) **BD**,   (c) **CD**,   (d) **DM**,   (e) **AM**,   (f) **BM**.

5. In tetrahedron $PQRS$, $\mathbf{PQ} = 3\mathbf{i} - \mathbf{j} - \mathbf{k}$, $\mathbf{PR} = -\mathbf{i} + 4\mathbf{j} + \mathbf{k}$ and $\mathbf{SQ} = 3\mathbf{i} - 4\mathbf{j} - 3\mathbf{k}$. The point T lies on RS produced such that $RS = ST$. Express in terms of $\mathbf{i}$, $\mathbf{j}$ and $\mathbf{k}$ the vectors
(a) **QR**,   (b) **PS**,   (c) **RS**,   (d) **PT**.

6. Find the magnitude of each of the following vectors
(a) $5\mathbf{i} - 12\mathbf{j}$,   (b) $-\mathbf{i} + 2\mathbf{k}$,   (c) $8\mathbf{j} + 6\mathbf{k}$,
(d) $2\mathbf{i} + \mathbf{j} - 2\mathbf{k}$,   (e) $2\mathbf{i} - 6\mathbf{j} + 3\mathbf{k}$,   (f) $-\mathbf{i} + 7\mathbf{j} - 5\mathbf{k}$.

7. Find unit vectors in the direction of
(a) $8\mathbf{i} - 4\mathbf{j} - \mathbf{k}$,   (b) $16\mathbf{i} - 8\mathbf{j} - 2\mathbf{k}$,   (c) $-8\mathbf{i} + 4\mathbf{j} + \mathbf{k}$.

In questions 8 to 10 take $\mathbf{a} = \mathbf{i} - 2\mathbf{j} + \mathbf{k}$, $\mathbf{b} = 3\mathbf{i} - \mathbf{j} - \mathbf{k}$, $\mathbf{c} = \mathbf{i} + 3\mathbf{j} - 2\mathbf{k}$.

8. Find (a) $|\mathbf{a}+\mathbf{b}|$,   (b) $|\mathbf{a}-\mathbf{b}|$,   (c) $|2\mathbf{b}-2\mathbf{a}|$.

9. Find (a) $|\mathbf{b}+\mathbf{c}|$,   (b) $|\mathbf{a}+\mathbf{b}+\mathbf{c}|$,   (c) $|5\mathbf{a}-\mathbf{b}+3\mathbf{c}|$.

10. Find unit vectors in the directions of
(a) $2\mathbf{b}-\mathbf{c}$,   (b) $5\mathbf{a}-5\mathbf{b}+3\mathbf{c}$,   (c) $5\mathbf{a}-\mathbf{b}+3\mathbf{c}$.

11. In a regular hexagon $OABCDE$ the position vectors of A and B relative to O are $\mathbf{a}$ and $\mathbf{b}$ respectively. Find expressions in terms of $\mathbf{a}$ and $\mathbf{b}$ for the vectors $\mathbf{AB}$ and $\mathbf{BC}$. Find also the position vectors of the points C, D and E.

12. In a quadrilateral $ABCD$ the point M is the mid-point of the diagonal BD. Given that the position vectors of A, B and C are $\mathbf{a}$, $\mathbf{b}$ and $\mathbf{c}$ respectively and that $ABCM$ is a parallelogram, find in terms of $\mathbf{a}$, $\mathbf{b}$ and $\mathbf{c}$ the vectors $\mathbf{BA}$, $\mathbf{BC}$ and $\mathbf{BM}$. Hence find the position vector of the point D.

13. The points A and B have position vectors $\mathbf{a}$ and $\mathbf{b}$ respectively. In each of the following cases, find the distance between A and B, the unit vector in the direction of $\mathbf{AB}$ and the position vector of the mid-point M of AB.
(a) $\mathbf{a} = 3\mathbf{i}-5\mathbf{j}-\mathbf{k}$, $\mathbf{b} = \mathbf{i}-\mathbf{j}+3\mathbf{k}$,
(b) $\mathbf{a} = -7\mathbf{i}+13\mathbf{j}$, $\mathbf{b} = 5\mathbf{i}-5\mathbf{j}-4\mathbf{k}$,
(c) $\mathbf{a} = \mathbf{i}-\mathbf{j}+3\mathbf{k}$, $\mathbf{b} = \mathbf{i}+2\mathbf{j}+2\mathbf{k}$,
(d) $\mathbf{a} = 5\mathbf{i}+4\mathbf{j}+\mathbf{k}$, $\mathbf{b} = -\mathbf{i}+\mathbf{j}-2\mathbf{k}$.

14. The points A, B and C have position vectors $\mathbf{a} = -\mathbf{i}+2\mathbf{j}+3\mathbf{k}$, $\mathbf{b} = 8\mathbf{i}+7\mathbf{j}-9\mathbf{k}$ and $\mathbf{c} = 2\mathbf{i}-3\mathbf{j}-\mathbf{k}$. Prove that the triangle ABC is right-angled and find its area.

Exercise 1.3 (*miscellaneous*)

1. If $\mathbf{a}$, $\mathbf{b}$ and $\mathbf{c}$ are vectors representing the edges of a parallelepiped, find vectors representing the four diagonals.

2. In a tetrahedron $OABC$ $\mathbf{OA} = \mathbf{a}$, $\mathbf{OB} = \mathbf{b}$ and $\mathbf{OC} = \mathbf{c}$. The points P and Q are constructed such that $\mathbf{OA} = \mathbf{AP}$ and $2\mathbf{OB} = \mathbf{BQ}$. The point M is the mid-point of PQ. Find, in terms of $\mathbf{a}$, $\mathbf{b}$ and $\mathbf{c}$, expressions for (a) $\mathbf{AB}$, (b) $\mathbf{PQ}$, (c) $\mathbf{CQ}$, (d) $\mathbf{QM}$, (e) $\mathbf{MB}$, (f) $\mathbf{OM}$.

3. If $\mathbf{a} = 2\mathbf{i}-4\mathbf{j}+2\mathbf{k}$ and $\mathbf{b} = 3\mathbf{i}+4\mathbf{j}-5\mathbf{k}$, find (a) the magnitudes of $\mathbf{a}$, $\mathbf{b}$ and $5\mathbf{a}+2\mathbf{b}$, (b) the unit vector in the direction of $\mathbf{a}+2\mathbf{b}$.

4. If P and Q are the points with position vectors

$$\mathbf{p} = -\mathbf{i}+3\mathbf{j}+2\mathbf{k} \text{ and } \mathbf{q} = \mathbf{i}-7\mathbf{j}+4\mathbf{k}$$

respectively, find (a) the distance PQ, (b) the unit vector in the direction of PQ, (c) the position vector of the mid-point of PQ.

5. Given that $\mathbf{a} = 6\mathbf{i}+(p-10)\mathbf{j}+(3p-5)\mathbf{k}$ and that $|\mathbf{a}| = 11$, find the possible values of p.

6. Given that the points A, B and C have position vectors $\mathbf{a} = \mathbf{i} - 2\mathbf{j} + 2\mathbf{k}$, $\mathbf{b} = 3\mathbf{i} - \mathbf{k}$ and $\mathbf{c} = -\mathbf{i} + \mathbf{j} + 4\mathbf{k}$, prove that the triangle ABC is isosceles.

7. In the parallelogram $OPQR$, the position vectors of P and R with respect to O are $6\mathbf{i} + \mathbf{j}$ and $3\mathbf{i} + 4\mathbf{j}$ respectively. M and N are the mid-points of the sides PQ and QR respectively. Find (a) the unit vector in the direction of $\overrightarrow{MN}$, (b) the magnitude of the vector $\overrightarrow{OM}$. (L)

8. In triangle OAB, $\mathbf{OA} = \mathbf{a}$ and $\mathbf{OB} = \mathbf{b}$. Points X, Y and Z are constructed so that $2\mathbf{AX} = 3\mathbf{AB}$, $\mathbf{OB} = \mathbf{BY}$ and Z is the point of intersection of OX and AY. If $\mathbf{AZ} = k\mathbf{AY}$, express $\mathbf{OZ}$ in terms of $\mathbf{a}$, $\mathbf{b}$ and k. Show that $\mathbf{OZ}$ is a scalar multiple of $3\mathbf{b} - \mathbf{a}$. Hence find the value of k and the position vector of Z.

9. In a parallelogram $OABC$, M is the mid-point of AB and P is the point of intersection of OM and AC. If the position vectors of A and B with respect to O as origin are $\mathbf{a}$ and $\mathbf{b}$, find the position vector of P.

10. The points $A(3, -2, 0)$, $B(-2, 5, -4)$ and $C(-1, 0, 4)$ are three vertices of a rhombus. Use vector methods to find the fourth vertex and the area of the rhombus.

2 Forces and equilibrium

2.1 Mathematical models

When applying mathematics to a practical problem, we try to set up what is called a mathematical model. In many cases this will take the form of a set of equations. However, it may also include diagrams, graphs or flow charts. As real situations are often very complicated, a mathematical model is usually a simplification of the original problem. Many scientific laws used in setting up systems of equations represent no more than good approximations to the true relationships between the quantities involved. Some factors governing a situation may be neglected altogether if their effect is likely to be small.

To set up a mathematical model we must first decide what factors are to be taken into account and what mathematical relationships are to be assumed, bearing in mind the degree of accuracy required in the result. We then find ways of giving numerical values to the variables involved, choosing suitable units of measurement.

To illustrate the process we now consider the problem of estimating the amount of petrol which will be consumed during a car journey. For a rough estimate we can use the distance, d miles, to be travelled and an approximate rate of petrol consumption for the car, c miles per gallon, based on past experience. We then assume that the amount of petrol used, P gallons, is proportional to the distance travelled and write $P = d \div c$. Clearly this single equation represents one of the simplest possible models which can be constructed to solve this problem. Many factors have been ignored, such as the load the car will be carrying, the type of road to be used, the traffic and weather conditions.

In elementary mechanics we set up simple models of practical situations in order to study the action of forces on various types of body. In early work we simplify the bodies involved as much as possible and take into account only the most important forces on them. For example, walls, floors and table tops are regarded as flat surfaces. A light rope or cable is assumed to be straight when pulled taut, whereas in practice, unless it is vertical, it hangs in a slight curve. We now list some of the other conventions observed when solving problems in mechanics.

A *particle* is a body of dimensions so small that its position in space can be represented by a single point.

A *lamina* is a flat object whose thickness is negligible but whose area is not.

A *rigid body* is one in which any pair of particles of matter remain a fixed distance apart. This means that rigid bodies are assumed to retain their shape when touching or colliding. For instance, when a sphere rests on a plane surface the area of contact is regarded as a single point.

A *light* string is taken to be weightless. If a body is suspended from one or more light strings, these can be represented by straight lines. Unless otherwise stated strings are assumed *inextensible*, i.e. of constant length.

A *smooth* surface is one which offers negligible frictional resistance to the motion of a body sliding across it. Wheels, pulleys, pivots and joints can also be described as smooth or frictionless.

For most purposes the surface of the earth is assumed to be flat and horizontal. Effects due to air currents and air resistance are usually ignored.

Exercise 2.1

Discuss the setting up of mathematical models in relation to various practical situations. Some problems for consideration are suggested below.

1.   To decide which is the quickest way to travel from home to work or college in the rush hour.

2.   To estimate the weekly cost of running a car.

3.   To budget for the household bills expected in the next three months.

4.   To plan orders of crisps, fruit, etc., for a college snack bar.

5.   To organise a school time-table.

6.   To plan a revision course for candidates taking a mathematics examination.

7.   To decide whether buying a domestic appliance such as a freezer or dish-washer will save a family (a) time, (b) money.

8.   To evaluate possible ways of saving energy at home or school, such as installing double glazing or switching off unnecessary lights.

2.2 The action of forces

The effect of a *force* is to set a body in motion or to change the speed and direction of its motion. If the forces on a stationary body cancel each other out, then the body is said to be in *equilibrium*. The two main branches of mechanics are *dynamics*, which is the study of the action of forces on bodies in motion, and *statics*, which is the study of forces in equilibrium. Closely related to dynamics is *kinematics*, which is the study of motion without reference to the forces involved.

A force may be completely specified by stating its magnitude, its direction and either its point of application or its line of action. Thus a force is a vector quantity associated with a particular point or line in space.

A force which is important in most problems is the gravitational attraction between the earth and any object close to it. This is the force which causes a body to fall to the ground and is called the *weight* of the body. Weight must not be confused with mass, which is not a force. The *mass* of a body is the amount of matter it contains. The weight of an object of fixed mass takes slightly different values at different points on the earth's surface. The gravitational pull on an object is much smaller on the surface of the moon, although its mass is unchanged.

When a body is attached to a string then the force acting along the string is called the *tension* in the string. The tension in a light string is assumed constant throughout its length. It is also possible to produce tension in rods and springs.

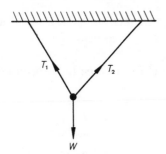

This diagram shows the forces on a particle of weight W, suspended from a beam by two light strings.

Another type of force called a *reaction* must be taken into account when two bodies are in contact. For a body resting on a smooth surface this force is referred to as the *normal reaction*, because its line of action is normal (i.e. perpendicular) to the surface. When two rough surfaces are in contact the total reaction is the sum of a normal reaction and a frictional force. [Friction will be considered further in Chapter 6.]

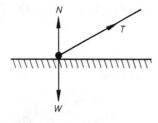

Shown here are the forces on a particle being pulled by a string across a smooth horizontal surface. The normal reaction is denoted by N.

Consider now a particle at rest on a rough inclined plane. As well as the normal reaction there will be a frictional force opposing the tendency of the particle to slide down the plane.

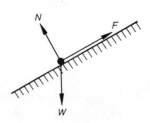

Force and other basic quantities are now usually measured in SI units, i.e. according to the Système International d'Unités. The SI unit of force is the newton, defined as the force needed to give a mass of 1 kilogramme an acceleration of 1 metre per second per second. [Students not familiar with the unit may find it helpful to remember that a cricket ball weighs approximately 1·5 N and a heavyweight boxer 800 N or more.]

We now give a table showing some of the SI units which are being used in this course.

Quantity	Name of unit	Symbol
length	metre	m
mass	kilogramme	kg
time	second	s
area	square metre	m^2
volume	cubic metre	m^3
velocity	metre per second	$m\,s^{-1}$ or m/s
acceleration	metre per second squared	$m\,s^{-2}$ or m/s^2
force	newton	N

[Note that 's' should never be added to a symbol to make a plural, because it is the symbol for second. For instance, 3 metres cannot be written as 3 ms because this means 3 milliseconds. Similarly the space in symbols for derived units is important, since without the space the symbol may have a different meaning. For example, $m\,s^{-1}$ means 'metre per second' but ms^{-1} means 'per millisecond'.]

Exercise 2.2

Draw diagrams to show the forces acting on a particle in each of the following situations.

1. At rest on a smooth horizontal plane.

2. At rest suspended from a fixed point by a string.

3. Sliding down a smooth inclined plane.

4. Sliding down a rough inclined plane.

5. Pulled across a rough horizontal plane by a string at an angle of 30° to the plane.

6. Held at rest on a smooth plane inclined at 25° to the horizontal by a string parallel to the plane.

7. Pulled up a rough plane inclined at 25° to the horizontal by a string parallel to the plane.

8.   Swinging at the end of a string, when the string is at an angle of $35°$ to the vertical.

9.   Sliding down the smooth inner surface of a hemispherical bowl.

2.3 Resultant forces

Since forces are vector quantities, they can be represented by directed line segments and added using either the triangle law or the parallelogram law as stated in §1.1. Thus, if $\mathbf{F}_1$ and $\mathbf{F}_2$ are two forces acting on a particle, their sum or resultant $\mathbf{R}$ may be represented by either the third side of a vector triangle or the diagonal of a parallelogram. A double arrow is used to emphasise that $\mathbf{R}$ is a resultant force rather than a third force acting on the particle.

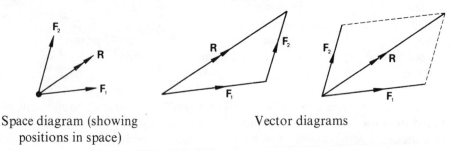

Space diagram (showing   Vector diagrams
    positions in space)

The magnitude and direction of the resultant can be found either by accurate scale drawing or by calculation. Although it is usually more convenient to use a vector triangle for this purpose, the parallelogram form of the vector diagram has the advantage that it shows the two forces and their resultant acting at a single point.

Example 1   Find the resultant of two forces of magnitudes $5\,\text{N}$ and $4\,\text{N}$ acting at right angles.

. Let R be the magnitude of the resultant and θ the angle it makes with the $5\,\text{N}$ force.

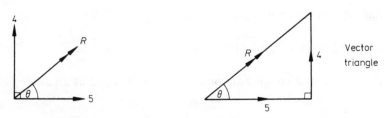

Vector
triangle

Using Pythagoras' theorem in the vector triangle,

$$R^2 = 5^2 + 4^2 = 25 + 16 = 41 \qquad \therefore \quad R \approx 6{\cdot}4$$
$$\tan\theta = 4/5 = 0{\cdot}8 \qquad\qquad\qquad \therefore \quad \theta \approx 38{\cdot}7°$$

The resultant is a force of magnitude $6{\cdot}4\,\text{N}$ at an angle $38{\cdot}7°$ to the $5\,\text{N}$ force.

Example 2 Two forces which act on a particle have magnitudes 2 N and 3 N. If the angle between their directions is 65°, find the resultant force on the particle.

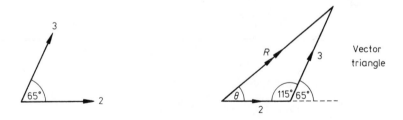

Vector triangle

By the cosine rule, $R^2 = 2^2 + 3^2 - 2.2.3 \cos 115°$
$$= 13 - 12 \cos 115°$$
$$\therefore \quad R \approx 4\cdot25$$

By the sine rule, $\dfrac{\sin \theta}{3} = \dfrac{\sin 115°}{R}$

$$\therefore \quad \sin \theta = \frac{3 \sin 115°}{R} \quad \text{and} \quad \theta \approx 39\cdot8°$$

Hence the resultant is a force of magnitude 4·25 N at an angle 39·8° to the 2 N force.

[Note that to achieve maximum accuracy the unrounded value of R should be used to find θ. The given results were obtained using a calculator, the value $R = 4\cdot251048811$ being stored in the memory.]

When the resultant of more than two forces is required a vector polygon can be constructed.

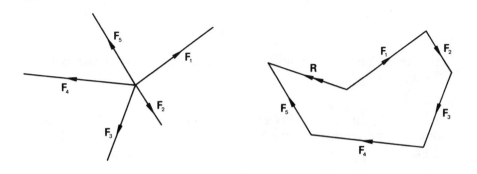

Example 3 Three forces, each of magnitude 10 N, act horizontally in the directions due west, N 30° E and S 50° E. Find the magnitude and direction of their resultant.

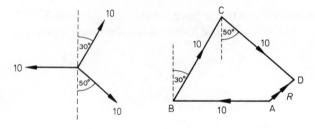
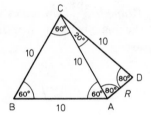

In the vector diagram, $\angle ABC = 60°$ and $AB = BC = 10$

$\therefore$ $\triangle ABC$ is an equilateral triangle.

Hence in $\triangle ACD$, $\angle ACD = 20°$ and $AC = CD = 10$

$\therefore$ $\triangle ACD$ is an isosceles triangle in which $\angle A = \angle D = 80°$ and $R = 2.10 \cos 80° \approx 3{\cdot}47$.

Thus the resultant force has magnitude 3·47 newtons and direction N 50° E.

The resultant of a set of forces can be found more quickly if the forces are expressed in terms of their Cartesian components. (See §1.2.)

Example 4   Find the magnitude and direction of the resultant of the forces represented by $2\mathbf{i} - 5\mathbf{j}$, $3\mathbf{j}$ and $\mathbf{i} + \mathbf{j}$, where $\mathbf{i}$ and $\mathbf{j}$ are unit vectors in the directions due east and due north respectively.

Let $\mathbf{R}$ be the resultant of the given forces and let θ be the angle between $\mathbf{R}$ and $\mathbf{i}$.

$$\mathbf{R} = (2\mathbf{i} - 5\mathbf{j}) + 3\mathbf{j} + (\mathbf{i} + \mathbf{j}) = (2 + 1)\mathbf{i} + (-5 + 3 + 1)\mathbf{j}$$
$$= 3\mathbf{i} - \mathbf{j}$$

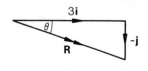

$R^2 = 3^2 + (-1)^2 = 10$

$\therefore$ $R = \sqrt{10} \approx 3{\cdot}16$

$\tan \theta = \frac{1}{3}$ $\therefore$ $\theta \approx 18{\cdot}4°$

Hence the resultant is represented by $3\mathbf{i} - \mathbf{j}$. Its magnitude is 3·16 and its direction is S 71·6° E.

Example 5   If $\mathbf{i}$, $\mathbf{j}$ and $\mathbf{k}$ are unit vectors parallel to the x-, y- and z-axes, find the magnitude of the resultant of the forces represented by $3\mathbf{i} - 2\mathbf{j} + 4\mathbf{k}$, $\mathbf{i} - 3\mathbf{k}$ and $2\mathbf{i} + 5\mathbf{j} + \mathbf{k}$.

The resultant is given by

$(3\mathbf{i} - 2\mathbf{j} + 4\mathbf{k}) + (\mathbf{i} - 3\mathbf{k}) + (2\mathbf{i} + 5\mathbf{j} + \mathbf{k})$,   i.e. $6\mathbf{i} + 3\mathbf{j} + 2\mathbf{k}$

$\therefore$ the magnitude of the resultant is

$|6\mathbf{i} + 3\mathbf{j} + 2\mathbf{k}| = \sqrt{(6^2 + 3^2 + 2^2)} = \sqrt{49} = 7.$

Example 6 Two forces **P** and **Q** act in the directions of the vectors $4\mathbf{i}+3\mathbf{j}$ and $\mathbf{i}-2\mathbf{j}$ respectively and the magnitude of **P** is 25 N. Given that the magnitude of the resultant of **P** and **Q** is also 25 N, find the magnitude of **Q**.

$$|4\mathbf{i}+3\mathbf{j}| = \sqrt{(4^2+3^2)} = \sqrt{25} = 5$$

∴ the force **P** can be represented in magnitude and direction by the vector $5(4\mathbf{i}+3\mathbf{j})$, i.e. $20\mathbf{i}+15\mathbf{j}$.

Since **Q** can be represented by a vector of the form $\lambda(\mathbf{i}-2\mathbf{j})$, we may write

$$\mathbf{P}+\mathbf{Q} = (20\mathbf{i}+15\mathbf{j})+\lambda(\mathbf{i}-2\mathbf{j}) = (20+\lambda)\mathbf{i}+(15-2\lambda)\mathbf{j}$$

∴ the magnitude of the resultant of **P** and **Q**

$$= \sqrt{\{(20+\lambda)^2+(15-2\lambda)^2\}} = 25$$

∴ $400+40\lambda+\lambda^2+225-60\lambda+4\lambda^2 = 625$

$$5\lambda^2-20\lambda = 0$$

∴ assuming λ is non-zero, $\lambda = 4$

Hence $\mathbf{Q} = 4(\mathbf{i}-2\mathbf{j})$ and $|\mathbf{Q}| = 4\sqrt{\{1^2+(-2)^2\}} = 4\sqrt{5}$.

Thus the magnitude of the force **Q** is $4\sqrt{5}$ N.

Exercise 2.3

1. The resultant of two forces **P** and **Q** is of magnitude R newtons and acts at an angle θ to the direction of **P**. Find R and θ, given that the magnitudes of **P** and **Q** and the angle between their directions are respectively
(a) 12 N, 5 N; 90°,
(b) 4 N, 7 N; 90°,
(c) 8 N, 11 N; 120°,
(d) 6 N, 10 N; 52°,
(e) 14 N, 9 N; 108°,
(f) 2 N, 7 N; 23°.

2. Find the angle between the lines of action of two forces of magnitudes 7 N and 11 N, given that their resultant is of magnitude 8 N.

3. The resultant of two forces **F** and **G** is a force of 20 N acting at an angle of 45° to the force **G**. Given that the magnitude of **G** is 12 N, find the magnitude and direction of **F**.

4. Two forces of magnitudes 7 N and 9 N act at an angle θ where $\sin\theta = 0\cdot4$. Find the magnitudes of the two possible resultants.

5. Find the resultant of three horizontal forces whose magnitudes and directions are 16 N in the direction N 70° W, 8 N in the direction N 20° E and 11 N in the direction S 70° E.

6. Four forces, each of magnitude 12 N, act horizontally in the directions N 30° E, S 60° E, S 15° E and S 75° W. Find the magnitude and direction of their resultant.

7. Horizontal forces of magnitudes 12 N, 9 N and 6 N act on a particle in the directions due north, due east and S 60° E respectively. Find the magnitude and direction of their resultant.

8. Find the magnitude and direction of the resultant of the forces represented by each of the following sets of vectors, where **i** and **j** are unit vectors in the directions due east and due north respectively.
(a) $2\mathbf{i}-\mathbf{j}$, $3\mathbf{i}$, $-\mathbf{i}+4\mathbf{j}$,
(b) $5\mathbf{i}-2\mathbf{j}$, $2\mathbf{i}+3\mathbf{j}$, $-\mathbf{j}$,
(c) $7\mathbf{i}+4\mathbf{j}$, $2\mathbf{i}-5\mathbf{j}$, $-3\mathbf{i}-2\mathbf{j}$,
(d) $\mathbf{i}+\mathbf{j}$, $-3\mathbf{i}-2\mathbf{j}$, $-3\mathbf{i}-4\mathbf{j}$.

9. If **i**, **j** and **k** are unit vectors parallel to the x-, y- and z-axes, find the magnitude of the resultant of the forces represented by
(a) $2\mathbf{i}-3\mathbf{j}$, $5\mathbf{i}+\mathbf{j}-3\mathbf{k}$ and $-3\mathbf{i}+4\mathbf{j}-\mathbf{k}$,
(b) $\mathbf{i}+6\mathbf{j}-3\mathbf{k}$, $8\mathbf{i}-\mathbf{j}-5\mathbf{k}$ and $3\mathbf{i}+3\mathbf{j}-\mathbf{k}$,
(c) $2\mathbf{j}-5\mathbf{k}$, $5\mathbf{i}-\mathbf{k}$ and $2\mathbf{i}+3\mathbf{j}+\mathbf{k}$.

10. Find the magnitude of the resultant of two forces of magnitudes 15 N and $4\sqrt{2}$ N acting in the directions of the vectors $3\mathbf{i}-4\mathbf{j}$ and $\mathbf{i}+\mathbf{j}$ respectively.

11. Two forces, each of magnitude $5P$ newtons, act in the directions of the vectors $7\mathbf{i}+\mathbf{j}$ and $\mathbf{i}-\mathbf{j}$. Show that their resultant acts in the direction of the vector $3\mathbf{i}-\mathbf{j}$. Given that the magnitude of the resultant is 20 newtons, find the value of P in surd form.

12. Two forces **F** and **G** act parallel to the vectors $3\mathbf{i}+\mathbf{j}$ and $\mathbf{i}+2\mathbf{j}$ respectively. If the resultant is a force of 10 newtons in the direction of the vector $3\mathbf{i}-4\mathbf{j}$, find the magnitudes of **F** and **G** in surd form.

2.4 Resolution into components

If p and q are two non-parallel lines in a plane, then any force **F** acting in that plane can be resolved into component forces **P** and **Q** in directions parallel to p and q by constructing a vector triangle or parallelogram as shown below.

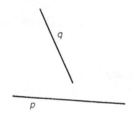 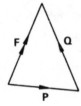 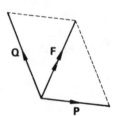

Consider now two forces and their resolution into components parallel to the lines p and q. Let $\mathbf{F}_1 = \mathbf{P}_1+\mathbf{Q}_1$, $\mathbf{F}_2 = \mathbf{P}_2+\mathbf{Q}_2$ and let the resultant of $\mathbf{F}_1$ and $\mathbf{F}_2$ be **R**.

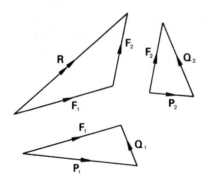

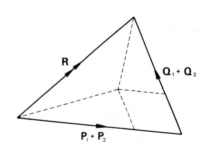

As shown in the diagrams,

$$\mathbf{R} = \mathbf{F}_1 + \mathbf{F}_2 = (\mathbf{P}_1 + \mathbf{Q}_1) + (\mathbf{P}_2 + \mathbf{Q}_2) = (\mathbf{P}_1 + \mathbf{P}_2) + (\mathbf{Q}_1 + \mathbf{Q}_2).$$

Thus the components of a resultant force are the sums of the corresponding components of the original forces. This property of forces and their components is often used to find resultant forces.

For most practical purposes forces are resolved into two components at right angles.

Example 1   Find the magnitudes of the horizontal and vertical components of a force of 6 N acting at an angle of 63° to the horizontal.

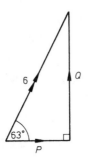

Let P and Q newtons be the magnitudes of the required components,

then $P = 6\cos 63° \approx 2{\cdot}72$

and $Q = 6\sin 63° \approx 5{\cdot}35$

$\therefore$ the magnitudes of the horizontal and vertical components are 2·72 N and 5·35 N respectively.

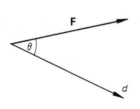

If a force $\mathbf{F}$ acts at an angle θ to a given direction d, then the quantity $F\cos\theta$ is called the *resolved part* of $\mathbf{F}$ in the direction d, or simply the component of $\mathbf{F}$ in the direction d. If θ is acute, $F\cos\theta$ is positive, but if θ is obtuse, $F\cos\theta$ is negative. Thus the sign of the resolved part indicates whether the direction of the component force is the same as d or opposite to d.

Example 2   A particle is sliding down a smooth plane inclined at an angle α to the horizontal. Find the components of the weight **W** and the normal reaction **N** down the plane and in the direction of an upward perpendicular to the plane.

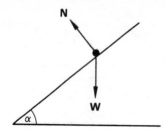
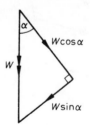

The components of **W** are $W \sin \alpha$ down the plane and $-W \cos \alpha$ along an upward perpendicular to the plane.

Since **N** acts at right angles to the plane, its component down the plane is 0 and its component along an upward perpendicular is N.

The resultant of a set of forces can now be found by resolving in two perpendicular directions.

Example 3   A small package of weight 20 N is attached to three light strings lying in the same vertical plane. If the tensions in the strings are as shown in the given diagram, find the resultant force on the package.

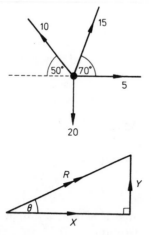

Let the resultant **R** have horizontal and vertical components X and Y. Resolving horizontally and vertically,

$$\rightarrow X = 5 + 15 \cos 70° - 10 \cos 50°.$$
$$\uparrow Y = 15 \sin 70° + 10 \sin 50° - 20$$

By calculator $X = 3 \cdot 70242$,
$$Y = 1 \cdot 755835.$$

$$\therefore \quad R = \sqrt{(X^2 + Y^2)} \approx 4 \cdot 10$$

and $\tan \theta = Y/X, \quad \theta \approx 25 \cdot 4°.$

Hence the resultant is a force of magnitude 4·10 N at an angle 25·4° to the horizontal.

It is sometimes convenient to express a set of forces in terms of perpendicular unit vectors **i** and **j**.

Example 4   A set of horizontal forces of magnitudes 3 N, 5 N, 6 N and 10 N act on a particle in directions due east, due south, N 30° W and N 60° E respectively. Find the magnitude and direction of the resultant.

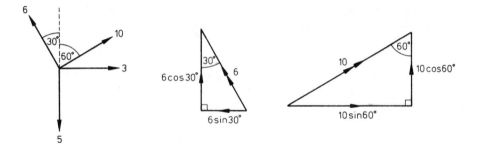

Let **i** and **j** be unit vectors in the directions due east and due north. The given set of forces can then be represented by

$$3\mathbf{i}, \; -5\mathbf{j}, \; -6\sin 30°\mathbf{i} + 6\cos 30°\mathbf{j} \quad \text{and} \quad 10\sin 60°\mathbf{i} + 10\cos 60°\mathbf{j}.$$

Hence the resultant **R** is given by

$$\mathbf{R} = 3\mathbf{i} + (-5\mathbf{j}) + (-3\mathbf{i} + 3\sqrt{3}\mathbf{j}) + (5\sqrt{3}\mathbf{i} + 5\mathbf{j}) = 5\sqrt{3}\mathbf{i} + 3\sqrt{3}\mathbf{j}$$

$$R^2 = (5\sqrt{3})^2 + (3\sqrt{3})^2 = 75 + 27 = 102$$

$$\therefore \quad R \approx 10 \cdot 1$$

$$\tan\theta = \frac{3\sqrt{3}}{5\sqrt{3}} = 0 \cdot 6 \quad \therefore \quad \theta \approx 31°.$$

The resultant is a force of magnitude 10·1 N and direction N 59° E.

Exercise 2.4

1. Find the magnitudes of the horizontal and vertical components of
(a) a force of 20 N acting at 40° to the horizontal,
(b) a force of 7 N acting at 78° to the horizontal,
(c) a force of 12 N acting at 36° to the vertical.

2. A particle is being pulled up a smooth plane, inclined at an angle α to the horizontal, by a string which makes an acute angle β with the plane. Find the resolved parts of the weight of the particle **W**, the normal reaction **N** and the tension in the string **T** (a) vertically upwards, (b) up the plane, (c) in the direction of a downward perpendicular to the plane.

3. A set of coplanar forces of magnitudes 12, 9, 15 and 16 newtons act on a particle in directions south-west, north, north-west and east respectively. Find the magnitude and direction of their resultant.

4. A particle is being pulled across a smooth horizontal plane by three strings. The directions of the strings are N 60° W, due north and N 30° E. If the tensions in the strings are of magnitude 15 N, 12 N and 10 N respectively, find the resultant force on the particle.

5. Four horizontal forces of equal magnitude act on a particle in the directions whose bearings are 050°, 100°, 250° and 290°. Calculate the bearing of the resultant.

6. *ABCDEF* is a regular hexagon. Forces of magnitude 2, 3, 4, 5 and 6 newtons act in the directions of **AB, AC, AD, AE** and **AF** respectively. If their resultant is a force of R newtons acting at an angle θ to **AB**, find R and θ.

7. *ABCD* is a rectangle in which AB is 3 m, BC is 4 m. Forces 3 N, 2 N, 10 N, 5 N act in the directions of **AB, AD, AC, BD** respectively. Find their resultant, giving the angle it makes with **AB**.

8. *ABCDE* is a regular pentagon. Find the magnitude of the resultant of forces 2 N, 3 N, 1 N, 4 N, 5 N in the directions of **AB, BC, CD, DE, EC** respectively.

9. A vertical flagpole of height 24 m is held in position by three straight wires fixed to its top and to points on the horizontal ground. The wires are of lengths 25 m, 30 m and 26 m and their fixing points are at bearings 060°, 150° and 270° respectively from the base of the pole. If the tensions in the wires are each 50 N, find (a) the vertical components of the tensions, (b) the horizontal components of the tensions. Hence find (c) the resultant force downwards caused by the wires, (d) the resultant horizontal force on the flagpole.

2.5 A particle in equilibrium

Forces on a particle are said to be in *equilibrium* if their resultant is zero. Thus when forces in equilibrium are resolved into components in two fixed directions, the sums of the components in each direction will be zero. This fact provides a basic approach to problem solving.

Example 1   A set of horizontal forces of magnitudes 5, 4 and 7 newtons act on a particle in the directions N 50° W, due north and S 80° E respectively. Find the magnitude and direction of a fourth force which holds the particle in equilibrium.

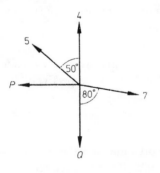

Let the components in the directions due west and due south of the fourth force **F** be P and Q respectively. Resolving in the directions west and south.

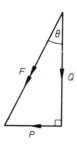

$$\leftarrow P + 5\sin 50° - 7\sin 80° = 0$$
$$\downarrow Q + 7\cos 80° - 5\cos 50° - 4 = 0$$
$$\therefore \quad P = 7\sin 80° - 5\sin 50°$$
$$Q = 4 + 5\cos 50° - 7\cos 80°.$$

By calculator $P = 3\cdot063436$,
$$Q = 5\cdot998404$$

$$\therefore \quad F = \sqrt{(P^2 + Q^2)} \approx 6\cdot74 \quad \text{and} \quad \tan\theta = P/Q, \quad \theta \approx 27\cdot1°.$$

Hence the fourth force is of magnitude 6·74 newtons in the direction S 27·1° W.

Example 2 A light inextensible string is attached to two points A and B on a horizontal beam. A smooth ring C of weight 10 N, which can move freely on the string, is held in equilibrium by a horizontal force P acting in the vertical plane containing A, B and C. Given that $\angle BAC = 36°$ and $\angle ABC = 48°$, find the magnitude of P and the tension T in the string.
    [Note that since the ring is smooth the tension is the same in both parts of the string.]

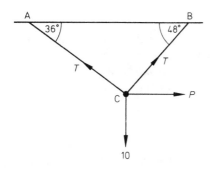

Resolving horizontally and vertically,

$$\rightarrow P + T\cos 48° - T\cos 36° = 0$$
$$\uparrow T\sin 48° + T\sin 36° - 10 = 0$$

$$\therefore \quad T = \frac{10}{\sin 48° + \sin 36°} \approx 7\cdot51$$

and $P = T(\cos 36° - \cos 48°) \approx 1\cdot05$.

Hence the magnitude of the horizontal force P is 1·05 N and the tension in the string is 7·51 N.

In §2.3 we saw that forces can be added by constructing a vector polygon. If a set of forces is in equilibrium the length of the side representing their resultant must be zero. Hence a set of forces in equilibrium can be represented by the sides of a closed polygon, often referred to as the *polygon of forces*.

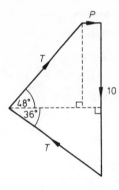

Example 2 could have been solved by drawing a polygon of forces. Using the right-angled triangles shown in the diagram,

$$T \sin 48° + T \sin 36° = 10$$
$$\text{and} \quad T \cos 48° + P = T \cos 36°$$

$\therefore$ as before we find that

$$T = \frac{10}{\sin 48° + \sin 36°},$$

$$P = T(\cos 36° - \cos 48°).$$

However, considering instead the angle properties of the figure, we could obtain the equivalent results,

$$P = 10 \tan 6° \text{ and}$$
$$2T \cos 48° \cos 6° = 10.$$

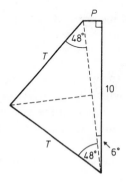

Of special interest are problems involving three forces in equilibrium, because in this case the vector diagram is simply a *triangle of forces*.

Example 3   A particle of weight $4W$ is attached to the end of a light inextensible string of length 2 m. The other end of the string is fixed to a point on a vertical wall. The particle is being held 1·2 m away from the wall by a horizontal force. Express the magnitudes of the horizontal force and the tension in the string in terms of W.

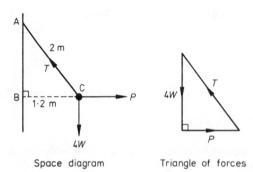

Space diagram   Triangle of forces

Let T be the tension in the string and P the horizontal force.

By Pythagoras' theorem in $\triangle ABC$,

$$AB^2 = AC^2 - BC^2 = 2^2 - (1·2)^2 = 2·56 \qquad \therefore \quad AB = 1·6$$

As shown in the diagrams, $\triangle ABC$ is similar to the triangle of forces

$$\therefore \quad \frac{T}{2} = \frac{P}{1\cdot2} = \frac{4W}{1\cdot6}.$$

Hence $T = 5W$ and $P = 3W.$

The magnitudes of the horizontal force and the tension in the string are $3W$ and $5W$ respectively.

Consider now three forces of magnitudes P, Q and R acting on a particle. If the angles between the forces are α, β and γ, then the exterior angles of the triangle of forces are also α, β and γ.

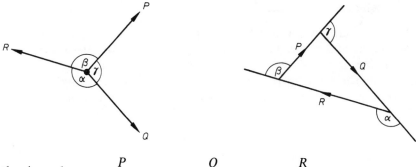

By the sine rule, $\dfrac{P}{\sin(180° - \alpha)} = \dfrac{Q}{\sin(180° - \beta)} = \dfrac{R}{\sin(180° - \gamma)}$

$$\therefore \quad \boxed{\frac{P}{\sin \alpha} = \frac{Q}{\sin \beta} = \frac{R}{\sin \gamma}}$$

This result is called *Lami's*† *Theorem.* It is often useful in solving three force problems in which angles rather than lengths are known.

Example 4   A small block of weight 20 N is at rest on a smooth plane inclined at an angle of 25° to the horizontal. The block is being held in position by a light rope. Given that the angle between the rope and the plane is 15°, find the magnitudes of the tension T in the rope and of the reaction R with the plane.

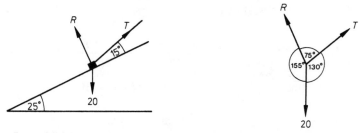

† *Lami, Bernard* (1640–1715) French scholar. He made a substantial contribution to the philosophical and mathematical theories of his time. His work on equilibrium appears in the *Traité de Mécanique* (1679).

By Lami's theorem, $\dfrac{T}{\sin 155°} = \dfrac{R}{\sin 130°} = \dfrac{20}{\sin 75°}$

$\therefore \quad T = \dfrac{20 \sin 155°}{\sin 75°} \approx 8\cdot75$ and $R = 20 \sin 130°/\sin 75° \approx 15\cdot9$

The tension in the rope is 8·75 N and the normal reaction with the plane is 15·9 N.

[This problem could, of course, also be solved by resolving the forces parallel and perpendicular to the plane or by drawing a triangle of forces.]

Problems involving more than one particle are often solved by considering the forces on each particle separately.

Example 5   A light inextensible string is suspended from two points A and D in the same horizontal plane. Particles of weight W and $2W$ are attached to the string at points B and C respectively. If AB and CD are inclined at 60° to the horizontal, find in terms of W the tensions T_1, T_2, T_3 in the strings AB, BC and CD respectively. Find also the angle θ, which BC makes with the horizontal.

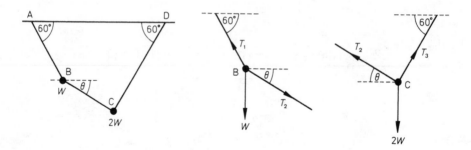

Resolving the forces on the particle at B

horizontally $\rightarrow T_2 \cos\theta - T_1 \cos 60° = 0$ (1)
vertically $\uparrow T_1 \sin 60° - T_2 \sin\theta - W = 0$ (2)

Resolving the forces on the particle at C

horizontally $\rightarrow T_3 \cos 60° - T_2 \cos\theta = 0$ (3)
vertically $\uparrow T_3 \sin 60° + T_2 \sin\theta - 2W = 0$ (4)

Adding (1) to (3): $T_3 \cos 60° - T_1 \cos 60° = 0$ $\therefore \quad T_1 = T_3$
Adding (2) to (4): $T_1 \sin 60° + T_3 \sin 60° - 3W = 0$

$\therefore \quad T_1 + T_3 = 3W/\sin 60° = 2\sqrt{3}W$ and $T_1 = T_3 = \sqrt{3}W$

Using (1) $T_2 \cos\theta = \sqrt{3}W . \cos 60° = \dfrac{\sqrt{3}}{2} W$

Using (2) $T_2 \sin\theta = \sqrt{3}W . \sin 60° - W = \dfrac{1}{2} W$

By squaring and adding these results:

$$T_2^2 = T_2^2(\cos^2\theta + \sin^2\theta) = \tfrac{3}{4}W^2 + \tfrac{1}{4}W^2 = W^2$$

Dividing: $\tan\theta = T_2\sin\theta/T_2\cos\theta = \dfrac{1}{2}W \Big/ \dfrac{\sqrt{3}}{2}W = 1/\sqrt{3}$

$$\therefore \quad T_2 = W \quad \text{and} \quad \theta = 30°.$$

Hence the tensions in the strings AB, BC and CD are $\sqrt{3}W$, W and $\sqrt{3}W$ respectively and BC is inclined at 30° to the horizontal.

Exercise 2.5

1.   A set of horizontal forces of magnitude 20 N, 12 N and 30 N act on a particle in the directions due south, due east and N 40° E respectively. Find the magnitude and direction of a fourth force which holds the particle in equilibrium.

2.   A set of four horizontal forces in equilibrium act in directions whose bearings are 020°, 110°, 230° and 320°. If the magnitudes of the forces are 8, 12, P and Q newtons respectively, find the values of P and Q.

3.   A smooth ring C of weight 15 N can move freely on a light inextensible string attached to two fixed points A and B in the same horizontal line. A horizontal force of magnitude P holds the ring in equilibrium, such that AC is vertical and $\angle ABC = 30°$. Find the value of P using a polygon of forces.

4.   A set of six forces in equilibrium act in the directions of the sides $\vec{AB}$, $\vec{BC}$, $\vec{CD}$, $\vec{DE}$, $\vec{EF}$ and $\vec{FA}$ of a regular hexagon. If the magnitudes of the forces are 7, 4, 10, 5, P and Q newtons respectively, use a polygon of forces to find the values of P and Q.

5.   A body of weight 20 newtons is held at rest on a smooth plane inclined at 60° to the horizontal by a force of magnitude P newtons. Find P given that the force is (a) horizontal, (b), vertical, (c) parallel to the plane.

6.   One end of a light inextensible string of length 75 cm is fixed to a point on a vertical pole. A particle of weight 12 N is attached to the other end of the string. The particle is held 21 cm away from the pole by a horizontal force. Find the magnitude of this force and the tension in the string.

7.   A small object of weight 4 N is suspended from a fixed point by a string. The object is held in equilibrium, with the string at an angle of 25° to the vertical, by a horizontal force. Find the magnitude of this force and the tension in the string.

8.   A particle P of weight 50 N is hanging in equilibrium supported by two strings inclined at 20° and 40° to the vertical. Find the tensions in the strings.

9.   A particle of weight $10W$ is held at rest on a smooth plane inclined at 30° to the horizontal by a light string. Find the tension in the string and the reaction

between the particle and the plane if (a) the string is parallel to the plane, (b) the string is at an angle of 30° to the plane.

10. A particle of weight 2 N hangs on a string. The particle is pulled to one side by a force of magnitude 3 N acting at an angle of 20° below the horizontal. Find the tension in the string and the inclination of the string to the vertical.

11. A particle P of weight $10W$ is supported by two light inextensible strings attached to fixed points X and Y which lie in the same horizontal plane. Given that $PX = 36$ cm, $PY = 48$ cm and $XY = 60$ cm, find the tension in each string.

12. A light inextensible string passes through a smooth ring fixed at a point P. Particles A and B of weights 10 N and 20 N respectively are attached to the ends of the string. The system is held in equilibrium by a horizontal force acting on the particle A. Find the magnitude of this force. Find also the magnitude and direction of the resultant force on the ring due to the tension in the string.

13. A light inextensible string ABC is fixed at the point A. Two particles each of weight W are attached to the string at B and C. The system is held in equilibrium by a horizontal force of magnitude $2W$ acting on the particle at C. Find (a) the tensions in BC and AB, (b) the inclinations of BC and AB to the vertical.

14. Two smooth straight rods XY and XZ are fixed at 45° to the vertical and at right angles to each other. Two small beads A and B, each of weight W, are free to slide on the rods XY and XZ respectively. The beads are connected by a light inextensible string, to the mid-point of which is attached a particle C of weight $2W$. Find the reaction between the bead A and the rod XY, the tension in the string AC and its inclination to the horizontal when the system is in equilibrium.

15. $ABCD$ is a light inextensible string. The ends A and D are fixed so that the line AD is horizontal. Particles of weight $3W$ and $4W$ are attached to the string at the points B and C respectively. Find the tensions in the strings AB, BC and CD given that (a) $\angle DAB = 45°$ and $\angle ABC = 150°$, (b) $\angle DAB = 45°$ and the strings BC and DC are equally inclined to the horizontal.

Exercise 2.6 (miscellaneous)

1. Find the angle between the lines of action of two forces of magnitudes 15 N and 9 N, given that their resultant is a force of magnitude 20 N.

2. Two forces of magnitude $3P$ and $4P$ newtons act on a particle. The magnitude of their resultant is 20 newtons. When one of the forces is reversed the magnitude of the resultant is halved. Calculate the value of P and the original angle between the forces.

3. Two forces of magnitude 5 N and 3 N act on a particle. Their resultant acts at an angle θ to the direction of the 5 N force. Find the range of possible values of θ.

4. Given that **i** and **j** are unit vectors in the directions due east and due north respectively, find the magnitude and direction of the resultant of the forces represented by the vectors $3\mathbf{i} - \mathbf{j}$, $-2\mathbf{i}$, $5\mathbf{i} + 7\mathbf{j}$ and $\mathbf{i} - 2\mathbf{j}$.

5. Two concurrent forces **X** and **Y** have resultant **R**. If $X = R$ and the angle between **R** and **Y** is α, prove (a) $Y = 2X \cos \alpha$, (b) the angle between **X** and **Y** is $180° - \alpha$.

6. A force of magnitude 10 N parallel to the vector $4\mathbf{i} + 3\mathbf{j}$ is the resultant of two forces parallel respectively to the vectors $2\mathbf{i} + \mathbf{j}$, $\mathbf{i} + \mathbf{j}$. Find the magnitudes of these two forces. (L)

7. The point O is the centre of a regular hexagon $ABCDEF$. Forces of magnitude 7, 3, 10, 9, 6 and 2 newtons act on a particle at O in the directions of **OA**, **OB**, **OC**, **OD**, **OE** and **OF** respectively. Find the magnitude of the resultant and show that it acts in the direction of **AC**.

8. Find the bearing of the resultant of five horizontal forces of equal magnitude which act in the directions whose bearings are 070°, 130°, 160°, 220° and 310°.

9. A set of four forces on a particle are in equilibrium. If **i** and **j** are unit vectors in the directions due east and due north respectively, three of the forces are represented by the vectors $\mathbf{i} + \mathbf{j}$, $3\mathbf{i} - 2\mathbf{j}$ and $2\mathbf{i} + 3\mathbf{j}$. Find the magnitude and direction of the fourth force.

10. A particle is in equilibrium under the action of a set of five horizontal forces. If four of the forces are of magnitude 6 N, 11 N, 8 N and 15 N acting in the directions N 72° W, N 15° W, N 35° E and S 63° E respectively, find the magnitude and direction of the fifth force.

11. A particle P of weight $10W$ is hanging in equilibrium from two strings PA and PB. If $\angle APB = 90°$ and the tensions in the strings are T and $2T$, find T in terms of W.

12. A particle P of weight 50 N is supported by two light inextensible strings attached to fixed points A and B. Given that A and B lie 2 m apart in the same horizontal plane and that $AP = 2$ m, $PB = 1$ m, find the tension in each string.

13. A small block of weight 20 N is held at rest on a smooth plane inclined at 20° to the horizontal by a string which makes an angle θ with the plane. If the tension in the string is 10 N, find the value of θ and the magnitude of the reaction between the block and the plane.

14. Show that the least force required to keep a particle of weight W in equilibrium on a smooth plane inclined at an angle α to the horizontal is of magnitude $W \sin \alpha$ and parallel to the plane.

15. The ends of a light inextensible string of length 80 cm are fixed to points A and B, which are 48 cm apart. A smooth ring C, of weight 5 N, which can move freely along the string, hangs in equilibrium. Find the tension in the string if (a) AB is horizontal, (b) AB is inclined at 60° to the horizontal.

16. One end of a light inextensible string is attached to a fixed point on a smooth straight wire inclined at 30° to the horizontal. The other end of the string is attached to a light ring which slides freely on the wire. A smooth bead of weight W, which is threaded on the string, is also free to slide. Find, in terms of W, the tension in the string when the system is in equilibrium.

17. A particle of weight 2 N is attached to a light string ABC at the point B. The ends A and C are threaded through two fixed smooth rings at points X and Y respectively, where the line XY makes an angle θ with the horizontal. A particle of weight 3 N is then attached to the string at A and a particle of weight 4 N at C. Show that equilibrium is possible only if Y lies above X and $1/4 < \sin\theta < 11/16$.

18. Two rods OA, OB are fixed in a vertical plane with O uppermost, each rod making an acute angle α with the vertical. Two smooth rings of equal weight W, which can slide one on each rod, are connected by a light inextensible string, upon which slides a third smooth ring of weight $2W$. Show that, in the symmetrical position of equilibrium, the angle between the two straight pieces of the string is 2β, where $\tan\beta = 2\cot\alpha$. Show that the tension in the string is $W\sqrt{(1+4\cot^2\alpha)}$ and that the reaction between the rings and the rods is $2W\operatorname{cosec}\alpha$. (W)

19. Four packages, each of weight 20 N, are fastened to a light rope at points B, C, D and E. The rope is attached to two fixed points A and F, which lie in the same horizontal plane. The points B and C are 1·2 m and 2·2 m respectively below the line AF and $AB = BC = CD = DE = EF$. Find the tension in the rope CD and the length of the rope.

20. Construct a flow chart for a procedure to find the resultant of a set of n horizontal forces, printing out its magnitude and bearing. Assume that the data is provided in the form of a list giving the magnitude x newtons and the bearing $y°$ of each force, where $x > 0$ and $0 \leqslant y < 360$.

3 Relative motion

3.1 Velocity and acceleration as vectors

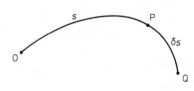

The diagram shows the path of a moving particle. The motion begins at the point O and after time t the particle reaches the point P. The *distance* travelled is the length s of the path OP. The *speed* of the particle is the rate at which it moves along its path. If the particle moves a further distance δs to a point Q in time δt, then its average speed in the motion from P to Q is $\delta s/\delta t$.

Hence the speed of the particle as it passes through $P = \lim\limits_{\delta t \to 0} \dfrac{\delta s}{\delta t} = \dfrac{ds}{dt}$.

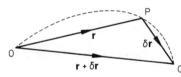

The *displacement* of the particle from O at time t is the vector $\mathbf{r}$ represented by the line segment $\overrightarrow{OP}$. The *velocity* of the particle is the rate of change of its displacement. Thus the average velocity of the particle in its motion from P to Q can be expressed as $\delta \mathbf{r}/\delta t$. Hence the velocity of the particle as it passes through

$P = \lim\limits_{\delta t \to 0} \dfrac{\delta \mathbf{r}}{\delta t} = \dfrac{d\mathbf{r}}{dt}$.

By considering the magnitude and direction of $\overrightarrow{PQ}$ as $\delta t \to 0$, we see that the magnitude of the velocity is the speed of the particle and the direction of the velocity is the direction of motion.

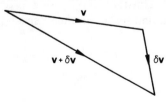

The *acceleration* of a particle is defined as the rate of change of its velocity. If the velocities of a particle at times t and $t+\delta t$ are $\mathbf{v}$ and $\mathbf{v}+\delta \mathbf{v}$ respectively, then the acceleration at

time $t = \lim\limits_{\delta t \to 0} \dfrac{\delta \mathbf{v}}{\delta t} = \dfrac{d\mathbf{v}}{dt}$.

[Note that unless a particle is moving in a straight line the magnitude of its acceleration does *not* correspond to the rate of change of its speed and the direction of the acceleration is *not* the same as the direction of motion.]

It is clear from these definitions that distance and speed are scalar quantities, whereas displacement, velocity and acceleration are vector quantities. We now give some examples illustrating the relationships between them. Unless otherwise stated we will assume that the magnitudes of vector quantities are measured in the appropriate SI units.

Example 1   A particle moving with uniform velocity $4\mathbf{i}+3\mathbf{j}$ passes through the point A whose position vector with respect to the origin O is $3\mathbf{i}-\mathbf{j}$. Find (a) the speed of the particle, (b) the distance of the particle from the origin 3 seconds after it passes through A.

(a) The speed of the particle
$$= |4\mathbf{i}+3\mathbf{j}| = \sqrt{(4^2+3^2)} = 5.$$
(b) After 3 seconds the displacement of the particle from A
$$= 3(4\mathbf{i}+3\mathbf{j}) = 12\mathbf{i}+9\mathbf{j}$$
$\therefore$ after 3 seconds its position vector
$$= (12\mathbf{i}+9\mathbf{j})+(3\mathbf{i}-\mathbf{j}) = 15\mathbf{i}+8\mathbf{j}.$$
Hence the distance of the particle from the origin
$$= |15\mathbf{i}+8\mathbf{j}| = \sqrt{(15^2+8^2)} = \sqrt{289} = 17.$$

Example 2   A particle moves for 2 seconds with velocity $6\mathbf{i}+3\mathbf{j}-2\mathbf{k}$, then for 3 seconds with velocity $\mathbf{i}-2\mathbf{j}-2\mathbf{k}$. Find (a) the average velocity and (b) the average speed of the particle during the motion.

(a) The total displacement of the particle
$$= 2(6\mathbf{i}+3\mathbf{j}-2\mathbf{k})+3(\mathbf{i}-2\mathbf{j}-2\mathbf{k}) = 15\mathbf{i}-10\mathbf{k}$$
$\therefore$ the average velocity during the 5 seconds of the motion is $3\mathbf{i}-2\mathbf{k}$.
(b) The distance moved in the first 2 seconds
$$= 2|6\mathbf{i}+3\mathbf{j}-2\mathbf{k}| = 2\sqrt{(6^2+3^2+2^2)} = 14.$$
The distance moved in the next 3 seconds
$$= 3|\mathbf{i}-2\mathbf{j}-2\mathbf{k}| = 3\sqrt{(1^2+2^2+2^2)} = 9$$
Hence the particle moves 23 m in 5 seconds
$\therefore$ the average speed during the motion is $4 \cdot 6 \, \mathrm{m\,s^{-1}}$.

Example 3 A particle moves in a plane with constant acceleration given by $-2\mathbf{i}+\mathbf{j}$. If the initial velocity of the particle is $3\mathbf{i}$, find its speed after 1 second and after 3 seconds.

The velocity of the particle after 1 second
$$= 3\mathbf{i}+(-2\mathbf{i}+\mathbf{j}) = \mathbf{i}+\mathbf{j}$$
$\therefore$ the speed of the particle after 1 second
$$= |\mathbf{i}+\mathbf{j}| = \sqrt{(1^2+1^2)} = \sqrt{2}.$$

The velocity of the particle after 3 seconds
$$= 3\mathbf{i} + 3(-2\mathbf{i} + \mathbf{j}) = -3\mathbf{i} + 3\mathbf{j}$$
$\therefore$ the speed of the particle after 3 seconds
$$= |-3\mathbf{i} + 3\mathbf{j}| = 3|-\mathbf{i} + \mathbf{j}| = 3\sqrt{2}.$$

Resultant velocities and accelerations can be found by the methods used to add forces in Chapter 2.

Example 4   An aircraft is heading due south with a velocity of 300 km/h. It is also being blown by a wind with velocity 45 km/h from the direction S 70°W. Find the velocity of the aircraft relative to the ground.

Let R km/h be the resultant velocity and θ the angle it makes with due south.
By the cosine rule, $R^2 = 300^2 + 45^2 - 2.300.45 \cos 70°$
$$\therefore \qquad R \approx 288$$

By the sine rule, $\dfrac{\sin \theta}{45} = \dfrac{\sin 70°}{R}$

$\therefore$ $\sin \theta = \dfrac{45 \sin 70°}{R}$ and $\theta \approx 8.5°$.

Hence the velocity of the aircraft relative to the ground is 288 km/h in the direction S 8·5° E.

Sums of three or more velocities can be found using a vector polygon. However, it is often more convenient to resolve the velocities in suitable directions and then add the components.

Example 5   A ship travelling through the water at 15 km/h is steering a course N 20°E. It is also being carried by a current with velocity 3 km/h to the north west. If a man is walking across the deck of the ship directly from port to starboard at 5 km/h, find his velocity relative to the shore.

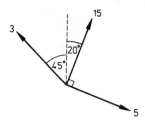

Let U and V be the components of the man's velocity along the perpendicular to the course steered by the ship, then resolving in those directions,
$$\nearrow \quad U = 15 + 3 \cos 65°$$
$$\rightarrow \quad V = 5 - 3 \sin 65°$$

$$R = \sqrt{(U^2 + V^2)} \approx 16{\cdot}4$$
$$\tan\theta = V/U \quad \therefore \quad \theta \approx 8°$$

Hence the man's velocity relative to the shore is 16·4 km/h in the direction N 28° E.

Exercise 3.1

1. A particle starts from a point A with position vector $\mathbf{i}-4\mathbf{j}$ and moves with velocity $12\mathbf{i}+5\mathbf{j}$. Find the speed of the particle and its position vector after 2 seconds.

2. A particle moves from A to B in 5 seconds. If the position vectors of A and B are $7\mathbf{i}-12\mathbf{j}$ and $-3\mathbf{i}+8\mathbf{j}$ respectively, find the average velocity of the particle.

3. A particle starts from the origin and moves with velocity $6\mathbf{i}-3\mathbf{j}+6\mathbf{k}$ for 2 seconds, then with velocity $12\mathbf{i}+9\mathbf{j}$ for 1 second. Find the position vector of the particle. Find also the average velocity and the average speed of the particle during its motion.

4. A particle with position vector $40\mathbf{i}+10\mathbf{j}+20\mathbf{k}$ moves with constant speed $5\,\mathrm{m\,s}^{-1}$ in the direction of the vector $4\mathbf{i}+7\mathbf{j}+4\mathbf{k}$. Find its distance from the origin after 9 seconds.

5. A particle moves with constant acceleration given by the vector $\mathbf{i}+\mathbf{j}$. If the initial velocity of the particle is $2\mathbf{i}+5\mathbf{j}$, find its velocity after 3 seconds. Given that the speed of the particle after k seconds is $15\,\mathrm{m\,s}^{-1}$, find the value of k.

6. The initial velocity of a particle moving with constant acceleration is $2\mathbf{i}-4\mathbf{j}$. After 2 seconds the particle is moving in the opposite direction with double the speed. Find the acceleration of the particle.

7. If $\mathbf{i}$ and $\mathbf{j}$ are unit vectors in the directions due east and due north respectively, find the magnitude and direction of the resultant of the velocities represented by each of the following sets of vectors
(a) $5\mathbf{i}+3\mathbf{j}$, $4\mathbf{i}$, $3\mathbf{i}+2\mathbf{j}$,   (b) $\mathbf{i}-2\mathbf{j}$, $3\mathbf{i}-\mathbf{j}$, $2\mathbf{i}+5\mathbf{j}$,
(c) $7\mathbf{i}-5\mathbf{j}$, $-\mathbf{i}+2\mathbf{j}$, $2\mathbf{i}-\mathbf{j}$,   (d) $-2\mathbf{i}+\mathbf{j}$, $\mathbf{i}-6\mathbf{j}$, $-3\mathbf{i}-4\mathbf{j}$.

8. Find the magnitudes and directions of the resultants of the given velocities
(a) $7\,\mathrm{m\,s}^{-1}$ due north and $10\,\mathrm{m\,s}^{-1}$ N 75°E;
(b) $50\,\mathrm{km/h}$ N 40°E and $60\,\mathrm{km/h}$ S 25°E;
(c) $12\,\mathrm{m\,s}^{-1}$ N 20°E, $6\,\mathrm{m\,s}^{-1}$ due west and $5\,\mathrm{m\,s}^{-1}$ due north;
(d) $30\,\mathrm{km/h}$ S 45°W, $50\,\mathrm{km/h}$ S 30°E and $70\,\mathrm{km/h}$ due east.

9. A stretch of river has straight parallel banks 100 m apart. A boat is being rowed at $4\,\mathrm{m\,s}^{-1}$ in a direction perpendicular to the banks. If the river is flowing at $1.2\,\mathrm{m\,s}^{-1}$, find (a) the magnitude of the resultant velocity of the boat, (b) the distance downstream that the boat is carried as it crosses from one bank to the other.

10. A ship travelling through the water at 12 km/h is steering a course S 75°E. It is also being carried by a current with velocity 2 km/h due E. If a passenger is walking across the deck of the ship directly from starboard to port at 4 km/h, find his velocity relative to the shore.

3.2 Relative velocity

If A and B are two moving objects, then the apparent velocity of B when observed from A is called the velocity of B relative to A, i.e.

> velocity of B relative to A = velocity of B – velocity of A.

Denoting the velocities of A and B by $\mathbf{v}_A$ and $\mathbf{v}_B$ respectively, the velocity of B relative to A is $\mathbf{v}_B - \mathbf{v}_A$ and may be found using a vector triangle.

Space diagram   Vector diagram

Example 1 A car is travelling due north on a straight stretch of motorway at 90 km/h. The car is observed by the driver of a lorry travelling north-east on an approach road at 60 km/h. Find the apparent speed of the car.

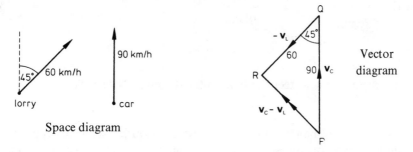

Space diagram

If the velocities of the car and the lorry are $\mathbf{v}_C$ and $\mathbf{v}_L$ respectively, then the velocity of the car relative to the lorry is $\mathbf{v}_C - \mathbf{v}_L$.

Using the cosine rule in the vector triangle PQR,

$$PR^2 = 90^2 + 60^2 - 2.90.60\cos 45° \qquad \therefore \quad PR \approx 63\cdot7.$$

Hence the apparent speed of the car is $63\cdot7$ km/h.

It follows from the definition of relative velocity that for moving objects A and B,

> velocity of B = velocity of B relative to A + velocity of A.

The advantage of using this result when solving problems is that it involves addition rather than subtraction of vectors.

Example 2   A man in a boat wishes to reach a small island due west of his present position. He knows that there is a current with a velocity of 3 km/h in the direction S 28°E. Given that the boat moves at 10 km/h through still water, find the course the man must steer to reach the island.

The true velocity of the boat

= velocity of boat relative to water + velocity of current.

If the boat is to reach the island its true velocity must be in the direction due west. Relative to the water the velocity of the boat is of magnitude 10 km/h. Let θ be the angle between these velocities.

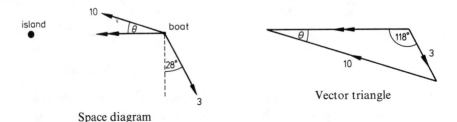

Space diagram   Vector triangle

By the sine rule, $\dfrac{\sin\theta}{3} = \dfrac{\sin 118°}{10}$

$\therefore \quad \sin\theta = \dfrac{3\sin 118°}{10}$ and $\theta \approx 15\cdot4°$

Hence the man must steer the boat in the direction N 74·6° W.

Example 3   To a man walking due west at 5 km/h the wind appears to be blowing from the north-west. However, to a man running due east at 10 km/h the wind appears to be blowing from the north-east. Find the true velocity of the wind.

Direction of walker

Direction of runner

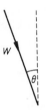

Apparent direction
of wind to walker

Apparent direction
of wind to runner

True magnitude
and direction
of wind

Velocity of wind
= velocity of wind relative to walker + velocity of walker
= velocity of wind relative to runner + velocity of runner

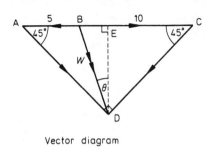

Vector diagram

From the symmetry of the diagram,

$$BE = 2 \cdot 5 \quad \text{and} \quad DE = 7 \cdot 5.$$

Using Pythagoras' theorem in $\triangle BDE$,

$$W^2 = (2 \cdot 5)^2 + (7 \cdot 5)^2$$
$$\therefore \quad W \approx 7 \cdot 9$$
$$\tan \theta = \frac{2 \cdot 5}{7 \cdot 5} = \frac{1}{3} \quad \therefore \quad \theta \approx 18 \cdot 4°$$

Hence the velocity of the wind is $7 \cdot 9$ km/h from the direction N $18 \cdot 4°$ W.

Exercise 3.2

1. A man is walking due south at 5 km/h. The wind is blowing from the west at 8 km/h. Find the magnitude and direction of the velocity of the wind relative to the man.

2. A ship is sailing south-east at 20 km/h and a second ship is sailing due west at 25 km/h. Find the magnitude and direction of the velocity of the first ship relative to the second.

3. If particles A and B have velocity vectors $7\mathbf{i} - 5\mathbf{j}$ and $-2\mathbf{i} + 7\mathbf{j}$ respectively, find the magnitude of the velocity of B relative to A and the angle its direction makes with the direction of $\mathbf{i}$.

4. Particles A and B have velocity vectors $3\mathbf{i} - 11\mathbf{j}$ and $5\mathbf{i} + \mathbf{j}$ respectively. The velocity of a particle C relative to A is $-2\mathbf{i} + 7\mathbf{j}$. Find, in vector form, the velocity of C and the velocity of B relative to C.

5. A boat A travels due west at a speed of 30 km/h. The velocity of a boat B relative to A is 14 km/h due south. Find the speed of boat B and the direction in which it is moving.

6.   To an observer on a ship P steaming at $20 \, \text{km/h}$ in the direction due west, a ship Q appears to be steaming at $20 \, \text{km/h}$ in the direction N $30°$W. Find the true velocity of Q.

7.   To a cyclist riding due east at $15 \, \text{km/h}$ the wind appears to be blowing from the north-east at $12 \, \text{km/h}$. Find the magnitude and direction of the true velocity of the wind.

8.   To the driver of a car travelling due north at $40 \, \text{km/h}$ the wind appears to be blowing at $50 \, \text{km/h}$ from the direction N $60°$E. The wind velocity remains constant, but the speed of the car is increasing. Find its speed when the wind appears to be blowing from the direction N $30°$E.

9.   A river with straight parallel banks $400 \, \text{m}$ apart flows due south at $3 \cdot 5 \, \text{km/h}$. Find the direction in which a boat, travelling at $12 \cdot 5 \, \text{km/h}$ relative to the water, must be steered in order to cross the river from east to west along a course perpendicular to the banks. Find also the time taken to make the crossing.

10. A stretch of river has straight parallel banks $120 \, \text{m}$ apart. A man rowing at $5 \, \text{ms}^{-1}$ relative to the water and heading directly across the river reaches the other bank $54 \, \text{m}$ downstream. Find the speed of the current and the direction in which the man would have to row in order to cross the river at right angles to the banks.

11. A helicopter whose speed in still air is $60 \, \text{km/h}$ is to fly to a village $80 \, \text{km}$ away in the direction N $40°$W. The wind is blowing at $10 \, \text{km/h}$ from the west. Find the direction in which the helicopter must fly and the time taken to reach the village to the nearest minute.

12. A plane flies in a straight line from A to B, where $AB = 580 \, \text{km}$ and the bearing of B from A is N $50°$E. The speed of the plane in still air is $300 \, \text{km/h}$. Given that the wind is blowing from the direction N $40°$W and that the flight takes 2 hours, calculate the speed of the wind and the course that should be set for the return journey, if the wind velocity remains unchanged.

3.3 Relative displacement

Some problems involve the positions as well as the velocities of objects in motion. In such cases it is usually best to select one of the objects and work with displacements and velocities relative to it.

If A and B are two moving objects then the displacement of B relative to A is given by the displacement vector **AB**. The velocity of B relative to A can be considered to be the rate of change of **AB**. The two objects can meet only if the relative velocity is parallel to the relative displacement.

Example 1 A motor-boat capable of 30 km/h wishes to intercept a yacht 5 km away on a bearing N 28°E. If the yacht is travelling at 20 km/h in the direction N 53°W, what course should the motor-boat take? Find also the time taken to reach the yacht.

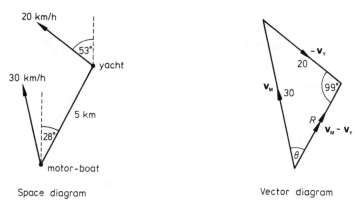

Space diagram   Vector diagram

If the velocities of the yacht and the motor-boat are v_Y and v_M respectively, then the velocity of the motor-boat relative to the yacht is $v_M - v_Y$ and must lie in the direction N 28°E. Let R be the magnitude of this relative velocity and θ the angle it makes with the course of the motor-boat.

By the sine rule, $\quad \dfrac{\sin \theta}{20} = \dfrac{\sin 99°}{30}$

$\therefore \quad \sin \theta = \dfrac{20 \sin 99°}{30} \quad$ and $\quad \theta \approx 41 \cdot 182°.$

Hence the motor-boat must be steered in the direction N 13·2° W.
The remaining angle in the vector triangle is 39·818°.

$\therefore \quad$ by the sine rule, $\quad \dfrac{R}{\sin 39 \cdot 818°} = \dfrac{30}{\sin 99°}$

$\therefore \quad R = \dfrac{30 \sin 39 \cdot 818°}{\sin 99°} \approx 19 \cdot 45.$

Thus on the course N 13·2° W the motor-boat can approach the yacht at a relative speed of 19·45 km/h

$\therefore \quad$ the time taken in minutes $= \dfrac{5}{19 \cdot 45} \times 60 \approx 15 \cdot 4.$

Hence the motor-boat can reach the yacht in 15·4 minutes.

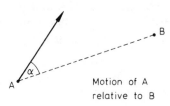

Motion of A
relative to B

We consider now two objects A and B with given speeds and positions. We assume that the direction of B is such that the objects can never meet. If α is the angle between the velocity of A relative to B and the initial displacement vector **AB**, then *A* will approach *B* as closely as possible when α takes its smallest possible value.

Example 2   A ship *A* is sailing due north at 20 km/h and a ship *B* is sailing due east at 15 km/h. At 12.00 hours *A* is 75 km due south of *B*. Find the shortest distance between the ships and the time at which they are closest, assuming that their velocities remain unchanged.

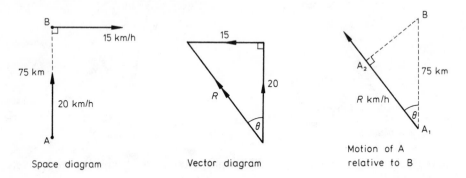

Space diagram   Vector diagram   Motion of A relative to B

Let the velocity of *A* relative to *B* be *R* km/h at an angle θ west of north.

Using the vector diagram, $R = \sqrt{(15^2 + 20^2)} = 25$

$$\therefore \quad \sin \theta = \frac{15}{25} = \frac{3}{5} \quad \text{and} \quad \cos \theta = \frac{20}{25} = \frac{4}{5}.$$

Let A_1 be the initial position of *A* and let A_2 be its position when closest to *B*. By considering the motion of *A* relative to *B*, we see that $A_2 B$ must be perpendicular to *A*'s relative path

$\therefore$ the shortest distance between the two ships is 75 sin θ km, i.e. 45 km.

Relative to *B* the apparent distance between A_1 and A_2 is 75 cos θ km, i.e. 60 km.

$\therefore$ the time *A* takes to move from A_1 to A_2

$$= \frac{\text{relative distance}}{\text{relative speed}} = \frac{60}{25}\text{hours} = 2 \text{ hours } 24 \text{ min.}$$

Hence the ships are closest together at 14.24 hours.

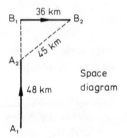

Space diagram

[A further diagram can be drawn to show the true paths of *A* and *B*. The true distance $A_1 A_2$ is 48 km and the distance moved by *B* is 36 km.]

Example 3 An aircraft A flying at a speed of 350 km/h is 50 km due west of another aircraft B. If B is flying at the same height on a course S 20°E at a speed of 400 km/h, find the direction in which A must fly to approach B as closely as possible. Find also the shortest distance between the two aircraft.

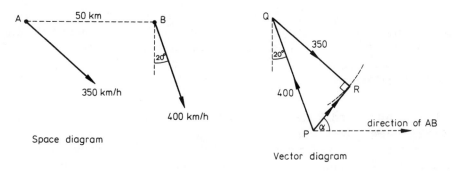

Space diagram

Vector diagram

In the vector diagram $\overrightarrow{QR}$ represents the velocity of A, $\overrightarrow{QP}$ represents the velocity of B and $\overrightarrow{PR}$ represents the velocity of A relative to B. Considering all possible directions for $\overrightarrow{QR}$, the smallest possible value of α occurs when $\angle PRQ$ is a right angle.

Hence $\angle PQR = \cos^{-1}(350/400) \approx 28 \cdot 955°$

∴ A must fly in the direction S 49° E to approach B as closely as possible.

Using the vector diagram, $\alpha = 49°$.

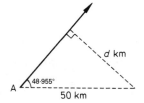

Let d km be the shortest distance between the aircraft, then by considering the direction of A's motion relative to B,

$$d = 50 \sin 48 \cdot 955° \approx 37 \cdot 7$$

∴ the shortest distance between the aircraft is 37·7 km.

Exercise 3.3

1. A destroyer must intercept a vessel 40 km away on a bearing of 110°. The vessel is sailing on a course of 200° at a speed of 20 km/h. If the speed of the destroyer is 30 km/h, find, to the nearest degree, the course it must steer. Find also the time taken for the destroyer to reach the vessel.

2. A man walking due north wishes to intercept a cyclist travelling due west at 12 km/h. The bearing of the cyclist from the man is N 60°E. Find the speed at which the man must walk if he does not change his direction. If the man walks at 8 km/h, find the direction in which he must go to intercept the cyclist as quickly as possible. What is the minimum speed at which the man can walk in order to intercept the cyclist?

3. A ship P is sailing due west at $16\,\text{km/h}$ and a ship Q is sailing due north at $24\,\text{km/h}$. At a certain instant Q is $10\,\text{km}$ due west of P. Find the velocity of P relative to Q and the shortest distance between the ships if they continue on these courses.

4. A cyclist A is riding along a straight level road on a bearing $030°$ at a steady speed of $5\,\text{m s}^{-1}$. A second cyclist B is travelling due east along another straight level road at a steady speed of $6\,\text{m s}^{-1}$. Find the magnitude and the direction of the velocity of A relative to B. At a certain instant A is $500\,\text{m}$ due south of B. Find the time that elapses before A is due west of B.   (JMB)

5. Two cyclists A and B are approaching a road junction at speeds of $20\,\text{km/h}$ and $15\,\text{km/h}$ respectively. A is $100\,\text{m}$ south of the junction riding due north, when B reaches the junction riding due east. Find the velocity of B relative to A. Find also the shortest distance between A and B, assuming their velocities remain unchanged.

6. At 10.00 hours a plane A passes through a point X travelling due south at $360\,\text{km/h}$. At the same instant a plane B is $50\,\text{km}$ due west of X travelling at $450\,\text{km/h}$ towards X. Find the magnitude and direction of the velocity of B relative to A and the shortest distance between A and B. Find also the time at which the planes are closest and the bearing of B from A at that time.

7. Two planes A and B, flying at the same height, are travelling at $500\,\text{km/h}$ in the directions due north and due east respectively. At a certain instant A is $100\,\text{km}$ from B on a bearing of $150°$. Find the velocity of B relative to A and the shortest distance between the planes if neither changes course.

8. (In this question the units of time and distance are the second and metre respectively.) Two particles A and B start simultaneously from points which have position vectors $3\mathbf{i}+4\mathbf{j}$ and $8\mathbf{i}+4\mathbf{j}$ respectively. Each moves with constant velocity, the velocity of B being $\mathbf{i}+4\mathbf{j}$. (i) If the velocity of A is $5\mathbf{i}+2\mathbf{j}$, show that the least distance between A and B subsequently is $\sqrt{5}$ metres. (ii) If the speed of A is $5\,\text{m/s}$ and the particles collide, find the velocity of A.   (L)

9. A destroyer sights a ship travelling with constant velocity $5\mathbf{j}$, whose position vector at the time of sighting is $2000(3\mathbf{i}+\mathbf{j})$ relative to the destroyer, distances being measured in m and speeds in m s^{-1}. The destroyer immediately begins to move with velocity $k(4\mathbf{i}+3\mathbf{j})$, where k is a constant, in order to intercept the ship. Find k and the time to interception. Find also the distance between the vessels when half the time to interception has elapsed.   (O&C)

10. A ship P sailing at $16\,\text{km/h}$ is $10\,\text{km}$ due south of a second ship Q. If Q is sailing in the direction $S\,70°E$ at a speed of $20\,\text{km/h}$, find the direction in which P must sail to approach Q as closely as possible. Find also the shortest distance between the ships.

Exercise 3.4 (*miscellaneous*)

[1 knot = 1 nautical mile per hour.]

1. During a race between two yachts, A and B, there is a wind of 9 knots blowing from due north. The resultant velocity of A is 6 knots on a bearing of 060°. Find the direction of the wind relative to A. At the same time, the resultant velocity of B is 6 knots on a bearing of 300°. Find, correct to the nearest degree, the direction of the wind relative to B and, in knots correct to one decimal place, the velocity of A relative to B.   (L)

2. A yacht A is sailing due east at 9 knots and a second yacht B is sailing on a bearing of 030° at 6 knots. At a certain instant a third yacht C appears to an observer on A to be sailing due south and appears to an observer on B to be sailing on a bearing of 150°. Find the speed of the yacht C and the bearing on which it is sailing.   (L)

3. A river flows at 5 m/s from west to east between parallel banks which are at a distance 300 metres apart. A man rows a boat at a speed of 3 m/s in still water. (i) State the direction in which the boat must be steered in order to cross the river from the southern bank to the northern bank in the shortest possible time. Find the time taken and the actual distance covered by the boat for this crossing. (ii) Find the direction in which the boat must be steered in order to cross the river from the southern bank to the northern bank by the shortest possible route. Find the time taken and the actual distance covered by the boat for this crossing.

(AEB 1978)

4. A river flows at a constant speed of 5 m/s between straight parallel banks which are 300 m apart. A boat, which has a maximum speed of $3\frac{1}{4}$ m/s in still water, leaves a point A on one bank and sails in a straight line to the opposite bank. Find, graphically or otherwise, the least time the boat can take to reach a point B on the opposite bank where $AB = 500$ m and B is downstream from A. Find also the least time the boat can take to cross the river. Find the time taken to sail from A to B by the slowest boat capable of sailing directly from A to B. (L)

5. A helicopter flies with constant airspeed 100 knots from position A to position B, which is 50 nautical miles north east of A, and then flies back to A. Throughout the whole flight the wind velocity is 30 knots from the west. Find, by drawing or calculation, the course set for each of the two legs of the flight. Find also the total time of flight from A to B and back.   (L)

6. A motorist A is travelling in a direction N 10°E at a constant speed of 60 km h^{-1}. The wind is blowing from the direction S 80°E at a constant speed of 25 km h^{-1}. Find the magnitude and direction of the velocity of the wind relative to the motorist. A second motorist B is travelling at a constant speed of 50 km h^{-1}. The velocity of B relative to A is in a direction S 30°W. Find graphically, or otherwise, the two possible directions in which B can be travelling.

(C)

7.   Three fixed buoys are at the vertices A, B and C of an equilateral triangle of side 12 km. The point B is due north of A, and C is to the east of the line AB. A steady current of speed 3 km h^{-1} flows from west to east. A boat which has a top speed of 8 km h^{-1} in still water does the triangular journey $ABCA$ at top speed. Find, graphically or otherwise, the time taken on each leg of the journey, giving your answers to the nearest minute.   (C)

8.   A helicopter, with a maximum speed in still air of 120 km h^{-1}, is to fly between airports A and B. B is 238 km from A in a direction N $\theta°$W where $\theta = \cos^{-1}\dfrac{12}{13}$. The helicopter leaves A at 12.00 hours in a wind blowing at 50 km h^{-1} from the west. What is the earliest possible time of arrival at B, and the corresponding direction in which it must head? At 13.00 hours the helicopter receives a radio message not to proceed but to return to A as soon as possible. Neglecting the time to change course, what is the earliest time it can be back at A?   (W)

9.   A small boat fitted with an outboard engine is 10 nautical miles due east of a trawler. The trawler. is travelling at 15 knots on a course N $\theta°$ E $[\theta = \sin^{-1}(24/25)]$. By considering the trawler's velocity components due east and due north, or otherwise, show that the minimum speed necessary for the boat to intercept the trawler is 4·2 knots, and find the corresponding direction in which it must steer. If the boat travels at 9 knots, show that it can steer in either of two directions to reach the trawler and calculate the shorter time needed to do so. (W)

10.   [In this question the units of distance and time are the metre and second respectively.] At time $t = 0$ a particle A is at the origin and a particle B is at the point with position vector $10\mathbf{i}$. Each particle is moving with constant velocity, the velocity of B being $-4\mathbf{i} + 3\mathbf{j}$. Subsequently the particles collide. Find (a) the least speed at which A can travel, (b) the velocity of A if the collision occurs at time $t = 2$. A third particle C is moving in the same plane. When the velocity of A is $\mathbf{i} + 3\mathbf{j}$ the velocity of C relative to A is in the direction of the vector $3\mathbf{i} + 2\mathbf{j}$ and relative to B is in the direction of the vector $7\mathbf{i} + 3\mathbf{j}$. Find the speed of C.   (L)

11.   A motorist A and a cyclist B are travelling along straight roads which cross at right angles at a point O. A is travelling at a constant speed of 48 km h^{-1} towards the east, and B at 14 km h^{-1} towards the north. At the moment that B is passing through O, A is 400 m from O and has not yet passed O. Calculate: (i) the velocity of B relative to A in magnitude and direction; (ii) the least distance between car and cycle; (iii) the distances of the car and cycle from O when they are nearest to one another.   (SU)

12.   A cruiser is moving due east at 30 km/h. Relative to the cruiser a frigate is moving on a course of 210° (S 30°W) at 48 km/h. Using a graphical method, or otherwise, find the magnitude and the direction of the velocity of the frigate relative to a coastguard who is recording the paths of these ships from a lighthouse. At 1300 hours the frigate is 10 km due east of the cruiser. If both ships

maintain their speeds and courses, find the time at which the distance between them is least and their actual distance apart at this instant. Find also the time at which the frigate is due south of the cruiser. (AEB 1977)

13. A ship A whose full speed is 40 km/h is 20 km due west of a ship B which is travelling uniformly with speed 30 km/h in a direction due north. The ship A travels at full speed on a course chosen so as to intercept B as soon as possible. Find the direction of this course and calculate to the nearest minute the time A would take to reach B. When half of this time has elapsed the ship A has engine failure and thereafter proceeds at half speed. Find the course which A should then set in order to approach as close as possible to B, and calculate the distance of closest approach (in kilometres to 2 decimal places). (JMB)

14. A ship A is travelling with constant velocity 20 km/h due east and a ship B has constant velocity 15 km/h in a direction 30° east of north. At noon B is 30 km due south of A. Find the magnitude of the velocity of B relative to A, and show that the direction of this relative velocity is approximately 44° west of north. Find, to the nearest minute, the time at which A and B are closest. At the time of closest approach a boat leaves A to intercept B. Find the least speed at which it must travel. (JMB)

15. Construct a flow chart for a procedure in which the input is the speeds and courses of two ships, A and B, in the form x km/h on a bearing $y°$. Assuming that initially ship A is 20 km due south of ship B, the following output is required:
(a) the time and distance of closest approach or an appropriate message if the ships are not moving closer to each other;
(b) the course A should steer to intercept B as soon as possible and the time of interception;
(c) if interception is not possible, the course A should steer to approach B as closely as possible.
[It may be helpful to consider velocity components due east and due north.]

4 Velocity and acceleration

4.1 Elementary kinematics

We consider now the motion of a particle in a straight line. Since in this type of motion the displacements, velocities and accelerations are parallel, there is no need to use vector notation. In general the displacement of the particle from a fixed point on the line after t seconds is denoted by s m, the velocity by v ms^{-1} and the acceleration by a ms^{-2}. This means that, $v = \dfrac{ds}{dt}$ and $a = \dfrac{dv}{dt}$ $= \dfrac{d^2s}{dt^2}$. Thus if a displacement-time graph is plotted the velocity is represented by the gradient of the curve. When the gradient is positive the motion of the particle is in the positive sense along the straight line and when the gradient is negative motion is in the opposite direction. At stationary points on the curve the velocity is zero and the particle is instantaneously at rest. Similarly the gradient of the velocity-time graph represents the acceleration of the particle.

Consider, for instance, the motion of a particle in a straight line as represented by the graphs given below. The first graph shows the displacement s from a fixed point O at time t and the second is the corresponding velocity-time graph.

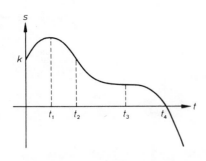

At the start of the motion the particle is at a distance k from O, moving away from O with positive velocity. It comes to rest at time t_1, then starts moving towards O. Its speed increases to a maximum value at $t = t_2$, then decreases so that the particle is again at rest when $t = t_3$. It then continues to move with negative velocity as t increases, passing through O at time t_4.

Considering the gradient of the velocity-time graph, we see that a negative acceleration produces the initial

46

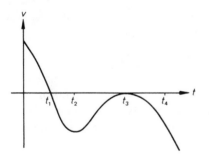

reduction in speed, the change of direction at time t_1, then an increasing speed towards O. The minimum point on the graph at $t = t_2$ corresponds to a maximum speed of the particle in the negative direction. The positive acceleration from $t = t_2$ to $t = t_3$ brings the particle to rest. The motion then continues with velocity and acceleration both negative and hence with increasing speed in the negative direction.

Example 1 A particle is moving in a straight line, so that after t seconds its displacement s metres from a fixed point O is given by $s = 9t + 3t^2 - t^3$. Find (a) the initial displacement, velocity and acceleration of the particle, (b) the time at which the particle is instantaneously at rest, (c) the greatest speed attained by the particle in the first 4 seconds of the motion.

Differentiating,
$$v = \frac{ds}{dt} = 9 + 6t - 3t^2$$

$$a = \frac{dv}{dt} = 6 - 6t.$$

(a) When $t = 0$, $s = 0$, $v = 9$ and $a = 6$

∴   initially the particle is at O moving with velocity $9\,\mathrm{m\,s}^{-1}$ and acceleration $6\,\mathrm{m\,s}^{-2}$ (both in the positive direction along the line of motion).

(b) $v = 0 \Leftrightarrow 9 + 6t - 3t^2 = 0 \Leftrightarrow 3(3 - t)(1 + t) = 0$

∴ $v = 0$ when $t = 3$ (assuming $t \geqslant 0$).

Hence the particle is instantaneously at rest after 3 seconds.

(c) $a = 0 \Leftrightarrow 6 - 6t = 0 \Leftrightarrow t = 1$.

When $t < 1$, $a > 0$ and   when $t > 1$, $a < 0$

∴   when $t = 1$, the velocity reaches a maximum value of $12\,\mathrm{m\,s}^{-1}$.

The velocity then decreases during the remainder of the motion. Since the particle is at rest when $t = 3$, it must move with increasing speed in the negative direction for $t > 3$. When $t = 4$, $v = -15$ ∴   the greatest speed attained by the particle in the first 4 seconds of the motion is $15\,\mathrm{m\,s}^{-1}$.

[These results are illustrated in the sketch graphs below.]

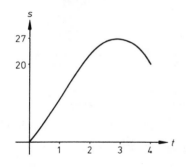

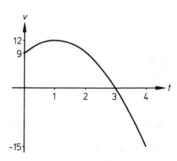

When the acceleration of a particle is represented by a known function of the time t, then expressions for the velocity and displacement can often be found by integration.

Example 2   A vehicle moves in a straight line so that its acceleration after t seconds is given by $a = 2t$. Initially it has a velocity of $20\,\mathrm{ms}^{-1}$. Find an expression for the displacement s metres of the vehicle from its starting point.

$$a = \frac{dv}{dt} = 2t$$

Integrating, $v = t^2 + c$

but $v = 20$ when $t = 0$, thus $c = 20$

$\therefore$ $v = \dfrac{ds}{dt} = t^2 + 20.$

Integrating, $s = \tfrac{1}{3}t^3 + 20t + k$

but $s = 0$ when $t = 0$, thus $k = 0$

$\therefore$ $s = \tfrac{1}{3}t^3 + 20t.$

The next example shows that the total displacement of a particle in any given interval of time is represented by the area under the velocity-time graph and that this can be found using a definite integral.

Example 3   A particle moves in a straight line so that after t seconds its velocity in ms^{-1} is given by $v = (2t^2 - 25)(t - 1)$. Find (a) the displacement of the particle from its starting point after 3 seconds, (b) the total distance moved by the particle in the first 3 seconds of the motion.

(a) The displacement of the particle from its starting point after 3 seconds (in metres)

$$= \int_0^3 v\,dt = \int_0^3 (2t^2 - 25)(t - 1)\,dt$$

$$= \int_0^3 (2t^3 - 2t^2 - 25t + 25)\,dt$$

$$= \left[\frac{1}{2}t^4 - \frac{2}{3}t^3 - \frac{25}{2}t^2 + 25t \right]_0^3$$

$$= \left(\frac{1}{2}\cdot 81 - \frac{2}{3}\cdot 27 - \frac{25}{2}\cdot 9 + 25\cdot 3 \right) - 0$$

$$= 40\tfrac{1}{2} - 18 - 112\tfrac{1}{2} + 75 = -15.$$

(b) Since $v = 0$ when $t = 1$, the particle is instantaneously at rest after 1 second.

For $0 < t < 1$, $v > 0$ and for $1 < t < 3$, $v < 0$.

Hence the direction of motion changes once in the first 3 seconds, i.e. when $t = 1$.

$$\int_0^1 v\,dt = \left[\frac{1}{2}t^4 - \frac{2}{3}t^3 - \frac{25}{2}t^2 + 25t\right]_0^1$$

$$= \left(\frac{1}{2} - \frac{2}{3} - \frac{25}{2} + 25\right) - 0 = \frac{1}{2} - \frac{2}{3} - 12\frac{1}{2} + 25 = 12\frac{1}{3}$$

$$\int_1^3 v\,dt = \left[\frac{1}{2}t^4 - \frac{2}{3}t^3 - \frac{25}{2}t^2 + 25t\right]_1^3$$

$$= \left(\frac{1}{2}.81 - \frac{2}{3}.27 - \frac{25}{2}.9 + 25.3\right) - \left(\frac{1}{2} - \frac{2}{3} - \frac{25}{2} + 25\right)$$

$$= -15 - 12\frac{1}{3} = -27\frac{1}{3}$$

$\therefore$ the total distance travelled in the first 3 seconds of the motion is $39\frac{2}{3}$ metres.

Exercise 4.1

Each of the questions in this exercise concerns a particle P moving along a straight line such that after t seconds its displacement from a fixed point A is s m, its velocity is $v\,\mathrm{m\,s}^{-1}$ and its acceleration is $a\,\mathrm{m\,s}^{-2}$.

1. Find expressions in terms of t for v and a, given that
(a) $s = 6 - 5t + 3t^3$,   (b) $s = (2t - 1)(t + 2)$.

2. Find expressions in terms of t for v and s, given that
(a) $a = 12t$ and when $t = 0$, $v = 7$ and $s = 0$,
(b) $a = -10$ and when $t = 0$, $v = 20$ and $s = 5$,
(c) $a = 24t(t - 1)$ and when $t = 1$, $v = s = 0$.

3. If $v = 2t^3 - 9t^2$, find the values of t for which $a = 0$. Given that $s = 20$ when $t = 0$, find the value of s when $t = 2$.

4. If $v = 12 + 3t^2$, find the value of v when $a = 12$. Find also the distance travelled in the first two seconds of the motion.

5. The particle P starts from rest at A and moves such that $a = 6 - 2t$. If the particle later comes to rest at a point B, find the distance AB and the greatest speed attained while moving from A to B.

6. Given that the initial velocity of the particle P is $9\,\mathrm{m\,s}^{-1}$ and that $a = 2t - 10$, find the times when the particle is instantaneously at rest and the maximum speed attained by the particle between these two times.

7.   Given that $a = 3t$ and that $v = 5$ when $t = 0$, find the value of v when $t = 4$ and the distance travelled in the first four seconds of the motion.

8.   If $s = t^3 - 12t$, find the initial velocity of the particle P and the distance between its positions when $t = 0$ and $t = 4$. Show that P changes direction between $t = 0$ and $t = 4$, then find the total distance travelled in this interval of time.

9.   Given that $v = 25 - 4t^2$, calculate (a) the value of t when the particle is instantaneously at rest, (b) the distance travelled by the particle in the third second.

10.   Given that $s = t^3 - 2t^2 - 15t$, find (a) the initial velocity and acceleration of P, (b) the times at which P passes through A, (c) the total distance travelled in the first five seconds of the motion.

11.   The particle P starts from rest at the point A and is again instantaneously at rest after 3 seconds. If $a = k - 6t$, where k is constant, find (a) expressions for v and s in terms of t, (b) the distance P travels before returning to A.

12.   Given that $s = 6t^2 - t^3$, sketch the displacement-time and velocity-time graphs for the motion of the particle P from $t = 0$ to $t = 6$. Find, in the interval $0 \leqslant t \leqslant 6$,
(a) the times at which the particle is at A,
(b) the greatest value of the distance AP,
(c) the total distance travelled,
(d) the greatest speed attained.

13.   Repeat question 12 for $s = t^2 - 5t + 4$.

14.   Repeat question 12 for $s = 4t^3 - 33t^2 + 54t$.

15.   Given that when $t = 1$, $s = 0$ and that when $t > 1$, $v = t^2 + \dfrac{9}{t^2}$, find the values of a, v and s when $t = 3$. Find also the minimum speed of the particle for $t > 1$.

16.   If the particle P starts from rest and moves such that $v = 4t^2(3 - t)$, find (a) the distance travelled by the particle before it next comes to rest, (b) the maximum speed attained by the particle in the first three seconds of its motion, (c) the maximum acceleration in the first two seconds of its motion.

4.2 Motion with constant acceleration

We now obtain general equations for the motion of a particle in a straight line with constant acceleration. These will then be used to solve a variety of problems.

Consider a particle with initial velocity u and constant acceleration a. Let its displacement from its initial position be s and its velocity v at time t.

$$\frac{dv}{dt} = a \quad \text{where } a \text{ is constant}$$

Integrating $\qquad\qquad\qquad\qquad v = at + c$

When $t = 0$, $v = u$ $\qquad\qquad\qquad \therefore \quad c = u$

Thus $\qquad\qquad\qquad\qquad\qquad v = u + at \qquad\qquad\qquad (1)$

and $\qquad\qquad\qquad\qquad\quad \dfrac{ds}{dt} = u + at$

Integrating $\qquad\qquad\qquad\qquad s = ut + \tfrac{1}{2}at^2 + k$

When $t = 0$, $s = 0$ $\qquad\qquad\quad \therefore \quad k = 0$

Thus $\qquad\qquad\qquad\qquad\qquad s = ut + \tfrac{1}{2}at^2 \qquad\qquad\quad (2)$

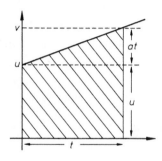

Results (1) and (2) can also be obtained by considering the velocity-time graph for the motion. As shown in the sketch this is a straight line with gradient a. The displacement s is represented by the shaded area under the line.

Rearranging (1) $\qquad\qquad\qquad\qquad at = v - u$

Substituting in (2) $\qquad\qquad\qquad s = ut + \tfrac{1}{2}(v - u)t$

$\qquad\qquad\qquad\qquad\qquad \therefore \quad s = \tfrac{1}{2}(u + v)t \qquad\qquad\qquad (3)$

Hence $\qquad\qquad 2as = (u + v)at = (u + v)(v - u) = v^2 - u^2$

$\qquad\qquad\qquad\qquad\therefore \quad v^2 = u^2 + 2as. \qquad\qquad\qquad (4)$

Eliminating u from equations (1) and (2),

$$s = vt - \tfrac{1}{2}at^2. \qquad\qquad\qquad (5)$$

We now have five equations connecting the quantities s, u, v, a and t. When using them it is advisable to check that the acceleration is constant and that the units of measurement are consistent.

$$\boxed{\begin{aligned} v &= u + at \\ s &= ut + \tfrac{1}{2}at^2 \\ s &= vt - \tfrac{1}{2}at^2 \\ s &= \tfrac{1}{2}(u + v)t \\ v^2 &= u^2 + 2as. \end{aligned}}$$

Example 1   A particle moving in a straight line accelerates uniformly from rest to a speed of $60\,\mathrm{m\,s^{-1}}$ in 10 seconds. Find the distance travelled in this time.

Given: $u = 0, v = 60, t = 10.$

Using the equation $s = \frac{1}{2}(u+v)t$
$$s = \frac{1}{2}(0+60)10 = 300.$$

Hence the particle travelled a distance of 300 metres.

Example 2   A train travelling in a straight line is brought to rest in 1 minute with a uniform retardation of $0.5\,\mathrm{m\,s}^{-2}$. Find the speed at which the train was travelling in km/h.

Given: $v = 0, a = -0.5, t = 60.$
Using the equation $v = u + at$
$$0 = u - 0.5 \times 60 \qquad \therefore \quad u = 30.$$

Hence the speed of the train $= 30\,\mathrm{m\,s}^{-1}$
$$= \frac{30 \times 60 \times 60}{1000}\,\mathrm{km/h} = 108\,\mathrm{km/h}.$$

Example 3   A particle moving in a straight line with constant acceleration travels 10 m in 2 seconds, then a further 30 m in the following 2 seconds. Find the acceleration of the particle.

When $s = 10, t = 2$ and when $s = 40, t = 4$

$\therefore$ using the equation $s = ut + \frac{1}{2}at^2$, $10 = 2u + 2a$
$$40 = 4u + 8a$$

Simplifying $u + a = 5$
$$u + 2a = 10 \qquad\qquad \therefore \quad a = 5.$$

Hence the acceleration of the particle is $5\,\mathrm{m\,s}^{-2}$.

Although the constant acceleration formulae are very useful, some problems are better solved by drawing a sketch of the velocity-time graph.

Example 4   A train takes 10 minutes to travel a distance of 12 km between two stations. It starts from rest at the first station, accelerating uniformly until it reaches a speed of V km/h. It travels at this speed for 5 minutes then decelerates uniformly, coming to rest at the second station. Find the value of V.

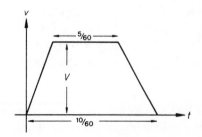

Consider the velocity-time graph for the motion, taking the units of distance and time as kilometres and hours.

Since the area of the trapezium under the graph represents the distance travelled,

$$\frac{1}{2}\left(\frac{5}{60}+\frac{10}{60}\right)V = 12, \quad \text{i.e.} \quad \frac{1}{8}V = 12.$$

Hence the value of V is 96.

An object falling freely under gravity has a downward acceleration usually denoted by g. The magnitude of this acceleration varies slightly over the surface of the earth. In m s^{-2} the variation is from about 9·78 at the equator to 9·83 at the poles. [On the moon the value of g is 1·62.] Although the pull of gravity on an object decreases as its distance from the earth's surface increases, this decrease can, in general, be regarded as negligible. Thus in most problems g is taken to be a constant with value 9·8 or 10 depending on the accuracy required.

Example 5   A boy standing at the edge of a cliff throws a stone vertically upwards with a velocity of $10\,\text{m s}^{-1}$. If the stone hits the sea below with a velocity of $40\,\text{m s}^{-1}$, find the height of the cliff above sea-level and the maximum height above sea-level reached by the stone. [Take $g = 10$.]

Taking the upward direction as positive, $u = 10$, $v = -40$ and $a = -10$.

Using the equation
$$v^2 = u^2 + 2as$$
$$1600 = 100 + 2(-10)s$$
$$1500 = -20s \qquad \qquad \therefore \quad s = -75.$$

Hence the height of the cliff above sea-level is 75 m.

When the stone reaches its maximum height its velocity is zero
$$\therefore \quad u = 10, v = 0 \text{ and } a = -10.$$

Using the equation
$$v^2 = u^2 + 2as$$
$$0 = 100 + 2(-10)s \qquad \qquad \therefore \quad s = 5.$$

Hence the maximum height reached by the stone is 5 m above the cliff, i.e. 80 m above sea-level.

Example 6   A particle is projected vertically upwards with a speed of $30\,\text{m s}^{-1}$. After 3 seconds another particle is projected vertically upwards from the same point with a speed of $25\,\text{m s}^{-1}$. Find the height at which the two particles collide. [Take $g = 10$.]

Let us assume that the collision occurs at a height of h m and T seconds after the projection of the second particle, then taking the upward direction as positive,

for the first particle: $s = h$, $u = 30$, $a = -10$, $t = T+3$
for the second particle: $s = h$, $u = 25$, $a = -10$, $t = T$.

Using the equation $s = ut + \frac{1}{2}at^2$ in both cases

$$h = 30(T+3) + \frac{1}{2}(-10)(T+3)^2$$
$$= 30T + 90 - 5T^2 - 30T - 45$$

i.e. $h = 45 - 5T^2$ (1)

and $h = 25T + \frac{1}{2}(-10)T^2$

i.e. $h = 25T - 5T^2$.   (2)

Hence $25T = 45$ so that $T = 9/5$.

Substituting in (1) $h = 45 - 5\left(\frac{9}{5}\right)^2 = 28\cdot8$

∴   the particles collide at a height of 28·8 metres.

Exercise 4.2

[Take g as $10\,\mathrm{m\,s^{-2}}$.]

In questions 1 to 10 a particle is moving in a straight line with constant acceleration a and initial velocity u. At time t its displacement from its initial position is s and its velocity is v.

1.   If $u = 5$, $a = 2$, $t = 3$, find v and s.

2.   If $v = 7$, $u = 5$, $a = 1$, find s and t.

3.   If $u = 10$, $v = -2$, $t = 4$, find s and a.

4.   If $s = 15$, $t = 5$, $u = 13$, find v and a.

5.   If $s = -5$, $v = 2$, $u = -3$, find a and t.

6.   If $t = 3$, $a = -8$, $s = 36$, find v and u.

7.   If $u = 50$, $s = 300$, $a = -4$, find t and v.

8.   If $a = 0\cdot4$, $t = 15$, $v = 7$, find u and s.

9.   If $v = -18$, $s = -64$, $t = 8$, find a and u.

10. If $s = 45$, $a = 40$, $v = 60$, find u and t.

11. A car accelerates uniformly from rest to $60\,\mathrm{km/h}$ in 30 seconds. Find the distance it travels in this time.

12. A cyclist travels $1\cdot25\,\mathrm{km}$ as he accelerates uniformly at a rate of $k\,\mathrm{m\,s^{-2}}$ from a speed of $15\,\mathrm{km/h}$ to $30\,\mathrm{km/h}$. Find the value of k.

13. A particle is projected vertically upwards from a point O with a speed of $25\,\mathrm{m\,s^{-1}}$. Find the maximum height reached by the particle and the time that elapses before it returns to O.

14. A boy on a bridge throws a pebble vertically upwards at a speed of $6\,\mathrm{m\,s^{-1}}$. After 2 seconds it hits the water below. Find the speed at which the pebble hits the water and its initial height above the water.

15. The points O, A, B and C lie in a straight line such that $AB = 28\,\mathrm{m}$ and $BC = 72\,\mathrm{m}$. A particle moving with constant acceleration starts from rest at O and passes through A, B and C, its velocities at B and C being $9\,\mathrm{m\,s^{-1}}$ and $15\,\mathrm{m\,s^{-1}}$ respectively. Find the velocity of the particle at A and the time it takes to travel from A to C.

16. A particle moving in a straight line with constant acceleration travels $10\,\mathrm{m}$ in 2 seconds, then a further $22\,\mathrm{m}$ in the next 2 seconds. Find the further distance travelled in 2 more seconds and the speed of the particle at the end of this 6-second interval of time.

17. A train, being brought to rest with uniform retardation, travels $30\,\mathrm{m}$ in 2 seconds, then a further $30\,\mathrm{m}$ in 4 seconds. Find the retardation of the train and the additional time it takes to come to rest.

18. A particle is projected vertically upwards from a point A. Given that it rises $15\,\mathrm{m}$ in the third second of its motion, find its initial speed and the maximum height above A that it reaches.

19. A bus sets off from a bus station P. It accelerates uniformly for T_1 seconds, covering a distance of $300\,\mathrm{m}$. It travels at a speed of $V\,\mathrm{km/h}$ for T_2 seconds, covering a further distance of $1250\,\mathrm{m}$. It then decelerates uniformly for T_3 seconds, coming to rest at a bus stop Q. If the total time taken is 3 minutes and $2T_1 = 3T_3$, find the distance from P to Q and the values of T_1, T_2, T_3 and V.

20. A train stops at a station A. It then accelerates at $0\cdot1\,\mathrm{m\,s^{-2}}$ for 5 minutes, reaching a speed of $V\,\mathrm{m\,s^{-1}}$. It continues at this speed for 12 minutes, then the brakes are applied for 3 minutes, bringing the train to rest with uniform retardation at a station B. Find the value of V and the distance AB.

21. A train stops at two stations $24\,\mathrm{km}$ apart. It takes 3 minutes to accelerate uniformly to a speed of $40\,\mathrm{m\,s^{-1}}$ then maintains this speed until it comes to rest with uniform retardation in a distance of $1200\,\mathrm{m}$. Find the time taken for the journey.

22. Two stations A and B are $10\,\mathrm{km}$ apart. A train travelling at a constant speed of $144\,\mathrm{km/h}$ passes station A at 10.00 hours. At a distance $d\,\mathrm{km}$ from B the brakes are applied, producing a constant retardation of $0\cdot4\,\mathrm{m\,s^{-2}}$. If the train comes to rest at station B, find the value of d and the time at which the train reaches B.

23. A particle accelerates from rest at a constant rate of $3\,\mathrm{m\,s^{-2}}$ to a speed of $V\,\mathrm{m\,s^{-1}}$. It continues to move at that speed for a certain time, then decelerates at a constant rate of $1\cdot5\,\mathrm{m\,s^{-2}}$. If the total time taken is one minute and the total distance travelled is $1\,\mathrm{km}$, find the value of V.

24. A car travelling along a straight level road at a constant speed of 54 km/h passes a second car as it starts to accelerate from rest at a uniform rate of $0.5\,\text{m}\,\text{s}^{-2}$. Find the time that elapses and the distance covered when the second car draws level with the first.

25. A ball is thrown vertically upwards from a point A with a speed of $20\,\text{m}\,\text{s}^{-1}$. At the same instant a second ball is dropped from a point B which is 60 m vertically above A. Find the time which elapses before the two balls meet and their height above A at this instant.

26. A stone is dropped from the top of a tower. After one second another stone is thrown vertically downwards from the same point at a speed of $15\,\text{m}\,\text{s}^{-1}$. If the stones reach the ground simultaneously, find the height of the tower.

4.3 Projectiles

Any particle which is given a non-zero initial velocity and then moves freely under gravity may be described as a *projectile*. In elementary work it is assumed that projectiles move in a vertical plane with constant downward acceleration g. The point of projection is taken as the origin O of a Cartesian coordinate system with the x-axis horizontal and the y-axis vertical. If at time t the projectile is at the point (x, y) then its displacement from O has horizontal component x and vertical component y. Thus the horizontal and vertical components of the velocity are dx/dt and dy/dt. Using a dot to indicate differentiation with respect to time these components are usually denoted by $\dot{x}$ and $\dot{y}$. Similarly the horizontal and vertical components of the acceleration are $\ddot{x}$ and $\ddot{y}$ respectively.

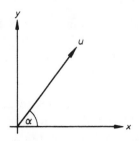

Consider a particle projected with initial velocity u at an angle α to the horizontal, the horizontal and vertical components of this velocity being $u\cos\alpha$ and $u\sin\alpha$ respectively. Since the particle has a constant downward acceleration of magnitude g, $\ddot{x} = 0$ and $\ddot{y} = -g$.

Thus the constant acceleration formulae derived in the previous section can now be applied to both horizontal and vertical motion. Using the equations $v = u + at$ and $s = ut + \frac{1}{2}at^2$,

$$\dot{x} = u\cos\alpha \qquad\qquad \dot{y} = u\sin\alpha - gt$$
$$x = ut\cos\alpha \qquad\qquad y = ut\sin\alpha - \tfrac{1}{2}gt^2.$$

Most projectile problems can be solved using one or more of these four equations.

The equation of the *trajectory* or path of the particle is obtained by eliminating from the expressions for x and y.

Writing $t = \dfrac{x}{u \cos \alpha}$, $\quad y = u \cdot \dfrac{x}{u \cos \alpha} \cdot \sin \alpha - \dfrac{1}{2}g\left(\dfrac{x}{u \cos \alpha}\right)^2$

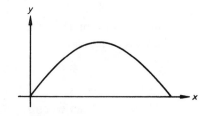

$$\therefore \quad y = x \tan \alpha - \frac{gx^2 \sec^2 \alpha}{2u^2}.$$

As shown in the sketch this is the equation of a parabola.

Example 1 A particle is projected from a point O on a horizontal plane with a speed of $50\,\mathrm{m\,s^{-1}}$ at an angle of $40°$ to the horizontal. Find (a) the velocity of the particle after 2 seconds, (b) the greatest height reached by the particle. [Take $g = 9\cdot8$.]

The equations for the motion of the particle are

$\dot{x} = 50 \cos 40°$ $\qquad\qquad$ $\dot{y} = 50 \sin 40° - gt$
$x = 50t \cos 40°$ $\qquad\qquad$ $y = 50t \sin 40° - \tfrac{1}{2}gt^2$.

(a)

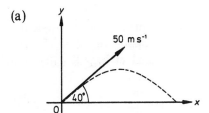 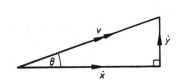

Let the velocity of the particle after 2 seconds be $v\,\mathrm{m\,s^{-1}}$ at an angle θ to the horizontal.

When $t = 2$, $\quad \dot{x} = 50 \cos 40°$ $\quad \dot{y} = 50 \sin 40° - 9\cdot8 \times 2$
$\therefore \quad v = \sqrt{(\dot{x}^2 + \dot{y}^2)} \approx 40\cdot3$
and $\quad \tan \theta = \dot{y}/\dot{x}$, $\quad \theta \approx 18\cdot1°$.

[These results were obtained using a calculator, storing the value $\dot{y} = 12\cdot5394$ in the memory.]

Thus the velocity after 2 seconds is $40\cdot3\,\mathrm{m\,s^{-1}}$ at an angle $18\cdot1°$ above the horizontal.

(b) When the particle reaches its greatest height, $\dot{y} = 0$

$\therefore \quad 50 \sin 40° - gt = 0 \quad$ and $\quad t = 50 \sin 40°/g$

For this value of t,

$$y = \frac{(50 \sin 40°)^2}{g} - \frac{1}{2}g\left(\frac{50 \sin 40°}{g}\right)^2 = \frac{(50 \sin 40°)^2}{2g} \approx 52\cdot7$$

$\therefore \quad$ the greatest height reached by the particle is $52\cdot7\,\mathrm{m}$.

Example 2 A stone is thrown horizontally from the edge of a cliff 40 m above the sea. Given that the stone travels 60 m horizontally before it hits the water, find the time for which it is in the air and its initial speed. [Take $g = 9 \cdot 8$.]

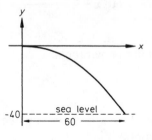

Let the initial speed of the stone be $u \, \mathrm{m\,s^{-1}}$, then after t seconds,

$$x = ut \quad y = -\tfrac{1}{2}gt^2.$$

Let the time for which the stone is in the air be T seconds, then when $t = T$, $x = 60$ and $y = -40$

$$\therefore \quad 60 = uT \text{ and } -40 = -\tfrac{1}{2} \times 9 \cdot 8 T^2.$$

Hence

$$T = \sqrt{\left(\frac{40}{4 \cdot 9}\right)} = \sqrt{\left(\frac{400}{49}\right)} = \frac{20}{7} = 2\frac{6}{7}$$

and

$$u = \frac{60}{T} = 60 \times \frac{7}{20} = 21$$

$\therefore$ the stone is in the air for $2\dfrac{6}{7}$ seconds and its initial speed is $21 \, \mathrm{m\,s^{-1}}$.

If a particle is projected from a point O on a horizontal plane and strikes the plane again at the point P, then the distance OP is called the *range* of the projectile. The time which the particle takes to travel from O to P is called the *time of flight*.

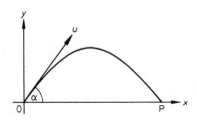

Consider again a particle projected from O with initial velocity u and angle of projection α. Let the range of the particle on the horizontal plane through O be R and the time of flight be T. The horizontal and vertical displacements of the particle at time t are given by

$$x = ut \cos \alpha, \quad y = ut \sin \alpha - \tfrac{1}{2}gt^2$$

When $t = T$, $x = R$ and $y = 0$

$$\therefore \quad R = uT \cos \alpha, \quad 0 = uT \sin \alpha - \tfrac{1}{2}gT^2$$

Since $T \neq 0$, $u \sin \alpha - \tfrac{1}{2}gT = 0 \quad \therefore \quad T = 2u \sin \alpha / g$

Thus

$$R = u \cos \alpha \cdot \frac{2u \sin \alpha}{g} = \frac{u^2}{g} \cdot 2 \sin \alpha \cos \alpha = \frac{u^2 \sin 2\alpha}{g}$$

Hence the range of the particle is $u^2 \sin 2\alpha / g$ and its time of flight is $2u \sin \alpha / g$.

If u is fixed, but α can be varied, the maximum range of the particle is given by $\sin 2\alpha = 1$, i.e. $\alpha = 45°$.

Hence the particle has a maximum range of u^2/g when projected at $45°$ to the horizontal.

Example 3   A particle projected from a point O on horizontal ground, with speed $35\,\mathrm{m\,s^{-1}}$ and angle of projection θ, strikes the ground again at a point $75\,\mathrm{m}$ from O. Find the two possible values of θ. [Take $g = 9{\cdot}8$.]

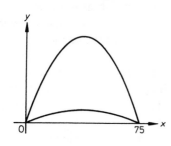

Taking O as origin, after t seconds

$$x = 35t \cos \theta$$
$$y = 35t \sin \theta - \tfrac{1}{2}gt^2$$

$\therefore$ $y = 0$ when $35t \sin \theta - \tfrac{1}{2}gt^2 = 0$
i.e. when $t = 0$ or $t = 70 \sin \theta / g$

$\therefore$ the time of flight of the particle is $70 \sin \theta / g$.
Since the range of the particle is $75\,\mathrm{m}$,

$$75 = 35 \cos \theta \, . \, \frac{70 \sin \theta}{g} = \frac{(35)^2}{9{\cdot}8} \, . \, 2 \sin \theta \cos \theta$$

Hence $$\sin 2\theta = 2 \sin \theta \cos \theta = \frac{75 \times 9{\cdot}8}{(35)^2} = 0{\cdot}6$$

Since θ is an acute angle, $2\theta = 36{\cdot}87°$ or $143{\cdot}13°$
$\therefore$ the two possible values of θ are $18{\cdot}4°$ and $71{\cdot}6°$.

Example 4   A particle is projected with speed $14\,\mathrm{m\,s^{-1}}$ at an angle θ to the horizontal. Find the values of θ for which the particle just clears an obstacle $5\,\mathrm{m}$ high and $10\,\mathrm{m}$ from the point of projection. [Take $g = 9{\cdot}8$.]

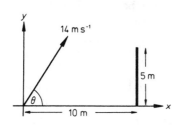

Taking the point of projection as origin, after t seconds

$$x = 14t \cos \theta$$
$$y = 14t \sin \theta - \tfrac{1}{2}gt^2$$

If the particle just clears the obstacle, then for some value of t, $x = 10$ and $y = 5$

$\therefore$ $10 = 14t \cos \theta$ and $5 = 14t \sin \theta - 4{\cdot}9t^2$.
Eliminating t from these equations,

$$5 = 14 \, . \, \frac{10}{14 \cos \theta} \, . \, \sin \theta - 4{\cdot}9 \left(\frac{10}{14 \cos \theta} \right)^2$$

$\Leftrightarrow$ $$5 = 10 \tan \theta - \frac{5}{2} \sec^2 \theta$$

$\Leftrightarrow$ $$2 = 4 \tan \theta - (1 + \tan^2 \theta)$$
$\Leftrightarrow$ $$\tan^2 \theta - 4 \tan \theta + 3 = 0$$
$\Leftrightarrow$ $$(\tan \theta - 1)(\tan \theta - 3) = 0.$$

Thus either $\tan \theta = 1$ or $\tan \theta = 3$.
Hence the particle just clears the obstacle if $\theta = 45°$ or $\theta = 71{\cdot}6°$.

Exercise 4.3

[In numerical questions take g as $9 \cdot 8 \, \mathrm{m \, s^{-2}}$.]

1. A particle is projected from a point on horizontal ground with speed $24 \cdot 5 \, \mathrm{m \, s^{-1}}$ at an angle of $30°$ to the horizontal. Find the time it takes to reach its greatest height. Find also the time of flight and the range of the particle.

2. A particle is projected horizontally with speed $30 \, \mathrm{m \, s^{-1}}$ from a point $19 \cdot 6 \, \mathrm{m}$ above horizontal ground. Find the horizontal distance it travels before striking the ground and its velocity as it strikes the ground.

3. A particle is projected from a point O on a horizontal plane with speed $35 \, \mathrm{m \, s^{-1}}$ at an angle of elevation θ, where $\tan \theta = 2$. Find the maximum height above the plane of the particle and the equation of its trajectory.

4. A golf ball is given initial velocity $30 \, \mathrm{m \, s^{-1}}$ at an angle α to the horizontal, where $\tan \alpha = 4/3$. The ball strikes the ground after T seconds at a horizontal distance of $90 \, \mathrm{m}$ from the point of projection and $k \, \mathrm{m}$ below it. Find the values of T and k. Find also the velocity of the ball when it strikes the ground.

5. A particle is projected from a point O $24 \cdot 5 \, \mathrm{m}$ above a horizontal plane. After 5 seconds it hits the plane at a point whose horizontal distance from O is $100 \, \mathrm{m}$. Find the horizontal and vertical components of the initial velocity of the particle and the greatest height it reaches above the plane.

6. A boy throws a ball horizontally from a point $4 \cdot 9 \, \mathrm{m}$ above horizontal ground. What is the minimum speed at which the ball must be thrown to clear a fence $2 \cdot 4 \, \mathrm{m}$ high at a horizontal distance of $8 \, \mathrm{m}$ from the point of projection? Find the distance beyond the fence of the point at which the ball strikes the ground if projected at this minimum speed.

7. A particle is projected from a point on a horizontal plane with velocity u and angle of projection α. The range of the particle is R and its time of flight T. Show that the particle reaches its greatest height h at time $\frac{1}{2}T$ and that $h = \frac{1}{4}R \tan \alpha$.

8. A gun fires shells with speed $210 \, \mathrm{m \, s^{-1}}$. Find the maximum range of the gun over horizontal ground. Find also the smaller angle of elevation at which a shell should be fired to hit a target at a distance of $3 \cdot 6 \, \mathrm{km}$.

9. A particle is projected from a point O on horizontal ground with an initial velocity whose horizontal and vertical components are $3u$ and $5u \, \mathrm{m \, s^{-1}}$ respectively. Find the equation of the trajectory of the particle. Given that it just clears an obstacle $5 \, \mathrm{m}$ high and $9 \, \mathrm{m}$ from O, find the value of u and the distance from O of the point at which the particle strikes the ground.

10. A ball thrown with speed $u \, \mathrm{m \, s^{-1}}$ and angle of projection α just clears the top of a fence $3 \cdot 6 \, \mathrm{m}$ high and a horizontal distance of $9 \cdot 6 \, \mathrm{m}$ from the point of

projection. Find u and α given that as the ball passes over the fence it is moving in a horizontal direction.

11. A projectile with initial speed $u\,\mathrm{m\,s}^{-1}$ has a maximum range of 80 m on a horizontal plane. Find the value of u. Given that the angle of projection is α, find the set of values of α for which the range is greater than 40 m.

12. The horizontal and vertical components of the initial velocity of a projectile are u and $3u$ respectively. Find in terms of u and g (a) the range of the projectile on the horizontal plane through the point of projection, (b) the times at which the particle is moving in a direction at $45°$ to the horizontal.

13. A particle is projected with speed u and angle of projection α. If after T seconds the velocity of the particle is perpendicular to its initial velocity, find an expression for T in terms of u, α and g. Comment on the significance of your answer in the cases $\alpha = 0°$ and $\alpha = 90°$.

14. A gun is fired from a vehicle moving along a straight horizontal road at speed U. Relative to the vehicle shells are fired with speed V and elevation θ. Find an expression for the range of the gun along the road ahead of the vehicle.

15. A particle is fired with speed V from a point O of a horizontal plane, the angle of elevation being $\arctan\left(\frac{2}{3}\right)$. The particle strikes the plane at a point A. Find the distance OA. Show that the same point A could have been reached by firing the particle with the same speed from O at an angle of elevation $\arctan\left(\frac{3}{2}\right)$. Find the difference in the times of flight for the two trajectories.   (O&C)

16. A projectile is fired with initial speed V at an angle θ to the horizontal. It passes through two points A and B at the same height h above the point of projection. Find the speed of the projectile at A, and the time it takes to travel from A to B. Given that $AB = 2h$ and $V^2 = 4gh$, find the angle θ.   (L)

17. Prove that two particles projected from the same point at the same time, but with different velocities, can never collide while moving freely under gravity.

18. Two particles are projected with the same speed from a point A, and land at B on the same horizontal level as A. If the greatest heights of the particles are in the ratio $4:1$, find the angles of projection and the ratio of AB to the maximum range with the same speed of projection.

19. A projectile is fired from a point P with speed $V\,\mathrm{m\,s}^{-1}$ and angle of elevation θ, where $\cos\theta = 0\cdot8$. At the same instant a target moving vertically upwards with constant speed $13\,\mathrm{m\,s}^{-1}$ passes through a point Q in the same horizontal plane as P and at a distance of 480 m from P. Given that the projectile hits the target, find the value of V. Find also the speed at which the projectile is travelling when it hits the target.

20. A particle is projected from a point A on horizontal ground such that the horizontal and vertical components of its initial velocity are u_1 and u_2 respectively. At the same instant a particle is projected from a point B at a height h vertically above A. The horizontal and vertical components of its initial velocity are v_1 and v_2. Find the time of flight of the first particle and show that the particles will collide before hitting the ground, provided that $u_1 = v_1$ and $2u_2(u_2 - v_2) > gh$.

4.4 Differentiation of position vectors

In §3.1 it was shown that if a moving particle has position vector $\mathbf{r}$, velocity $\mathbf{v}$ and acceleration $\mathbf{a}$, then

$$\mathbf{v} = \frac{d\mathbf{r}}{dt} \text{ or } \dot{\mathbf{r}} \quad \text{and} \quad \mathbf{a} = \frac{d\mathbf{v}}{dt} = \frac{d^2\mathbf{r}}{dt^2} \text{ or } \ddot{\mathbf{r}}.$$

In general, the basic rules for differentiation still hold when vectors are involved.

Thus
$$\frac{d}{dt}\left(\mathbf{r}_1 + \mathbf{r}_2\right) = \frac{d\mathbf{r}_1}{dt} + \frac{d\mathbf{r}_2}{dt},$$

and if $\mathbf{r}$ is of the form $f(t)\mathbf{c}$, where $\mathbf{c}$ is a constant vector,

then
$$\frac{d\mathbf{r}}{dt} = \frac{d}{dt}\left\{f(t)\mathbf{c}\right\} = \frac{df}{dt}\mathbf{c}.$$

Hence if a position vector $\mathbf{r}$ is expressed in terms of the standard set of unit vectors $\mathbf{i}$, $\mathbf{j}$ and $\mathbf{k}$, then

$$\boxed{\begin{aligned} \mathbf{r} &= x\mathbf{i} + y\mathbf{j} + z\mathbf{k} \\ \mathbf{v} &= \dot{\mathbf{r}} = \dot{x}\mathbf{i} + \dot{y}\mathbf{j} + \dot{z}\mathbf{k} \\ \mathbf{a} &= \ddot{\mathbf{r}} = \ddot{x}\mathbf{i} + \ddot{y}\mathbf{j} + \ddot{z}\mathbf{k}. \end{aligned}}$$

Using these results we can extend some of the earlier work in this chapter to motion in two and three dimensions.

Example 1   A particle moves so that after t seconds its position vector $\mathbf{r}$ is given by $\mathbf{r} = (4t-1)\mathbf{i} + t^2\mathbf{j} + (15t - t^3)\mathbf{k}$. Find vector expressions for its velocity and acceleration at time t. Find also its speed after 3 seconds.

$$\mathbf{r} = (4t-1)\mathbf{i} + t^2\mathbf{j} + (15t - t^3)\mathbf{k}$$
$$\therefore \quad \mathbf{v} = \dot{\mathbf{r}} = 4\mathbf{i} + 2t\mathbf{j} + (15 - 3t^2)\mathbf{k}$$
$$\therefore \quad \mathbf{a} = \ddot{\mathbf{r}} = 2\mathbf{j} - 6t\mathbf{k}.$$

Hence the velocity and acceleration at time t are given by

$$\mathbf{v} = 4\mathbf{i} + 2t\mathbf{j} + (15 - 3t^2)\mathbf{k} \quad \text{and} \quad \mathbf{a} = 2\mathbf{j} - 6t\mathbf{k}.$$

When $t = 3$, $\mathbf{v} = 4\mathbf{i} + 6\mathbf{j} - 12\mathbf{k}$

$\therefore$ $|\mathbf{v}| = \sqrt{\{4^2 + 6^2 + (-12)^2\}} = \sqrt{(16 + 36 + 144)} = \sqrt{196} = 14$.

Hence after 3 seconds the speed of the particle is $14\,\mathrm{m\,s}^{-1}$.

Example 2   A particle moves so that at time t its velocity is given by $\mathbf{v} = 10t\mathbf{i} + (3 - 6t^2)\mathbf{k}$. Given that when $t = 1$ the particle is at the point with position vector $\mathbf{j} + \mathbf{k}$, find an expression for its position vector $\mathbf{r}$ at time t.

$$\mathbf{v} = \dot{\mathbf{r}} = 10t\mathbf{i} + (3 - 6t^2)\mathbf{k}$$

Integrating $\mathbf{r} = 5t^2\mathbf{i} + (3t - 2t^3)\mathbf{k} + \mathbf{c}$

where $\mathbf{c}$ is a constant vector.

When $t = 1$, $\mathbf{r} = \mathbf{j} + \mathbf{k}$ $\therefore$ $\mathbf{j} + \mathbf{k} = 5\mathbf{i} + \mathbf{k} + \mathbf{c}$

i.e. $\mathbf{c} = -5\mathbf{i} + \mathbf{j}$

Hence $\mathbf{r} = 5t^2\mathbf{i} + (3t - 2t^3)\mathbf{k} - 5\mathbf{i} + \mathbf{j}$

i.e. $\mathbf{r} = (5t^2 - 5)\mathbf{i} + \mathbf{j} + (3t - 2t^3)\mathbf{k}$.

Consider now a particle with initial velocity $\mathbf{u}$ and constant acceleration $\mathbf{a}$.

$$\frac{d\mathbf{v}}{dt} = \mathbf{a}, \text{ where } \mathbf{a} \text{ is constant}$$

Integrating $\mathbf{v} = \mathbf{a}t + \mathbf{c}$, where $\mathbf{c}$ is constant

When $t = 0$, $\mathbf{v} = \mathbf{u}$ $\therefore$ $\mathbf{c} = \mathbf{u}$.

Thus $\mathbf{v} = \dfrac{d\mathbf{r}}{dt} = \mathbf{u} + \mathbf{a}t$.

Integrating again and taking the initial position of the particle as origin,
$$\mathbf{r} = \mathbf{u}t + \tfrac{1}{2}\mathbf{a}t^2.$$
Hence $\mathbf{v} = \mathbf{u} + \mathbf{a}t$ $\mathbf{r} = \mathbf{u}t + \tfrac{1}{2}\mathbf{a}t^2$.
Eliminating $\mathbf{a}$, we also have $\mathbf{r} = \tfrac{1}{2}(\mathbf{u} + \mathbf{v})t$.
These results are the vector forms of the constant acceleration formulae derived in §4.2.

If the acceleration due to gravity is denoted by the constant vector $\mathbf{g}$, then by substituting $\mathbf{a} = \mathbf{g}$ we obtain the vector equations governing the motion of a projectile, namely

$$\mathbf{v} = \mathbf{u} + \mathbf{g}t \quad \text{and} \quad \mathbf{r} = \mathbf{u}t + \tfrac{1}{2}\mathbf{g}t^2.$$

Using the notation of §12.3 and horizontal and vertical unit vectors $\mathbf{i}$ and $\mathbf{j}$, let $\mathbf{r} = x\mathbf{i} + y\mathbf{j}$, $\mathbf{v} = \dot{x}\mathbf{i} + \dot{y}\mathbf{j}$, $\mathbf{u} = (u\cos\alpha)\mathbf{i} + (u\sin\alpha)\mathbf{j}$ and $\mathbf{g} = -g\mathbf{j}$, then

$$\dot{x}\mathbf{i} + \dot{y}\mathbf{j} = (u\cos\alpha)\mathbf{i} + (u\sin\alpha - gt)\mathbf{j}$$
and $x\mathbf{i} + y\mathbf{j} = (ut\cos\alpha)\mathbf{i} + (ut\sin\alpha - \tfrac{1}{2}gt^2)\mathbf{j}$.

Clearly in this form the vector equations correspond exactly to the results derived in the previous section.

Example 3   A particle is projected from a point O with initial velocity represented by the vector $\mathbf{i}+2\mathbf{j}$. Find vector expressions for its velocity $\mathbf{v}$ and its displacement $\mathbf{r}$ from O at time t. [Take $g = 10$.]

Using the equations $\mathbf{v} = \mathbf{u}+\mathbf{g}t$ and $\mathbf{r} = \mathbf{u}t+\frac{1}{2}\mathbf{g}t^2$,
where $\mathbf{u} = \mathbf{i}+2\mathbf{j}$ and $\mathbf{g} = -10\mathbf{j}$,

$$\mathbf{v} = (\mathbf{i}+2\mathbf{j})-10t\mathbf{j} = \mathbf{i}+(2-10t)\mathbf{j}$$

and
$$\mathbf{r} = (\mathbf{i}+2\mathbf{j})t+\tfrac{1}{2}(-10\mathbf{j})t^2 = t\mathbf{i}+(2t-5t^2)\mathbf{j}.$$

[Note that although vector equations can be used in any projectile problem, in elementary work many students will prefer the methods of §4.3.]

Exercise 4.4

[Use SI units and take $g = 10$.]

1.   A particle moves such that its position vector at time t is $\mathbf{r}$. Find vector expressions for its velocity and acceleration at time t given that
(a) $\mathbf{r} = 3t\mathbf{i}-2\mathbf{j}+2t^3\mathbf{k}$,   (b) $\mathbf{r} = (t^2+1)\mathbf{i}+t^4\mathbf{j}-6t\mathbf{k}$.

2.   A particle moves such that at time t its position vector is $\mathbf{r} = t^2\mathbf{i}+(2-3t)\mathbf{j}+3t^2(t-2)\mathbf{k}$. Find the initial speed of the particle and its speed after 2 seconds.

3.   A particle moves such that at time t its velocity is given by $\mathbf{v} = 3\mathbf{i}+4t\mathbf{j}+(1-3t^2)\mathbf{k}$. Given that when $t = 2$ the position vector of the particle is $6(\mathbf{j}-\mathbf{k})$, find an expression for its position vector at time t.

4.   A particle moves such that at time t its acceleration is given by $\mathbf{a} = 6t\mathbf{i}-4\mathbf{k}$. Initially the particle has velocity vector $\mathbf{i}+\mathbf{j}$ and position vector $3\mathbf{j}$. Find expressions for its velocity and position vectors at time t.

In questions 5 to 8 the directions of the unit vectors $\mathbf{i}$ and $\mathbf{j}$ are horizontal and vertically upward respectively.

5.   A particle is projected from a point O with initial velocity represented by the vector $3\mathbf{i}+2\mathbf{j}$. Find vector expressions for its velocity $\mathbf{v}$ and its displacement $\mathbf{r}$ from O at time t.

6.   A particle is projected from a point O on a horizontal plane with initial velocity represented by the vector $40\mathbf{i}+25\mathbf{j}$. Find the greatest height reached by the particle, its range and time of flight.

7.   A particle is projected from a point O with speed $20\,\mathrm{m\,s^{-1}}$ at an angle of $60°$ to the horizontal. Find vector expressions for its velocity $\mathbf{v}$ and its displacement $\mathbf{r}$ from O at time t.

8.   A stone is thrown from the top of a cliff with initial velocity vector $8\mathbf{i}-\mathbf{j}$. If the stone hits the sea below after 3 seconds, find the height of the cliff and the horizontal distance travelled by the stone. Find also the speed at which the stone is travelling when it hits the water.

Exercise 4.5 (miscellaneous)

[In numerical questions take g as $10 \, \text{m s}^{-2}$.]

1. A particle is moving in a straight line such that its displacement from a fixed point after t seconds is s metres, where $s = 2t^3 - 13t^2 + 20t$. Find the total distance travelled and the maximum speed attained by the particle in the first 4 seconds of its motion. Find also the range of values of t for which the acceleration of the particle is negative.

2. A particle moving in a straight line starts from rest at a point A. Its acceleration at time t is $(45 + 12t - 9t^2) \, \text{m s}^{-2}$. If the particle comes to rest instantaneously at a point B, find the distance AB and the time the particle takes to reach B. Find also the maximum acceleration and the maximum speed attained in that time.

3. Two particles A and B move along a straight line starting from a point O such that at time t their displacements from O are s_1 and s_2 respectively. If $s_1 = 5t^2(t+7)$ and $s_2 = t^3(t+3)$, find (a) the time at which the particles again meet, (b) an expression for the velocity of A relative to B, (c) the range of values of t for which A is travelling at a greater speed than B.

4. Due to track repairs a train retards uniformly, with retardation $1 \, \text{m s}^{-2}$, from a speed of $40 \, \text{m s}^{-1}$ at A to a speed of $10 \, \text{m s}^{-1}$ at B. The train travels from B to C, a distance of $3 \cdot 5 \, \text{km}$, at a constant speed of $10 \, \text{m s}^{-1}$ and then accelerates uniformly, with acceleration $0 \cdot 2 \, \text{m s}^{-2}$ so that its speed at D is $40 \, \text{m s}^{-1}$. Sketch the velocity-time graph for the journey from A to D, and show that the distance from A to D is $8 \, \text{km}$. Show that the journey from A to D takes $330 \, \text{s}$ more than it would if the train travelled at a constant speed of $40 \, \text{m s}^{-1}$ from A to D.   (C)

5. Two trains, P and Q, travel by the same route from rest at station A to rest at station B. Train P has constant acceleration f for the first third of the time, constant speed for the second third and constant retardation f for the last third of the time. Train Q has constant acceleration f for the first third of the distance, constant speed for the second third and constant retardation f for the last third of the distance. Show that the times taken by the two trains are in the ratio $3\sqrt{3} : 5$.   (L)

6. A bus starts from rest and moves along a straight road with constant acceleration f until its speed is V; it then continues at constant speed V. When the bus starts, a car is at a distance b behind the bus and is moving in the same direction with constant speed u. Find the distance of the car behind the bus at time t after the bus has started (i) for $0 < t < V/f$, (ii) for $t > V/f$. Show that the car cannot overtake the bus during the period $0 < t < V/f$ unless $u^2 > 2fb$. Find the least distance between the car and the bus in the case when $u^2 < 2fb$ and $u < V$. State briefly what will happen if $u^2 < 2fb$ and $u > V$.   (JMB)

7. A man descending in a lift at constant speed $V \, \text{m s}^{-1}$ throws a ball vertically upwards with speed $U \, \text{m s}^{-1}$ relative to the lift. Find the time that elapses before the ball (a) has zero velocity relative to the lift, (b) returns to the man's hand.

8.   A batsman hits a cricket ball with initial speed 25 m/s at an elevation of 50°. Find the greatest height attained, the range on level ground and the time of flight. Show that it will clear the roof of a pavilion 10 m high which is at a distance of 50 m from the batsman.   (L)

9.   A particle P, projected from a point A on horizontal ground, moves freely under gravity and hits the ground again at B. Referred to A as origin, AB as x-axis and the upward vertical at A as y-axis, the equation of the path of P is $y = x - x^2/40$, where x and y are measured in metres. Calculate (i) the distance AB, (ii) the greatest height above AB attained by P, (iii) the magnitude and the direction of the velocity of P at A, (iv) the time taken by P to reach B from A. Calculate the coordinates of the points on the path of P at the two instants when the speed of P is 15 m/s.   (AEB 1978)

10. A particle P is projected from a point A on a horizontal plane with speed V m/s at an angle of elevation α. The particle strikes the horizontal plane again at B, where $AB = 160$ metres. Show that $V^2 \sin 2\alpha = 1600$. A second particle Q is projected from A with the same speed V m/s at an angle of elevation $\alpha - 30°$ and strikes the horizontal plane at C, where C is the mid-point of AB. Find the values of V and α and show that the time of flight of Q is $8 \sin 15°$ seconds. Given that P and Q are projected from A simultaneously, find, at the instant when Q reaches C, the angle between the tangent to the path of P and the horizontal.   (AEB 1978)

11. A particle is projected from a point O with a speed of $10 \, \mathrm{m \, s^{-1}}$ and angle of elevation θ. Given that the projectile just clears an obstacle of height h at a horizontal distance D from O, express in the form of a quadratic equation in $\tan \theta$ the relationship connecting θ, h and D. Show that provided that $D^2 + 20h < 100$, there are two distinct possible values of θ. Show further that if $h = 0$ the sum of these two values is 90°.

12. A point O lies on a horizontal plane, and the point A is at a height h vertically above O. A particle is projected from A with speed V at an angle α above the horizontal. Taking O as the origin and Oy vertically upwards, show that the equation of the path of the particle can be written in the form
$y = h - \dfrac{gx^2}{2V^2} + x \tan \alpha - \dfrac{gx^2}{2V^2} \tan^2 \alpha$. The particle hits the plane at the point
$B(r, 0)$. In the case when $V^2 = gh$ derive a quadratic equation for $\tan \alpha$ in terms of h and r, and show that $r \leqslant \sqrt{3h}$. For the same value of V show that $r = \sqrt{3h}$ when $\alpha = 30°$.   (JMB)

13. A particle is fired from the origin O with speed V at an angle of inclination α above the x-axis, which is horizontal. At the instant when the particle is at the highest point of its path, a second particle is fired from O with speed U at an angle of inclination β above the horizontal so that the particles collide at a point on the x-axis. Show that $\tan \beta = \frac{1}{4} \tan \alpha$. Show also that, if $\tan \alpha = 3$, then $8U^2 = 5V^2$.

14. *A* and *B* are points distant *a* apart on horizontal ground. A ball is thrown from *A* towards *B* with velocity *u* at an angle 2α ($< 90°$) to the horizontal, and simultaneously a second ball is thrown from *B* towards *A* with velocity v at an angle α to the horizontal. If the balls collide, show that $v = 2u\cos\alpha$ and hence that they collide after a time $t = a/u(2\cos 2\alpha + 1)$. Show also that (i) the two trajectories would have the same maximum height above *AB*, (ii) the range of the ball from *B* would always exceed the range of the ball from *A*. (W)

15. A particle *P* is set in motion at a point *A* and then moves such that at time *t* its position vector is $\mathbf{r} = 3(t-2)^2\mathbf{i} + 2\mathbf{j} - 4t(t-4)\mathbf{k}$. By considering the vector **AP**, show that the particle moves in a straight line and find a unit vector parallel to the direction of motion. Find also the time that has elapsed and the position vector of *P* when it comes instantaneously to rest.

16. [In this question the directions of the unit vectors **i** and **j** are horizontal and vertically upwards.] A particle projected from the origin *O* with initial velocity represented by the vector $u\mathbf{i} + v\mathbf{j}$ passes through the points *A* and *B* with position vectors $20(\mathbf{i}+\mathbf{j})$ and $25\mathbf{i}$ respectively. Find the values of *u* and *v*. Show that a particle projected from *O* with velocity vector $v\mathbf{i} + u\mathbf{j}$ also passes through *B*.

5 Newton's laws of motion

5.1 Newton's laws

The theory of elementary dynamics is based on three laws first stated by Newton† in the seventeenth century. Although slight discrepancies can be detected when comparing the predictions of Newtonian mechanics with the true motion of atomic particles travelling at high speed, and with certain astronomical observations (when results based on the theory of relativity are more reliable), Newton's laws can be used to describe the behaviour of moving objects with great accuracy.

> *Newton's first law*:   Every body continues in its state of rest or of uniform motion in a straight line unless compelled to change that state by external forces.

This law implies that a force changes the velocity of the body it acts upon. However, if two or more forces act on a body there will be no change in velocity unless the forces have a non-zero resultant. Newton's first law also implies that no force is required to maintain uniform motion, but practical experience tells us that the thrust of an engine is needed to drive a car along a horizontal road with uniform velocity. The explanation of this apparent contradiction is that the resultant force on the car is zero, the thrust of the engine exactly balancing the various forces opposing motion.

> *Newton's second law*:   The rate of change of momentum of a body is proportional to the applied force and has the direction of that force.

---

† *Newton, Sir Isaac* (1642–1727) English scientist and mathematician. He invented, a little before the German mathematician Leibnitz, differential calculus (1665) and integral calculus (1666). He did significant work on the nature of light and the construction of telescopes. However, Newton is chiefly remembered for his statement of the laws of dynamics and his theory of gravitation, which are explained in *Philosophiae Naturalis Principia Mathematica* (1687).

The *momentum* of a body is defined as the product of its mass and its velocity, i.e. the momentum of a particle of mass m moving with velocity v is the vector quantity mv. Thus for a particle of constant mass m,

$$\text{rate of change of momentum} = \frac{d}{dt}(mv) = m\frac{dv}{dt} = ma,$$

where a is the acceleration of the particle.

Hence Newton's second law states that, for a body of constant mass m, the quantity ma is proportional to the force F acting on the body, i.e. $F = kma$, where k is constant. The value of k depends on the units of measurement chosen for F, m and a. A newton is defined as the force which gives a mass of $1\,kg$ an acceleration of $1\,ms^{-2}$. Hence when using SI units, $k = 1$ and we obtain the fundamental equation of motion for a body of constant mass

$$\boxed{F = ma.}$$

Example 1   A particle of mass $5\,kg$ is moving with an acceleration of $3\,ms^{-2}$. Find the magnitude of the resultant force acting on the particle.

If the resultant force on the particle is F newtons, by Newton's second law, $F = 5 \times 3$.
Hence there is a force of $15\,N$ acting on the particle.

In Chapter 2 various ways of finding the resultant of a set of forces were discussed. Any of these methods, together with Newton's second law, can be used when finding the acceleration of a body moving under the action of two or more forces.

Example 2   A body of mass $8\,kg$ on a smooth horizontal plane is acted upon by horizontal forces of magnitudes 20, 12 and 16 newtons in the directions $N\,45°\,E$, due south and $S\,30°\,E$ respectively. Find the magnitude and direction of the acceleration of the body.

Let F be the resultant force on the body acting at an angle θ east of south and let a be the acceleration produced. If P and Q are the components of F in the directions south and east respectively, then resolving in these directions

$$\downarrow P = 12 + 16\cos 30° - 20\cos 45°$$
$$\rightarrow Q = 16\sin 30° + 20\sin 45°.$$

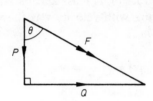

[By calculator $P = 11{\cdot}71426$, $Q = 22{\cdot}14214$.]

Using Newton's second law, $\mathbf{F} = 8\mathbf{a}$

$$\therefore \quad a = \frac{1}{8}F = \frac{1}{8}\sqrt{(P^2 + Q^2)} \approx 3{\cdot}13$$

and $\tan \theta = Q/P$, $\theta \approx 62{\cdot}1°$.

Hence the body moves with an acceleration of $3{\cdot}13\,\mathrm{m\,s}^{-2}$ in the direction S $62{\cdot}1°$ E.

When a body is moving in a straight line under the action of constant forces then its acceleration is constant. Hence the motion is governed by the constant acceleration equations derived in §4.2.

Example 3   A particle of mass $2\,\mathrm{kg}$ starting from rest is acted on by a force of $4\,\mathrm{N}$ for 5 seconds. Find its acceleration and the speed attained. The particle is then brought to rest in a further 8 seconds by a constant resistance of $R\,\mathrm{N}$. Find the value of R and the total distance travelled by the particle.

Let $a_1\,\mathrm{m\,s}^{-2}$ and $a_2\,\mathrm{m\,s}^{-2}$ be the accelerations of the particle in the two parts of its motion and let $V\,\mathrm{m\,s}^{-1}$ be the speed attained after 5 seconds.

By Newton's 2nd law, $4 = 2a_1$ $\therefore$ $a_1 = 2$.

Using the formula $v = u + at$, substituting $u = 0$, $v = V$, $a = 2$, $t = 5$:
$V = 0 + 2 \times 5 = 10$.

Hence the initial acceleration of the particle is $2\,\mathrm{m\,s}^{-2}$ and the speed attained is $10\,\mathrm{m\,s}^{-1}$.

Using the formula $v = u + at$, substituting $u = 10$, $v = 0$, $a = a_2$, $t = 8$
$0 = 10 + 8a_2$ $\therefore$ $a_2 = -1{\cdot}25$.

By Newton's 2nd law $R = 2 \times 1{\cdot}25 = 2{\cdot}5$.

Hence the resistance is of magnitude $2{\cdot}5\,\mathrm{N}$.

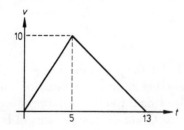

The total distance travelled is represented by the area under the velocity-time graph for the motion

$\therefore$ total distance travelled

$= \frac{1}{2} \times 10 \times 13\,\mathrm{m} = 65\,\mathrm{m}$.

Newton's third law: To every action there is an equal and opposite reaction.

This means that if a body A exerts a force on a body B, then B exerts an equal and opposite force on A. For instance, consider a body of weight W. The gravitational pull of the earth on the body is W, but Newton's third law tells us that the body also exerts a force of magnitude W on the earth. Similarly, when a body is in contact with a smooth surface, the surface exerts a force called the normal reaction on the body. As stated in Newton's third law, the body exerts an equal and opposite force on the surface. This law will be particularly useful when examining systems involving two or more objects in contact.

Exercise 5.1

[Vector quantities are measured in SI units.]

1. A particle of mass $12\,\text{kg}$ is moving with an acceleration of $4\,\text{m s}^{-2}$. Find the magnitude of the resultant force on the particle.

2. Find the acceleration of a mass of $45\,\text{kg}$ acted upon by a single force of $9\,\text{N}$.

3. A resultant force of $36\,\text{N}$ acting on a particle produces an acceleration of $3\,\text{m s}^{-2}$. Find the mass of the particle.

4. A particle of mass $8\,\text{kg}$ is pulled along a smooth horizontal plane by a horizontal string. Find the tension in the string when the acceleration of the particle is $5\,\text{m s}^{-2}$.

5. A particle of mass $15\,\text{kg}$ is acted upon by a resultant force represented by the vector $30\mathbf{i} - 75\mathbf{j}$. Find, in vector form, the acceleration of the particle.

6. A particle of mass $4\,\text{kg}$ is moving with acceleration vector $3\mathbf{i} + \mathbf{j}$. Find a vector representing the resultant force on the particle.

7. Forces of magnitude $5\,\text{N}$ and $9\,\text{N}$ act at an angle of $50°$ on a particle of mass $2\,\text{kg}$. Find the magnitude and direction of the acceleration produced.

8. Two forces of magnitude $16\,\text{N}$ and $24\,\text{N}$ act on a particle of mass $5\,\text{kg}$. Given that an acceleration of $6\,\text{m s}^{-2}$ is produced, find the angle between the lines of action of the two forces.

9. Forces represented by the vectors $3\mathbf{i} + \mathbf{j}$, $-5\mathbf{i} + 2\mathbf{j}$, $4\mathbf{i} - 5\mathbf{j}$ and $2\mathbf{i} - \mathbf{j}$ act on a particle of mass $0\cdot8\,\text{kg}$ moving on a smooth horizontal plane. Given that $\mathbf{i}$ and $\mathbf{j}$ are unit vectors in the directions due east and due north respectively, find the magnitude and direction of the acceleration of the particle.

10. A body of mass $2\,\text{kg}$ on a smooth horizontal plane is acted upon by horizontal forces of magnitudes 9, 4 and 7 newtons in the directions due west, $\text{N}\,20°\,\text{W}$ and $\text{S}\,75°\,\text{E}$ respectively. Find the magnitude and direction of the acceleration of the body.

11. A train of mass 300 000 kg travelling at $0.3\,\mathrm{m\,s^{-1}}$ is brought to rest at a station by buffers exerting an average force of 50 000 N. Find the time taken to bring the train to rest.

12. A particle of mass 20 kg is brought to rest in a distance of 600 m from a speed of $30\,\mathrm{m\,s^{-1}}$ by a constant retarding force. Find the magnitude of this force.

13. A body is moving in a straight line with a speed of $40\,\mathrm{m\,s^{-1}}$. A retarding force of 25 N reduces its speed to $15\,\mathrm{m\,s^{-1}}$ in 10 seconds. Find the mass of the body.

14. A car of mass 800 kg is moving along a straight horizontal road under the action of a constant resultant force of 1000 N. Find its speed when it has moved 40 m from rest.

15. A particle of mass 5 kg starting from rest is acted on by a force of 12 N for 10 seconds. The particle continues to move with constant velocity for a further 10 seconds. It is then brought to rest by a constant resistance of R N in a further time of 15 seconds. Find the value of R and the total distance travelled.

16. A particle of mass 4 kg starts from rest and moves under the action of a constant force of F newtons for 12 seconds. It is then brought to rest in a further 8 seconds by a constant retarding force of R newtons. If the total distance travelled is 200 m, find the maximum speed attained and the values of F and R.

5.2 Further applications

As stated in §4.2, an object falling freely under gravity has a constant downward acceleration denoted by g. Thus if a body of mass m kg has a weight of W N, then by Newton's second law,

$$W = mg.$$

Hence the force due to the gravitational pull of the earth on a body of mass m kg is of magnitude mg N.

[In this and later chapters the value of g will be taken as $9.8\,\mathrm{m\,s^{-2}}$ unless otherwise stated.]

Example 1   A package of mass 5 kg is being lifted by means of a vertical cable. If the tension in the cable is 60 N, find the acceleration of the package.

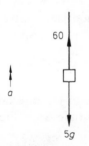

Let the acceleration of the package be $a\,\mathrm{m\,s^{-2}}$ vertically upwards.
Applying Newton's 2nd law vertically

$$\uparrow\,60 - 5g = 5a$$

$$\therefore\quad a = 12 - g = 12 - 9.8 = 2.2.$$

Hence the acceleration of the package is $2.2\,\mathrm{m\,s^{-2}}$.

[Note that to avoid confusion in diagrams showing both forces and accelerations, the forces are denoted by single-headed arrows and the accelerations by double-headed arrows.]

Example 2 A lift descends with an acceleration of $1\cdot5\,\mathrm{m\,s^{-2}}$, then moves with constant speed until it is retarded at $1\,\mathrm{m\,s^{-2}}$. A suitcase of mass 20 kg stands on the floor of the lift during the journey. Find the magnitude of the force it exerts on the floor of the lift at each stage of the journey.

Let R_1, R_2 and R_3 newtons be the reactions of the floor on the suitcase.

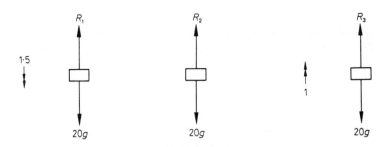

Applying Newton's 2nd law vertically in each case

$\downarrow 20g - R_1 = 20 \times 1\cdot5$ $\therefore$ $R_1 = 20g - 30 = 196 - 30 = 166$
$\uparrow R_2 - 20g = 0$ $\therefore$ $R_2 = 20g = 196$
$\uparrow R_3 - 20g = 20 \times 1$ $\therefore$ $R_3 = 20g + 20 = 196 + 20 = 216.$

By Newton's third law, the force exerted by the suitcase on the floor is equal in magnitude to the reaction of the floor on the suitcase. Hence the forces exerted by the suitcase on the floor of the lift are 166, 196 then 216 newtons.

Example 3 A particle of mass 4 kg is being pulled across a smooth horizontal plane by a string inclined at 40° to the horizontal. If the acceleration of the particle is $5\,\mathrm{m\,s^{-2}}$, find the tension in the string and the reaction between the particle and the plane.

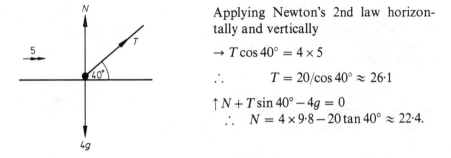

Applying Newton's 2nd law horizontally and vertically

$\rightarrow T\cos 40° = 4 \times 5$

$\therefore$ $T = 20/\cos 40° \approx 26\cdot1$

$\uparrow N + T\sin 40° - 4g = 0$
$\therefore$ $N = 4 \times 9\cdot8 - 20\tan 40° \approx 22\cdot4.$

Hence the tension in the string is 26·1 N and the reaction between the particle and the plane is 22·4 N.

Example 4   A particle of mass 10 kg slides down a smooth plane inclined at 30° to the horizontal. If the particle starts from rest, find its speed after sliding a distance of 5 m.

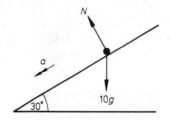

Let the acceleration of the particle down the plane be $a \, \mathrm{m\,s^{-2}}$.

Applying Newton's 2nd law down the plane

$$\nwarrow \quad 10g \sin 30° = 10a$$
$$\therefore \quad a = g \sin 30° = 4 \cdot 9$$

Using the formula $v^2 = u^2 + 2as$, where $u = 0$, $s = 5$, $a = 4\cdot9$,

$$v^2 = 0 + 2 \times 4\cdot9 \times 5 = 49 \qquad \therefore \quad v = 7$$

Hence the particle attains a speed of $7 \, \mathrm{m\,s^{-1}}$.

Exercise 5.2

1.   Find the weight in newtons of an object with mass
(a) 10 kg,   (b) 1·5 kg,   (c) 250 grammes.

2.   A particle of mass 2 kg is being lifted by a vertical force of 32 N. Find its acceleration.

3.   A package of mass 8 kg is being lowered by means of a vertical cable with a downward acceleration of $2 \, \mathrm{m\,s^{-2}}$. Find the tension in the cable.

4.   A boy of mass 40 kg is ascending in a lift. Find the force exerted by the floor of the lift on the boy when the lift is (a) accelerating at $1\cdot2 \, \mathrm{m\,s^{-2}}$, (b) moving with constant speed, (c) decelerating at $0\cdot8 \, \mathrm{m\,s^{-2}}$.

5.   A man descends in a lift carrying a parcel of mass 3 kg. Describe the motion of the lift when the parcel has an apparent weight of (a) 33 N, (b) 27 N, (c) 29·4 N.

6.   A box of mass 30 kg is being towed across a smooth horizontal surface by means of a light chain inclined at an angle of 25° to the horizontal. If the box is accelerating at $1 \, \mathrm{m\,s^{-2}}$, find the tension in the chain and the reaction between the box and the surface.

7.   A particle of mass 6 kg is being pushed across a smooth horizontal plane by a force of 30 N acting downwards at 20° to the vertical. Find the acceleration of the particle and the force the particle exerts on the plane.

8.   A particle of mass 0·5 kg is suspended from a string. If the acceleration of the particle is horizontal and of magnitude $2 \, \mathrm{m\,s^{-2}}$, find the tension in the string and its angle of inclination to the vertical.

9. A particle of mass 5 kg slides down a smooth plane inclined at an angle of 60° to the horizontal. Find the acceleration of the particle down the plane and the reaction between the particle and the plane.

10. A body of mass 12 kg slides down a smooth plane inclined at an angle of 20° to the horizontal. If it starts from rest, find the time it takes to slide a distance of 10 m.

11. A particle of mass 2 kg is being pulled up a smooth plane inclined at 25° to the horizontal by a string parallel to the plane. Find the tension in the string if the particle is (a) moving with uniform velocity, (b) accelerating at $3 \, m \, s^{-2}$.

12. An object of mass 4 kg is being pushed up a smooth plane inclined at an angle α to the horizontal by a horizontal force of 40 N. If $\sin \alpha = 0.6$, find the acceleration of the particle and the reaction between the particle and the plane.

5.3 Connected particles

When considering a set of objects which are connected in some way, it is necessary to apply Newton's third law. Any force exerted by one of the objects upon another is matched by an equal and opposite reaction. For instance, in the case of a railway engine pulling a truck, the truck exerts a pull on the engine equal in magnitude to the pull of the engine on the truck. In problems involving such systems it is usually helpful to examine the forces on one or more of the objects separately.

Example 1   An engine of mass 50 tonnes is pulling several trucks of total mass 200 tonnes along a horizontal track. The resistance to the motion of the engine is 60 N per tonne and the resistance to the motion of the trucks is 35 N per tonne. If the tractive force exerted by the engine is 60 kN, find (a) the acceleration, (b) the tension in the coupling between the engine and the trucks.

$$[1 \text{ tonne} = 1000 \, kg, \; 1 \, kN = 1000 \, N.]$$

Let $a \, m \, s^{-2}$ be the acceleration and let T N be the tension in the coupling.
(a) Considering the forces on the whole train, the total resistance to motion is $(50 \times 60) + (200 \times 35)$ N, i.e. 10 000 N.

Applying Newton's 2nd law

$$\leftarrow 60\,000 - 10\,000 = 250\,000a$$

$$\therefore \quad a = \frac{50\,000}{250\,000} = 0.2.$$

Hence the acceleration of the train is $0.2 \, m \, s^{-2}$.

(b) Considering the forces on the trucks, the resistance to motion is $(200 \times 35)\,\text{N}$, i.e. 7000 N.

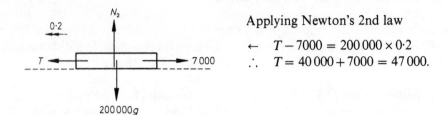

Applying Newton's 2nd law

$\leftarrow \quad T - 7000 = 200\,000 \times 0{\cdot}2$

$\therefore \quad T = 40\,000 + 7000 = 47\,000.$

Hence the tension in the coupling is 47 kN.

Each of the remaining examples in this section involves two particles connected by a light inextensible string passing over a smooth fixed light pulley. Under these conditions we can assume that the tension in the string is constant throughout its length.

Example 2   Two particles of mass 3 kg and 4 kg are connected by a light inextensible string passing over a smooth fixed pulley. The particles are released from rest with the strings taut and vertical. Find the acceleration of the particles and the tension in the string.

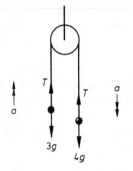

Let the acceleration be $a\,\text{m s}^{-2}$ and the tension $T\,\text{N}$.
Using Newton's 2nd law

for the 3 kg mass: $T - 3g = 3a$ (1)
for the 4 kg mass: $4g - T = 4a$ (2)

Adding (1) to (2) $g = 7a$ $\therefore \quad a = \dfrac{1}{7}g = 1{\cdot}4$

Substituting in (1) $T - 3g = \dfrac{3}{7}g$ $\therefore \quad T = 33{\cdot}6.$

Hence the acceleration of the system is $1{\cdot}4\,\text{m s}^{-2}$ and the tension in the string is 33·6 N.

Example 3   A particle of mass 15 kg rests on a smooth horizontal table. It is connected by a light inextensible string passing over a smooth pulley fixed at the edge of the table to a particle of mass 10 kg which hangs freely. Find the acceleration of the system when it is released from rest. Find also the force exerted by the string on the pulley.

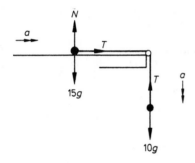

Let $a\,\mathrm{m\,s^{-2}}$ be the acceleration and let $T\,\mathrm{N}$ be the tension in the string. Let $F\,\mathrm{N}$ be the force exerted by the string on the pulley.

Using Newton's 2nd law,

horizontally for the 15 kg mass: $T = 15a$ (1)

vertically for the 10 kg mass: $10g - T = 10a$ (2)

Adding (1) to (2), $10g = 25a$ $\therefore\quad a = \dfrac{2}{5}g = 3\cdot92.$

Hence the acceleration of the system is $3\cdot92\,\mathrm{m\,s^{-2}}$.

Substituting in (1) $T = 15\cdot\dfrac{2}{5}g = 6g.$

The string exerts on the pulley a force T horizontally and a force T vertically.

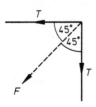

Since these forces are equal in magnitude, their resultant F acts along the bisector of the angle between the strings.

Resolving along this bisector:

$$F = 2T\cos 45° = 12g\cos 45° \approx 83\cdot2$$

Hence the string exerts a force on the pulley of $83\cdot2\,\mathrm{N}$ at $45°$ to the horizontal.

Example 4   A particle of mass m rests on a smooth plane inclined at an angle α to the horizontal where $\sin\alpha = \dfrac{3}{5}$. It is connected by a light inextensible string passing over a smooth pulley fixed at the top of the plane to a particle of mass $3\,m$ which hangs freely. Find the acceleration of the system when it is released from rest and the tension in the string.

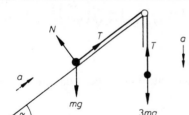

Let a be the acceleration and let T be the tension in the string.

Using Newton's 2nd law,

parallel to the plane for the mass m: $T - mg \sin \alpha = ma$ (1)
vertically for the mass $3m$: $3mg - T = 3ma$ (2)

Adding (1) to (2) $3mg - mg \sin \alpha = 4ma$

$$\therefore \quad a = \frac{1}{4}g\left(3 - \frac{3}{5}\right) = \frac{3}{5}g.$$

Substituting in (2) $3mg - T = 3m \cdot \frac{3}{5}g$

$$\therefore \quad T = 3mg\left(1 - \frac{3}{5}\right) = \frac{6}{5}mg.$$

Hence the acceleration of the system is $\frac{3}{5}g$ and the tension in the string is $\frac{6}{5}mg$.

Example 5   Two particles of mass 2 kg and 3 kg are connected by a light inextensible string passing over a fixed smooth pulley. Initially the system is at rest with the strings taut and vertical with both particles at a height of 2 m above the ground. When the system is released, find the time which elapses before the 3 kg mass hits the ground and the maximum height reached by the 2 kg mass.

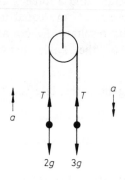

2g   3g

Let $a \, \mathrm{m\,s^{-2}}$ be the acceleration and let $T \, \mathrm{N}$ be the tension in the string. Using Newton's 2nd law,

for the 2 kg mass: $T - 2g = 2a$ (1)
for the 3 kg mass: $3g - T = 3a$ (2)

$(1) + (2)$ $g = 5a$ $\therefore \quad a = \frac{1}{5}g.$

Using the formula $s = ut + \frac{1}{2}at^2$

where $s = 2, u = 0, a = \frac{1}{5}g$

$$2 = 0 + \frac{1}{2} \cdot \frac{1}{5}gt^2$$

$$\therefore \quad t = \sqrt{\left(\frac{20}{g}\right)} = \sqrt{\left(\frac{20}{9 \cdot 8}\right)} = \sqrt{\left(\frac{100}{49}\right)}$$

$$= \frac{10}{7}.$$

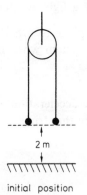

2 m

initial position

Hence the 3 kg mass hits the ground after $1\frac{3}{7}$ seconds.

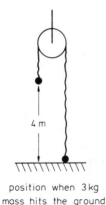

4 m

position when 3 kg
mass hits the ground

Using the formula $v^2 = u^2 + 2as$,

where $u = 0, a = \dfrac{1}{5}g, s = 2$,

$$v^2 = 0 + 2 \cdot \dfrac{1}{5}g \cdot 2 = \dfrac{4}{5}g.$$

Hence when the 3 kg mass hits the ground both particles are travelling at $\sqrt{(4g/5)}\,\mathrm{m\,s^{-1}}$. Since the string is no longer taut, the 2 kg mass now moves freely under gravity with a downward acceleration of $g\,\mathrm{m\,s^{-2}}$.

Using the formula $v^2 = u^2 + 2as$, where $u = \sqrt{(4g/5)}, v = 0, a = -g$:

$$0 = \dfrac{4}{5}g - 2gs \qquad \therefore \quad s = \dfrac{2}{5}.$$

Hence the 2 kg mass rises a further 0·4 m, reaching a maximum height above the ground of 4·4 m.

Exercise 5.3

1.   A motor-boat of mass 1000 kg is towing a water-skier of mass 75 kg by means of a horizontal cable. The resistance to the motion of the boat is 650 N and the resistance to the motion of the skier is 125 N. If the thrust of the boat's engine is 4000 N, find (a) the acceleration, (b) the tension in the cable.

2.   A car of mass 800 kg tows a trailer of mass 400 kg. The resistance to motion for both car and trailer is 0·2 N per kg. Find the tractive force exerted by the car engine and the tension in the coupling between the car and the trailer when they are travelling (a) with uniform velocity, (b) with an acceleration of $2\,\mathrm{m\,s^{-2}}$.

3.   A railway engine of mass 60 tonnes is pulling two trucks each of mass 12 tonnes along a horizontal track. The resistance to motion is 80 N per tonne for the engine and 50 N per tonne for the trucks. Given that the train is travelling at constant speed, find the tractive force exerted by the engine, the tension in the coupling between the engine and the first truck and the tension in the coupling between the two trucks. If the tractive force is increased to 27 kN, find the acceleration and the new tensions in the couplings.

4.   Two particles of mass 2 kg and 5 kg are connected by a light inextensible string passing over a smooth fixed pulley. If the system is moving freely with the strings taut and vertical, find the acceleration of the particles and the tension in the string.

5.   Repeat question 4 for particles of mass 9 kg and 3 kg.

6. Repeat question 4 for particles of mass m and M, where $m < M$.

7. Two particles of mass $2m$ and $3m$ are connected by a light inextensible string passing over a smooth fixed pulley. If the system is moving freely with the strings vertical, find the force exerted by the string on the pulley.

8. A particle of mass $3.6\,kg$ rests on a smooth horizontal table. It is connected by a light inextensible string passing over a smooth pulley fixed at the edge of the table to a particle of mass $1.2\,kg$ which hangs freely. Find the acceleration of the system when it is released from rest and the tension in the string.

9. A particle of mass m rests on a smooth horizontal table. It is connected by a light inextensible string passing over a smooth pulley fixed at the edge of the table to a second particle of mass m which hangs freely. If the system is released from rest find the distance travelled in the first 0.4 seconds of the subsequent motion. Find also the force exerted by the string on the pulley.

10. A particle of mass $2\,kg$ rests on a smooth plane inclined at an angle of $30°$ to the horizontal. It is connected by a light inextensible string passing over a smooth pulley fixed at the top of the plane to a particle of mass $3\,kg$ which hangs freely. Find the acceleration of the system when it is released from rest and the tension in the string. Find also the force exerted by the string on the pulley.

11. A particle of mass m rests on a smooth plane inclined at an angle α to the horizontal. It is connected by a light inextensible string passing over a smooth pulley fixed at the top of the plane to a particle of mass M which hangs freely. Find the condition that the mass m should slide down the plane when the system is released from rest.

12. Two particles of mass $3m$ and $5m$ are connected by a light inextensible string passing over a fixed smooth pulley. The system is released from rest with the strings taut and vertical. After 2 seconds the $5m$ mass hits the ground. Find the further time which elapses before the $3m$ mass reaches its greatest height.

13. Two particles of mass $0.5\,kg$ and $0.7\,kg$ are connected by a light inextensible string passing over a fixed smooth pulley. Initially both parts of the string are taut and vertical, and the $0.5\,kg$ mass is moving vertically downwards with a speed of $3.5\,ms^{-1}$. Find the distance it travels before coming instantaneously to rest.

14.

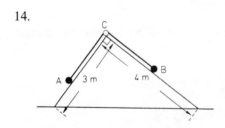

Two particles A and B, of mass $5\,kg$, rest on the smooth inclined faces of a fixed wedge as shown. They are connected by a light inextensible string passing over a smooth pulley C which lies in the same vertical plane as the particles. Find the acceleration of the system when moving freely and the tension in the string. If the system is released from rest with the string taut and both particles 2 m from the pulley, find the speed of the particles when *A* hits the horizontal plane. Find also the distance that B has travelled when it first comes to rest.

5.4 Related accelerations

Some problems involve bodies moving with different but related accelerations. A system including both fixed and moving pulleys can be dealt with by the methods of the previous section when the relationships between the accelerations have been established.

Example 1   A light inextensible string attached to the ceiling passes under a smooth movable pulley of mass 2 kg and then over a smooth fixed pulley. A particle of mass 3 kg hangs freely from the end of the string. All parts of the string not touching the pulleys are vertical. If the system is released from rest, find the acceleration of the particle and the tension in the string.

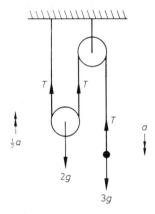

If the particle moves a distance s m, then the movable pulley moves a distance $\frac{1}{2}s$ m in the opposite direction. Hence if the acceleration of the particle is a m s^{-2} downwards, then the acceleration of the movable pulley is $\frac{1}{2}a$ m s^{-2} upwards.

Using Newton's 2nd law,

$$
\begin{array}{llr}
\text{for the particle} & 3g - T = 3a & (1) \\
\text{for the pulley} & 2T - 2g = 2.\tfrac{1}{2}a & (2) \\
2 \times (1) + (2) & 4g = 7a &
\end{array}
$$

$$\therefore \quad a = \frac{4}{7}g = \frac{4}{7} \times 9{\cdot}8 = 5{\cdot}6.$$

Substituting in (1) $3g - T = 3.\dfrac{4}{7}g$

$$\therefore \quad T = \frac{9}{7}g = \frac{9}{7} \times 9{\cdot}8 = 12{\cdot}6.$$

Hence the acceleration of the particle is $5{\cdot}6$ m s^{-2} and the tension in the string is $12{\cdot}6$ N.

Example 2   A light inextensible string which passes over a smooth fixed pulley P carries at one end a particle A of mass $2\,\text{kg}$ and at the other end a smooth light pulley Q. A light inextensible string passes over pulley Q and carries at its ends a particle B of mass $1\,\text{kg}$ and a particle C of mass $2\,\text{kg}$. Find the acceleration of particle A when the system is moving freely and the tensions in the two strings.

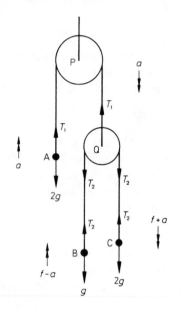

The tensions and accelerations in the different parts of the system are shown in the diagram, f being the acceleration of particles B and C relative to pulley Q.

Applying Newton's 2nd law, to pulley Q (which is assumed to have zero mass):

$$2T_2 - T_1 = 0 \qquad\qquad\qquad (1)$$

to A: $\quad T_1 - 2g = 2a \qquad\qquad (2)$

to B: $\quad T_2 - g = f - a \qquad\qquad (3)$

to C: $\quad 2g - T_2 = 2(f+a) \qquad (4)$

$(1)+(2)$ $\qquad\qquad\qquad\qquad 2T_2 - 2g = 2a \qquad\qquad\qquad\qquad \therefore\quad T_2 = a+g.$

Substituting in (3) $\qquad a+g-g = f-a \qquad \therefore\quad f = 2a$

Substituting in (4) $\qquad 2g-(a+g) = 2(2a+a)$

$$g-a = 6a$$

$$\therefore\quad a = \frac{1}{7}g = 1\cdot4.$$

Hence the acceleration of particle A is $1\cdot4\,\text{m s}^{-2}$ upwards.

Thus $\quad T_2 = a+g = 1\cdot4+9\cdot8 = 11\cdot2$

and $\quad T_1 = 2T_2 = 22\cdot4.$

Hence the tensions in the strings over pulleys P and Q are $22\cdot4\,\text{N}$ and $11\cdot2\,\text{N}$ respectively.

The last example concerns two bodies in contact, which are free to move with different accelerations. In problems of this kind it is helpful to consider the acceleration of one body relative to the other.

Example 3   A particle of mass m rests on a smooth face of a wedge which stands on a smooth horizontal plane. The face of the wedge is inclined at an angle of $45°$ to the horizontal and the mass of the wedge is $10m$. Find the acceleration of the wedge when the system is released.

Motion of the particle   Motion of the wedge

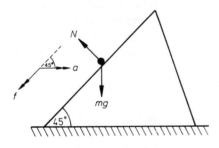   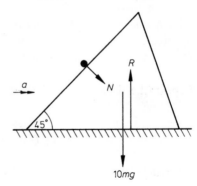

Let a be the acceleration of the wedge and let f be the acceleration of the particle relative to the wedge. [This means that the true acceleration of the particle has components of magnitudes a and f as shown in the diagram.]

Applying Newton's second law to the motion of the particle in a direction perpendicular to the wedge:

$$\searrow mg \cos 45° - N = ma \sin 45°.$$

Applying Newton's second law horizontally to the motion of the wedge:
$$\rightarrow N \sin 45° = 10ma$$

Hence
$$mg . \frac{1}{\sqrt{2}} - N = ma . \frac{1}{\sqrt{2}} \qquad (1)$$

and
$$N . \frac{1}{\sqrt{2}} = 10ma \qquad (2)$$

$\dfrac{1}{\sqrt{2}} \times (1) + (2)$
$$\tfrac{1}{2}mg = \tfrac{1}{2}ma + 10ma$$
$$\therefore \quad g = a + 20a$$

i.e. $\quad a = \dfrac{g}{21} = \dfrac{9\cdot8}{21} = \dfrac{1\cdot4}{3} = \dfrac{7}{15}.$

Hence the acceleration of the wedge is $7/15\,\mathrm{m\,s^{-2}}$ horizontally.

Exercise 5.4

1. A light inextensible string attached to the ceiling passes under a smooth movable pulley of mass 6 kg and then over a smooth fixed pulley. A particle of mass 1 kg hangs freely from the end of the string. All parts of the string not touching the pulleys are vertical. If the system is released from rest, find the acceleration of the particle and state its direction. Find also the tension in the string.

2. Repeat question 1 for a movable pulley of mass 5 kg and a particle of mass 4 kg.

3.   A light inextensible string which passes over a smooth fixed pulley P carries at one end a particle A of mass $2\,$kg and at the other end a smooth light pulley Q. Particles B and C of masses $4\,$kg and $5\,$kg respectively are connected by a light inextensible string passing over pulley Q. Find the accelerations of particles A and B when the system is moving freely. Find also the tensions in the two strings.

4.   Repeat question 3 for particles A, B and C of masses $4\,$kg, $1\,$kg and $2\,$kg.

5.   Repeat question 3 for particles A, B and C of masses $5\,$kg, $2\,$kg and $1\,$kg. Assume in this case that pulley Q has a non-zero mass of $1\,$kg.

6.   A particle of mass $2\,$kg is in contact with a smooth face of a wedge which stands on a smooth horizontal plane. The face of the wedge is inclined at $30°$ to the horizontal and the mass of the wedge is $4\,$kg. Find the acceleration of the wedge when the system is released.

7.   A particle of mass m is placed on a smooth face of a wedge which stands on a smooth horizontal plane. The face of the wedge is inclined at an angle α to the horizontal and the mass of the wedge is $4m$. If the system is released from rest, find the speed of the particle relative to the wedge after 1 second.

8.   A particle of mass $1\,$kg is placed on the smooth horizontal upper face of a wedge, which is itself standing on a smooth plane inclined at an angle α to the horizontal. The mass of the wedge is $3\,$kg and $\sin \alpha = \frac{1}{4}$. Find the accelerations of the particle and the wedge when the system is released.

Exercise 5.5 (*miscellaneous*)

1.   Two forces of magnitude $10\,$N and $7\,$N act on a particle producing an acceleration of $4\,\mathrm{m\,s}^{-2}$. If the forces act at an angle of $60°$, find the mass of the particle.

2.   A body of mass $5\,$kg rests on a smooth horizontal plane. Horizontal forces of magnitudes 6, 12, 5 and F newtons act on the body in the directions $015°$, $130°$, $180°$ and $270°$ respectively. Given that the acceleration of the body is $3\,\mathrm{m\,s}^{-2}$, find the value of F and the direction of the acceleration.

3.   A vehicle of mass $2000\,$kg is travelling along a straight horizontal road at $90\,$km/h. It is brought to rest by a constant force of F newtons in a distance of $500\,$m. Find F and the time taken for the car to come to rest.

4.   A particle A of mass $2\,$kg is acted upon by a constant force of magnitude $10\,$N in the direction of the vector $3\mathbf{i} - 4\mathbf{j}$ and a constant force of magnitude $50\,$N in the direction of the vector $7\mathbf{i} + 24\mathbf{j}$. Find the acceleration of A. Initially the particle is at the origin moving with speed $39\,\mathrm{m\,s}^{-1}$ in the direction of the vector $12\mathbf{i} - 5\mathbf{j}$. Find the position vector of the particle $2\,$s later.   (O & C)

5.   A particle of mass 3 kg is being pulled across a smooth horizontal surface by a string inclined at an angle of 35° to the horizontal. If the particle started from rest and moved a distance of 5 m in the first 2 seconds of its motion, find the constant tension in the string.

6.   A man of mass 70 kg is travelling in a lift. Find the force between the man and the floor of the lift when the lift is (a) ascending with an acceleration of $1.5 \, \text{m s}^{-2}$, (b) descending with an acceleration of $0.5 \, \text{m s}^{-2}$.

7.   A load of 200 kg is lifted by means of a vertical cable through a distance of 50 m. The load accelerates uniformly from rest for 20 seconds, then continues with constant speed for 10 seconds. It then decelerates uniformly to rest in a further 10 seconds. Find the maximum speed attained and the tensions in the cable at every stage of the motion.

8.   A package of mass 80 kg is suspended by a rope from a helicopter. Find the tension in the rope and its angle of inclination to the vertical when the helicopter is flying (a) with uniform velocity, (b) with a constant acceleration of $2.5 \, \text{m s}^{-2}$ horizontally.

9.   A particle of mass m slides down a smooth plane inclined at an angle α to the horizontal. Find the speed attained by the particle when it has travelled a distance x from rest.

10.   A particle of mass 5 kg rests on a smooth plane inclined at an angle α to the horizontal, where $\sin \alpha = 0.2$. If the particle is projected up the plane with an initial speed of $7 \, \text{m s}^{-1}$, find the distance up the plane that it travels.

11.   A ring of mass m kg slides down a smooth wire inclined at an angle α to the horizontal. The ring is released 4.9 m vertically above a horizontal plane and hits the plane t seconds later. Find (a) the value of t if $\alpha = 30°$, (b) the value of α if $t = 1.2$.

12.   A car of mass 1200 kg is pulling a trailer of mass 500 kg up a road inclined at an angle α to the horizontal where $\sin \alpha = 0.1$. The resistance to motion for both car and trailer is 0.15 N per kg. Find the tractive force exerted by the car engine and the tension in the coupling between the car and the trailer if they are decelerating at $0.5 \, \text{m s}^{-2}$.

13.   Two particles of mass 1.5 kg and 2 kg are connected by a light inextensible string passing over a smooth fixed pulley. If the system is released from rest with the strings taut and vertical, find the distance moved by the 1.5 kg mass relative to the 2 kg mass in the first $1\frac{1}{2}$ seconds of the subsequent motion.

14.   A particle of mass 4 kg rests on a smooth horizontal platform at a distance of 2.5 m from the edge. It is connected by a light inextensible string passing over a smooth pulley at the edge of the platform to a particle of mass 0.5 kg which is

hanging freely. If the particles are released from rest, find the speed of the 4 kg mass when it reaches the edge of the platform given that initially the 0·5 kg mass is (a) 3 m, (b) 1·6 m above the ground.

15. A particle of mass 10 kg rests on a smooth plane inclined at an angle of 40° to the horizontal. It is connected by a light inextensible string passing over a smooth pulley fixed at the top of the plane to a particle of mass 4 kg which is hanging freely. Find the acceleration of the system when it is released from rest and the force exerted by the string on the pulley.

16. A particle *A* of mass 4 kg is connected by a light inextensible string passing over a smooth fixed pulley to a particle *B* of mass 3 kg. Particle *B* is connected by another light inextensible string to a particle *C* of mass 3 kg. The system is released from rest with the strings taut and vertical. Find the tensions in the strings. Given that *B* and *C* are initially 2 m and 1 m respectively above the ground, find the distance travelled by *A* before it first comes to rest.

17. A particle *A* of mass 2*m* is initially at rest on a smooth plane inclined at an angle α to the horizontal. It is supported by a light inextensible string which passes over a smooth light pulley *P* at the top edge of the plane. The other end of the string supports a particle *B*, of mass *m*, which hangs freely. Given that the system is in equilibrium, find α, and the magnitude and direction of the resultant force exerted by the string on the pulley.

A further particle of mass *m* is now attached to *B* and the system is released. Find, for the ensuing motion, the tension in the string, the acceleration of *B* and the magnitude and direction of the resultant force exerted by the string on the pulley.   (L)

18. A light inextensible string has one end attached to a ceiling. The string passes under a smooth movable pulley of mass *m* and then over a smooth fixed pulley. A particle of mass 2*m* is attached at the free end of the string. The sections of the string not in contact with the pulleys are vertical. If the system is released from rest and moves in a vertical plane, show that the acceleration of the particle is 2*g*/3 and find the tension in the string.   (AEB 1977)

19.

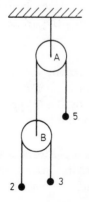

The figure shows a light inextensible string which passes over a smooth light fixed pulley *A* and carries at one end a mass 5 kg and at the other end a smooth light pulley *B*. A light inextensible string passes over the pulley *B* and carries masses 3 kg and 2 kg at its ends. The system is in motion with the masses moving vertically. Find the tensions in the two moving strings stating the units.   (C)

20. A crate of mass 50 kg is suspended by a light cable from a helicopter. The helicopter has a horizontal acceleration of $2\,\mathrm{m\,s^{-2}}$. The crate is being winched aboard the helicopter with an acceleration relative to the helicopter of $0{\cdot}5\,\mathrm{m\,s^{-2}}$. Find the tension in the cable and its angle of inclination to the vertical.

6 Friction; Hooke's law

6.1 The laws of friction

When two objects are in contact each exerts a force upon the other. As stated in Newton's third law, these forces are equal and opposite. The force exerted by a smooth surface on a body in contact with it is perpendicular to the surface. Thus there is no resistance to sliding motion across the surface. However, the force exerted by a rough surface on a body has a component perpendicular to the surface, but may also have a component which acts along or tangentially to the surface and which opposes sliding or a tendency to slide. These components are referred to as the *normal reaction* **N** and the *frictional force* **F**. Their resultant is called the *total reaction* **R**.

It can be shown experimentally that the following laws provide a fairly good approximation to the behaviour of frictional forces.

(1) When two rough surfaces are in contact friction acts to oppose the sliding of one surface relative to the other.

(2) When there is no sliding the frictional force is just sufficient to prevent the relative motion of the surfaces. However, the friction between two surfaces cannot exceed a maximum value called *limiting friction*.

(3) The limiting value of the frictional force F is proportional to the normal reaction N. Thus the maximum value of F is μN, where μ is a constant called the *coefficient of friction*.

(4) The value of μ depends only on the nature of the two surfaces involved.

(5) When sliding occurs the frictional force takes its limiting value μN and acts in the direction that opposes the relative motion of the surfaces.

[In practice, the magnitude of the frictional force that acts during sliding is found to be slightly less than the limiting value reached just before sliding begins. Thus for any pair of surfaces the coefficient of sliding friction is slightly less than the coefficient of static friction. However, in elementary work the difference is assumed to be negligible and a single value of μ is used.]

Example 1 A block of weight 50 N rests in equilibrium on a rough horizontal plane. It is attached to a string inclined at 30° to the horizontal and the tension in the string is 30 N. Find the magnitude of the frictional force acting on the block.

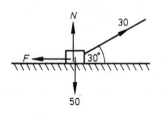

Resolving horizontally

$$\leftarrow F - 30 \cos 30° = 0$$

$$\therefore \quad F = 30 \times \frac{\sqrt{3}}{2} = 15\sqrt{3}.$$

Hence the magnitude of the frictional force is $15\sqrt{3}$ N.

Example 2 A block of weight 50 N rests on a horizontal plane. The coefficient of friction between the block and the plane is 0·4. A horizontal force of P N is applied to the block. Find the value of P given that the block is just about to slide.

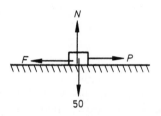

Resolving horizontally and vertically,

$$\leftarrow F - P = 0, \quad \text{i.e.} \quad F = P$$
$$\uparrow N - 50 = 0, \quad \text{i.e.} \quad N = 50.$$

When the block is just about to slide friction is limiting, i.e. $F = \mu N$

$$\therefore \quad P = 0·4 \times 50 = 20.$$

Example 3 A block of mass 5 kg is sliding down a plane inclined at 35° to the horizontal. If the coefficient of friction between the block and the plane is 0·3, find the acceleration of the block.

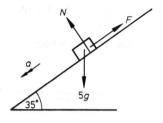

Let the acceleration of the block be $a \, \text{m s}^{-2}$ down the plane.

Applying Newton's second law parallel and perpendicular to the plane

$$\nearrow \quad 5g \sin 35° - F = 5a \qquad (1)$$
$$\nwarrow \quad N - 5g \cos 35° = 0 \qquad (2)$$

Since the block is sliding, $\quad F = \mu N$

$\therefore \quad$ using (2), $\quad F = 0·3 \times 5g \cos 35°.$

Substituting in (1) $\quad 5g \sin 35° - 0·3 \times 5g \cos 35° = 5a$

$$\therefore \quad a = g(\sin 35° - 0·3 \cos 35°) \approx 3·21.$$

Hence the acceleration of the block down the plane is $3·21 \, \text{m s}^{-2}$.

Exercise 6.1

1.   A block of weight 20 N rests in equilibrium on a rough horizontal plane under the action of a force of 10 N. Find the magnitude of the frictional force on the block, given that the external force acts (a) horizontally, (b) vertically downwards, (c) downwards at 30° to the vertical.

2.   A block of weight 20 N rests in equilibrium on a rough plane inclined at 30° to the horizontal. Find the magnitude and direction of the frictional force on the block, given that there is a force on the block acting up the plane, which has magnitude (a) 15 N, (b) 10 N, (c) 5 N.

3.   A block of weight 12 N rests on a horizontal plane. The coefficient of friction between the block and the plane is $\frac{1}{4}$. A force of P N is applied to the block, such that the block is just about to slide. Find the value of P, given that this force acts (a) horizontally, (b) upwards at 45° to the horizontal, (c) downwards at 45° to the horizontal.

4.   A block of weight W rests on a rough plane inclined at 25° to the horizontal. Given that the block is just about to slide down the plane, find the coefficient of friction.

5.   A particle of weight 5 N is at rest on a plane inclined at 40° to the horizontal under the action of a force of P N up the plane. The coefficient of friction is 0·2. Find the value of P if the particle is just about to slide (a) up the plane, (b) down the plane.

6.   A particle of mass 2 kg is being pulled across a horizontal plane by a horizontal force of magnitude 8 N. Find the acceleration of the particle if the coefficient of friction is $\frac{1}{3}$.

7.   A particle of mass 3 kg is being pulled across a rough horizontal plane by a string inclined at 35° to the horizontal. The coefficient of friction between the particle and the plane is 0·6. Find the acceleration of the particle when the tension in the string is 30 N.

8.   A particle of mass 10 kg is sliding down a plane inclined at 30° to the horizontal. If the coefficient of friction is 0·2, find the acceleration of the particle.

9.   A particle of mass 4 kg is sliding down a plane inclined at 20° to the horizontal. If its acceleration is 2 m s^{-2}, find the coefficient of friction between the particle and the plane.

10. A particle of mass 5 kg is being pulled up a plane inclined at 45° to the horizontal by a string parallel to the plane. If the coefficient of friction is $\frac{1}{4}$ and the tension in the string is 50 N, find the acceleration of the particle.

6.2 Motion on a rough surface

When a particle is in motion on a rough surface the frictional force F and the normal reaction N are connected by the equation $F = \mu N$. Many problems can be solved using this relationship together with the methods of Chapter 5.

Example 1 A particle of mass 4 kg is being pulled across a rough horizontal plane by a string inclined at an angle of $20°$ above the horizontal. When the tension in the string is 25 N the particle accelerates at $4\,\mathrm{m\,s^{-2}}$. Find the coefficient of friction between the particle and the plane.

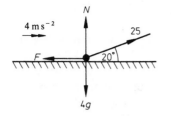

Applying Newton's second law horizontally and vertically

$$\rightarrow 25\cos 20° - F = 4 \times 4$$
$$\uparrow N + 25\sin 20° - 4g = 0$$
$$\therefore F = 25\cos 20° - 16$$
$$N = 4g - 25\sin 20°.$$

Since the particle is in motion, $\quad F = \mu N$

$$\therefore \quad \mu = \frac{F}{N} = \frac{25\cos 20° - 16}{4 \times 9 \cdot 8 - 25\sin 20°} \approx 0.244.$$

Hence the coefficient of friction is 0·244.

Example 2 A particle of mass 6 kg rests on a rough horizontal plane, the coefficient of friction between the particle and the plane being 0·4. The particle is connected by a light inextensible string passing over a smooth pulley at the edge of the plane to a second particle of mass 3 kg which hangs freely. If the system is released from rest, find the distance moved by each of the particles in the first 3 seconds of the subsequent motion.

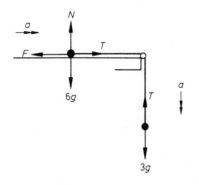

Let the tension in the string be T N and the acceleration of the particles $a\,\mathrm{m\,s^{-2}}$.

Using Newton's second law for the 6 kg mass:

$$\rightarrow \quad T - F = 6a \qquad (1)$$
$$\uparrow N - 6g = 0 \qquad (2)$$

for the 3 kg mass: $\quad \downarrow 3g - T = 3a \qquad (3)$

When the 6 kg mass is sliding $F = \mu N$

$\therefore$ using (2) $F = 0 \cdot 4N = 0 \cdot 4 \times 6g = 2 \cdot 4g$

Substituting in (1) $T - 2 \cdot 4g = 6a$

Adding (3) $0 \cdot 6g = 9a$

$$\therefore \quad a = \frac{1}{9} \times \frac{3}{5}g = \frac{1}{15}g.$$

Using the formula $s = ut + \frac{1}{2}at^2$, where $u = 0, t = 3, a = \dfrac{g}{15}$

$$s = 0 + \frac{1}{2} \times \frac{g}{15} \times 9 = \frac{3g}{10} = 2 \cdot 94.$$

Hence the distance moved by the particles in the first 3 seconds is $2 \cdot 94 \, \text{m}$.

Example 3   A particle A of mass 3 kg rests on a rough plane inclined at 30° to the horizontal, the coefficient of friction between the particle and the plane being 1/10. It is connected by a light inextensible string passing over a smooth pulley at the top edge of the plane to a particle B of mass 2 kg which hangs freely. Find the acceleration of the system when it is released from rest and the tension in the string.

The component of the weight of particle A acting down the plane is $3g \sin 30°$, i.e. $\dfrac{3}{2}g$. Since this is less than the weight of particle B, A will have a tendency to move up the plane. Thus the force of friction will act down the plane.

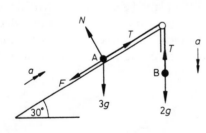

Using Newton's second law, for particle A:

$$\nearrow T - F - 3g \sin 30° = 3a \qquad (1)$$

$$\nwarrow N - 3g \cos 30° = 0 \qquad (2)$$

for particle B:

$$\downarrow 2g - T = 2a. \qquad (3)$$

When particle A is sliding $F = \mu N$

$\therefore$ using (2) $F = \dfrac{1}{10}N = \dfrac{3}{10}g \cdot \dfrac{\sqrt{3}}{2} = \dfrac{3\sqrt{3}}{20}g.$

Substituting in (1) $T - \dfrac{3\sqrt{3}}{20}g - 3g \cdot \dfrac{1}{2} = 3a.$

Adding (3) $2g - \dfrac{3\sqrt{3}}{20}g - \dfrac{3}{2}g = 5a.$

$$\therefore \quad a = \frac{1}{5}g\left(\frac{1}{2} - \frac{3\sqrt{3}}{20}\right) = \frac{g}{100}(10 - 3\sqrt{3}) \approx 0\cdot47.$$

Rearranging (3) $\qquad T = 2(g - a) \approx 18\cdot7.$

Hence the acceleration of the particles is approximately $0\cdot47\,\mathrm{m\,s}^{-2}$ and the tension in the string $18\cdot7\,\mathrm{N}$.

Exercise 6.2

1. A particle of mass $4\,\mathrm{kg}$ is projected across a horizontal plane with a speed of $7\,\mathrm{m\,s}^{-1}$. If it comes to rest in a distance of $10\,\mathrm{m}$, find the magnitude of the frictional force acting on the particle and the coefficient of friction between the particle and the plane.

2. A body of mass $5\,\mathrm{kg}$ is at rest on a horizontal plane, the coefficient of friction being $0\cdot3$. A horizontal force of $21\,\mathrm{N}$ is applied to the body. If after $3\frac{1}{2}$ seconds this force ceases to act, find the further time that elapses before the particle comes to rest.

3. A block of mass $2\,\mathrm{kg}$ rests on a horizontal plane. The coefficient of friction is $\frac{1}{2}$. Find the acceleration of the block when a force of $20\,\mathrm{N}$ acts on it (a) upwards at an angle of $20°$ to the horizontal, (b) downwards at an angle of $20°$ to the horizontal.

4. A particle slides down a plane inclined at an angle of $30°$ to the horizontal. The coefficient of friction is $1/7$. Find the distance the particle slides in 2 seconds from rest.

5. A particle is sliding down a plane inclined at an angle α to the horizontal. Find an expression for the coefficient of friction, given that the particle moves with (a) uniform velocity, (b) constant acceleration a.

6. A block of mass $2\,\mathrm{kg}$ rests on a rough plane inclined at an angle α to the horizontal, where $\sin\alpha = 7/25$. The coefficient of friction is $\frac{1}{2}$. Find the acceleration of the block when a force of $50\,\mathrm{N}$ acts on it down the plane. Find the magnitude of the force acting parallel to the plane that would give the block an equal acceleration up the plane.

7. A body of mass $8\,\mathrm{kg}$ is projected down a plane inclined at an angle of $15°$ to the horizontal with a velocity of $10\,\mathrm{m\,s}^{-1}$. If the body comes to rest after travelling a distance of $25\,\mathrm{m}$, find the magnitude of the frictional force acting on the body during its motion and the coefficient of friction.

8. A particle is placed at a point O on a plane inclined at $45°$ to the horizontal. The particle is projected up the plane along a line of greatest slope with velocity $15\,\mathrm{m\,s}^{-1}$. Find the condition that must be satisfied by the coefficient of friction μ if the particle is to return through 0 after it comes to rest. Given that the particle does return through 0 with a velocity of $10\,\mathrm{m\,s}^{-1}$, find the value of μ.

9.   A particle of mass 3 kg rests on a rough horizontal table, the coefficient of friction between the particle and the table being $\frac{1}{3}$. The particle is connected by a light inextensible string passing over a smooth pulley at the edge of the table to a second particle of mass 4 kg which hangs freely. If the system is released from rest, find the acceleration of the particles and the tension in the string.

10. A particle A of mass 6 kg rests on a rough horizontal plane. It is connected by a light inextensible string passing over a smooth pulley at the edge of the plane to a particle B of mass 2 kg which hangs vertically. If particle B is projected vertically downwards with a velocity of $3\cdot5\,\mathrm{m\,s^{-1}}$, it comes to rest after travelling a distance of $2\cdot5$ m. Find the coefficient of friction between particle A and the plane. Find also the force exerted by the string on the pulley during the motion.

11. A particle of mass 5 kg rests on a rough plane inclined at 25° to the horizontal, the coefficient of friction between the particle and the plane being $0\cdot2$. The particle is connected by a light inextensible string passing over a smooth pulley at the top of the plane to a second particle of mass 5 kg which hangs freely. Find the acceleration of the system and the tension in the string.

12. A particle of mass 5 kg rests on a rough plane inclined at an angle α to the horizontal, the coefficient of friction between the particle and the plane being $1/8$. The particle is connected by a light inextensible string passing over a smooth pulley at the top of the plane to a particle of mass 3 kg which hangs freely. Find the acceleration of the system when it is released from rest if (a) $\alpha = 10°$, (b) $\alpha = 60°$.

6.3 Equilibrium on a rough surface

When a particle is in equilibrium on a rough surface the frictional force F and the normal reaction N satisfy the inequality $F \leqslant \mu N$. When the particle is on the point of sliding $F = \mu N$. This state is sometimes called limiting equilibrium.

Example 1   A particle is placed on a rough plane inclined at an angle α to the horizontal. The coefficient of friction between the particle and the plane is μ. Find the condition that the particle should be in equilibrium.

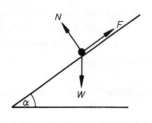

If the particle is in equilibrium, resolving along and perpendicular to the plane,

$$\nearrow \; F - W \sin \alpha = 0$$
$$\nwarrow \; N - W \cos \alpha = 0$$

i.e. $F = W \sin \alpha$ and $N = W \cos \alpha$.

Since $F \leqslant \mu N$, $W \sin \alpha \leqslant \mu W \cos \alpha$ $\therefore$ $\tan \alpha \leqslant \mu$.

Hence equilibrium will be possible if $\mu \geqslant \tan \alpha$.

In some problems it is necessary to find the least force required to maintain the equilibrium of a particle on a rough surface. As this least force just prevents motion, when it is applied the frictional force F takes its limiting value μN.

Example 2   A particle of weight 6 N is placed on a rough plane inclined at 45° to the horizontal, the coefficient of friction being $\frac{1}{2}$. Find the magnitude of the least horizontal force required to maintain equilibrium.

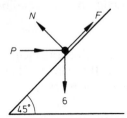

Consider a horizontal force of $P\,$N acting on the particle to maintain equilibrium.

Resolving along and perpendicular to the plane

$$\nearrow \quad P\cos 45° + F - 6\sin 45° = 0$$
$$\nwarrow \quad N - P\sin 45° - 6\cos 45° = 0$$

$$\therefore \quad F = 6\sin 45° - P\cos 45° = \frac{1}{\sqrt{2}}(6-P)$$

$$N = 6\cos 45° + P\sin 45° = \frac{1}{\sqrt{2}}(6+P).$$

The value of P is least when friction is limiting, i.e. when

$$F = \mu N$$

$$\therefore \quad \text{since} \quad \mu = \tfrac{1}{2}, \quad \frac{1}{\sqrt{2}}(6-P) = \frac{1}{2} \cdot \frac{1}{\sqrt{2}}(6+P)$$

i.e. $12 - 2P = 6 + P$ $\therefore \quad P = 2$

Hence the least horizontal force required to maintain equilibrium is 2 N.

[A similar method can be used to find the least force required to move a particle across a rough surface.]

Exercise 6.3

1.   A particle is at rest on a rough plane inclined at an angle α to the horizontal. The coefficient of friction is $\frac{1}{4}$. Given that the particle is on the point of sliding down the plane, find α.

2.   A horizontal force of magnitude $P\,$N acts on a particle of weight 10 N at rest on a plane inclined at 40° to the horizontal. The coefficient of friction between the particle and the plane is 0·2. Find the value of P if the particle is just about to slide (a) up the plane, (b) down the plane.

3.   A particle of weight 3 N rests on a rough horizontal plane. The coefficient of friction is μ. A force of 1 N acts on the particle. Find the condition that the particle should be in equilibrium if this force acts (a) horizontally, (b) upwards at 30° to the horizontal, (c) downwards at 30° to the horizontal.

4.   A body of weight 4 N is placed on a rough plane inclined at an angle α to the horizontal. The coefficient of friction between the body and the plane is $\frac{1}{2}$. A force of 1·5 N acting downwards parallel to the plane is applied to the particle. Prove that the condition that the particle should be in equilibrium is $3 \sec \alpha + 8 \tan \alpha \leqslant 4$.

5.   A body of weight 6 N is kept in equilibrium on a rough plane inclined at 30° to the horizontal by a force of P N acting up the plane. If the least value of P for which equilibrium is maintained is 1·5, find the coefficient of friction.

6.   A block of weight 5 N is on a plane inclined at 50° to the horizontal. The coefficient of friction is 0·3. The block is kept in equilibrium by a force of P N acting up the plane. Find the range of possible values of P.

7.   A particle of weight 20 N rests on a rough plane inclined at an angle α to the horizontal, where $\tan \alpha = \frac{3}{4}$. The coefficient of friction is $\frac{1}{4}$. The particle moves up the plane under the action of a force of P N. Find the least value of P, given that this force acts (a) up the plane, (b) horizontally.

8.   A particle of mass M rests on a rough horizontal plane, the coefficient of friction being $\frac{1}{3}$. The particle is connected by a light inextensible string passing over a smooth pulley at the edge of the plane to a particle of mass m which hangs vertically. Find the condition that the system should remain at rest when released.

6.4 Angle of friction

The total reaction $\mathbf{R}$ of a surface on a body in contact with it is the resultant of the normal reaction $\mathbf{N}$ and the frictional force $\mathbf{F}$.

If $\mathbf{R}$ acts at an angle θ to the normal to the surface then

$$F = R \sin \theta \quad \text{and} \quad N = R \cos \theta.$$

Since $F \leqslant \mu N, \quad R \sin \theta \leqslant \mu R \cos \theta, \quad$ i.e. $\tan \theta \leqslant \mu.$

If λ is the acute angle such that $\tan \lambda = \mu$, then $\tan \theta \leqslant \tan \lambda$ and hence $\theta \leqslant \lambda$. The angle λ is called the *angle of friction*. It is the maximum angle which the total reaction can make with the normal to the surface. Thus the total reaction can lie anywhere on or within a 'cone of friction' with the normal to the surface as axis and λ as semi-vertical angle.

Some problems are simplified by using the total reaction **R** instead of its components **F** and **N**.

Example 1 A particle of weight **W** is suspended by a light inextensible string from a light ring. The ring can slide along a rough horizontal rod, the coefficient of friction being $\frac{1}{3}$. A horizontal force **P** is applied to the particle. Given that the system is at rest with the ring on the point of sliding along the rod, find P in terms of W.

Since the only forces acting on the ring are the tension in the string and the reaction of the rod on the ring, these forces must be equal and opposite. If the reaction makes an angle θ with the vertical, then since the ring is about to slide, $\theta = \lambda$.

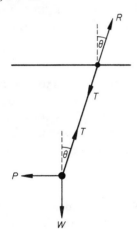

Resolving the forces on the particle horizontally and vertically

$$\leftarrow \quad P - T \sin \lambda = 0$$
$$\downarrow \quad W - T \cos \lambda = 0$$

$$\therefore \quad P = T \sin \lambda, \quad W = T \cos \lambda,$$

Hence $\dfrac{P}{W} = \tan \lambda = \frac{1}{3}$ so that

$$P = \tfrac{1}{3}W.$$

Example 2 A particle of weight **W** is placed on a rough plane inclined at an angle α to the horizontal. The coefficient of friction is μ, where $\mu < \tan \alpha$. Find the magnitude and direction of the least force required to prevent motion down the plane.

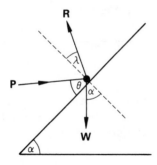

Suppose that sliding is prevented by a force of magnitude P acting at an angle θ to the plane. When P takes its least value, friction will be limiting and the reaction **R** will make an angle λ with the normal to the plane, where $\tan \lambda = \mu$.

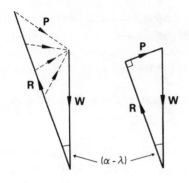

Assuming that the particle is on the point of sliding, the value of P depends on the value chosen for θ. By considering the triangle of forces as θ varies, we see that the magnitude of **P** is least when its direction is perpendicular to that of **R**, i.e. when $\theta = \lambda$. Hence the least force required to prevent motion down the plane is of magnitude $W \sin (\alpha - \lambda)$ and acts at an angle λ to the plane where $\tan \lambda = \mu$.

Exercise 6.4

1.   A particle of weight 12 N is suspended by a light inextensible string from a light ring. The ring can slide along a rough horizontal rod, the coefficient of friction being $\frac{1}{2}$. A force of P N is acting on the particle. The system is in equilibrium with the ring on the point of sliding along the rod. Find P given that the force is acting (a) horizontally, (b) upwards at 45° to the horizontal, (c) downwards at 30° to the horizontal.

2.   One end of a light inextensible string is attached to a fixed point on a horizontal rod. The other end is fastened to a light ring which can slide on the rod. The coefficient of friction is $\frac{3}{4}$. A particle of weight 20 N is suspended from the mid-point of the string. Given that the system is in equilibrium with the ring on the point of sliding along the rod, find the tension in each part of the string and the angle of inclination to the vertical.

3.   A block of weight 8 N rests on a horizontal plane. The coefficient of friction between the block and the plane is $\frac{1}{4}$. Find the magnitude and direction of the least force required to move the block.

4.   A particle of weight W rests on a horizontal plane. If the angle of friction is λ, find the magnitude and direction of the least force required to move the block.

5.   A particle of weight 6 N is placed on a rough plane inclined at 30° to the horizontal. The coefficient of friction is $\frac{1}{3}$. Find the magnitude and direction of the least force required (a) to prevent motion down the plane, (b) to move the particle up the plane.

6.   A particle of weight W is placed on a rough plane inclined at an angle α to the horizontal. The angle of friction is λ, where $\lambda > \alpha$. Find the magnitude and direction of the least force required to move the particle (a) down the plane, (b) up the plane.

6.5 Hooke's† law

In this section we examine the behaviour of springs and elastic strings. The length of an elastic string when it is unstretched is called its *natural length*. When the string is stretched by forces exerted on its ends, its increase in length is called the *extension* of the string. It can be shown experimentally that as an elastic string is stretched the tension in the string is proportional to the extension. This result is called *Hooke's law* after the man who discovered it.

When a string is stretched beyond a certain point it ceases to obey Hooke's law. However, in elementary work with elastic strings it is assumed that conditions are such that Hooke's law can be used.

For a string of natural length *l*, tension *T* and extension *x*, the law is written in the form

$$T = \lambda \frac{x}{l}$$

where λ is a constant called the *modulus of elasticity*. The value of λ depends on the nature of the string in use. Since x/l is a ratio of two lengths it has a purely numerical value. Hence the modulus λ must be measured in the same units as T, i.e. in units of force. By writing $x = l$, we see that λ is equal to the tension required to double the length of an elastic string.

Example 1 An elastic string of natural length 1·5 m is stretched to 2 m. If its modulus of elasticity is 12 N, find the tension in the string.

By Hooke's law $\qquad\qquad T = \frac{\lambda x}{l}.$

Putting $\lambda = 12, l = 1\cdot5, x = 0\cdot5$:

$$T = \frac{12 \times 0\cdot5}{1\cdot5} = 4$$

∴   the tension in the string is 4 N.

Example 2 A light elastic string of natural length 1 m is fixed at one end and a particle of weight 4 N is attached to the other end. When the particle hangs freely

† *Hooke, Robert* (1635–1703) English experimental physicist. He contributed to many of the important inventions of his time including the microscope. He worked on planetary motion and proposed a law of gravitation similar to Newton's. A pamphlet containing his theory of elasticity was published in 1678.

in equilibrium the length of the string is 1·4 m. The string is now held at an angle θ to the vertical by a horizontal force of 3 N acting on the particle. Find the value of θ and the new length of the string.

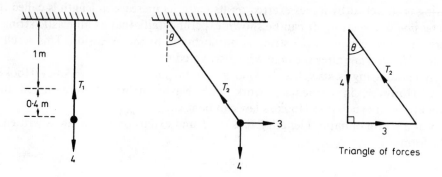

Triangle of forces

In the first equilibrium position $T_1 = 4$.

Using Hooke's law, $T = \dfrac{\lambda x}{l}$, where $T = 4$, $x = 0\cdot4$, $l = 1$,

$$4 = \frac{\lambda \times 0\cdot4}{1} \qquad \therefore \quad \lambda = 10.$$

Hence the modulus of elasticity for the string is 10 N.

Using the triangle of forces for the second equilibrium position

$$\tan \theta = \tfrac{3}{4} \qquad \therefore \quad \theta = 36° \, 52'$$
$$T_2 = \sqrt{(3^2 + 4^2)} = 5.$$

Using Hooke's law for $T = 5, \lambda = 10, l = 1$

$$5 = \frac{10x}{1} \qquad \therefore \quad x = 0\cdot5.$$

Hence the value of θ is 36° 52′ and the new length of the string is 1·5 m.

Hooke's law also applies to the stretching of springs.

Example 3   A spring AB of natural length 0·8 m and modulus 16 N is fixed at A. The other end is joined to a second spring BC of natural length 0·5 m and modulus 20 N. A particle of weight W N is then attached at the point C. When the system is hanging freely in equilibrium, the point C is a distance of 2·5 m vertically below A. Find the value of W.

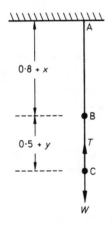

Let the extensions in springs AB and BC be x m and y m respectively.

Applying Hooke's law to both springs

$$T = \frac{16x}{0 \cdot 8} = 20x \quad \text{and} \quad T = \frac{20y}{0 \cdot 5} = 40y$$

Since the tensions in the springs are equal,

$$20x = 40y, \quad \text{i.e.} \quad x = 2y \qquad (1)$$

Considering the two springs together, the natural length is $1 \cdot 3$ m and the stretched length is $2 \cdot 5$ m.

Hence $\qquad x + y = 2 \cdot 5 - 1 \cdot 3 = 1 \cdot 2$

Using (1) $\qquad 3y = 1 \cdot 2, \qquad \text{i.e.} \quad y = 0 \cdot 4$

$$\therefore \quad T = 40y = 40 \times 0 \cdot 4 = 16.$$

Since the particle is in equilibrium, $\quad W = T = 16$.

Thus the value of W is 16.

A spring also obeys Hooke's law when compressed. We again write $T = \lambda x / l$, where in this case T represents a thrust and x a compression, i.e. a reduction in length.

Exercise 6.5

1.   An elastic string of natural length 2 m is stretched to $2 \cdot 5$ m. If its modulus of elasticity is 20 N, find the tension in the string.

2.   A spring of natural length 60 cm is stretched to a length of 1 m. If the tension in the spring is 6 N, find its modulus of elasticity.

3.   A spring of natural length 10 cm is compressed to a length of 8 cm. If its modulus of elasticity is 12 N, find the thrust in the spring.

4.   When the tension in an elastic string is 8 N, its length is $1 \cdot 6$ m. If the modulus of elasticity of the string is 24 N, find its natural length.

5.   An elastic string of natural length $3a$ is fixed at one end and a particle of weight W is attached to the other end. When the particle hangs freely in equilibrium the length of the string is $5a$. If the string is held at an angle θ to the vertical by a horizontal force of magnitude $\frac{1}{2}W$, find the value of θ and the new length of the string.

6.   A particle of mass 3 kg is suspended from an elastic string of natural length $0 \cdot 5$ m and modulus 48 N. If the particle is pulled vertically downwards and then

released when the length of the string is 1 m, find its acceleration at the instant that it is released.

7.   An elastic string AB of natural length 1·2 m and modulus 10 N lies along a line of greatest slope of a smooth plane inclined at 30° to the horizontal. The end A is fixed and to the end B is attached a particle of weight 10 N. Find the length of the string when the particle at B rests in equilibrium on the plane.

8.   The ends of an elastic string of natural length $4a$ are fixed to points A and B on the same horizontal level, where $AB = 3a$. A particle P of weight W is attached to the mid-point of the string and hangs in equilibrium at a depth of $2a$ below the level of AB. Find the modulus of elasticity of the string in terms of W.

9.   A particle P of weight 5·2 N is hanging in equilibrium attached to two strings PA and PB, where A and B are fixed points on the same horizontal level. The string PA is inextensible, but the string PB is elastic with modulus of elasticity 6 N. Given that $AB = 1·3$ m, $PA = 0·5$ m and $\angle APB = 90°$, find the tension in each string and the natural length of the elastic string.

10. A spring PQ of natural length 1·5 m and modulus λ N is fixed at P. The other end is joined to a second spring QR of natural length 1 m and modulus 2λ N. A particle of weight 15 N is then attached to the end R of the second spring. When the system is hanging freely in equilibrium, the distance PR is 4 m. Find the value of λ.

11. Three light springs of natural lengths 80 cm, 100 cm and 120 cm whose moduli of elasticity are 320 N, 240 N and 180 N respectively are attached end to end and confined in a horizontal tube of length 276 cm. Calculate the thrust on the ends of the tube and the amount by which each spring is compressed.

12. A body of weight 50 N is suspended from a ceiling by a spring of natural length 1 m and modulus of elasticity 120 N. It is supported by another spring of natural length 2 m and modulus 160 N attached to the floor. The springs are vertical, and the distance from floor to ceiling is 3 m. Find the lengths of the springs.

Exercise 6.6 (miscellaneous)

1.   A box of weight 400 N will just move across a rough horizontal floor when a horizontal force of 100 N is applied to it. Find the least force required to move the box if it acts (a) upwards at 60° to the horizontal, (b) downwards at 30° to the horizontal.

2.   A particle of weight W rests on a horizontal plane, the coefficient of friction between the particle and the plane being $\frac{1}{3}$. When a horizontal force of magnitude P is applied to the particle its acceleration is a. When a horizontal force of magnitude $2P$ is applied, the acceleration is $4a$. Find P in terms of W.

3.   A particle of mass 2 kg is placed on a rough plane inclined at an angle α to the horizontal, where $\sin \alpha = 3/5$. The coefficient of friction between the particle and the plane is 1/4. Initially the particle is at rest under the action of a force P N acting upwards parallel to the plane. Find the value of P given that the particle is about to move (a) up the plane, (b) down the plane. If the force is then removed, find the acceleration of the particle down the plane.

4.   A block of weight W is placed on a rough plane inclined at an angle α to the horizontal, where $\tan \alpha = 5/12$. The block is on the point of sliding when a force of 5 N acts directly down the plane and when a force of 55 N acts directly up the plane. Find the value of W and the coefficient of friction between the block and the plane.

5.   A particle of weight W rests on a rough plane inclined to the horizontal at an angle whose tangent is 2μ, where μ is the coefficient of friction between the particle and the plane. The particle is acted on by a force of magnitude P. (i) Given that the force acts horizontally in a vertical plane through a line of greatest slope, and that the particle is on the point of sliding down the plane, find the magnitude of P. (ii) Given that the force acts along a line of greatest slope and that the particle is on the point of sliding up the plane, find the magnitude of P.   (C)

6.   Two small light rings which are connected by a light inextensible string of length a can slide on a rough horizontal rod. A weight is attached to the mid-point of the string and the system hangs in equilibrium. If the coefficient of friction between the rings and the rod is μ, show that the greatest possible distance between the rings is $\mu a/(1 + \mu^2)^{1/2}$.   (O)

7.   A mass of 5 kg is moved along a rough horizontal table by means of a light inextensible string which passes over a smooth light pulley at the edge of the table and is attached to a mass of 1 kg hanging over the edge of the table. The system is released from rest with the string taut, each portion being at right angles to the edge of the table. If the masses take twice the time to acquire the same velocity from rest that they would have done had the table been smooth, prove that the coefficient of friction is 1/10. After falling a distance 1/5 m, the 1 kg mass reaches the floor and comes to rest. Prove that the 5 kg mass then moves a further 1/6 m before coming to rest. [Assume throughout that the 5 kg mass does not leave the table.]   (O & C)

8.   Two particles A and B, of masses 5 kg and 10 kg respectively, lie with B above A on a rough slope inclined at an angle of 30° to the horizontal. The coefficient of friction between the particles and the slope is 0·2. A light inextensible string along a line of greatest slope joins A to B and a force of P N acts on B up the slope. If the system is in equilibrium with both particles just about to move up the slope, find the value of P and the tension in the string.

9.   Three particles, A, B, C, are of masses 4, 4, 2 kg respectively. They lie at rest on a horizontal table in a straight line, with particle B attached to the mid-point of a light inextensible string. The string has particle A attached at one end and

particle C at the other, and is taut. A force of 60 N is applied to A in the direction CA produced, and a force of 15 N is applied to C in the opposite direction. Find the acceleration of the particles and the tension in each part of the string, (a) if the table is smooth, (b) if the coefficient of friction between each particle and the table is $\frac{1}{4}$. [Take g as $10\,\mathrm{m/s^2}$.]   (L)

10. A particle of mass m moves on a line of greatest slope of a plane inclined to the horizontal at an angle θ. The coefficient of friction between the particle and the plane is μ. The particle is released from rest at a point A and it slides down to B, where the distance $AB = d$. Prove that $\mu < \tan\theta$, and that V, the particle's speed at B, is given by $V^2 = 2gd(\sin\theta - \mu\cos\theta)$. The particle is projected up the plane from B with speed U, comes instantaneously to rest at A and then returns to B. If $U = 2V$, prove that (i) $\mu = \dfrac{3}{5}\tan\theta$, (ii) $V^2 = \dfrac{4}{5}gd\sin\theta$.   (C)

11. A particle of mass $2m$ rests on a rough plane inclined at an angle α to the horizontal. It is connected by a light inextensible string passing over a smooth pulley at the top edge of the plane to a second particle of mass m which hangs freely. Given that when the system is released from rest it begins to move, find the condition that must be satisfied by μ, the coefficient of friction if (a) $\tan\alpha = 3/4$, (b) $\tan\alpha = 5/12$.

12.

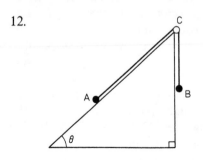

The diagram shows a fixed wedge whose sloping face is inclined at an angle θ to the horizontal. Two particles A and B are connected by a light inextensible string which passes over a smooth pulley C at the top of the wedge.

The particle A rests on the sloping face of the wedge, the string between A and C being parallel to a line of greatest slope, and B hangs freely. Particle A has mass M, particle B has mass m and the coefficient of friction between A and the sloping plane is μ. The system is released from rest.

(i) Show that, if $\sin\theta - \mu\cos\theta \leqslant \dfrac{m}{M} \leqslant \sin\theta + \mu\cos\theta$, the masses remain at rest.

(ii) If $M = m$, $\theta = 30°$ and $\mu = \frac{1}{2}$, find expressions for the acceleration of the system and the tension in the string.   (C)

13. The inclined faces of a fixed triangular wedge make angles α and β with the horizontal. Two particles of equal weight, connected by a light inextensible string which passes without friction over the vertex of the wedge, rest on the two faces of the wedge. The system rests in equilibrium with the plane containing the string perpendicular to both faces of the wedge. If both particles are in limiting equilibrium, show that $\mu = \tan\frac{1}{2}|\alpha - \beta|$, where μ is the coefficient of friction between each particle and the face of the wedge.   (O)

14. A body of weight W N is being pulled across a rough horizontal plane by a string inclined at an angle θ to the horizontal. The tension in the string is $\frac{1}{2}W$N and the coefficient of friction between the body and the plane is $\frac{1}{4}$. Find the value of θ for which the acceleration of the body is greatest and the magnitude of the maximum acceleration.

15. A particle of weight 4 N is placed on a rough plane inclined at an angle of $10°$ to the horizontal. The coefficient of friction between the particle and the plane is $0\cdot2$. Find the magnitude and direction of the least force required to move the particle (a) down the plane, (b) up the plane.

16.

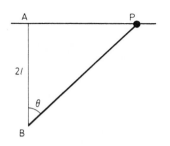

A small rough ring P of weight W is threaded on to a fixed horizontal straight wire which passes through a point A, as shown in the diagram. The ring is joined by a light elastic string of natural length l and modulus λ to a fixed point B which is at a distance $2l$ vertically below A. The ring is in equilibrium with the angle $ABP = \theta$. Find the tension in the string and the vertical and horizontal components of the force exerted by the wire on the ring. Show that

$$W \geqslant \lambda(2-\cos\theta)\left(\frac{\tan\theta}{\mu} - 1\right),$$

where μ is the coefficient of friction between the ring and the wire.   (JMB)

17. A particle of mass $3m$ is tied to the end C and a particle of mass m is tied at the mid-point B of a light unstretched elastic string ABC. The end A of the string is fixed and a horizontal force of magnitude $4mg$ is applied to the particle at C so that the system hangs in equilibrium as shown. Calculate (i) the tensions in BC and AB, (ii) the inclinations of BC and AB to the vertical. Given that the modulus of elasticity of the string is $6mg$, show that, for this position of equilibrium, $AB:BC = (6+4\sqrt{2}):11$.   (AEB 1978)

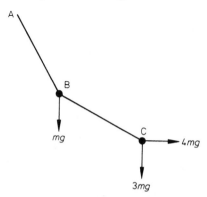

18. A light elastic string is of natural length a, and is such that when it is stretched by a length a, the tension in it is mg.
(i) The string is fastened to two points, $2a$ apart, which are in the same

horizontal line. A particle of mass m is attached to the mid-point, and gently lowered until it comes to rest. Show that, in its equilibrium position, each of the parts of the string is inclined at θ to the horizontal, where θ is given by $2\tan\theta - \sin\theta = \frac{1}{2}$.

(ii) The same string is now fastened to two points, $2a$ apart, which are in the same vertical line. A particle of mass m is attached to the mid-point and gently released until it comes to rest. Show that, when the system comes to rest, the particle is $\frac{1}{4}a$ below its original position.   (SU)

19. A wedge of mass M is resting on a smooth horizontal table. A particle of mass m is placed gently on a rough face of the wedge which is inclined at an angle θ to the horizontal, and slides down this face. Given that the coefficient of friction between the particle and the face is μ, where $\mu < \tan\theta$, prove that the acceleration of the wedge is $\dfrac{mg\cos\theta(\sin\theta - \mu\cos\theta)}{M + m\sin\theta(\sin\theta - \mu\cos\theta)}$.   (O)

7 Work, energy and power

7.1 Work and kinetic energy

The *work done by a force* is the product of the force and the distance moved in the direction of the force by its point of application.

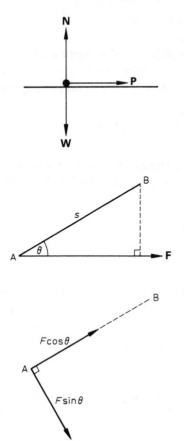

If a particle of weight **W** is pulled a distance s along a smooth horizontal plane by a horizontal force **P**, then the work done by this force is Ps. However, since the direction of motion is perpendicular to the directions of the weight **W** and the normal reaction **N**, these forces do no work.

Consider now a particle which moves a distance s from A to B under the action of a force **F**, where the angle between the displacement **AB** and the force **F** is θ.

The particle moves a distance $s\cos\theta$ in the direction of the force **F**. Hence the work done by the force is $Fs\cos\theta$.

Another way of obtaining the same result is to consider the force **F** as a sum of components along and perpendicular to **AB**. The component $F\sin\theta$ does no work but, since the particle moves a distance s in the direction of the component $F\cos\theta$, the work done is $F\cos\theta \times s$, i.e. $Fs\cos\theta$ as before.

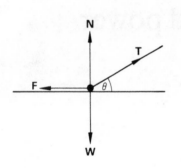

If a particle is pulled a distance s along a rough horizontal plane by a string inclined at an angle θ to the horizontal, then the work done by the tension $\mathbf{T}$ in the string is $Ts\cos\theta$. The weight $\mathbf{W}$ and the normal reaction $\mathbf{N}$ do no work. However, the displacement of the particle in the direction of the frictional force $\mathbf{F}$ which opposes motion is $-s$. Hence the work done by the force $\mathbf{F}$ is $-Fs$. The quantity Fs is called the work done *against* friction.

The SI unit of work is the joule (J). When the point of application of a force of 1 newton moves 1 metre, the work done is 1 joule, i.e. $1\,J = 1\,Nm$.

To establish a relationship between the motion of a body and the work done on it, we consider a particle of mass m moving in a straight line under the action of a constant force F. We assume that the acceleration of the particle is a and that its initial velocity is u. If when the particle has moved a distance s its velocity is v, then, as shown in §4.2, $v^2 = u^2 + 2as$. By Newton's second law,

$$F = ma$$

$$\therefore \quad Fs = mas \quad \text{and} \quad as = \tfrac{1}{2}(v^2 - u^2)$$

Hence
$$Fs = \tfrac{1}{2}mv^2 - \tfrac{1}{2}mu^2.$$

The quantity $\tfrac{1}{2}mv^2$ is called the *kinetic energy* (K.E.) of a particle of mass m moving with velocity v and is measured in the same units as work, i.e. in joules.

Thus when a particle is moving in a straight line under the action of a constant force,

$$\text{work done by force} = \text{increase in kinetic energy}.$$

Example 1   A body of mass $4\,kg$ is moving in a straight line under the action of a constant force. Given that its speed increases from $3\,ms^{-1}$ to $7\,ms^{-1}$, find the work done by the force.

Work done = increase in K.E. $= \tfrac{1}{2}.4.7^2 - \tfrac{1}{2}.4.3^2\,J$
$$= 98 - 18\,J.$$

Hence the work done by the force is $80\,J$.

Example 2   A car of mass $1200\,kg$ travelling along a straight horizontal road accelerates uniformly from $10\,ms^{-1}$ to $15\,ms^{-1}$ in a distance of $200\,m$. If the thrust of the engine is $500\,N$, find the resistance to motion.

Let the resistance to motion be $R\,N$, then the total horizontal force acting on the car is $(500 - R)\,N$.

$$\text{Work done} = \text{increase in K.E.}$$
$$\therefore \quad (500 - R)200 = \tfrac{1}{2}.1200.15^2 - \tfrac{1}{2}.1200.10^2 = 600(225 - 100)$$
$$\therefore \quad 500 - R = 3 \times 125 = 375.$$

Hence there is resistance to motion of $125\,N$.

When the motion of a particle in a straight line is opposed by a constant force, it may be convenient to express the relationship between work and kinetic energy in the form:

Work done again resistance = loss of K.E.

Exercise 7.1   [Take $g = 10$.]

1.   A particle of weight W is pulled a distance s across a rough horizontal plane by a horizontal force P. Find the work done by the weight W, the normal reaction N, the force P and the frictional force F.

2.   A body of weight W is lifted through a distance x by a force P directed vertically upwards. Find the work done by the weight W and the force P.

3.   A particle of weight W slides a distance s down a rough plane inclined at an angle α to the horizontal. Find the work done by the weight W and the normal reaction N. Find also the work done against the frictional force F.

4.   A particle of weight W is pulled a distance s up a rough plane inclined at an angle α to the horizontal by a string parallel to the plane. Find the work done by the tension T and the normal reaction N. Find also the work done against the frictional force F and against gravity.

5.   A body of mass 10 kg moving under the action of a constant force accelerates from $2\,\mathrm{m\,s}^{-1}$ to $5\,\mathrm{m\,s}^{-1}$. Find the work done by the force. Given that the magnitude of the force is 7 N, find the distance moved by the body.

6.   A railway truck of mass 2 tonnes moving on a straight horizontal track is brought to rest from a speed of $3\,\mathrm{m\,s}^{-1}$ by a force of P N. Find the work done by this force. Given that the truck travels 20 m before coming to rest, find the value of P.

7.   A bullet of mass 0·04 kg travelling at $300\,\mathrm{m\,s}^{-1}$ hits a fixed wooden block and penetrates a distance of 4 cm. Find the average resistance of the wood.

8.   A car of mass 1000 kg travelling along a straight horizontal road accelerates uniformly from $15\,\mathrm{m\,s}^{-1}$ to $25\,\mathrm{m\,s}^{-1}$ in a distance of 320 m. If the resistance to motion is 145 N, find the driving force of the engine.

9.   A box of mass 16 kg is pulled from rest a distance of 5 m across a smooth horizontal floor by a cable inclined at 60° to the horizontal. Find the work done by the tension in the cable given that its magnitude is 25 N.

10. A particle of mass 6 kg sliding across a rough horizontal plane comes to rest in a distance of 8 m. Given that its initial velocity was $10\,\mathrm{m\,s}^{-1}$, find the work done against friction. Find also the coefficient of friction between the particle and the plane.

11. Find the kinetic energy gained by a body of mass 2 kg falling freely from rest through a distance of 10 m. If a vertical force of P N brings the body to rest in a further distance of 8 m, find the value of P.

12. A particle of mass 5 kg slides a distance 9 m down a rough plane inclined at an angle α to the horizontal, where $\sin \alpha = \frac{3}{5}$. The coefficient of friction is $\frac{1}{2}$. Find the work done by gravity and the work done against friction. Find also the velocity attained by the particle.

7.2 Conservation of mechanical energy

The *energy* of a body can be regarded as its capacity for doing work. For instance, the kinetic energy of a body is its capacity to do work by virtue of its motion. As we saw in the previous section, a moving body does work against forces opposing motion as it loses kinetic energy. There are many other forms of energy such as heat, light, sound, chemical and electrical energy. However, our interest will be confined to forms of *mechanical energy*, i.e. energy by virtue of motion or position.

A body is said to have *potential energy* if its position is such that when released it begins to move and to gain kinetic energy. For instance, a body of mass m released at a height h above the ground will fall freely under gravity until it hits the ground with velocity v.

$$\text{Work done by gravity} = \text{gain in K.E.}$$
$$\therefore \quad mgh = \tfrac{1}{2}mv^2.$$

Thus, initially the body is said to have *gravitational potential energy mgh* by virtue of its height h above the ground.

In any given situation a *zero level* for gravitational potential energy must be decided, and then the potential energy of a body can be calculated relative to this level. Bodies above the zero level will have positive potential energy and bodies below it negative potential energy.

As stated earlier, if a particle is moving in a straight line under the action of a resultant force F then,

$$\text{work done by } F = \text{gain in K.E.}$$

If the only force doing work is gravity this result becomes,

$$\text{work done by gravity} = \text{gain in K.E.}$$

However, by definition, when a mass m falls from a height h the work done by gravity, mgh, is equal to the loss of potential energy.

Hence,   loss of P.E. = gain in K.E.
so that   K.E. + P.E. = constant.

This result is a simple form of the *principle of conservation of mechanical energy*.

If a particle is moving such that no external force other than gravity is doing work, then the total mechanical energy of the particle remains constant.

Example 1   A particle of mass m kg is released from rest at a point A on a smooth plane inclined at an angle α to the horizontal, where $\sin \alpha = 3/5$. Find the velocity acquired by the particle after travelling a distance of 6 m down the plane to a point B.

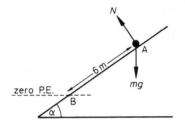

Let us assume that at B the particle has zero P.E. and velocity v m s^{-1}, then

at A: K.E. $= 0$, P.E. $= mg \times 6 \sin \alpha$

at B: K.E. $= \frac{1}{2}mv^2$, P.E. $= 0$.

Using the conservation of mechanical energy

$$\tfrac{1}{2}mv^2 + 0 = 0 + 6mg \sin \alpha$$

$$\therefore \quad v^2 = 2 \times 6 \times 9 \cdot 8 \times \frac{3}{5} = \frac{6^2 \times 7^2}{5^2}$$

$$\therefore \quad v = \frac{6 \times 7}{5} = 8 \cdot 4.$$

Hence the velocity acquired by the particle is $8 \cdot 4$ m s^{-1}.

[Note that although this problem could be solved using Newton's second law and one of the constant acceleration formulae, it is quicker to use an energy equation, since only velocity and distance moved are involved.]

It can be shown that the principle of conservation of mechanical energy also applies to the motion of a particle along a curved path, provided that no work is done by any external force other than gravity.

Example 2   A ring of mass m is threaded on a smooth circular wire fixed in a vertical plane. If the ring is projected from the lowest point A of the wire with velocity v and first comes to rest at a point B on the wire, express the vertical height h of B above A in terms of g and v.

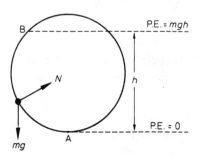

Since the wire is smooth the force exerted by the wire on the ring is always perpendicular to the direction of motion and therefore does no work. Hence mechanical energy is conserved throughout the motion, i.e.

(K.E. $+$ P.E.) at B = (K.E. $+$ P.E.) at A

$$0 + mgh = \tfrac{1}{2}mv^2 + 0.$$

Thus $h = v^2/2g.$

When using energy equations to solve problems it is helpful to distinguish between *conservative* and *non-conservative* forces. When work is done against a conservative force such as gravity, there is a gain in potential energy. However, when work is done against a non-conservative force, such as friction, energy is produced in various forms, including heat and sound, but there is no gain in potential energy. Thus the principle of conservation of mechanical energy can be applied to systems of particles provided that (i) no work is done by external forces other than gravity, (ii) no work is done against non-conservative internal forces such as friction.

Example 3   A particle A of mass $2\,\text{kg}$ is connected to a particle B of mass $3\,\text{kg}$ by means of a light inextensible string which passes over a smooth light pulley. The system is released from rest with both parts of the string taut and vertical. Find the speed attained by each particle when A has risen $2\,\text{m}$.

Let the initial P.E. of the system be zero and let the final speed of each particle be $v\,\text{m}\,\text{s}^{-1}$.

Thus initially the system has zero mechanical energy.

Final P.E. of $A = 2g \times 2\,\text{J} = 4g\,\text{J}$.

Final P.E. of $B = 3g \times (-2)\,\text{J} = -6g\,\text{J}$.

Final K.E. of $A = \frac{1}{2} \times 2 \times v^2\,\text{J} = v^2\,\text{J}$.

Final K.E. of $B = \frac{1}{2} \times 3 \times v^2\,\text{J} = \frac{3}{2}v^2\,\text{J}$.

Thus the final mechanical energy of the system

$$= \left(v^2 + \frac{3}{2}v^2 + 4g - 6g\right)\text{J} = \left(\frac{5}{2}v^2 - 2g\right)\text{J}.$$

Using conservation of mechanical energy, $\dfrac{5}{2}v^2 - 2g = 0$.

$$\therefore \qquad v = \sqrt{\left(\frac{4g}{5}\right)} = \sqrt{\left(\frac{4}{5} \times \frac{49}{5}\right)} = \frac{2 \times 7}{5} = 2 \cdot 8.$$

Hence each particle attains a speed of $2 \cdot 8\,\text{m}\,\text{s}^{-1}$.

When the total mechanical energy of a particle or system of particles is changed by the action of external forces an energy equation similar to the following may be used,

$$\boxed{\text{initial (P.E.} + \text{K.E.)} + \text{work done} = \text{final (P.E.} + \text{K.E.).}}$$

If the mechanical energy of a system is reduced by work done against non-conservative forces a more convenient form may be,

> initial (P.E. + K.E.) − work done against resistance = final (P.E. + K.E.).

Example 4 A small block of mass m slides down a rough plane inclined at an angle 30° to the horizontal. If the block acquires velocity v after travelling a distance x from rest, find an expression for the work done against friction.

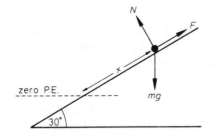

Let the final P.E. of the block be zero, then the initial P.E. is $mg \times x \sin 30°$, i.e. $\frac{1}{2}mgx$.
The initial K.E. is zero and the final K.E. is $\frac{1}{2}mv^2$.

Initial (P.E. + K.E.) − work done against friction = final (P.E. + K.E.).
Work done against friction
$\quad$ = initial (P.E. + K.E.) − final (P.E. + K.E.)
$\quad$ = $(\frac{1}{2}mgx + 0) − (0 + \frac{1}{2}mv^2)$
$\quad$ = $\frac{1}{2}m(gx − v^2)$.

Exercise 7.2

1. A ball is thrown vertically downwards with a speed of $3\cdot5\,\text{m s}^{-1}$. Find its speed when it has travelled a distance of 5 m.

2. A particle is projected vertically upwards from a point A with a speed of $21\,\text{m s}^{-1}$. Find its position relative to A when its speed is (a) $4\cdot2\,\text{m s}^{-1}$, (b) $35\,\text{m s}^{-1}$.

3. A stone is thrown vertically upwards from a point A with velocity $v\,\text{m s}^{-1}$. Find an expression for the greatest height above A reached by the stone.

4. A small block is released from rest on a smooth plane inclined at 30° to the horizontal. Find the distance the particle has travelled down the plane when its speed is $6\cdot3\,\text{m s}^{-1}$.

5. A particle is projected with velocity $9\,\text{m s}^{-1}$ up a line of greatest slope of a smooth plane inclined at an angle α to the horizontal, where $\sin \alpha = 4/7$. Find the speed of the particle when it has travelled 5 m up the plane.

6. A tile slides from rest down a smooth roof inclined at an angle α to the horizontal, where $\sin \alpha = \frac{2}{3}$. It reaches the edge after travelling a distance of 4·5 m,

then falls to the ground 7 m below. Find the speed at which the tile is travelling as it hits the ground.

7. A particle is attached to a fixed point by means of a light inextensible string of length 0·8 m. If when the particle is released from rest the string makes an angle of 60° with the downward vertical, find the speed of the particle as it passes through its lowest point.

8. A force acts vertically upwards on a body of mass 4 kg. If the body rises vertically from rest through 5 m and acquires a speed of $3\,\mathrm{m\,s^{-1}}$, find the work done by the force.

9. Find the kinetic energy acquired by a body of mass 5 kg which falls freely from rest through a distance of 3 m. If the particle is then brought to rest by a vertical force of 70 N, find the further distance that it falls.

10. A particle of mass m is connected to a particle of mass M by means of a light inextensible string which passes over a smooth light pulley. The system is released from rest with both parts of the string taut and vertical. Given that $M > m$, find an expression for the distance moved by each particle when the velocity attained is v.

11. A particle of mass 3 kg standing on a smooth horizontal table is connected by means of a light inextensible string passing over a smooth pulley at the edge of the table to a particle of mass 2 kg hanging freely. Find the speed of the particles when they have travelled a distance of 25 cm from rest.

12. A cyclist travelling initially at $2\,\mathrm{m\,s^{-1}}$ free-wheels down a hill. At the bottom of the hill his speed is $10\,\mathrm{m\,s^{-1}}$. If the total mass of the cyclist and his machine is 90 kg and the work done against resistance is 4500 J, find the difference in level between the top and bottom of the hill.

13. In a fairground ride a car of mass 500 kg starts from rest at a point A, 30 m above the ground. After travelling 73 m along a track against a constant resistance of 600 N the car passes through a point B with a speed of $16\,\mathrm{m\,s^{-1}}$. Find the height of B above the ground.

14. A particle is moving at a speed of $7\,\mathrm{m\,s^{-1}}$ when it begins to ascend a slope inclined at an angle α to the horizontal where $\sin\alpha = 5/13$. The coefficient of friction between the particle and the slope is 5/8. Find (a) the speed of the particle when it has travelled 1·95 m up the slope, (b) the total distance the particle travels up the slope before coming to rest.

15. A block of mass 5 kg is projected with velocity $5\cdot6\,\mathrm{m\,s^{-1}}$ up a line of greatest slope of a rough plane inclined at an angle α to the horizontal where $\sin\alpha = 0\cdot6$. If the block travels 2 m up the slope before coming to rest, find the work done against friction. Find also the coefficient of friction between the block and the plane.

7.3 Work done by a variable force

Consider a particle moving in a straight line under the action of a variable force **F** acting along the line. The work done by **F** in a small displacement δs is approximately equal to $F\delta s$. Thus an approximate value of the total work done in a displacement from $s = 0$ to $s = x$ is given by a sum of the form $\sum\limits_{s=0}^{s=x} F\delta s$.

Remembering that sums of this kind can be evaluated by integration, we write:

$$\text{work done} = \lim_{\delta s \to 0} \sum_{s=0}^{s=x} Fds = \int_0^x Fds.$$

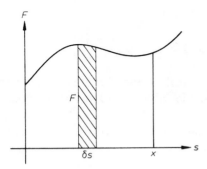

Geometrically this quantity is represented by the area under the force-displacement graph for the motion.

An important application of this theory is to the stretching of a spring or elastic string. By Hooke's law, when the extension in an elastic string is x, then the tension T is given by

$$T = \frac{\lambda x}{l}$$

where λ is the modulus of elasticity and l is the natural length of the string. Hence the work done against the tension when the extension is increased from x_1 to x_2 is

$$\int_{x_1}^{x_2} Tdx = \int_{x_1}^{x_2} \frac{\lambda x}{l} dx = \left[\frac{\lambda x^2}{2l} \right]_{x_1}^{x_2} = \frac{\lambda}{2l} \left(x_2^2 - x_1^2 \right).$$

> In particular, the work done when an elastic string is stretched from its natural length l to length $(l+x)$ is $\dfrac{\lambda x^2}{2l}$.

[A similar result can be obtained for the work done when a spring is compressed.]

Example 1   A particle of weight $10\,\text{N}$ is suspended from a fixed point by a light elastic string of natural length $1\cdot5\,\text{m}$. When the particle hangs in equilibrium the length of the string is $2\,\text{m}$. Find the modulus of elasticity of the string. Find also the work done in stretching the string from its natural length to a length of $2\,\text{m}$.

When the particle is in equilibrium the tension in the string is equal in magnitude to the weight of the particle.

Hence, using Hooke's law $T = \dfrac{\lambda x}{l}$, where $T = 10$, $l = 1\cdot5$ and $x = 0\cdot5$,

$$10 = \frac{\lambda \times 0\cdot5}{1\cdot5} \qquad \therefore \quad \lambda = 30$$

$\therefore$ the modulus of elasticity of the string is 30 N.

The work done in extending a string from its natural length by an amount x is $\dfrac{\lambda x^2}{2l}$

$\therefore$ the work done in extending this string by $0\cdot5$ m

$$= \frac{30 \times (0\cdot5)^2}{2 \times 1\cdot5}\,\text{J} = 2\cdot5\,\text{J}.$$

Let us suppose that an elastic string is stretched and then released. As the tension acts to restore the string to its original length the work it does is equal to the work done against the tension in stretching the string. Thus, since no mechanical energy is lost, the tension in an elastic string is a conservative force. A spring or elastic string stretched from its natural length l to a length $(l+x)$ is said to have *elastic potential energy* of $\lambda x^2/2l$.

The principle of conservation of mechanical energy can be applied to systems involving springs and elastic strings, provided that no work is done by external forces (other than gravity).

Example 2   A particle of mass 2 kg is suspended from a fixed point by a spring of natural length 20 cm and modulus 10 N. Given that the extension in the spring when the particle is hanging in equilibrium is x m, find x. If the particle is released from rest with the spring vertical and unstretched, find the speed, $v\,\text{m s}^{-1}$, of the particle when it passes through its equilibrium position.

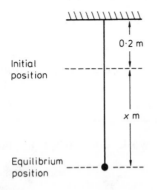

In the equilibrium position the tension in the spring is equal to the weight of the particle, i.e. $2g\,$N.

Using Hooke's law, $T = \dfrac{\lambda x}{a}$

Substituting $T = 2g$, $\lambda = 10$, $a = 0\cdot2$

$$2g = \frac{10x}{0\cdot2}$$

$\therefore$ $x = 0\cdot04\,g = 0\cdot04 \times 9\cdot8 = 0\cdot392.$

Considering mechanical energy in the initial position,
let gravitational P.E. $= 0$,
energy stored in spring $= 0$,
kinetic energy $= 0$.

Considering mechanical energy in the equilibrium position,
gravitational P.E. $= 2\,g \times (-x)\,\mathrm{J} = -0\!\cdot\!08\,g^2\,\mathrm{J}$

energy stored in spring $= \dfrac{\lambda x^2}{2a}\mathrm{J} = \dfrac{10(0\!\cdot\!04\,g)^2}{2+0\!\cdot\!2}\mathrm{J} = 0\!\cdot\!04\,g^2\,\mathrm{J}$

kinetic energy $= \frac{1}{2} \times 2 \times v^2\,\mathrm{J} = v^2\,\mathrm{J}$.

Using the principle of conservation of mechanical energy

$$-0\!\cdot\!08\,g^2 + 0\!\cdot\!04\,g^2 + v^2 = 0$$

$$\therefore \quad v^2 = 0\!\cdot\!04\,g^2, \text{ i.e. } v = 0\!\cdot\!2\,g = 1\!\cdot\!96.$$

Hence the speed with which the particle passes through its equilibrium position is $1\!\cdot\!96\,\mathrm{m\,s^{-1}}$.

[Note that in practice it is virtually impossible to construct a system in which there is no loss of mechanical energy, since there are no truly frictionless pulleys, smooth surfaces nor perfectly elastic strings. In this chapter we are dealing with mathematical models of systems in which the work done against friction and other non-conservative forces is negligible compared with the total energy involved.]

Exercise 7.3

1. Find the work done in stretching a spring of natural length 1 m and modulus 10 N to a length of (a) 1·2 m, (b) 2 m.

2. Find the energy stored in an elastic string of natural length 4 m and modulus 2 N when its length is (a) 5 m, (b) 10 m.

3. Find the work done in stretching a spring of natural length 1·5 m and modulus 9 N from a length of 2 m to length 2·5 m.

4. The work done in stretching an elastic string of natural length 2·5 m from 3 m to 4 m in length is 6 J. Find the modulus of the string.

5. When an elastic string of natural length 1·5 m is stretched to the length 1·8 m the energy stored in it is 2·7 J. Find the energy stored in the string when its length is 2 m.

6. The work done in extending a spring from its natural length $6a$ to a length $7a$ is ka. Find the modulus of the spring in terms of k and the work done in extending the length of the spring from $7a$ to $8a$.

7. A particle of mass 8 kg is suspended from a fixed point by a spring of natural length 0·5 m and modulus 140 N. If the particle is released from rest with the spring vertical and unstretched, find the distance it falls before coming to rest instantaneously.

8. A particle of mass 5 kg on a smooth horizontal plane is attached to one end

of a string of natural length 1 m and modulus 20 N. The other end of the string is attached to a fixed point in the same plane. If the particle is released from rest with the string stretched to a length of 2 m, find its speed at the instant the string returns to its natural length.

9.   A particle of mass m is attached by a light elastic string of natural length $4a$ and modulus $7mg$ to a fixed point. The particle is released from rest with the string taut and vertical, but unstretched. Find an expression for its speed when it has fallen a distance a.

10. A particle is suspended from a fixed point A by a light elastic string of natural length 2 m. When the particle hangs in equilibrium the length of the string is 2·5 m. Given that the particle is released from rest at A, find the distance it has fallen when it first comes to rest.

11. A particle of mass 7 kg is attached to one end of an elastic string of modulus $9g$ N and natural length 1·8 m. The other end of the string is fastened to a fixed point A. The point B is the position of the particle when it hangs in equilibrium. If the particle is released from rest at A, find its speed when it passes through B.

12. A particle is attached by a light elastic string of natural length 60 cm to a fixed point O. When the particle hangs in equilibrium its distance below O is 80 cm. If the particle is released from rest at a point 1 m vertically below O, find the distance of the particle from O when it next comes to rest. Find also the speed of the particle when it passes through its equilibrium position.

13. The ends of an elastic string of modulus 30 N and natural length 2 m are attached to fixed points A and B 2 m apart on the same horizontal level. A particle P is attached to the mid-point of the string then released at the mid-point of AB. If the particle falls 0·75 m before coming to rest instantaneously, find its weight.

14. A particle P of mass 2 kg is suspended from a point O by a light elastic string of length 1 m and modulus 98 N. Find the length of the string when P hangs in equilibrium. The particle is now pulled down and released from rest 1·6 m below O. Find (a) the speed of P as the string goes slack, (b) the depth below O at which P comes instantaneously to rest.

7.4 Power

Power is the rate at which a force does work. The SI unit of power is the watt (W). One watt is a rate of working of one joule per second, i.e. $1\,W = 1\,J\,s^{-1}$.
[For those who are familiar with the watt only as a unit of electrical power, it may be helpful to remember that a family saloon car has a maximum power output of approximately 40–50 kW. A sprinter may generate kinetic energy at an

average rate of about 1 kW for short periods, but most people produce mechanical energy at much lower rates.]

Example 1 Find the average power developed by a crane which lifts a load of 8 kN through a vertical distance of 15 m in 6 s.

Work done by the crane in 6 s is $8 \times 15 \text{kJ}$, i.e. 120 kJ
$\therefore$ average work done in 1 s is $120 \div 6 \text{kJ}$, i.e. 20 kJ.
Hence the average power of the crane is 20 kW.

Example 2 A pump raises water at a rate of 750 litres per minute through a vertical distance of 4 m and projects it into a reservoir at a speed of 6m s^{-1}. Find the power developed by the pump.

Since the mass of 1 litre of water is 1 kg, the mass of water raised per second
$$= \frac{750}{60} \text{kg} = \frac{25}{2} \text{kg}.$$
Thus the P.E. given to the water each second
$$= \frac{25}{2}g \times 4 \text{J} = 25 \times 9 \cdot 8 \times 2 \text{J} = 490 \text{J}.$$

The K.E. given to the water each second
$$= \frac{1}{2} \times \frac{25}{2} \times 6^2 \text{J} = 25 \times 9 \text{J} = 225 \text{J}.$$

Hence the total power developed by the pump is

$(490 + 225) \text{W}$, i.e. 715 W.

If the engine of a vehicle, such as a car or a train, produces a tractive force F newtons, then the power of the engine is the rate at which this force does work. When the vehicle is travelling at constant speed $v \text{m s}^{-1}$, since the distance travelled each second is v m, the work done each second is Fv J. Hence the power of the engine is Fv watts.

A similar result is obtained for non-uniform motion by considering the work done when the vehicle moves a small distance δs in time δt. The rate of working in this interval is approximately $\dfrac{F\delta s}{\delta t}$, i.e. $F\dfrac{\delta s}{\delta t}$. However, as $\delta t \to 0$, $\dfrac{\delta s}{\delta t} \to \dfrac{ds}{dt}$. Thus the rate of working at the instant when the vehicle is moving with velocity $v \text{m s}^{-1}$ must be Fv watts. Hence the power P watts, the tractive force F newtons and the velocity $v \text{m s}^{-1}$ are connected by the formula

$$\boxed{P = Fv.}$$

Example 3 A car of mass 1200 kg is moving along a horizontal road against resistance to motion of 500 N. Find the power developed by the engine when the car is travelling at $15\,\mathrm{m\,s^{-1}}$ and accelerating at $0{\cdot}25\,\mathrm{m\,s^{-2}}$. Find also the maximum speed reached by the car if the engine continues to work at the same rate.

If the pull of the engine is F newtons, then by Newton's second law,

$$F - 500 = 1200 \times 0{\cdot}25$$
$$\therefore \qquad F = 300 + 500 = 800.$$

Hence the power of the engine

$$= 800 \times 15\,\mathrm{W} = 12\,000\,\mathrm{W} = 12\,\mathrm{kW}.$$

Let the maximum speed of the car be $v\,\mathrm{m\,s^{-1}}$. When maximum speed is reached the pull of the engine is equal in magnitude to the resistance to motion

$$\therefore \quad 12\,000 = 500\,v, \text{ i.e. } v = 24.$$

Hence the maximum speed when the engine is working at the rate of $12\,\mathrm{kW}$ is $24\,\mathrm{m\,s^{-1}}$.

Example 4   A train of mass 150 tonnes is ascending an incline of 1 in 70 at a constant speed of $25\,\mathrm{m\,s^{-1}}$. If the power being exerted by the engine is $750\,\mathrm{kW}$, find the resistance to motion.

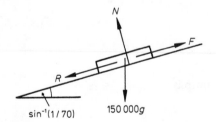

Let $F\,\mathrm{N}$ be the tractive force of the engine and $R\,\mathrm{N}$ the resistance to motion.
Using the formula $P = Fv$,
$$750\,000 = F \times 25$$
$$\therefore \quad F = 30\,000.$$

Applying Newton's second law up the incline

$$F - R - 150\,000\,g \times \frac{1}{70} = 0$$

$$\therefore \quad R = 30\,000 - \frac{150\,000 \times 9{\cdot}8}{70} = 30\,000 - 21\,000 = 9000.$$

Hence the resistance to motion is $9\,\mathrm{kN}$.

Example 5   When a cyclist rides along a horizontal road at $v\,\mathrm{m\,s^{-1}}$ the resistance to motion is $(16 + \frac{1}{4}v^2)\,\mathrm{N}$. Find the rate at which the cyclist must work to maintain a steady speed of $6\,\mathrm{m\,s^{-1}}$.

When travelling at a steady speed the force exerted by the cyclist is equal to the resistance to motion,
$$\therefore \quad \text{his rate of work} = (16 + \tfrac{1}{4}v^2)v\,\mathrm{W}$$
$$= (16 + \tfrac{1}{4} \times 6^2)6\,\mathrm{W}$$
$$= (16 + 9)6\,\mathrm{W}$$

Hence to maintain a steady speed of $6\,\mathrm{m\,s^{-1}}$ the cyclist must work at a rate of $150\,\mathrm{W}$.

Exercise 7.4

1.   A man of mass 80 kg climbs a staircase of height 5 m in 10 s. Find his average rate of work against gravity.

2.   If the effective power developed by a crane is 15 kW, find the time taken to lift a load of weight 50 kN through a vertical distance of 12 m.

3.   Find the minimum power needed to pull an object of weight 500 N a distance of 8 m up a smooth slope inclined at 30° to the horizontal in 5 seconds.

4.   A lift of mass 1500 kg is being raised by an engine working at the rate of 24·5 kW. If the lift rises 50 m in 40 s, find the load it is carrying.

5.   Water from a river, flowing at $4 \, \mathrm{m \, s^{-1}}$, completely fills a pipe of cross-sectional area $3 \, \mathrm{m^2}$. If, when the water is used to drive a generator, 30% of its kinetic energy is converted into electrical energy, find the power supplied by the generator.

6.   A pump raises 40 kg of water a second through a vertical distance of 10 m and delivers it in a jet with speed $12 \, \mathrm{m \, s^{-1}}$. Find the effective power developed by the pump.

7.   A pump raises water at the rate of 250 litres per minute through a vertical distance of 8 m and projects it into a lake at $2 \, \mathrm{m \, s^{-1}}$. Find the power developed by the pump.

8.   If the engine of a train travelling at a steady speed of $25 \, \mathrm{m \, s^{-1}}$ is working at a rate of 1800 kW, find the magnitude of the resistance to motion.

9.   A motor-cyclist is riding along a horizontal road at a constant speed of $15 \, \mathrm{m \, s^{-1}}$ against a resistance of 80 N. Find the power at which the motor-cycle engine is working. Given that the total mass of the rider and his machine is 200 kg, find the initial acceleration when the power is increased to 1·5 kW.

10.   A car of mass 900 kg is travelling at $20 \, \mathrm{m \, s^{-1}}$ along a horizontal road against a constant resistance of 600 N. Find the power developed by the engine if the car is (a) moving with constant speed, (b) accelerating at $0·15 \, \mathrm{m \, s^{-2}}$, (c) decelerating at $0·5 \, \mathrm{m \, s^{-2}}$.

11.   A cable car of mass 1500 kg is pulled at a constant speed of $10 \, \mathrm{m \, s^{-1}}$ up a smooth slope inclined at an angle α to the horizontal where $\sin \alpha = 1/7$. Find the power exerted on the car.

12.   A car of mass 1000 kg is travelling down an incline of 1 in 28 against a constant resistance of 750 N. Find the maximum speed that can be reached by the car when the engine is working at the rate of 12 kW.

13. A lorry of mass 2400 kg is moving at a steady speed of 60 km/h against a constant frictional resistance of 2 kN. Find the power developed by the engine if the lorry is travelling (a) along a horizontal road, (b) up a hill of inclination $\sin^{-1}$ (1/21), (c) down the same hill.

14. A train of mass 50 tonnes is ascending an incline of 1 in 60 with the engine working at the rate of 200 kW. When the train is travelling at $10\,\mathrm{m\,s^{-1}}$, its acceleration is $0\cdot1\,\mathrm{m\,s^{-2}}$. Find the frictional resistance to motion. Assuming that the resistance and the power of the engine remain constant, find the maximum speed the train can attain on this slope.

15. The constant non-gravitational resistance to the motion of a car of mass 1500 kg is 750 N. The engine of the car works at a constant rate of 20 kW. Find, in km/h, the maximum speed (a) on the level, and (b) directly up a road inclined at an angle arcsin (1/12) to the horizontal. Find also, in m/s², the acceleration of the car when it is travelling at 72 km/h on a level road. [Take g as 10 m/s².]   (L)

16. The frictional resistance to the motion of a car of mass 1000 kg is $30v\,\mathrm{N}$ where $v\,\mathrm{m\,s^{-1}}$ is the speed of the car. The car ascends a hill of inclination arcsin $\left(\dfrac{1}{10}\right)$, the power exerted by the engine being 12·8 kW. If the car is moving at a steady speed, prove (do not merely verify) that this steady speed is $10\,\mathrm{m\,s^{-1}}$. On reaching the top of the hill, find the immediate acceleration of the car, assuming the road becomes level.   (O&C)

17. The resistance to the motion of a car is $(160+cV^2)$ newtons, where c is a constant and V is the speed of the car in m/s. The mass of the car is 900 kg and, when the engine is working at the rate of 19·2 kW, the maximum speed on a level road is 20 m/s. Find the value of c. The car ascends a slope inclined to the horizontal at an angle θ, where $\sin\theta = 1/30$. If the engine continues to work at the same rate, find the acceleration of the car when its speed is 10 m/s. [Take g as 10 m/s².]   (L)

18. A car of mass 1·2 tonnes is travelling along a straight, horizontal road at a constant speed of 120 km/h against a resistance of 600 newtons. Calculate, in kW, the effective power being exerted. Given that the resistance is proportional to the square of the velocity, calculate also (i) the power required to go down a hill of 1 in 30 (along the slope) at a steady speed of 120 km/h, (ii) the acceleration of the car up this hill with the engine working at 20 kW at the instant when the speed is 80 km/h.   (AEB 1978)

Exercise 7.5 (miscellaneous)

1. A particle is projected at a speed of $3\cdot5\,\mathrm{m\,s^{-1}}$ across a rough horizontal plane. Given that it comes to rest after travelling a distance of 5 m, find the coefficient of friction.

2.   A particle released from rest on a smooth plane inclined at an angle α to the horizontal reaches a speed of $6\,\text{m}\,\text{s}^{-1}$ after travelling $3\,\text{m}$ down the plane. Find $\sin \alpha$.

3.   A body of mass $2\,\text{kg}$ is pulled from rest across a rough horizontal plane by a string inclined at an angle α to the horizontal where $\sin \alpha = 3/5$. The coefficient of friction is $1/3$. After travelling $7 \cdot 8\,\text{m}$ the body attains a speed of $5 \cdot 2\,\text{m}\,\text{s}^{-1}$. Assuming the tension in the string is constant, find its magnitude.

4.   A particle is attached to a fixed point by means of a light inextensible string of length $1\,\text{m}$. If the particle is projected horizontally through its lowest point with a speed of $2 \cdot 8\,\text{m}\,\text{s}^{-1}$, find the angle the string makes with the vertical when the particle first comes to rest.

5.   A particle of mass $5\,\text{kg}$ is projected with a speed of $2 \cdot 8\,\text{m}\,\text{s}^{-1}$ down a rough plane inclined at an angle α to the horizontal, where $\sin \alpha = 5/13$. If the particle comes to rest after travelling $2 \cdot 6\,\text{m}$, find the work done against friction. Find also the coefficient of friction between the particle and the plane.

6.   The work done in stretching an elastic string from $3\,\text{m}$ to $5\,\text{m}$ in length is $4\,\text{J}$. If the modulus of the string is $3\,\text{N}$, find its natural length.

7.   A particle of mass $2\,\text{kg}$ on a smooth plane inclined at $30°$ to the horizontal is attached by means of a light inextensible string passing over a smooth pulley at the top edge of the plane to a particle of mass $3\,\text{kg}$ which hangs freely. If the system is released from rest with both parts of the string taut, find the speed acquired by the particles when both have moved a distance of $1\,\text{m}$.

8.   A curved chute with a smooth surface is fixed so that a point A on the chute is $2 \cdot 5\,\text{m}$ above a horizontal plane. A particle is released from A and is travelling horizontally when it leaves the chute at a point B $1 \cdot 6\,\text{m}$ above the horizontal plane. Find the speed of the particle as it hits this plane and the horizontal distance it has travelled since leaving the chute.

9.   A particle P of mass m is attached to two elastic strings each of length $0 \cdot 6\,\text{m}$ and modulus kmg. The other ends of the strings are fixed to two points A and B $1 \cdot 2\,\text{m}$ apart on the same horizontal level. P is released from rest at M, the mid-point of AB and falls vertically $0 \cdot 8\,\text{m}$ before coming instantaneously to rest. Find k and also the speed of P as it passes through C, where $MC = 0 \cdot 45\,\text{m}$.

10. A light elastic string obeys Hooke's law, so that when it is stretched by an amount x the tension in it is given by $T = kx$ for some constant k. Prove that the elastic energy stored in the string when its extension is x is given by $E = \frac{1}{2}kx^2$.

   One end of such a string is attached to a fixed point A, and the other end is attached to a particle of mass m. The unstretched length of the string is a, and the particle hangs freely in equilibrium at a point B which is at a distance $\frac{5}{4}a$ below

A. Prove that $k = 4mg/a$. The particle is held at *A*, and released from rest. Find its velocity as it passes *B*, and the total distance it falls before coming instantaneously to rest.   (C)

11. A bead of mass *m* slides on a smooth vertical rod and is attached to a light inextensible string which passes over a smooth peg at a distance *a* from the rod and has a particle of mass *2m* fastened to its other end. The bead is held at the level of the peg and then released. Prove that it will descend $\frac{4}{3}a$ before coming to rest and find the tension in the string at this instant.   (O)

12. *A, B, C, D* are fixed points situated at the mid-points of the sides of a square of side *2a* with *AC* vertical (*C* above *A*) and *BD* horizontal. A weight *W* is held in the plane of the square by four springs, of modulus λ and natural length *a*, whose other ends are attached to *A, B, C* and *D* respectively. Show that in the equilibrium position the springs attached to *B* and *D* are inclined to the upward drawn vertical at an angle α where $2\cot\alpha - \cos\alpha = W/2\lambda$. Show that the amount of energy needed to raise the weight to the centre of the square must be at least $2a\lambda(\cot^2\alpha + \sin\alpha - 1)$.   (W)

13. A small bead of mass *m* is threaded on a smooth wire which is shaped in the form of the curve $by = x^2 + b^2$ ($x \leqslant 0$). The positive *y*-axis is vertically upwards and the *x*-axis lies in a horizontal plane. The bead is released from rest at the point where $x = -2b$ and slides down the wire to its end at the point $(0, b)$, after which the bead moves freely under gravity until it strikes the horizontal plane at a point on the *x*-axis. Find expressions for (i) the speed of the bead on leaving the wire, (ii) the speed of the bead on striking the *x*-axis, (iii) the angle that the direction of motion of the bead makes with the *x*-axis when it meets the *x*-axis, (iv) the *x*-coordinate of the point where the bead meets the *x*-axis.

Suppose instead that it is required that the bead should hit a small target which is to be placed on the *x*-axis at the point $(c, 0)$. Find the *x*-coordinate of the point on the curve at which the bead has to be released from rest if it is to achieve this.   (JMB)

14. An elastic string is such that when stretched from its natural length *l* to a length $l + x$ the tension in the string becomes kx, where *k* is a positive constant. Show that the work done when the length of the string is increased from $l + x_1$ to $l + x_2$ is $\frac{1}{2}k(x_2^2 - x_1^2)$.

A particle of mass *m* is attached to one end of the string, the other end of which is attached to a fixed point *O* in a smooth inclined plane of inclination α. The particle rests in equilibrium on the plane and the extension of the string is $\frac{1}{2}l$. Show That $kl = 2mg\sin\alpha$. The particle is then pulled a further distance $b - \frac{1}{2}l$ down the line of greatest slope, and released. By considerations of energy or otherwise, determine the distance up the plane, measured from the point of release, that the particle will travel, distinguishing the cases (i) $b \leqslant l$, (ii) $l < b \leqslant 2l$. Describe briefly in words what happens if $b > 2l$.   (JMB)

15. A train of mass 3×10^5 kg travels along a straight level track. The resistance to motion is 1.5×10^4 N. Find the tractive force required to produce an acceleration of 0.1 m s^{-2}, and the power in kW which is then developed by the engine when the speed of the train is 10 m s^{-1}. Find also the maximum speed attainable on the same track when the engine is working at a rate of 360 kW. (JMB)

16. A car of mass 1000 kg is travelling along a level road at a steady speed of 45 km/h with its engine working at $22\frac{1}{2}$ kW. Calculate in newtons the total resistance (assumed constant) due to friction, etc. The engine is disconnected and simultaneously the brakes are applied, bringing the car to rest in 30 metres. Find the force, assumed constant, exerted by the brakes.   (O & C)

17. A cable car in the Alps gains height at an average rate of 900 m in $2\frac{1}{2}$ minutes. Given that the cable car has mass 1300 kg and carries 30 passengers of average mass 90 kg, determine the average power required if the efficiency of the machinery is 75%. [Take g to be 10 m s^{-2}.]   (C)

18. A pump raises water through a vertical height of 15 m and delivers it at a speed of 10 m s^{-1} through a circular pipe of internal diameter 12 cm. Find the mass of water raised per second and the effective power of the pump, giving your answers to 3 significant figures.

19. A motor lorry weighing 5 metric tonnes can develop up to $15\,000$ watts. It is moving up a hill with slope 1 in 20 $\left(\theta = \sin^{-1}\dfrac{1}{20} \right)$ against a frictional force of 300 N. This frictional force is independent of the speed. (i) Find the maximum steady speed in kilometres per hour at which the lorry can travel up this slope. (ii) Find the acceleration capable of being developed when the lorry travels up this slope at 10 km h^{-1}. The lorry travels on a straight horizontal road at a speed of v kilometres per hour against a braking force of $10v$ newtons and other resistances of 300 N. What is the maximum value of v?   (W)

20. A locomotive of mass $15\,000$ kg, working at the rate of 220 kW, pulls a train of mass $35\,000$ kg up a straight track which rises 1 m vertically for every 50 m travelled along the track. When the speed is 10 m/s the acceleration is 0.23 m/s^2. Find the frictional resistance at this speed. Given that the resistance is proportional to the speed of the train, find, in m/s, the greatest speed of the train up the slope if the rate of working is unchanged. [Take $g = 10$ m/s^2.]   (L)

21. The engine of a car, of mass M kg, works at a constant rate of H kW. The non-gravitational resistance to the motion of the car is constant. The maximum speed on level ground is V m/s. Find, in terms of M, V, H, α and g, expressions for the accelerations of the car when it is travelling at speed $\frac{1}{2}V$ m/s (a) directly up a road of inclination α, (b) directly down this road. Given that the acceleration in case (b) is twice that in case (a), find $\sin \alpha$ in terms of M, V, H and g. Find also, in terms of V alone, the greatest steady speed which the car can maintain when travelling directly up the road.   (L)

22. An engine is travelling at a steady speed of 10 m/s on a level track against a constant resistance of 40 000 N. Calculate, in kW, the power output of the engine. The engine is then coupled to a carriage by a towbar. The constant resistance to the motion of the carriage is 20 000 N. If the power output of the engine is now 900 kW, calculate, in m/s, the maximum speed of the train on a level track. State the tension, in newtons, in the towbar. The train then ascends an incline of inclination arcsin (1/50) to the horizontal with the same power output, 900 kW, against the same constant frictional forces. If the total mass of the train is 340 tonne, show that the acceleration of the train when it is travelling at 5 m/s is $13/85$ m/s^2. [Take g as 10 m/s^2.] (L)

23. A car of mass $2 \cdot 5 \times 10^3$ kg travels at a constant speed of $20 \, \text{m s}^{-1}$ up a hill of inclination of $\sin^{-1}$ (1/20) to the horizontal, with the engine working at a power of 8×10^4 W. Given that the resistance is proportional to the cube of the speed show that the resistance at a speed of $24 \, \text{m s}^{-1}$ is $4 \cdot 8 \times 10^3$ N, correct to 2 significant figures. Given that the engine is working at the same power, find the acceleration at an instant when the car is moving down a hill of inclination $\sin^{-1}$ (1/10) to the horizontal at a speed of $24 \, \text{m s}^{-1}$. (C)

24. A motor-cyclist, whose total mass with his machine is 200 kg, is ascending a hill of inclination θ to the horizontal, where $\sin \theta = 1/8$. If the resistance forces total 150 N and the engine is working at 9 kW, calculate (i) the acceleration of the motor-cycle when the speed is 20 m/s, (ii) the maximum speed that can be attained by the motor-cycle up this hill. The motor-cyclist descends the same hill with a pillion rider whose mass is 80 kg. The resistive forces now total 170 N and the engine is switched off. Find the distance covered and the time taken as the speed of the motor-cycle increases from 10 m/s to 20 m/s. [Take the acceleration due to gravity to be 10 m/s^2.] (AEB 1977)

25. A car has a maximum speed of 108 km/h when moving along a horizontal road with the engine working at 36 kW. Calculate, in newtons, the total resistance to the motion of the car. The car, which is of mass 800 kg, can move down a road inclined at an angle α to the horizontal at a maximum speed of 108 km/h with the engine working at 30 kW against the same total resistance. Calculate $\sin \alpha$. Given that the total resistance varies as the square of the speed, find, in kW, the rate at which the engine is working at the instant when the car is moving along a horizontal road with an acceleration of 0·5 m/s^2 at a speed of 54 km/h. [Take the acceleration due to gravity to be 10 m/s^2.] (AEB 1978)

26. Two points A and B are at the same level, and they are connected by a road consisting of two straight sections AC and CB, each of uniform gradient. The point C is at a height h vertically above the line AB, and the inclinations to the horizontal of AC and CB are α and β respectively. A car of mass m starts from rest at A, accelerates uniformly to reach a speed $2U$ at C, and then moves with constant retardation, attaining a speed U at B. Show that the time taken to move from A to B is $h(\operatorname{cosec} \alpha + \frac{2}{3} \operatorname{cosec} \beta)/U$. The resistance to the motion of the car is a constant force R. Find the force exerted by the engine during the climb from A

to C, the maximum power developed by the engine and the total work done by the engine. Show that the described motion from C to B can be achieved by using the brakes, with the engine switched off, only if $R \leqslant \dfrac{m \sin \beta}{2h} (2gh + 3U^2)$.   (JMB)

8 Uniform motion in a circle

8.1 Angular velocity

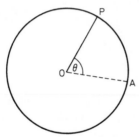

Consider a particle P moving round the circumference of a circle with centre O. If A is any fixed point on the circle and $\angle POA = \theta$, then the *angular velocity* of P is defined as the rate of change of θ and often denoted by ω.

Thus $\omega = \dot{\theta}$, i.e. $\omega = d\theta/dt$.

The value of ω may be positive or negative according to the direction of motion. Anti-clockwise rotations are usually taken to be positive. The *angular speed* of P is the magnitude of its angular velocity. The *angular acceleration* of P is the rate of change of the angular velocity, denoted by $\dot{\omega}$ or $\ddot{\theta}$.

The SI unit of angular velocity is one radian per second, i.e. $1 \, \text{rad s}^{-1}$. Angular velocity can also be measured in revolutions per minute (rev min^{-1}).

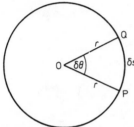

Suppose now that a particle is moving round the circumference of a circle radius r such that when the angular velocity of the particle is ω, its speed is v. If the particle moves from P to Q in time δt, let arc $PQ = \delta s$ and $\angle POQ = \delta \theta$.

Since $\delta s = r \, \delta\theta$ we have $\dfrac{\delta s}{\delta t} = r \dfrac{\delta\theta}{\delta t}$.

As $\delta t \to 0$, $\dfrac{\delta s}{\delta t} \to \dfrac{ds}{dt}$ and $\dfrac{\delta\theta}{\delta t} \to \dfrac{d\theta}{dt}$.

Hence
$$\frac{ds}{dt} = r\frac{d\theta}{dt}.$$

$\therefore$

$$v = r\omega \quad \text{and} \quad \omega = \frac{v}{r}.$$

Example 1 The tip of the second hand of a large clock is 60 cm from the centre of the clock face. Find the angular speed of the second hand and the speed at which the tip is travelling.

The second hand makes 1 revolution per minute, i.e. it moves through 2π rad in 60 s

$\therefore$ its angular speed $= \dfrac{2\pi}{60}$ rad s^{-1} $= \dfrac{\pi}{30}$ rad s^{-1}.

Hence the speed of the tip of the hand

$$= \frac{60}{100} \times \frac{\pi}{30} \text{m s}^{-1} = \frac{\pi}{50} \text{m s}^{-1} \approx 0.063 \text{ m s}^{-1}.$$

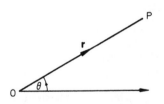

The definition of angular velocity can be extended to the motion in a plane of a point P with position vector $\mathbf{r}$. If the angle between $\mathbf{r}$ and some fixed direction is θ, then the angular velocity of P about O (i.e. the angular velocity of **OP**) is $\dot{\theta}$.

Example 2 At time t, the position vector of a point P with respect to the origin O is $2t\mathbf{i} + t^2\mathbf{j}$. Find the angular velocity of **OP** at time t.

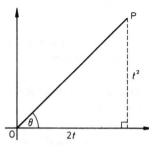

Let θ be the angle between **OP** and the direction of $\mathbf{i}$, then at time t,

$$\tan \theta = \frac{t^2}{2t} = \frac{t}{2}.$$

Differentiating with respect to t

$$\sec^2 \theta \frac{d\theta}{dt} = \frac{1}{2}.$$

$\therefore$

$$(1 + \tan^2 \theta)\frac{d\theta}{dt} = \frac{1}{2}$$

$$\left(1 + \frac{t^2}{4}\right)\frac{d\theta}{dt} = \frac{1}{2}$$

i.e.

$$(4 + t^2)\frac{d\theta}{dt} = 2.$$

Hence the angular velocity at time t is given by $\dfrac{d\theta}{dt} = \dfrac{2}{4+t^2}$.

Example 3   A particle P is moving anti-clockwise with constant angular speed ω round a circle with centre O and radius 5. Given that initially the position vector of P is 5i, find its position vector at time t. Deduce vector expressions for the velocity and acceleration of P at time t.

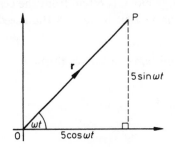

Since the angular speed is ω, at time t **OP** makes an angle ωt with the direction of **i**. Hence at time t the position vector of P is

$$\mathbf{r} = 5(\cos \omega t\,\mathbf{i} + \sin \omega t\,\mathbf{j}).$$

Differentiating with respect to t, the velocity of P is given by

$$\mathbf{v} = \dot{\mathbf{r}} = 5(-\omega \sin \omega t\,\mathbf{i} + \omega \cos \omega t\,\mathbf{j})$$

i.e.
$$\mathbf{v} = 5\omega(-\sin \omega t\,\mathbf{i} + \cos \omega t\,\mathbf{j}).$$

Similarly the acceleration of P is given by

$$\mathbf{a} = \ddot{\mathbf{r}} = 5\omega(-\omega \cos \omega t\,\mathbf{i} - \omega \sin \omega t\,\mathbf{j})$$

i.e.
$$\mathbf{a} = -5\omega^2(\cos \omega t\,\mathbf{i} + \sin \omega t\,\mathbf{j})$$

[We note that $v = 5\omega\sqrt{(\sin^2 \omega t + \cos^2 \omega t)} = 5\omega$, which is consistent with the result $v = r\omega$ obtained earlier in the section. We also see that $\mathbf{a} = -\omega^2\mathbf{r}$. Thus the acceleration of the particle is directed towards O and has magnitude $5\omega^2$.]

Exercise 8.1

1.   A record of diameter 18 cm is rotating at 45 rev min^{-1}. Find its angular velocity in rad s^{-1} and the speed of a point on the rim of the record.

2.   A point is travelling round a circle of radius 5 m at a speed of 20 m s^{-1}. Find the angular speed of the point about the centre of the circle.

3.   Find the angular speed with which the earth is rotating about its axis. Hence, taking the radius of the earth to be 6400 km, find the speed of a point on the equator in m s^{-1}.

4.   Find an approximate value for the angular speed at which the earth is moving about the sun. Assuming that the earth moves round the sun in an approximately circular orbit of radius 150 million kilometres, find the speed of the earth relative to the sun.

5. Given that the tip of the minute hand of a clock is moving at a speed of $0.001 \, \mathrm{m \, s^{-1}}$, find the length of the hand to the nearest cm.

6. Find the angular velocity of a point P about the origin O at time $t > 0$, given that the position vector of P is

(a) $\mathbf{i} + t\mathbf{j}$,   (b) $2t\mathbf{i} - 3\mathbf{j}$,   (c) $\dfrac{1}{t}\mathbf{i} + t\mathbf{j}$.

7. A particle P moves anti-clockwise with constant angular speed ω round a circle with centre O and radius r. Write down the position vector of P at time t given that when $t = 0$ its position vector is (a) $r\mathbf{i}$, (b) $r\mathbf{j}$.

8. Use the results of question 7 to find the angular velocity of a particle P about the origin O and the speed at which the particle is travelling given that at time t its position vector is
(a) $3(\cos 2t\mathbf{i} + \sin 2t\mathbf{j})$,   (b) $5(-\sin t\mathbf{i} + \cos t\mathbf{j})$,
(c) $\cos 2\pi t\mathbf{i} - \sin 2\pi t\mathbf{j}$,   (d) $a(\sin kt\mathbf{i} - \cos kt\mathbf{j})$.

9. The points S and T are moving anti-clockwise round a circle with centre O (the origin) and radius a, with the same constant speed $a\omega$. When T is passing through the point with position vector $a\mathbf{j}$, S is passing through the point with position vector $a\mathbf{i}$. Find, at time t later, the position vectors of S and T. Find also, in vector form, the velocity of T relative to S.   (L)

8.2 Acceleration in circular motion

Consider a particle moving with angular velocity ω round the circumference of a circle centre O, radius r. Suppose that in time δt it moves from P to Q, where $\angle POQ = \delta\theta$. Let the speed of the particle be v at P and $v + \delta v$ at Q.

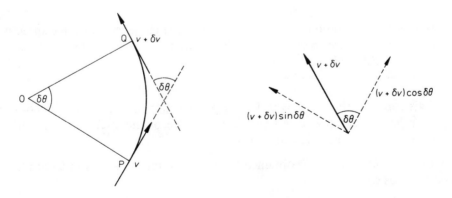

From the diagrams we see that the velocity of the particle at Q has components $(v + \delta v) \sin \delta\theta$ in the direction of $\overrightarrow{PO}$ and $(v + \delta v) \cos \delta\theta$ perpendicular to $\overrightarrow{PO}$.

Thus in the direction of $\vec{PO}$, the change in velocity in time δt

$$= (v + \delta v)\sin\delta\theta$$

∴   average acceleration $= \dfrac{(v+\delta v)\sin\delta\theta}{\delta t} = (v+\delta v)\dfrac{\sin\delta\theta}{\delta\theta}\cdot\dfrac{\delta\theta}{\delta t}.$

As $\delta t \to 0,\ \ \delta v \to 0,\ \ \dfrac{\sin\delta\theta}{\delta\theta} \to 1$ and $\dfrac{\delta\theta}{\delta t} \to \dfrac{d\theta}{dt}$

∴   acceleration along $\vec{PO} = v\dfrac{d\theta}{dt} = v\omega = \dfrac{v^2}{r}.$

Similarly, perpendicular to $\vec{PO}$, the change in velocity in time δt

$$= (v + \delta v)\cos\delta\theta - v$$

∴   average acceleration $= \dfrac{(v+\delta v)\cos\delta\theta - v}{\delta t}$

$$= \dfrac{v(\cos\delta\theta - 1)}{\delta t} + \dfrac{\delta v}{\delta t}\cos\delta\theta$$

$$= -\dfrac{v\,.\,2\sin^2\frac{1}{2}\delta\theta}{\delta t} + \dfrac{\delta v}{\delta t}\cos\delta\theta$$

$$= -v\dfrac{\delta\theta}{\delta t}\left(\dfrac{\sin\frac{1}{2}\delta\theta}{\frac{1}{2}\delta\theta}\right)\sin\tfrac{1}{2}\delta\theta + \dfrac{\delta v}{\delta t}\cos\delta\theta.$$

As $\delta t \to 0,\ \ \dfrac{\sin\frac{1}{2}\delta\theta}{\frac{1}{2}\delta\theta} \to 1,\ \ \dfrac{\delta\theta}{\delta t} \to \dfrac{d\theta}{dt},\ \ \dfrac{\delta v}{\delta t} \to \dfrac{dv}{dt}$

but $\sin\tfrac{1}{2}\delta\theta \to 0$ and $\cos\delta\theta \to 1$

∴   acceleration perpendicular to $\vec{PO} = \dfrac{dv}{dt}.$

Hence the acceleration of a particle moving in a circle with variable speed v has, at any instant, components v^2/r towards the centre of the circle and dv/dt in the direction of motion.

If v is constant, then $dv/dt = 0$. Thus a particle moving in a circle with constant speed v has acceleration v^2/r towards the centre of the circle. In terms of the angular velocity ω the acceleration is $r\omega^2$.

[This last result can also be obtained by the vector methods used in Example 3 of the previous section.]

Using Newton's second law, we find that the resultant force acting on a particle of mass m, which moves in a circle radius r with constant speed v, is of magnitude mv^2/r and is directed towards the centre of the circle.

Example 1   One end of a light inextensible string of length 0·5 m is attached to a fixed point O on a smooth horizontal table and a particle of mass 2 kg is attached to its other end. If the particle moves in a horizontal circle, centre O, with a speed of 5 m s^{-1}, find the tension in the string and the reaction of the table on the particle.

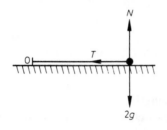

The acceleration of the particle is $5^2/0·5$ m s^{-2}, i.e. 50 m s^{-2} towards O

$\therefore$ using Newton's second law horizontally and vertically,

$$\uparrow N - 2g = 0$$
$$\leftarrow \qquad T = 2 \times 50 = 100.$$
$$\therefore \quad N = 2g = 19·6$$

Hence the tension in the string is 100 N and the reaction of the table is 19·6 N.

Example 2   A particle is placed at a point 20 cm from the centre O of a rough circular disc. When the disc rotates about a vertical axis through O at an angular speed of 3·5 rad s^{-1}, the particle is on the point of slipping. Find the coefficient of friction between the particle and the disc.

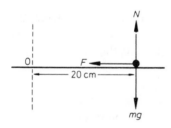

The acceleration of the particle is $0·2 \times (3·5)^2$ m s^{-2} towards O. Using Newton's second law horizontally and vertically,

$$\uparrow N - mg = 0 \quad \therefore \quad N = mg$$

$$\leftarrow \qquad F = m \times 0·2(3·5)^2 = m \times \frac{1}{5} \times \left(\frac{7}{2}\right)^2 = \frac{49m}{20}.$$

Since the particle is on the point of slipping, $F = \mu N$

$$\therefore \quad \frac{49m}{20} = \mu mg = 9·8\,\mu m.$$

Hence $\mu = \dfrac{49}{20 \times 9·8} = \dfrac{1}{4}$

$\therefore$ the coefficient of friction between the particle and the disc is $\frac{1}{4}$.

Exercise 8.2

1.   Find the acceleration of a particle moving uniformly along a circular path
(a) radius 4 m at a speed of 6 m s^{-1},

(b) radius 25 m at a speed of 36 km/h,
(c) radius 80 cm with angular velocity $5 \, \text{rad s}^{-1}$,
(d) radius 10 m with angular velocity 24 rev/min.

2.   Find the magnitude of the resultant force acting on a particle of mass 5 kg which is moving in a circle of radius 2 m with a constant speed of $3 \, \text{m s}^{-1}$.

3.   Find the magnitude of the resultant force acting on a particle of mass 1·5 kg which is moving in a circle of radius 50 cm with a constant angular velocity of $4 \, \text{rad s}^{-1}$.

4.   One end of a light inextensible string of length 3 m is attached to a fixed point O on a smooth horizontal surface and a particle of mass 5 kg is attached to its other end. If the particle is moving in a horizontal circle, centre O, at a speed of $15 \, \text{m s}^{-1}$, find the tension in the string and the reaction of the surface on the particle.

5.   One end of a light inextensible string of length 1·6 m is attached to a fixed point O on a smooth horizontal surface and a particle of mass 4 kg is attached to the other end. If the string will break when the tension in it exceeds 90 N, find the maximum speed at which the particle can move in a horizontal circle with centre O.

6.   A particle is placed at a point 0·5 m from the centre O of a rough circular disc. When the disc rotates about a vertical axis through O at an angular speed of $2·8 \, \text{rad s}^{-1}$, the particle is on the point of slipping. Find the coefficient of friction between the particle and the disc.

7.   A small ring A is threaded on a horizontal rod PQ, the coefficient of friction between the rod and the ring being 2/7. When the rod rotates horizontally about P with a constant angular velocity of $2 \, \text{rad s}^{-1}$, the ring does not slip along the rod. Find the maximum possible distance AP.

8.   A particle A is placed on a rough horizontal platform, the coefficient of friction between the particle and the platform being 3/8. The platform rotates about a vertical axis through a fixed point O on the platform. If $OA = 1·2 \, \text{m}$, find the angular velocity of the platform when the particle is on the point of slipping.

8.3 Further problems

Consider a particle P of mass m attached by means of a light inextensible string of length l to a fixed point O. The particle is set in motion so that it moves in a horizontal circle of radius r with constant angular velocity ω. Since the string traces out a cone in space, this system is called a *conical pendulum*.

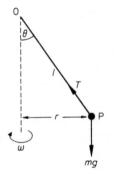

Applying Newton's second law horizontally and vertically,

$$\leftarrow T\sin\theta = mr\omega^2$$
$$\uparrow T\cos\theta - mg = 0.$$

Substituting $r = l\sin\theta$,

$$T\sin\theta = ml\sin\theta\omega^2$$

$\therefore$ the tension in the string is $ml\omega^2$.

Example 1 A particle of mass 2 kg is attached by a light inextensible string of length 1 m to a fixed point O. The particle is made to move in a horizontal circle whose centre is 0·8 m vertically below O. Find the tension in the string and the speed of the particle.

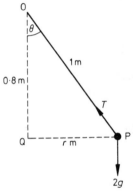

Let the speed of the particle be $v\,\mathrm{m\,s^{-1}}$, then applying Newton's second law horizontally and vertically

$$\leftarrow T\sin\theta = \frac{2v^2}{r} \qquad (1)$$

$$\uparrow T\cos\theta - 2g = 0 \qquad (2)$$

In $\triangle OPQ$, by Pythagoras' theorem

$$r = \sqrt{\{1^2 - (0\cdot8)^2\}} = 0\cdot6$$

$\therefore \quad \sin\theta = 0\cdot6 \quad$ and $\quad \cos\theta = 0\cdot8$

Using (2)
$$T = \frac{2\times9\cdot8}{0\cdot8} = 24\cdot5$$

$\therefore \quad$ the tension in the string is 24·5 N.

Using (1)
$$v^2 = 24\cdot5\times0\cdot6\times\frac{0\cdot6}{2} = 7^2\times(0\cdot3)^2$$

$$\therefore \qquad v = 7\times0\cdot3 = 2\cdot1.$$

Hence the speed of the particle is $2\cdot1\,\mathrm{m\,s^{-1}}$.

The methods used in Example 1 can also be applied to a particle sliding round the inner surface of a smooth sphere or cone in a horizontal circle. In such problems the acceleration towards the centre of the circle is produced by the horizontal component of the normal reaction of the surface on the particle.

Example 2   One end of a light inextensible string of length l is attached to a fixed point A and a particle P is attached to the other end. The ends of a second string of the same length are attached to P and to a fixed point B at a distance h ($<2l$) vertically below A. If the particle moves in a horizontal circle with uniform angular speed ω, find the least value of ω for which both strings are taut.

Let $\angle PAB = \theta$, then $h = 2l\cos\theta$ and the radius of the circle described by the particle is $l\sin\theta$.

Hence the acceleration of the particle

$$= \omega^2 l\sin\theta.$$

Applying Newton's second law horizontally and vertically

$$\uparrow T_1\cos\theta - T_2\cos\theta - mg = 0$$
$$\leftarrow T_1\sin\theta + T_2\sin\theta = m\omega^2 l\sin\theta$$

$$\therefore \quad T_1 + T_2 = m\omega^2 l$$

$$T_1 - T_2 = \frac{mg}{\cos\theta} = \frac{2mgl}{h}.$$

Subtracting
$$2T_2 = m\omega^2 l - \frac{2mgl}{h}$$

$$\therefore \quad T_2 = \frac{ml}{h}(h\omega^2 - 2g).$$

Since $T_1 > T_2$, both strings will be taut if $T_2 \geqslant 0$

i.e.   if $h\omega^2 - 2g \geqslant 0.$

Hence the least value of ω for which both strings are taut is $\sqrt{(2g/h)}$.

When a vehicle travels at constant speed round a bend, regarded as a circular arc, its acceleration is directed towards the centre of the arc. If the road surface is horizontal then this acceleration is produced by the frictional force between the wheels and the ground. However, if the road is banked, the horizontal components of the frictional force and of the normal reaction between the vehicle and the ground together provide the required acceleration. [We will ignore at this stage the possibility that the vehicle could overturn.]

Example 3   A car of mass m travels at constant speed v round a bend of radius r on a road banked at an angle α. The coefficient of friction between the car's tyres and the road surface is μ. Find an expression for v^2 given that (a) the car travels with no tendency to slip, (b) the car is about to slip outwards, (c) the car is about to slip inwards.

(a) 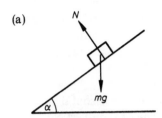 (b) 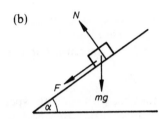 (c)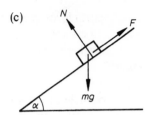

(a) In this case there is no frictional force acting.
Applying Newton's second law horizontally and vertically

$$\leftarrow N \sin \alpha = mv^2/r$$
$$\uparrow N \cos \alpha - mg = 0$$

$$\therefore \quad v^2 = \frac{rN \sin \alpha}{m} = \frac{r \sin \alpha}{m} \cdot \frac{mg}{\cos \alpha} = rg \tan \alpha.$$

Hence when there is no tendency to slip $v^2 = rg \tan \alpha$.

(b) The frictional force acts down the slope and takes its limiting value μN.
Applying Newton's second law horizontally and vertically

$$\leftarrow N \sin \alpha + \mu N \cos \alpha = mv^2/r$$
$$\uparrow N \cos \alpha - \mu N \sin \alpha - mg = 0$$

$$\therefore \quad v^2 = \frac{rN}{m}(\sin \alpha + \mu \cos \alpha) \quad \text{and} \quad N = \frac{mg}{\cos \alpha - \mu \sin \alpha}.$$

Hence when the car is about to slip outwards

$$v^2 = \frac{rg(\sin \alpha + \mu \cos \alpha)}{\cos \alpha - \mu \sin \alpha}, \quad \text{i.e.} \quad \frac{rg(\tan \alpha + \mu)}{1 - \mu \tan \alpha}.$$

(c) The frictional force acts up the slope and takes its limiting value μN.
Applying Newton's second law horizontally and vertically

$$\leftarrow N \sin \alpha - \mu N \cos \alpha = mv^2/r$$
$$\uparrow N \cos \alpha + \mu N \sin \alpha - mg = 0.$$

Hence when the car is about to slip inwards

$$v^2 = \frac{rg(\sin \alpha - \mu \cos \alpha)}{\cos \alpha + \mu \sin \alpha}, \quad \text{i.e.} \quad \frac{rg(\tan \alpha - \mu)}{1 + \mu \tan \alpha}.$$

[Note that if we substitute $\mu = \tan \lambda$, where λ is the angle of friction, the results in parts (b) and (c) may be written in the form $v^2 = rg \tan (\alpha + \lambda)$ and $v^2 = rg \tan (\alpha - \lambda)$ respectively.]

Exercise 8.3

1. A particle of mass 3 kg is attached by a light inextensible string of length 75 cm to a fixed point. The particle moves in a horizontal circle with constant speed such that the string makes an angle θ with the vertical, where $\tan \theta = 4/3$. Find the tension in the string and the speed of the particle.

2. A particle of mass 5 kg is attached by a light inextensible string of length 3·25 m to a fixed point. The particle moves in a horizontal circle with a constant angular velocity of 2·8 rad s^{-1}. Find the tension in the string and the radius of the circle.

3. A particle of mass m is moving with constant speed v in a horizontal circle of radius r around the smooth inner surface of a hollow cone of semi-vertical angle θ. Find the reaction between the particle and the cone and express v^2 in terms of r, θ and g.

4. A particle moving on the smooth inner surface of a sphere describes a horizontal circle with constant angular speed 2 rad s^{-1}. Find the depth of the circle below the centre of the sphere.

5. A particle of mass 2 kg is suspended from a fixed point by a light elastic string of natural length 1 m and modulus 19·6 N. The particle is moving in a horizontal circle with constant speed v m s^{-1}. Given that the length of the string is 2·25 m, find the value of v.

6. A light inextensible string of length $4a$ has one end fixed at a point A and the other end fixed at a point B which is at a distance $2a$ vertically below A. A smooth ring R of mass m is threaded on the string and moves in a horizontal circle with centre B such that the string is taut. Show that $AR = 5a/2$ and, assuming that the ring is free to move on the string, find its speed.

7. A light inextensible string of length $5a$ has one end fixed at a point A and the other end fixed at a point B which is vertically below A and at a distance $4a$ from it. A particle P of mass m is fastened to the midpoint of the string and moves with speed u, and with the parts AP and BP of the string both taut, in a horizontal circular path whose centre is the midpoint of AB. Find, in terms of m, u, a and g, the tensions in the two parts of the string, and show that the motion described can take place only if $8u^2 \geqslant 9ga$.   (JMB)

8. A car is moving in a horizontal circle of radius 100 m on a track banked at an angle α, where $\tan \alpha = 5/16$. Find the speed of the car when there is no tendency for it to slip sideways.

9. A car travels at 90 km/h round a bend of radius 200 m on a road banked at an angle α. Find α, given that there is no tendency to skid sideways.

10. A car travels round a bend of radius 125 m on a road banked at an angle α where $\tan \alpha = 0·5$. The coefficient of friction between the car's tyres and the road is $\frac{1}{3}$. Find the maximum and minimum speeds at which the car can travel without slipping sideways.

11. A vehicle is approaching a bend of radius 50 m. The coefficient of friction between its wheels and the road is $\frac{1}{2}$. If the road surface is horizontal, find the

maximum speed at which the vehicle can negotiate the bend without skidding. If the vehicle is to drive round the bend at $20\,\mathrm{m\,s^{-1}}$ without skidding, find the least angle at which the road must be banked.

12.

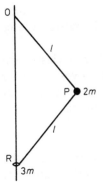

The figure shows a particle P of mass $2m$ which is attached to a fixed point O by a light inextensible string of length l. A ring R of mass $3m$, which is attached to P by another light inextensible string of length l, is free to slide on a smooth vertical wire passing through O.

The plane OPR rotates about the wire with constant angular velocity ω, where $\omega^2 > 4g/l$. Show that $OR = 8g/\omega^2$. What happens if $\omega^2 \leqslant 4g/l$?   (C)

Exercise 8.4 (miscellaneous)

1. A record is rotating at $33\frac{1}{3}$ rev/min. Find its angular speed in $\mathrm{rad\,s^{-1}}$. Find also the speed of a point on the record at a distance of $12\,\mathrm{cm}$ from the centre.

2. A van, whose wheels are of diameter $0.8\,\mathrm{m}$, is travelling at $72\,\mathrm{km/h}$. If the wheels do not slip on the road, find the number of revolutions made each second and hence the angular velocity of the wheels in $\mathrm{rad\,s^{-1}}$.

3. A point P moves such that at time t its position vector is $2t\mathbf{i}+(3-t)\mathbf{j}$. Find an expression for the angular velocity of P about the origin O at time t.

4. A particle A is moving in a horizontal circle of radius $3\,\mathrm{m}$ with constant speed $6\,\mathrm{m\,s^{-1}}$. A second particle B is moving in a concentric circle of radius $9\,\mathrm{m}$ with the same constant speed. At a given instant both particles are due east of the centre of the circles and are moving northwards. Find, in magnitude and direction, the velocity of A relative to B after a time $\frac{1}{4}\pi\,\mathrm{s}$.   (O & C)

5. On an icy morning a car travelling at $42\,\mathrm{km/h}$ drives safely round a bend of radius $100\,\mathrm{m}$ but skids on a bend of radius $25\,\mathrm{m}$. Assuming that the road surface is horizontal, find the range of possible values of the coefficient of friction between the car's tyres and the road.

6. One end of a light inextensible string of length $1.2\,\mathrm{m}$ is attached to a fixed point A on a smooth horizontal surface. A particle of mass $2\,\mathrm{kg}$ is attached to the other end C and a particle of mass $1\,\mathrm{kg}$ is attached to the mid-point B. Each

particle is moving in a horizontal circle centre A, such that the string remains straight. If the particle at C is moving at a constant speed of $6\,\text{m}\,\text{s}^{-1}$, find the tensions in BC and AB.

7. Show that when a particle moves in a circle of radius r with constant speed u its acceleration is of magnitude u^2/r and is directed towards the centre of the circle.

A particle of mass m is attached to one end A of a light inelastic string of length a, the other end being attached to a fixed point O. A moves in a horizontal circle below O with constant speed $\sqrt{(3ag/2)}$. Find (i) the angle that OA makes with the vertical, (ii) the tension in the string, (iii) the time taken to complete one revolution.   (SU)

8. A particle P is attached by a light inextensible string of length l to a fixed point O. The particle is held with the string taut and OP at an acute angle α to the downward vertical, and is then projected horizontally at right angles to the string with speed u chosen so that it describes a circle in a horizontal plane. Show that $u^2 = gl\sin\alpha\tan\alpha$. The string will break when the tension exceeds twice the weight of P. Find the greatest possible value of α.   (JMB)

9. A particle moves in a circle, of radius a and centre O, at constant speed u. Prove that the acceleration of the particle is u^2/a towards O. The end A of a light rigid rod AB of length 1 metre is smoothly hinged at a fixed point. A ring is threaded on AB and the coefficient of friction between the ring and the rod is $\frac{1}{3}$. The rod is made to rotate horizontally at 2 rad/s about A. Show that the ring can remain at rest relative to the rod at any position between A and C, where $AC = 5/6$ metres. The ring is placed at C and a second identical ring is threaded on the rod and placed at the mid-point of AB. The rings are connected by a taut, light inextensible string. When the rod rotates horizontally at ω rad/s, the rings are on the point of sliding on the rod. Given that the mass of each ring is $0.2\,\text{kg}$, calculate (i) the value of ω, (ii) the tension in the string. [Take the acceleration due to gravity to be $10\,\text{m/s}^2$.]   (AEB 1977)

10. One end of a light inelastic string of length a is attached to a particle P of mass m, and the other end of the string is attached to a fixed point O. P moves with constant speed in a horizontal circle whose centre C is a fixed point vertically below O. If the angular velocity at which CP rotates is ω, show that $OC = g/\omega^2$. A second string, also of length a, is fixed to P and C, and the new system rotates about OC with uniform angular velocity Ω and with both strings taut. Find expression in terms of m, a, ω and Ω for the tensions in OP and PC, and deduce that $\Omega > \omega\sqrt{2}$.   (C)

11. A particle moves in a horizontal circle on the smooth inner surface of a fixed spherical bowl of radius a. If the depth of the circle below the centre of the sphere is h, find an expression for the speed of the particle.

12.

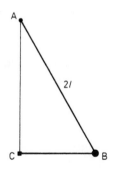

The ends of a light inextensible string *ABC* of length $3l$ are attached to fixed points *A* and *C*, *C* being vertically below *A* at a distance $\sqrt{3}l$ from *A*. At a distance $2l$ along the string from *A* a particle *B* of mass *m* is attached. When both portions of the string are taut, *B* is given a horizontal velocity *u*, and then continues to move in a circle with constant speed. Find the tensions in the two portions of the string and show that the motion is possible only if $u^2 \geqslant \frac{1}{3}gl\sqrt{3}$.

(JMB)

13.

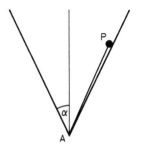

A circular cone of semi-vertical angle α is fixed with its axis vertical and its vertex, *A*, lowest, as shown in the diagram. A particle *P* of mass *m* moves on the inner surface of the cone, which is smooth. The particle is joined to *A* by a light inextensible string *AP* of length *l*. The particle moves in a horizontal circle with constant speed *v* and with the string taut. Find the reaction exerted on *P* by the cone. Find the tension in the string and show that the motion is possible only if $v^2 \geqslant gl\cos\alpha$. (JMB)

14. A car moves in a horizontal circle of radius 500 m on a track which is banked at an angle α to the horizontal. When the speed is 60 m/s there is no sideways force on the wheels. Find the angle α. Find also the maximum speed round the track to avoid slipping if the coefficient of friction is 0·5. (AEB 1978)

15. A light elastic string *AB* of natural length *a* and modulus of elasticity *mg* is joined to a light inextensible string *BC* of length *a*. The ends *A* and *C* of the string are fastened to two fixed points with *A* vertically above *C* and $AC = a$. A particle of mass *m* is fixed at *B* and rotates with speed *v* in a horizontal circle. Show that if *AB* makes an angle $\pi/6$ with the downward vertical then $v^2 = \frac{1}{2}\sqrt{3}ag$, and find the tension in *BC*. (O)

16. A car moves with constant speed in a horizontal circle of radius *r* on a track which is banked at an angle α to the horizontal, where $\tan\alpha = \frac{3}{4}$. The coefficient of friction between the tyres and the track is $\frac{1}{2}$. Find, in terms of *r* and *g*, the range of speeds at which the car can negotiate this bend without the tyres slipping on the road surface. Show that the greatest possible speed is $\sqrt{11}$ times the least possible speed. [It may be assumed that the car will not overturn at these speeds.] (L)

17. A small ring of mass m can slide on a smooth fixed vertical rod. One end of a light inextensible string of length $2a$ is fastened to the ring, and its other end is fastened to a point of the rod. A particle of mass $4m$ attached to the mid-point of the string is moving in a horizontal circle. Show that the angular velocity of the particle in this circle is greater than $\sqrt{(3g/2a)}$. Find the speed of the particle if the tension in the lower half of the string is $4mg$.   (L)

9 Coplanar forces; centre of gravity

9.1 Parallel forces, moments and couples

In earlier chapters we considered forces acting on bodies small enough to be treated as particles and represented by single points in space. Applying Newton's laws of motion, we found that if the forces acting on such a body have a non-zero resultant then the effect produced is an acceleration in the direction of the resultant. However, if the vector sum of the forces on the body is zero, the body either remains at rest or continues to move with unchanged velocity.

There are many situations in which this elementary approach is inadequate. From experience we know that the forces on a body may tend to produce rotation as well as the types of motion discussed in earlier work. A projectile, such as a cricket ball, may spin as it moves. A block placed on an inclined plane may topple rather than slide. Thus, when solving a problem in which the rotational effects of forces could be important, we must use a more realistic representation of the bodies involved. We will then find that the effect produced by a set of forces depends not only on the magnitude and direction of the resultant, but also on its line of action.

We now develop these ideas by considering the effect of coplanar forces on a variety of rigid bodies i.e. bodies whose shapes are not changed by the forces acting on them.

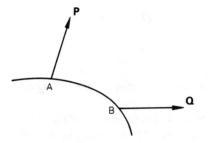

Let **P** and **Q** be *non-parallel* coplanar forces acting at points A and B of a rigid body. The magnitude and direction of their resultant **R** can be found using the parallelogram law. If the lines of action of **P** and **Q** intersect at the point C, then the line of action of **R** also passes through C.

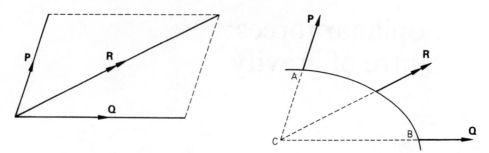

To find the line of action of the resultant of *parallel* forces **P** and **Q** acting at points *A* and *B* of a rigid body, we introduce forces **F** and −**F** acting along *AB*. The application of these equal and opposite forces will have no effect on the body and leave the line of action of the resultant unaltered.

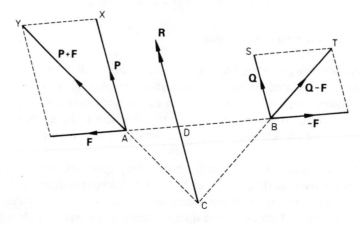

The diagram shows how the parallelogram law is used to construct a point *C* on the line of action of the resultant **R**, when **P** and **Q** are *like parallel forces* i.e. forces in the same sense.

In similar triangles ADC, YXA: $\dfrac{AD}{DC} = \dfrac{YX}{XA} = \dfrac{F}{P}$

In similar triangles DBC, STB: $\dfrac{DC}{DB} = \dfrac{SB}{ST} = \dfrac{Q}{F}$

$$\therefore \quad \frac{AD}{DB} = \frac{AD}{DC} \times \frac{DC}{DB} = \frac{F}{P} \times \frac{Q}{F} = \frac{Q}{P}$$

By vector addition, the magnitude of **R** is $P + Q$.

Hence the resultant of the like parallel forces **P** and **Q** is of magnitude $P + Q$ and divides *AB* internally in the ratio $Q:P$.

Using similar arguments it can be shown that the resultant of *unlike parallel forces* **P** and **Q**, where $P > Q$, is of magnitude $P - Q$ and divides *AB* externally in the ratio $Q:P$.

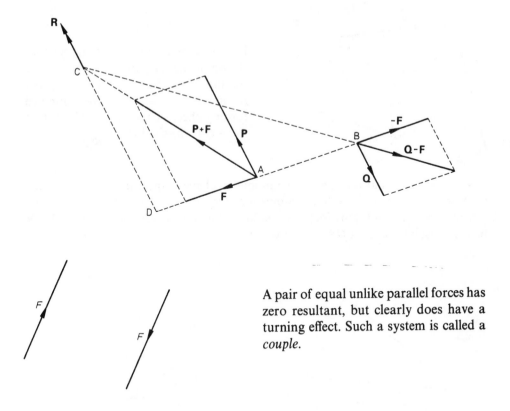

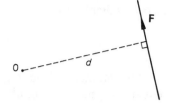

A pair of equal unlike parallel forces has zero resultant, but clearly does have a turning effect. Such a system is called a *couple*.

A quantity called the *moment of a force* or *torque* is used as a measure of "turning effect". The moment of a force about a given point is defined as the product of the magnitude of the force and its distance from the point. If the line of action of a force **F** is at a perpendicular distance d from a point O, then the moment of **F** about O is Fd.

[In three-dimensional work the quantity Fd is more accurately described as the moment or torque about an axis through O perpendicular to the plane containing O and the force **F**.]

The SI unit of torque is the newton metre (N m). Thus, if a force of magnitude 40 N acts along a line whose perpendicular distance from a point A is 2 m, then the moment of the force about A is 80 N m.

When finding the sum of the moments of a set of coplanar forces about a point, the moment of each force is taken to be positive or negative according to the sense of the rotation it would produce. The moment of a force about any point on its line of action is zero.

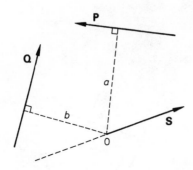

For instance, if forces **P**, **Q** and **S** act as shown in the diagram, then the sum of the anti-clockwise moments of **P**, **Q** and **S** about O is $Pa - Qb$, i.e. the combined turning effect of the system about O is $Pa - Qb$ anti-clockwise.

We now show that the sum of the moments of two coplanar forces about any point in their plane is equal to the moment of their resultant about the same point.

Suppose that **P** and **Q** are forces whose lines of action intersect at a point C. Let **R** be their resultant and let O be a point in the same plane such that $OC = d$.

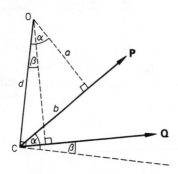
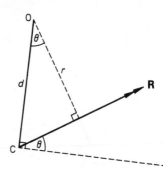

Using the notation of the above diagrams, the sum of the moments of **P** and **Q** about O

$$= Pa + Qb = Pd \cos \alpha + Qd \cos \beta = d(P \cos \alpha + Q \cos \beta)$$

The moment of **R** about O

$$= Rr = Rd \cos \theta = d(R \cos \theta).$$

Considering the components of **P**, **Q** and **R** in a direction perpendicular to OC, we have

$$P \cos \alpha + Q \cos \beta = R \cos \theta.$$

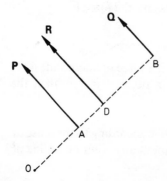

Hence the sum of the moments about O of **P** and **Q** is equal to the moment about O of **R**.

If **P** and **Q** are like parallel forces with resultant **R**, as shown in the diagram, then

$$\frac{AD}{DB} = \frac{Q}{P}$$

$$\therefore \qquad P \times AD = Q \times DB$$

Thus the sum of the moments of **P** and **Q** about *O*

$$= P \times OA + Q \times OB$$
$$= P(OD - AD) + Q(OD + DB)$$
$$= (P + Q)OD - P \times AD + Q \times DB$$
$$= R \times OD$$
$$= \text{the moment of } \mathbf{R} \text{ about } O.$$

By extending these arguments to any set of coplanar forces with a non-zero resultant it is possible to establish the following general result called the *principle of moments*.

The sum of the moments of a system of coplanar forces about any point in their plane is equal to the moment of their resultant about the same point

---

A couple has zero resultant but non-zero moment. Consider a couple consisting of a pair of equal and opposite forces of magnitude *F* with lines of action at a distance *d* apart. Suppose that *O* is any point in the plane of this couple.

(a) 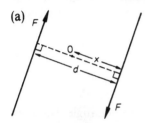   (b)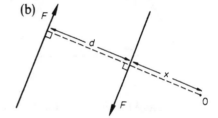

In diagram (a) the sum of the moments about *O*

$$= F(d - x) + Fx = Fd - Fx + Fx = Fd.$$

In diagram (b) the sum of the moments about *O*

$$= F(d + x) - Fx = Fd + Fx - Fx = Fd.$$

Since both results are independent of *x*, the couple has the same moment, i.e. *Fd* clockwise, for all positions of *O*.

Hence the *moment of a couple* about any point in its plane is the product of the magnitude of one of the forces and the perpendicular distance between the forces.

Exercise 9.1

1.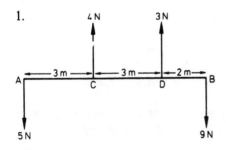

Forces act on a rod *AB* of length 8 m as shown in the diagram. Find the sum of the anti-clockwise moments of these forces about each of the points *A, B, C* and *D*.

2.

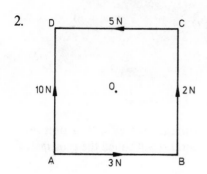

ABCD is a square of side 6 m with centre O. Forces act along the sides
AB, BC, CD, AD as shown in the diagram. Find the sum of the anti-clockwise
moments of these forces about each of
the points A, B, C, D and O.

3.

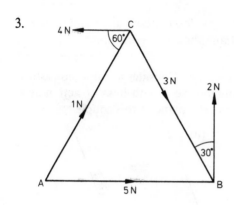

ABC is an equilateral triangle of side
2 m. Find the sum of the anti-clockwise
moments of the forces shown in the
diagram about each of the points A, B
and C. [You may leave your answers in
surd form.]

In questions 4 to 9 forces **F**, **G**, **P** and **Q** act along the sides of the rectangle ABCD as
shown in the diagram.

4.

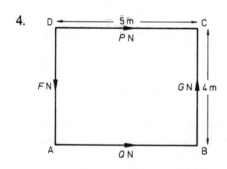

The resultant of **P** and **Q** acts
through a point X on BC. Find the
magnitude of the resultant and the
length of BX if (a) $P = Q = 3$,
(b) $P = 6, Q = 2$.

5.   The resultant of **F** and **G** acts through a point Y on AB produced. Find the
magnitude of the resultant and the length of AY if
(a) $F = 1, G = 2$,   (b) $F = 2, G = 3$.

6.   Find the moment of the couple formed by forces **F** and **G** if $F = G = 10$.

7.   If the forces **F** and **G** form a couple of moment 20 N m, find F and G.

8.   The resultant of **F** and **P** acts through a point S on AB. Find the magnitude of
the resultant and the length of AS if (a) $F = P = 5$, (b) $F = 12, P = 9$.

9. The resultant of **G** and **Q** acts through a point *T* on *DA* produced. Find the magnitude of the resultant and the length of *AT* if (a) $G = Q = 4$, (b) $G = 6, Q = 2.5$.

10. Four forces each of magnitude 3 N act along the sides *BA, BC, CD, AD* of a square *ABCD*, in the directions indicated by the order of the letters. Find the magnitude and the line of action of their resultant.

11. Three forces each of magnitude 10 N act along the sides *AB, DE, AF* of a regular hexagon *ABCDEF* of side 2 m. Find the sum of the moments of these forces about each of the points *A, B, C, D, E* and *F*. Find also the magnitude and the line of action of the resultant of the three forces.

9.2 Systems of coplanar forces

We consider first a system of parallel coplanar forces with non-zero resultant. The magnitude and direction of the resultant is found by vector addition. Its line of action can be determined using the principle of moments.

Example 1   Find the magnitude and line of action of the resultant of the system of parallel forces shown in the diagram.

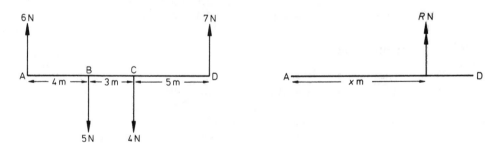

Let the resultant of the given system of forces be of magnitude *R* N acting at a distance *x* m from *A*.
Comparing magnitudes and moments about *A*⟩

$$\uparrow \quad R = 6 - 5 - 4 + 7 = 4$$
$$A\rangle \quad Rx = 0 - 5 \times 4 - 4 \times 7 + 7 \times 12 = 36$$
$$\therefore \quad R = 4 \quad \text{and} \quad x = 9.$$

Hence the resultant has magnitude 4 N and its line of action cuts *AD* at a point 9 m from *A*.

Similar methods can be applied to any set of coplanar forces with a non-zero resultant. The magnitude and direction of the resultant is found by means of a vector polygon or by resolving in two perpendicular directions. As before the line of action of the resultant is determined using the principle of moments.

Example 2

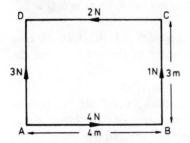

The resultant of the system of forces shown in the diagram is a force **R** acting through a point T on AB. Find the magnitude and direction of **R** and the length of AT.

Let X and Y be the components of **R** parallel and perpendicular to AB.

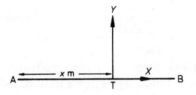

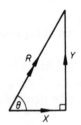

Resolving parallel and perpendicular to AB

$\rightarrow$ $X = 4 - 2$ $\therefore$ $X = 2$

$\uparrow$ $Y = 3 + 1$ $\therefore$ $Y = 4$

Taking moments about $A\,\widehat{)}$

$Yx = 1 \times 4 + 2 \times 3 = 10$ $\therefore$ $x = 2{\cdot}5$

$\therefore$ $R = \sqrt{(X^2 + Y^2)} = \sqrt{(4 + 16)} = \sqrt{20} = 2\sqrt{5}$ and

$\tan \theta = \dfrac{Y}{X} = \dfrac{4}{2} = 2,$ $\theta \approx 63{\cdot}4°.$

Hence the resultant has magnitude $2\sqrt{5}$ N and acts at $63{\cdot}4°$ to AB. The length of AT is $2{\cdot}5$ m.

Example 3

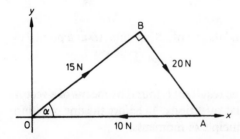

Find the equation of the line of action of the resultant of the forces shown in the diagram, given that $\tan \alpha = \frac{3}{4}$ and that A is the point $(7, 0)$.

Let X and Y be the components of the resultant in the directions of the x- and y-axes respectively. Let the line of action cut the y-axis at the point $(0, c)$.

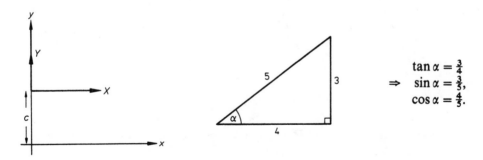

Resolving in the directions of the x- and y- axes,

$$\rightarrow \qquad X = 15 \cos \alpha + 20 \sin \alpha - 10$$
$$\uparrow \qquad Y = 15 \sin \alpha - 20 \cos \alpha$$

$$\therefore \quad X = 12 + 12 - 10 = 14, \quad Y = 9 - 16 = -7.$$

Taking moments about O: $\quad Xc = 20 \times 7 \cos \alpha$

$$\therefore \quad c = \frac{20 \times 7 \cos \alpha}{X} = \frac{20 \times 7 \times 4}{14 \times 5} = 8$$

Hence the line of action of the resultant has gradient $Y/X = -7/14 = -1/2$ and intercept on the y-axis $c = 8$,

$\therefore \quad$ the equation of the line of action is

$$y = -\tfrac{1}{2}x + 8 \quad \text{i.e.} \quad x + 2y = 16.$$

Two systems of forces are said to be *equivalent* if their effects are the same. In particular, two sets of coplanar forces are equivalent if
(i) the sums of the components of the forces in any given direction are equal and
(ii) the sums of the moments of the forces about any given point are equal.
Thus, the *resultant* of a system of forces is the single force equivalent to the whole system.

It also follows from conditions (i) and (ii) that any two coplanar *couples* with the same moment are equivalent. Similarly a set of coplanar couples with moments $G_1, G_2, G_3, \ldots, G_n$ is equivalent to a single couple with moment

$$G_1 + G_2 + G_3 + \ldots + G_n.$$

We next consider the resultant of a force $\mathbf{P}$ acting at a point O and a couple of moment G in the same plane. The couple is equivalent to a pair of equal and opposite forces of magnitude P and perpendicular distance d apart, provided that

$$Pd = G.$$

Therefore the force and the couple are equivalent to the three forces shown in diagram (a) and hence to the single force shown in diagram (b).

(a)

(b)

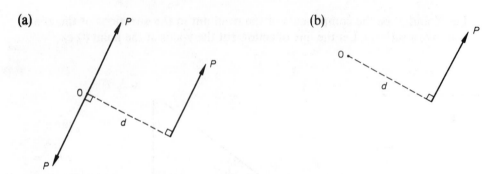

Thus the resultant of a force **P** acting at O and a couple of moment G is a force **P** acting at a distance d from O, where $d = G/P$.

Reversing the argument we may also deduce that a force **P** acting at a distance d from a point O is equivalent to a force **P** acting at O together with a couple of moment Pd.

This result can be used to find a simple equivalent system for any set of coplanar forces. Let $\mathbf{P_1}, \mathbf{P_2}, \ldots, \mathbf{P_n}$ be a system of coplanar forces acting at distances $d_1, d_2, \ldots, d_n$ respectively from a fixed point O in their plane. A typical force $\mathbf{P_r}$ acting at a distance d_r from O is equivalent

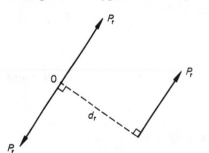

to a force $\mathbf{P_r}$ acting at O together with a couple of moment $P_r d_r$. Applying this reasoning to all the forces in the system we obtain an equivalent system of forces $\mathbf{P_1}, \mathbf{P_2}, \ldots, \mathbf{P_n}$ acting at 0 together with couples of moments $P_1 d_1, P_2 d_2, \ldots, P_n d_n$.

If **R** is the vector sum of the forces and G is the sum of the moments of the original forces about O, then this new system can be replaced by a single force **R** acting at O and a couple of moment G.

> Thus, in general, any system of coplanar forces is equivalent to a single force acting through a given point together with a couple.

We consider further four possible types of system.
(1) $R = 0$, $G = 0$. The system is in equilibrium.
(2) $R = 0$, $G \neq 0$. The system is equivalent to a couple of moment G.
(3) $R \neq 0$, $G = 0$. The system is equivalent to a single force **R** acting through O.
(4) $R \neq 0$, $G \neq 0$. The system is equivalent to a single force **R** acting at a distance G/R from O.

> Hence any system of coplanar forces which is not in equilibrium may be reduced either to a single force or to a couple.

Example 4   A square $ABCD$ of side 3 m has forces of magnitude 8, 3, 3, 4 and $2\sqrt{2}$ newtons acting along AB, CB, CD, AD and BD respectively. If the system is reduced to a force acting through A together with a couple, find the magnitude and direction of the force and the moment of the couple. If the system is reduced to a single force acting through a point E on AB at a distance d metres from A, find d.

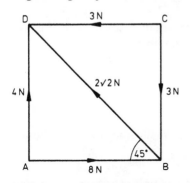

Suppose that the given system is equivalent to forces X and Y acting along AB and AD respectively, together with a couple of moment G in the sense $ABCD$.

Resolving in the directions of AB and AD:

$\rightarrow$
$$X = 8 - 3 - 2\sqrt{2}\cos 45° = 3$$
$\uparrow$
$$Y = 4 - 3 + 2\sqrt{2}\sin 45° = 3$$

Taking moments about A↺:

$$G = 3 \times 3 - 3 \times 3 + 2\sqrt{2} \times 3 \sin 45° = 6$$

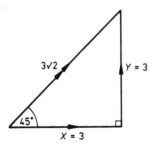

Hence the system is equivalent to a force of $3\sqrt{2}$ N acting along AC together with a couple of moment 6 N m in the sense $ABCD$.

The single equivalent force through E has moment G about A and components X and Y in the directions of AB and AD respectively.

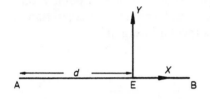

Taking moments about A↺:

$$G = Yd$$
i.e. $6 = 3d$
$\therefore$ $d = 2.$

Example 5 $ABCDEF$ is a regular hexagon of side 2 m. Forces of magnitude P, 3, 5 and Q newtons act along AB, DC, EF and AE respectively. Show that this system of forces is not in equilibrium.

(a) If the system is equivalent to a couple, find its moment and the values of P and Q.
(b) If the system is equivalent to a single force through E, find P.

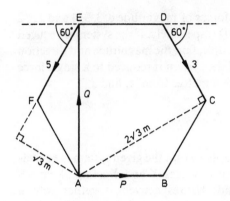

The sum of the moments of the forces about A (in N m)
$$= 3 \times 2\sqrt{3} - 5 \times \sqrt{3} = \sqrt{3}.$$
Since this sum is not zero, the forces are not in equilibrium.

(a) If the system is equivalent to a couple, it will have the same moment about any point in the plane,
∴   the moment of the couple is $\sqrt{3}$ N m.
The sum of the components of the forces in a couple is zero in any direction,
∴   resolving in the directions of AB and AE:

→ $\qquad\qquad\qquad P + 3\cos 60° - 5\cos 60° = 0$

↑ $\qquad\qquad\qquad Q - 3\sin 60° - 5\sin 60° = 0$

∴ $P = 2\cos 60° = 1$ and $Q = 8\sin 60° = 4\sqrt{3}.$

(b) If the system is equivalent to a single force through E, then the sum of the moments about E will be zero.
Taking moments about E: $P \times 2\sqrt{3} - 3 \times \sqrt{3} = 0$

∴ $P = \dfrac{3\sqrt{3}}{2\sqrt{3}} = 1\cdot5.$

Exercise 9.2

In questions 1 to 4 the resultant of the given forces acts through a point T on AB or AB produced. In each case find the magnitude and direction of the resultant and the length of AT. [In question 4 $ABCDEF$ is a regular hexagon.]

1.

2.

3.
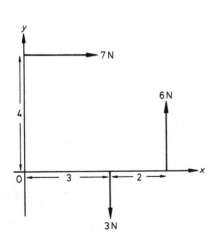

2 N

2√3 N

8 N

30°   60°

A   3 m   B

4.
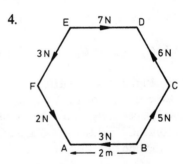

E   7 N   D

3 N   6 N

F   C

2 N   5 N

3 N

A   2 m   B

5. Forces of magnitude $8P, 7P, 5P$ and $3P$ act along the sides AB, BC, CD and DA respectively of a square $ABCD$ of side $2a$. The resultant of this system of forces cuts AB produced at E. Find
(a) the magnitude and direction of the resultant,
(b) the length of AE.

In questions 6 and 7 find the equation of the line of action of the resultant of the given forces.

6.
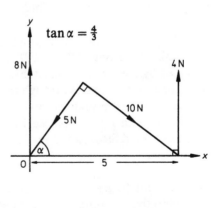

y

7 N

6 N

O   3   2   x

3 N

7.

y $\tan \alpha = \frac{4}{3}$

8 N   4 N

10 N

5 N

α

O   5   x

In questions 8 to 19 a system of forces acts in the plane of perpendicular axes Ox and Oy. The sums of the components of the forces in the directions of Ox and Oy are X and Y respectively. The sums of the anti-clockwise moments of the forces about three non-collinear points A, B and C in the plane are G_A, G_B and G_C respectively. In each question use the given facts to decide which of the following statements could be true.

a: the system is in equilibrium,
b: the system is equivalent to a couple,
c: the system is equivalent to a single force.

8. $X = 0, Y = 0.$

9. $X = 0, Y \neq 0.$

10. $Y = 0, G_A = 0.$

11. $X = 0, G_B \neq 0.$

12. $Y \neq 0, G_C = 0.$

13. $G_A \neq 0, G_B = 0.$

14. $G_A = G_B = 0.$ 15. $G_A = G_B \neq 0.$ 16. $G_A = G_B \neq G_C.$

17. $G_A = G_B = G_C = 0.$ 18. $G_A = G_B = G_C \neq 0$ 19. $X = 0, G_A = G_B = 0.$

20. In the square $OABC$ of side 2 m, O, A and B are the points $(0, 0)$, $(2, 0)$ and $(2, 2)$ respectively. Forces of magnitude 5, 8, 3 and $5\sqrt{2}$ newtons act along OA, BA, OC and AC respectively. Show that this system of forces is equivalent to a couple and find its moment. If a fifth force of magnitude $6\sqrt{2}$ newtons acts along OB, find the equation of the line of action of the resultant of the enlarged system.

21. In a rectangle $ABCD$, $AB = 12$ m, $BC = 5$ m. Forces of magnitude 6, P, 18, 10 and Q newtons act along AB, CB, CD, AD and DB respectively. Show that this system of forces is not in equilibrium. Find P and Q given that the system reduces to (a) a couple, (b) a single force acting along DC.

22. In a rectangle $ABCD$, $AB = 3$ m, $BC = 2$ m. Forces of magnitude 5, 8, 12, 6 and P newtons act along BA, BC, DC, AD and EA respectively, where E is a point on CD. Given that the forces are in equilibrium, find P and the distance DE. If the force along EA is replaced by an equal force acting through C, show that the system now reduces to a couple and find its moment.

23. $ABCDEF$ is a regular hexagon of side 1 m. Forces of magnitude 4, 6, 10, 8, P and 2 newtons act along AB, BC, CD, ED, FE and AF respectively, directions being indicated by the order of the letters.
(a) If the resultant passes through the centre of the hexagon find the value of P and the magnitude and direction of the resultant.
(b) The force in FE is replaced by another so that the new system reduces to a couple. Find the magnitude of the force and the moment of the couple indicating its sense.   (SU)

24. The points A, B and C have coordinates $(9a, 0), (0, -4a)$ and $(6a, 4a)$ respectively referred to the coordinate axes Ox and Oy.
(a) Forces $12P, 15P, 5P$ and P act along $\overrightarrow{OA}, \overrightarrow{BC}, \overrightarrow{CA}$ and $\overrightarrow{OB}$ respectively. Calculate the magnitude of the resultant of these forces and the equation of the line of action of this resultant.
(b) Forces $15P, S$ and T act along $\overrightarrow{BC}, \overrightarrow{OA}$ and $\overrightarrow{CA}$ respectively.
Given that these forces reduce to a couple, calculate (i) the values of S and T, in terms of P, (ii) the magnitude of the couple, in terms of a and P, (iii) the sense of the couple.   (AEB 1979)

9.3 Centre of gravity; centre of mass

A solid body may be regarded as a tightly packed collection of small particles. The *weight* of the body is the resultant of the weights of the particles. For relatively small bodies on or near the earth's surface the weights of the constituent particles are assumed to form a system of parallel forces acting vertically downwards.

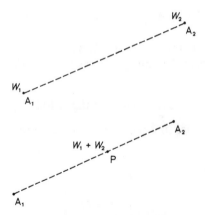

Suppose that at points A_1 and A_2 of a body there are particles of weights W_1 and W_2 respectively. As shown in §9.1, the resultant of the weights of these particles is a force of magnitude $W_1 + W_2$ acting through the point P which divides A_1A_2 in the ratio $W_2 : W_1$.

By extending this argument to include all the particles forming the body, we deduce that the resultant weight force is equal to the sum of the weights of the particles and acts through a fixed point in the body.

> The *centre of gravity* of a body is the fixed point through which its weight acts.

The *symmetries* of a body can be used to determine its centre of gravity. If the particles in a body are evenly distributed about an axis or a plane of symmetry, then the centre of gravity of the body must lie on this axis or plane. Thus the centre of gravity of a thin uniform rod is at its mid-point and the centre of gravity of a uniform sphere is at its centre.

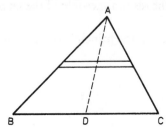

To find the centre of gravity of a *uniform triangular lamina ABC*, suppose that the triangle is divided into n strips parallel to the side BC. If the value of n is increased the strips become thin uniform rods with centres of gravity at their mid-points. Hence the centre of gravity of the whole lamina must lie on the line joining these mid-points i.e. on the median AD. Similarly the centre of gravity must also lie on the medians through B and C.

Thus the centre of gravity of a uniform triangular lamina is at the point of intersection of the medians.

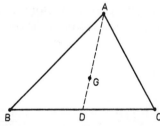

Consider now three particles each of weight W placed at the vertices of a triangle ABC. The resultant of the weights of the particles at B and C is a force of $2W$ acting at D, the mid-point of BC. Hence the resultant of the weights of all three particles is a force of $3W$ acting at the point G on AD which divides

AD in the ratio 2:1. Using similar arguments we find that *G* is also the point which divides the medians through *B* and *C* in the ratio 2:1.

Thus the centre of gravity of the three equal particles at *A*, *B* and *C* is at the point of intersection of the medians of triangle *ABC*, i.e. at the same point as the centre of gravity of the uniform lamina *ABC*.

[Note that we have also verified that this point divides each median in the ratio 2:1.]

In general the centre of gravity of a set of particles in a plane is found using the principle of moments.

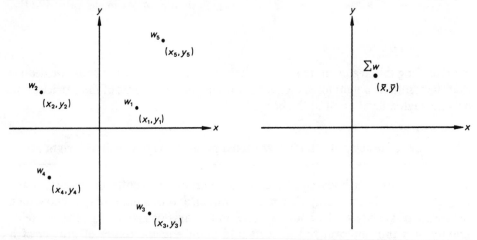

Let particles with weights $w_1, w_2, \ldots, w_n$ have positions $(x_1, y_1), (x_2, y_2), \ldots, (x_n, y_n)$ relative to *x*- and *y*-axes in their plane. Suppose that the resultant weight of the set of particles acts through the point $(\bar{x}, \bar{y})$.

Assuming the *x*, *y* plane to be horizontal and applying the principle of moments we have,
for moments about the *y*-axis:

$$w_1 x_1 + w_2 x_2 + \cdots + w_n x_n = (w_1 + w_2 + \cdots + w_n)\bar{x}$$

and for moments about the *x*-axis:

$$w_1 y_1 + w_2 y_2 + \cdots + w_n y_n = (w_1 + w_2 + \cdots + w_n)\bar{y}.$$

Hence the centre of gravity of the particles is at the point $(\bar{x}, \bar{y})$,

where
$$\bar{x} = \frac{\sum wx}{\sum w}, \quad \bar{y} = \frac{\sum wy}{\sum w}.$$

This result can be expressed in vector notation by letting the position vectors of the particles be $\mathbf{r}_1 = x_1\mathbf{i} + y_1\mathbf{j}, \mathbf{r}_2 = x_2\mathbf{i} + y_2\mathbf{j}, \ldots$ and the position vector of the centre of gravity be $\bar{\mathbf{r}} = \bar{x}\mathbf{i} + \bar{y}\mathbf{j}$, so that

$$\bar{\mathbf{r}} = \frac{(w_1 x_1 + w_2 x_2 + \cdots)\mathbf{i}}{\sum w} + \frac{(w_1 y_1 + w_2 y_2 + \cdots)\mathbf{j}}{\sum w}$$

$$= \frac{w_1(x_1\mathbf{i} + y_1\mathbf{j}) + w_2(x_2\mathbf{i} + y_2\mathbf{j}) + \cdots}{\sum w}$$

Thus the position vector of the centre of gravity is $\bar{\mathbf{r}} = \dfrac{\sum w\mathbf{r}}{\sum w}$.

Note that in the case of three particles of weight W at the points $A(x_1, y_1)$, $B(x_2, y_2)$, $C(x_3, y_3)$ we have

$$\bar{x} = \frac{Wx_1 + Wx_2 + Wx_3}{3W} = \tfrac{1}{3}(x_1 + x_2 + x_3)$$

and similarly $\qquad \bar{y} = \tfrac{1}{3}(y_1 + y_2 + y_3)$.

Hence the centre of gravity of three equal particles at A, B, C and also of a uniform triangular lamina ABC has coordinates $(\tfrac{1}{3}\{x_1 + x_2 + x_3\}, \tfrac{1}{3}\{y_1 + y_2 + y_3\})$ and position vector $\tfrac{1}{3}\{\mathbf{r}_1 + \mathbf{r}_2 + \mathbf{r}_3\}$.

Example 1 Find the coordinates of the centre of gravity of particles of weights $4\,\text{N}$, $7\,\text{N}$, $3\,\text{N}$ and $6\,\text{N}$ at the points $(1, 2)$, $(-2, -1)$, $(6, -3)$ and $(0, 4)$ respectively.

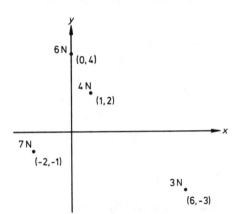

Let the centre of gravity of the particles be at the point $(\bar{x}, \bar{y})$, then the resultant weight of the particles has magnitude $20\,\text{N}$ and acts through $(\bar{x}, \bar{y})$.

Taking moments about the y-axis,

$$20\bar{x} = 4 \times 1 + 7 \times (-2) + 3 \times 6 + 6 \times 0$$

$$\therefore \quad \bar{x} = \frac{4 - 14 + 18 + 0}{20} = \frac{8}{20} = \frac{2}{5}$$

Taking moments about the x-axis,

$$20\bar{y} = 4 \times 2 + 7 \times (-1) + 3 \times (-3) + 6 \times 4$$

$$\therefore \quad \bar{y} = \frac{8 - 7 - 9 + 24}{20} = \frac{16}{20} = \frac{4}{5}$$

Hence the centre of gravity has coordinates $\left(\dfrac{2}{5}, \dfrac{4}{5}\right)$.

Example 2 Find the coordinates of the centre of gravity of a uniform lamina in the form of a trapezium with vertices $A(1, 0)$, $B(7, 0)$, $C(3, 4)$ and $D(0, 4)$.

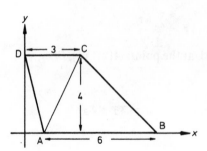

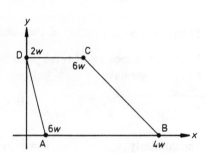

The weight of the lamina $ABCD$ is the resultant of the weights of lamina ABC and lamina ACD. Let w be the weight per unit area of the lamina, then the weight of ABC is $12w$ and is equivalent to three weights of $4w$ at points A, B and C.

Similarly the weight of ACD is $6w$ and is equivalent to three weights of $2w$ at points A, C and D.

Hence the centre of gravity $(\bar{x}, \bar{y})$ of the lamina $ABCD$ is the same as the centre of gravity of particles of weights $6w, 4w, 6w$ and $2w$ at the points A, B, C and D respectively.

Taking moments about the y-axis,

$$18w\bar{x} = 6w \times 1 + 4w \times 7 + 6w \times 3$$

Taking moments about the x-axis,

$$18w\bar{y} = 6w \times 4 + 2w \times 4$$

$$\therefore \bar{x} = \frac{52w}{18w} = \frac{26}{9}, \quad \bar{y} = \frac{32w}{18w} = \frac{16}{9}.$$

Hence the centre of gravity has coordinates $\left(\dfrac{26}{9}, \dfrac{16}{9}\right)$.

The principle of moments is also used to find the centre of gravity of any body which can be divided into smaller bodies, each with known weight and centre of gravity.

Example 3   A thin uniform wire is bent to form a triangle ABC in which $AB = AC = 30$ cm and $BC = 48$ cm. Find its centre of gravity.

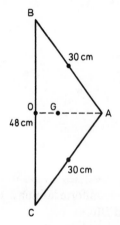

From symmetry the centre of gravity G lies on OA, where O is the mid-point of BC.

Each of the wires AB, AC and BC has its centre of gravity at its mid-point.

By Pythagoras' theorem, $OA = 18$ cm.

Letting w be the weight per cm of the wire, we have:

Body	Weight	Distance of centre of gravity from BC
Wire AB	$30w$	9
Wire AC	$30w$	9
Wire BC	$48w$	0
Whole body	$108w$	$\bar{x}$

Taking moments about BC,

$$108w\bar{x} = 30w \times 9 + 30w \times 9 + 48w \times 0$$

$$\therefore \quad \bar{x} = \frac{2 \times 30w \times 9}{108w} = 5$$

∴ the centre of gravity is 5 cm from BC on the line OA.

Example 4

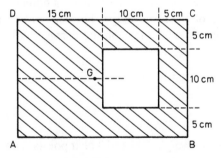

A square hole is cut in a uniform rectangular lamina as shown in the diagram. Find the centre of gravity of the resulting body.

From symmetry the centre of gravity G lies on the line joining the mid-points of AD and BC.

We use the positions of the centres of gravity of the complete rectangle and of the square removed to find the distance $\bar{x}$ of G from AD.
Letting w be the weight per unit area, we have:

Body	Weight	Distance of centre of gravity from AD
Rectangle	$600w$	15
Square	$100w$	20
Remainder	$500w$	$\bar{x}$

Taking moments about AD,

$$500w\bar{x} + 100w \times 20 = 600w \times 15$$

$$\therefore \quad 500w\bar{x} = 600w \times 15 - 100w \times 20$$

$$\therefore \quad \bar{x} = \frac{9000w - 2000w}{500w} = 14$$

∴ the centre of gravity is 14 cm from AD on the line joining the mid-points of AD and BC.

As shown earlier the centre of gravity of a set of particles in a plane is the point $\left(\dfrac{\sum wx}{\sum w}, \dfrac{\sum wy}{\sum w}\right)$. If $m_1, m_2, \ldots$ are the masses of the particles, their *centre of mass* is defined to be the point

$$\left(\frac{\sum mx}{\sum m}, \frac{\sum my}{\sum m}\right).$$

The weight w and the mass m of a typical particle are connected by the relationship $w = mg$, where g is the acceleration due to gravity. Thus, provided that g takes the same value for all the particles, $\dfrac{\sum wx}{\sum w} = \dfrac{\sum mgx}{\sum mg} = \dfrac{\sum mx}{\sum m}$ and similarly $\dfrac{\sum wy}{\sum w} = \dfrac{\sum my}{\sum m}$.

It follows that, in general, the centre of gravity and the centre of mass of a body are at the same point.

[We note, however, that if a body is so large that the weights of its constituent particles are not parallel forces, then its centre of gravity cannot be found by elementary methods and does not necessarily coincide with the centre of mass.]

A *centroid* is a centre of area or volume. The centroid of a plane area coincides with the centre of mass of a uniform lamina of the same shape. The centroid of a three-dimensional figure coincides with the centre of mass of the corresponding uniform solid.

Exercise 9.3

1. Find the centre of gravity of two particles of weight $2\,\text{N}$ and $3\,\text{N}$ at points A and B respectively, given that $AB = 30\,\text{cm}$.

2. Find the centre of gravity of two particles of weight $30\,\text{N}$ and $70\,\text{N}$ at points P and Q respectively, given that $PQ = 1\cdot5\,\text{m}$.

3. A uniform triangular lamina ABC has $AB = AC = 17\,\text{cm}$ and $BC = 16\,\text{cm}$. Find the distance of the centre of gravity from BC.

4. A uniform triangular lamina PQR has $PQ = 9\,\text{cm}$, $QR = 15\,\text{cm}$ and $PR = 12\,\text{cm}$. Find the distances of the centre of gravity from PR and PQ.

5. Find the coordinates of the centre of gravity of particles of weight $5\,\text{N}, 7\,\text{N}, 1\,\text{N}$ and $3\,\text{N}$ at the points $(1,0), (3,1), (6,3)$ and $(0,2)$ respectively.

6. Find the coordinates of the centre of mass of particles of mass $9\,\text{kg}, 4\,\text{kg}, 6\,\text{kg}$ and $5\,\text{kg}$ at the points $(4,3), (6,-6), (-3,0)$ and $(6,-3)$ respectively.

7. Find the position vector of the centre of mass of a uniform triangular lamina, given that the position vectors of its vertices are $3\mathbf{i} - 5\mathbf{j}, 7\mathbf{i} + 2\mathbf{j}$ and $-\mathbf{i} + 6\mathbf{j}$.

8.   Find the position vector of the centre of gravity of three particles of weight 7 N, 9 N and 4 N with position vectors $4\mathbf{i} + \mathbf{j}$, $3\mathbf{j}$ and $3\mathbf{i} + 4\mathbf{j}$.

9.   A uniform lamina in the form of a quadrilateral has vertices $O(0,0)$, $A(4, -6)$, $B(7,0)$ and $C(0,6)$. If the weight per unit area of the lamina is w, show that it has the same centre of gravity as particles of weight $14w$, $7w$, $14w$ and $7w$ at O, A, B and C respectively. Hence find the centre of gravity of the lamina.

10. Use the method of the previous question to find the centre of gravity of a uniform lamina in the form of a pentagon with vertices $O(0,0)$, $A(3,0)$, $B(3,2)$, $C(0,4)$ and $D(-3,1)$.

11. A thin uniform wire is bent to form a triangle ABC in which $AB = 24$ cm, $AC = 10$ cm and $\angle A = 90°$. Find the distances of the centre of gravity from AC and AB.

12. A thin uniform wire is bent into the shape of an isosceles trapezium $ABCD$ in which $AB = 24$ cm, $AD = BC = 25$ cm and $CD = 10$ cm. Find the distance of the centre of gravity from AB.

In questions 13 to 16 find the position of the centre of gravity of the uniform lamina shown in the given diagram.

13.

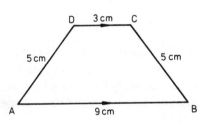

14.

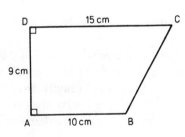

15.

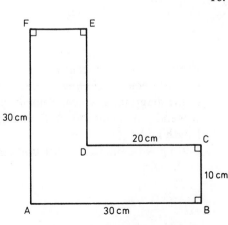

16.

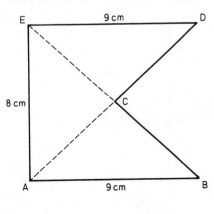

17.

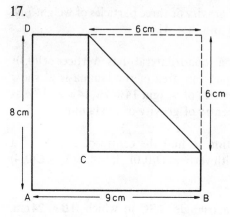

Find the centre of gravity of a uniform rectangular lamina *ABCD* folded as shown in the diagram.

18.

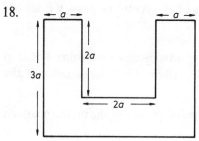

The diagram shows the central cross-section of a uniform cylindrical container weighing $2w$ per unit volume. Find its centre of gravity. If the container is now filled with a liquid weighing w per unit volume, find the new position of the centre of gravity.

9.4 Standard results by integration

As we saw in the previous section the principle of moments can be used to find the centre of gravity of any body which can be divided into smaller bodies with known weights and centres of gravity. In certain cases it is necessary to divide a body into a large number of small parts or elements. The sums of the moments of these elements about appropriate axes are then found by integration.

Example 1 Find the centre of gravity of a uniform wire in the form of an arc of a circle, radius r, subtending an angle 2α at the centre.

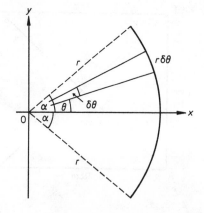

From symmetry the centre of gravity lies on the bisector of the angle 2α. As shown in the diagram, a typical element of arc subtends an angle $\delta\theta$ at O and is of length $r\,\delta\theta$.

Letting w be the weight per unit length of the wire, we have:

Body	Weight	Distance of centre of gravity from the y-axis
Element	$wr\,\delta\theta$	$r\cos\theta$
Whole arc	$wr\,2\alpha$	$\bar{x}$

Taking moments about the y-axis,

$$wr\,2\alpha\bar{x} \approx \sum(wr\,\delta\theta \times r\cos\theta)$$

$$\therefore \quad 2wr\,\alpha\bar{x} = \int_{-\alpha}^{\alpha} wr^2\cos\theta\,d\theta$$

$$= wr^2\left[\sin\theta\right]_{-\alpha}^{\alpha} = 2wr^2\sin\alpha$$

$$\therefore \qquad \bar{x} = \frac{r\sin\alpha}{\alpha}$$

Hence the centre of gravity of the wire is at a distance $(r\sin\alpha)/\alpha$ from the centre.

Example 2   Find the centre of gravity of a uniform lamina in the form of a sector of a circle, radius r, subtending an angle 2α at the centre.

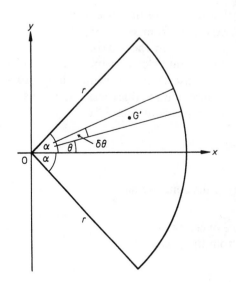

From symmetry the centre of gravity lies on the bisector of the angle 2α. A typical element is a sector subtending an angle $\delta\theta$ at O and having area $\frac{1}{2}r^2\,\delta\theta$. This sector is approximately triangular with its centre of gravity G' at a distance $\frac{2}{3}r$ from O.

Letting w be the weight per unit area of the lamina, we have:

Body	Weight	Distance of centre of gravity from the y-axis
Element	$w\frac{1}{2}r^2\,\delta\theta$	$\frac{2}{3}r\cos\theta$
Whole sector	$w\frac{1}{2}r^2\,2\alpha$	$\bar{x}$

Taking moments about the y-axis,

$$w\tfrac{1}{2}r^2\, 2\alpha\bar{x} \approx \sum(w\tfrac{1}{2}r^2\,\delta\theta \times \tfrac{2}{3}r\cos\theta)$$

$$\therefore \quad wr^2\alpha\bar{x} = \int_{-\alpha}^{\alpha} \tfrac{1}{3}wr^3\cos\theta\, d\theta$$

$$= \tfrac{1}{3}wr^3\left[\sin\theta\right]_{-\alpha}^{\alpha} = \tfrac{2}{3}wr^3\sin\alpha$$

$$\therefore \quad \bar{x} = \frac{2r\sin\alpha}{3\alpha}$$

Hence the centre of gravity of the lamina is at a distance $(\tfrac{2}{3}r\sin\alpha)/\alpha$ from the centre.

[This result can also be produced by showing that a uniform sector of radius r has the same centre of gravity as a uniform arc of radius $\tfrac{2}{3}r$.]

Example 3   Find the centre of gravity of a uniform solid right circular cone of base radius r, height h.

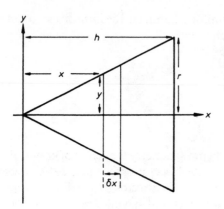

Let the axis of the cone lie along the x-axis, then from symmetry the centre of gravity is on the x-axis. If the cone is divided into elements by planes parallel to its base, then each element is approximately a disc, thickness δx, radius y, which has volume $\pi y^2\, \delta x$.

Letting w be the weight per unit volume of the cone, we have:

Body	Weight	Distance of centre of gravity from the y-axis
Element	$w\pi y^2\, \delta x$	x
Whole cone	$w\tfrac{1}{3}\pi r^2 h$	$\bar{x}$

Taking moments about the y-axis

$$w\tfrac{1}{3}\pi r^2\, h\bar{x} \approx \sum(w\pi y^2\,\delta x \times x)$$

$$\therefore \quad \tfrac{1}{3}\pi r^2\, hw\bar{x} = \int_0^h \pi wxy^2\, dx$$

From similar triangles, $\dfrac{y}{x} = \dfrac{r}{h}$

$$\therefore \quad \tfrac{1}{3}\pi r^2 hw\bar{x} = \int_0^h \frac{\pi r^2 w}{h^2} x^3 \, dx$$

$$= \frac{\pi r^2 w}{h^2}\left[\tfrac{1}{4}x^4\right]_0^h = \tfrac{1}{4}\pi r^2 h^2 w$$

$$\therefore \qquad \bar{x} = \tfrac{3}{4}h$$

Hence the centre of gravity of the cone is on its axis at a distance $\tfrac{1}{4}h$ from its base.

Example 4   Find the centre of gravity of a uniform solid tetrahedron.

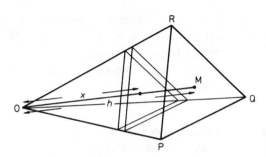

In tetrahedron $OPQR$, let M be the point of intersection of the medians of $\triangle PQR$. Let the length of OM be h and let the area of $\triangle PQR$ be A.

If the tetrahedron is divided into elements by planes parallel to the face PQR, then a typical element is a triangular lamina of thickness δx, which cuts OM at a distance x from O. Since this element is similar to $\triangle PQR$, its medians intersect on OM and its area is Ax^2/h^2.

Letting w be the weight per unit volume, we have:

Body	Weight	Distance of centre of gravity from 0
Element	$wAx^2\,\delta x/h^2$	x
Whole body	$w\tfrac{1}{3}Ah$	$\bar{x}$

Taking moments about an axis perpendicular to OM

$$w\tfrac{1}{3}Ah\bar{x} \approx \sum\left(\frac{wAx^2\,\delta x}{h^2} \times x\right)$$

$$\therefore \quad \tfrac{1}{3}Ahw\bar{x} = \int_0^h \frac{Aw}{h^2} x^3 \, \delta x$$

$$= \frac{Aw}{h^2}\left[\tfrac{1}{4}x^4\right]_0^h = \tfrac{1}{4}Awh^2$$

$$\therefore \qquad \bar{x} = \tfrac{3}{4}h$$

Hence the centre of gravity of the tetrahedron lies one quarter of the way up a line joining the centroid of one face to the opposite vertex.

Example 5   Find the centre of gravity of a uniform solid hemisphere of radius r.

If we take x- and y-axes along and perpendicular to the axis of symmetry of the hemisphere, then its centre of gravity will be on the x-axis.

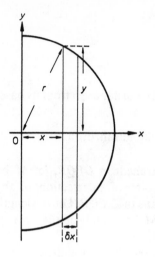

A typical element is approximately a disc of thickness δx, radius y at a distance x from the y-axis.

Letting w be the weight per unit volume of the hemisphere:

Body	Weight	Distance of centre of gravity from the y-axis
Element	$w\pi y^2\,\delta x$	x
Whole hemisphere	$w\frac{2}{3}\pi r^3$	$\bar{x}$

Taking moments about the y-axis,

$$w\tfrac{2}{3}\pi r^3 \bar{x} \approx \sum(w\pi y^2\,\delta x \times x)$$

$$\therefore \quad \tfrac{2}{3}\pi r^3 w\bar{x} = \int_0^r \pi wxy^2\,dx$$

By Pythagoras' theorem, $x^2 + y^2 = r^2$,

$$\therefore \quad \tfrac{2}{3}\pi r^3 w\bar{x} = \int_0^r \pi w(r^2 x - x^3)\,dx$$

$$= \pi w\left[\tfrac{1}{2}r^2 x^2 - \tfrac{1}{4}x^4\right]_0^r = \tfrac{1}{4}\pi r^4 w$$

$$\therefore \qquad \bar{x} = 3r/8$$

Hence the centre of gravity of the hemisphere is on its axis of symmetry at a distance $3r/8$ from its plane face.

Example 6   Find the centre of gravity of a uniform hemispherical shell of radius r.

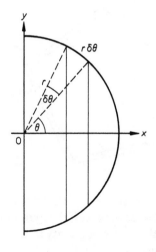

If we take x- and y-axes along and perpendicular to the axis of symmetry of the hemispherical shell, then its centre of gravity will be on the x-axis.

If the shell is divided into narrow bands by planes perpendicular to the x-axis, then a typical elemental band is approximately cylindrical with radius $r \sin \theta$ and width $r \, \delta\theta$. Letting w be the weight per unit area of the shell, we have:

Body	Weight	Distance of centre of gravity from the y-axis
Element	$w2\pi r^2 \sin \theta \, \delta\theta$	$r \cos \theta$
Whole body	$w2\pi r^2$	$\bar{x}$

Taking moments about the y-axis

$$w2\pi r^2 \bar{x} \approx \sum(w2\pi r^2 \sin \theta \, \delta\theta \times r \cos \theta)$$

$$\therefore \quad 2\pi w r^2 \bar{x} = \int_0^{\pi/2} 2\pi w r^3 \sin \theta \cos \theta \, d\theta$$

$$= \int_0^{\pi/2} \pi w r^3 \sin 2\theta \, d\theta$$

$$= \pi w r^3 [-\tfrac{1}{2}\cos 2\theta]_0^{\pi/2} = \pi w r^3$$

$$\therefore \qquad \bar{x} = \frac{r}{2}$$

Hence the centre of gravity of the hemispherical shell is at a distance $\tfrac{1}{2}r$ from its base.

[For an alternative method see Exercise 9.6, question 11.]

It is not necessary to use integration to find the centres of gravity of hollow pyramids and cones.

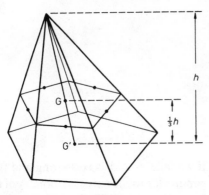
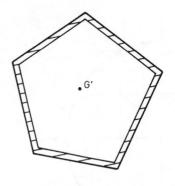

Let us consider a thin hollow pyramid of height h, without base. Each of the faces is a triangular lamina with centre of gravity at a height $\frac{1}{3}h$ above the base. If the pyramid is divided into sections parallel to the base, we see that the centre of gravity must lie on the line joining the centres of gravity of these sections.

Hence the centre of gravity of the *hollow pyramid* lies one third of the way up a line joining the centroid of the base to the vertex.

As the number of sides of the base of the pyramid is increased indefinitely, it tends to become a cone. Hence the centre of gravity of a *hollow right circular cone*, without base, is on the axis of the cone at a distance of one third of the height of the cone from the base.

[Note that the results obtained in this section may be quoted without proof when finding the centres of gravity of composite bodies. A list of standard results will be found in the "Formulae for reference" section near the end of the book.]

Exercise 9.4

1.   Prove that the centre of gravity of a uniform wire in the form of a semi-circle of radius r is at a distance $2r/\pi$ from the centre.

2.   Prove that the centre of gravity of a uniform semi-circular lamina of radius r is at a distance $4r/3\pi$ from the centre.

In questions 3 to 6 find the distance from AD of the centre of gravity of the given uniform lamina.

3.
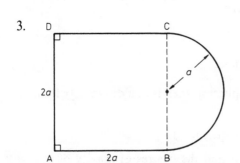

4.
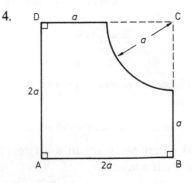

5.

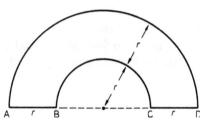

6.

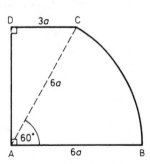

7. A frustum is cut from a solid right circular cone of base radius r and height $2h$ by a plane parallel to the base and at a distance h from it. Find the distance of the centre of gravity of the frustum from the base.

8. A circular lamina of radius $2r$ is divided into two segments by a line at a distance r from the centre. Find the distance from the centre of the centre of gravity of (a) the larger segment, (b) the smaller segment.

9. A solid sphere of radius $3a$ is divided into two parts by a plane at a distance a from the centre. Find, by integration, the volume of the smaller part and the distance of its centre of gravity from the centre of the sphere.

10. Prove that the centre of gravity of a uniform solid pyramid with a square base lies one quarter of the height of the pyramid above the base and on the line joining the vertex to the point of intersection of the diagonals of the base.

11. Prove that the centre of gravity of a uniform solid hemisphere of radius r is a distance $3r/8$ from the centre.

   A child's toy is made up from a uniform and solid right circular cone and hemisphere. The radius of the cone is r, and its height $3r$. The radius of the hemisphere is r. The base of the cone and hemisphere are sealed together. The material from which the hemisphere is made is 3 times as heavy per unit volume as the cone material. Find the distance of the centre of gravity of the toy from the vertex of the cone.   (SU)

12. Prove that the centre of gravity of a uniform thin hemispherical cup of radius r is at a distance $r/2$ from the centre.

   A goblet consists of a uniform thin hemispherical cup of radius r, a circular base of the same material, thickness and radius as the cup, and an intervening stem of length r and whose weight is one-quarter of that of the cup. Show that the height of the centre of gravity above the base is $13r/14$. If the weight of the goblet is W and that of the amount of liquid that fills it is W', show that filling it raises the centre of gravity through a distance $\dfrac{39}{56}\left(\dfrac{W'}{W + W'}\right)r$.   (W)

9.5 Centroids of areas and volumes

The *centroid* of a plane figure is its centre of area i.e. the point about which the area is evenly distributed. In simple cases we can use symmetry to find the centroid of a figure. However, to arrive at a more general method, we define a quantity called the *first moment of area*.

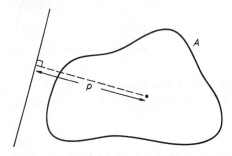

If the centroid of an area A is at a perpendicular distance p from an axis, then the first moment of A about this axis is pA.

If an area is divided into a number of parts, then the sum of the first moments of the parts about any axis is equal to the first moment of the whole area about that axis.

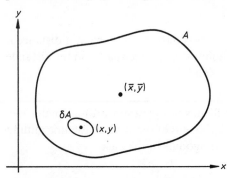

Suppose that a region of the x, y plane has area A and centroid $(\bar{x}, \bar{y})$. If a typical element of area δA has centroid (x, y) then, comparing first moments about the coordinates axes, we have:

$$\bar{x}A = \sum x \, \delta A, \quad \bar{y}A = \sum y \, \delta A.$$

Example 1   Find the centroid of the region bounded by the curve $y^2 = x$ and the line $x = 4$.

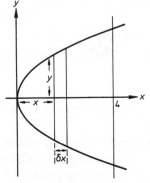

A typical element of area is a strip of width δx, length $2y$ at a distance x from the y-axis. From symmetry the centroids of such strips and of the whole region lie on the x-axis.

Thus, we may write:

	Area	Coordinates of centroid
Element	$2y \, \delta x$	$(x, 0)$
Whole region	A	$(\bar{x}, 0)$

First moment of area about the y-axis

$$= \bar{x}A \approx \sum(x \times 2y\,\delta x)$$

$$\bar{x}A = \int_0^4 2xy\,dx$$

$$= \int_0^4 2x^{3/2}\,dx = 2\left[\frac{2}{5}x^{5/2}\right]_0^4 = \frac{128}{5}$$

But $$A = \int_0^4 2y\,dx$$

$$= \int_0^4 2x^{1/2}\,dx = 2\left[\frac{2}{3}x^{3/2}\right]_0^4 = \frac{32}{3}$$

$$\therefore \quad \bar{x} = \frac{128}{5}\bigg/\frac{32}{3} = \frac{128}{5}\times\frac{3}{32} = \frac{12}{5}$$

Hence the centroid of the region is the point $(12/5, 0)$.

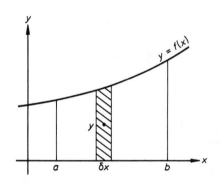

Let us consider now the area bounded by the curve $y = f(x)$, the x-axis and the lines $x = a$, $x = b$. A typical element of area is an approximately rectangular strip of width δx and height y.

	Area	Coordinates of centroid
Element	$y\,\delta x$	$(x, \frac{1}{2}y)$
Whole region	A	$(\bar{x}, \bar{y})$

First moment of area about the y-axis

$$= \bar{x}A \approx \sum(x \times y\,\delta x)$$

$$\therefore \qquad \bar{x}A = \int_a^b xy\,dx$$

First moment of area about the x-axis

$$= \bar{y}A \approx \sum(\tfrac{1}{2}y \times y\,\delta x)$$

$$\therefore \qquad \bar{y}A = \int_a^b \tfrac{1}{2}y^2\,dx$$

But $A = \displaystyle\int_a^b y\,dx$, so the centroid has coordinates

$$\bar{x} = \int_a^b xy\,dx \Big/ \int_a^b y\,dx \qquad \bar{y} = \int_a^b \tfrac{1}{2}y^2\,dx \Big/ \int_a^b y\,dx$$

Example 2   Find the centroid of the area bounded by the curve $y = x^2$, the x-axis and the line $x = 1$.

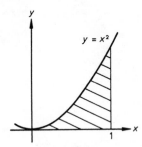

Area of the given region

$$= \int_0^1 y\,dx = \int_0^1 x^2\,dx = \left[\frac{1}{3}x^3\right]_0^1 = \tfrac{1}{3}$$

First moment about the y-axis

$$= \int_0^1 xy\,dx = \int_0^1 x^3\,dx = \left[\frac{1}{4}x^4\right]_0^1 = \tfrac{1}{4}$$

First moment about the x-axis

$$= \int_0^1 \tfrac{1}{2}y^2\,dx = \int_0^1 \tfrac{1}{2}x^4\,dx = \left[\frac{1}{10}x^5\right]_0^1 = \frac{1}{10}$$

$$\therefore\quad \bar{x} = \int_0^1 xy\,dx \Big/ \int_0^1 y\,dx = \frac{1}{4} \div \frac{1}{3} = \frac{3}{4}$$

$$\therefore\quad \bar{y} = \int_0^1 \tfrac{1}{2}y^2\,dx \Big/ \int_0^1 y\,dx = \frac{1}{10} \div \frac{1}{3} = \frac{3}{10}$$

Hence the centroid of the area is the point $(\tfrac{3}{4}, \tfrac{3}{10})$.

The centroid of a solid three-dimensional figure is its centre of volume i.e. the point about which the volume is evenly distributed. The methods used to find centroids of similar to those used to find centroids of area.

Example 3   Find the centroid of the volume obtained by rotating completely about the x-axis the area bounded by the curve $y = x^2$, the x-axis and the line $x = 1$.

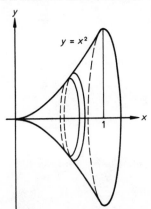

A typical element of volume is approximately a disc of thickness δx, radius y at a distance x from the y-axis. From symmetry the centroids of such discs and of the whole solid lie on the x-axis.

Thus we may write:

	Volume	Coordinates of centroid
Element	$\pi y^2 \, \delta x$	$(x, 0)$
Whole solid	V	$(\bar{x}, 0)$

First moment of volume about the y-axis

$$= \bar{x} V \approx \sum (x \times \pi y^2 \, \delta x)$$

$$\therefore \quad \bar{x} V = \int_0^1 \pi x y^2 \, dx$$

$$= \pi \int_0^1 x^5 \, dx = \pi \left[\frac{1}{6} x^6 \right]_0^1 = \frac{\pi}{6}$$

But $\quad V = \int_0^1 \pi y^2 \, dx$

$$= \pi \int_0^1 x^4 \, dx = \pi \left[\frac{1}{5} x^5 \right]_0^1 = \frac{\pi}{5}$$

$$\therefore \quad \bar{x} = \frac{\pi}{6} \bigg/ \frac{\pi}{5} = \frac{\pi}{6} \times \frac{5}{\pi} = \frac{5}{6}$$

Hence the centroid of the solid is at the point $(5/6, 0)$.

Exercise 9.5

Find the first moments about the y-axis and the x-axis of the areas bounded by the following curves and straight lines. In each case use your results to find the coordinates of the centroid of the area.

1. $y = x^2 + 1$, $y = 0$, $x = 0$ and $x = 2$.

2. $y = x(x + 2)$ for $x \geqslant 0$, $y = 0$ and $x = 3$.

3. $y = \dfrac{1}{x^2}$, $y = 0$, $x = 1$ and $x = 2$.

4. $y = x^2$ for $x \geqslant 0$, $x = 0$ and $y = 1$.

Find the centroids of the areas bounded by the following curves and straight lines.

5. $y^2 = x^3$ and $x = 4$.

6. $y^2 = 4x$ and $x = 1$.

7. $y = \cos x$ for $-\frac{1}{2}\pi \leqslant x \leqslant \frac{1}{2}\pi$ and $y = 0$.

8. $x^2y = 4$, $y = 1$ and $y = 4$.

9. $y = e^x$, $y = 0$, $x = 0$ and $x = 1$.

10. $y = \sin x$ for $0 \leqslant x \leqslant \frac{1}{2}\pi$, $y = 0$ and $x = \frac{1}{2}\pi$.

Find the centroids of the solids formed by rotating completely about the x-axis the regions defined by the following inequalities.

11. $y \geqslant x(x - 4)$, $y \leqslant 0$. 　　　　　　　　12. $y^2 \leqslant 9x$, $y \geqslant 0$, $x \leqslant 1$.

13. $xy \leqslant 4$, $y \geqslant 0$, $1 \leqslant x \leqslant 2$. 　　　　14. $0 \leqslant y \leqslant e^{-x}$, $0 \leqslant x \leqslant 1$.

15. Sketch the curve $y^2 = x(3 - x)^2$. Find the centroid of the area enclosed by the loop.

16. Find the centroid of the solid formed by rotating through π radians about the y-axis the region bounded by the curve $y = 4x^2$ and the straight lines $y = 1$ and $y = 4$.

17. Use integration by parts to evaluate

$$\int_1^2 \ln x \, dx, \quad \int_1^2 x \ln x \, dx \quad \text{and} \quad \int_1^2 (\ln x)^2 \, dx.$$

Hence find, correct to 2 decimal places, the coordinates of the centroid of the area bounded by the curve $y = \ln x$, the x-axis and the line $x = 2$.

18. Find the area of the region R bounded by the curve $y = x^2$ and the straight line $y = x$. Show that the first moments of R about the x- and y-axes are given by

$$\int_0^1 \tfrac{1}{2}(x^2 - x^4) \, dx \quad \text{and} \quad \int_0^1 (x^2 - x^3) \, dx \text{ respectively.}$$

Hence find the centroid of the region R.

Exercise 9.6 (miscellaneous)

1. All forces in this question act in the plane of a triangle ABC in which $AB = 4a$, $AC = 3a$ and the angle $A = 90°$. Forces of magnitude $17P$, $15P$, $3P$ act along AB, BC, AC respectively in the directions indicated by the order of the letters. Calculate
(a) the magnitude of the resultant of these three forces and the tangent of the angle made by its line of action with AB,
(b) the distance from A of the point where the line of action of the resultant cuts AB. A couple G is now added to the system and the resultant of this enlarged system acts through the point B. Calculate the magnitude and sense of G.　　(L)

2. A rigid square lamina $ABCD$ of side a is subject to forces of magnitude $1, 2, 3, 1, 3\sqrt{2}$ and $\lambda\sqrt{2}$ units acting along AB, BC, CD, AD, AC and DB respectively

in the directions indicated by the order of the letters. Given that the direction of the resultant force is parallel to AC, find λ. With this value of λ, find the total moment about A of the forces acting on the lamina. Hence, or otherwise, find AE in terms of a, where E is the intersection of AB with the line of action of the resultant force.

(JMB)

3. (a) State conditions which will ensure that a system of forces in a plane will reduce to a couple.
   (b) State conditions which will ensure that a system of forces in a plane is in equilibrium.
   (c) $ABCD$ is a square of side a. Forces of size 1, 3, 3 and 7 act respectively along AB, BC, CD and DA in the directions indicated by the letters. (i) Find the sizes of the forces which must act along AC and BD so that the six forces will be equivalent to a couple, and find the moment of the couple. (ii) If the forces in DA, AC and BD are to be replaced so that the system is in equilibrium, how will this have to be done? (SU)

4. An equilateral triangle ABC has side $2a$ and D, E are the mid-points of BC, CA respectively. Fixed forces of magnitude $P, 2P, 4P$ act along AB, BC, CA respectively and variable forces of magnitude x, y act along AD, BE respectively, the direction of each force being indicated by the order of the letters. Find (in terms of P) the values of x and y if
(a) the system is equivalent to a force through B parallel to AD, stating the magnitude of this force;
(b) the system is equivalent to a couple, stating the moment of the couple. (O&C)

5. Forces $2, 4, 6, 2p, 2q$ and 18 newtons act along the sides AB, CD, ED, EF and AF respectively of a regular hexagon $ABCDEF$, the directions of the forces being indicated by the order of the letters. If the system is in equilibrium, find, by resolving parallel and perpendicular to AB, the values of p and q. Check your results by finding the moment of the forces about O, the centre of the hexagon.

The forces along ED, EF and AF are now replaced by a coplanar force through O and a coplanar couple. If the resulting system is in equilibrium and if the length of each side of the hexagon is 2 metres, calculate

(a) the magnitude of this force through O,
(b) the magnitude of the couple. (L)

6. The centre of a regular hexagon $ABCDEF$ of side a is O. Forces of magnitude $P, 2P, 3P, 4P, mP$ and nP act along $\overrightarrow{AB}, \overrightarrow{BC}, \overrightarrow{CD}, \overrightarrow{DE}, \overrightarrow{EF}$, and $\overrightarrow{FA}$ respectively. Given that the resultant of these six forces is of magnitude $3P$ acting in a direction parallel to $\overrightarrow{EF}$,
(i) determine the values of m and n,
(ii) show that the sum of the moments of the forces about O is $9Pa\sqrt{3}$.
   The mid-point of EF is M.
(iii) Find the equation of the line of action of the resultant referred to OM as x-axis and OA as y-axis.

The forces mP and nP acting along $\overrightarrow{EF}$ and $\overrightarrow{FA}$ are removed from the system. The remaining four forces and an additonal force Q, which acts through O, reduce to a couple. Calculate the magnitude of Q and the moment of the couple. (AEB 1979)

7.

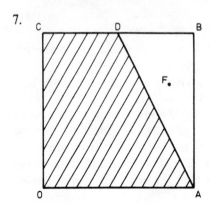

The diagram shows a square $OABC$ of side a. The mid-point of BC is D. Show that, with respect to OA and OC as axes, the coordinates of the centroid F of the triangular region ABD are $(5a/6, 2a/3)$. Find the coordinates of the centre of mass of a uniform lamina in the form of the figure $OADC$.   (JMB)

8. A uniform thin sheet of paper has the shape of a rectangle $OABC$, where $OA = 20$ cm and $OC = 12$ cm. The side AB is folded down so as to lie entirely along OA. Find the distances of the centre of gravity of the folded sheet from OA and OC.

(O&C)

9. A uniform solid hemisphere of radius a is cut into two parts by a plane parallel to the plane face of the hemisphere and at a distance $\frac{1}{2}a$ from it. Find the volume of each of the two parts and the position of the centre of mass of each of the two parts.

(AEB 1980)

10. Prove that the centre of gravity of a uniform circular arc subtending an angle 2θ at the centre of a circle of radius a is $a \sin\theta/\theta$ from the centre. Deduce that the centre of gravity of a uniform sector bounded by that arc and the radii to its extremities is $\frac{2}{3}a \sin\theta/\theta$ from the centre.

Show also that the centre of gravity of a segment of a circular lamina cut off by a chord subtending a right angle at the centre of the circle is $\frac{2}{3}\sqrt{2}a/(\pi - 2)$ from the centre.   (W)

11. Find by integration the distance of the centroid of a uniform solid hemisphere of radius a from its plane face.

A hollow sphere of external radius R and internal radius r is cut in half by a plane through its centre. Show that the distance of the centroid of each half from the centre of the sphere is

$$\frac{3(R + r)(R^2 + r^2)}{8(R^2 + Rr + r^2)}.$$

Deduce that the centroid of a hemispherical shell of radius R is at a distance $R/2$ from its centre.   (L)

12. Find the area A of the loop of the curve $y^2 = x^2(2 - x)$. Find also the first moment about the y-axis of the volume generated when the area A is rotated through π radians about the x-axis.   (AEB 1975)

13. Find the area of the region in the first quadrant enclosed between the curve $y = x^2 + 4$, the line $y = 8$ and the y-axis. The region is rotated through four right-angles about Oy to form a uniform solid. Find the volume and the coordinates of the centre of mass of the solid.   (C)

14. Sketch on one diagram the graphs of $x^3y = 1$ and $y = \sqrt{x}$, for positive values of x. Show that the area of the finite region bounded by the straight lines $y = 0$ and $x = 2$ and an arc of each of the above curves is $25/24$. Find also the coordinates of the centroid of the region.   (C)

15. Find the area of the finite region between the curve $y = x^2 + 1$ and the line $y = 2x + 1$. The region is rotated through four right angles about Ox, to produce a uniform solid of revolution. Find the volume and the coordinates of the centre of gravity of this solid.   (C)

16. Sketch the arc of the curve given parametrically by $x = a(\theta - \sin \theta)$, $y = a(1 - \cos \theta)$, for which $0 \leqslant \theta \leqslant 2\pi$. Find the area of the finite region enclosed by this arc and the x-axis. Find also the coordinates of the centroid of the region. (L)

10 Equilibrium of rigid bodies

10.1 Parallel forces in equilibrium

If a set of coplanar forces is in equilibrium then
(i) the sum of the components of the forces in any given direction is zero and
(ii) the sum of the moments of the forces about any given point is zero.
These facts are used to find unknown quantities in many statics problems.

Example 1   A non-uniform rod AB of length 5 m and weight 75 N is supported in a horizontal position by two vertical strings attached to its ends. A weight of 15 N is attached to the rod at the point C, where $AC = 1$ m. If the tensions in the strings at A and B are $2T$ N and T N respectively, find the value of T. Find also the distance, x m, of the centre of gravity of the rod from A.

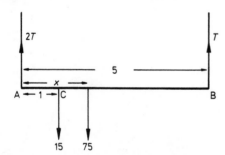

Considering the vertical forces on the rod,

$$\uparrow \qquad 2T - 15 - 75 + T = 0$$
$$\therefore \qquad\qquad 3T = 90$$
$$\text{Hence} \qquad\qquad T = 30.$$

Taking moments clockwise about A,

$$A \curvearrowright \qquad\qquad 15 \times 1 + 75 \times x - T \times 5 = 0$$

$$\therefore \qquad 75x = 5T - 15 = 135$$
$$\text{Hence} \qquad x = 1\cdot8.$$

When a rigid body rests on an object described as *smooth*, (e.g. a smooth support or a smooth table,) then the reaction on the body at any point of contact is assumed to be perpendicular to the surfaces in contact.

180

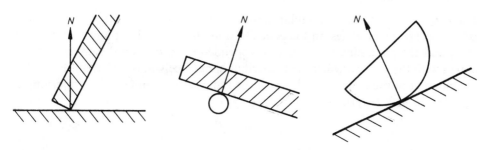

Example 2 A uniform plank AB of length 4 m and weight 300 N rests horizontally on smooth supports at P and Q, where $AP = QB = 1\cdot2$ m. Find the maximum weight that can be placed at B without tilting the plank.

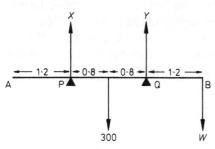

Let us assume that the plank is in equilibrium with reactions of X N and Y N at P and Q respectively and a weight of W N at B.

Taking moments about Q,

$$X \times 1\cdot6 + W \times 1\cdot2 - 300 \times 0\cdot8 = 0$$
$$\therefore \quad 1\cdot2W = 240 - 1\cdot6X$$

Since the reaction at P acts vertically upwards, $X \geqslant 0$,

$$\therefore \quad 1\cdot2W \leqslant 240 \quad \text{i.e.} \quad W \leqslant 200.$$

Hence the maximum weight that can be placed at B without tilting the plank is 200 N.

[Note that when a weight of 200 N is placed at B, the reaction at P is zero and the plank just fails to rotate about Q.]

When a body is in equilibrium under the action of *two forces*, these forces must be equal in magnitude and act in opposite directions along the same line.

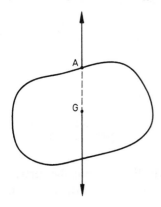

In particular, when a body freely suspended from a point A is in equilibrium, the two forces acting on it, namely its weight and the force at A, must act along the same vertical line. We deduce that the body hangs in equilibrium with its centre of gravity G vertically below A.

Example 3   A uniform rectangular lamina $ABCD$ of weight $5W$ has $AB = 5a$ and $BC = 4a$. The point P lies on the edge DC and $DP = 3a$. The triangle BCP is cut away and the remaining trapezium is suspended from P. Find the angle that DP makes with the vertical when the trapezium hangs freely in equilibrium. Find also the moment of the couple which would be required to maintain the trapezium in equilibrium with D vertically below P.

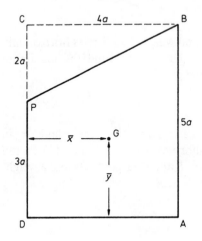

We first find the position of G, the centre of gravity of the lamina $ABPD$.

Rectangle $ABCD$ has area $20a^2$ and weight $5W$. Since triangle BCP has area $4a^2$, its weight must be W.

Body	Weight	Distance of centre of gravity from CD	Distance of centre of gravity from DA
Rectangle $ABCD$	$5W$	$2a$	$5a/2$
Triangle BCP	W	$4a/3$	$13a/3$
Remainder	$4W$	$\bar{x}$	$\bar{y}$

Taking moments about CD,

$$4W \times \bar{x} + W \times \frac{4a}{3} = 5W \times 2a$$

$$\therefore \quad \bar{x} = \frac{1}{4}\left(10a - \frac{4a}{3}\right) = \frac{13a}{6}$$

Taking moments about DA,

$$4W \times \bar{y} + W \times \frac{13a}{3} = 5W \times \frac{5a}{2}$$

$$\therefore \quad \bar{y} = \frac{1}{4}\left(\frac{25a}{2} - \frac{13a}{3}\right) = \frac{49a}{24}$$

When the trapezium hangs in equilibrium from P, the line PG must be vertical. Let θ be the angle DP then makes with the vertical and let Q be the foot of the perpendicular from G to DP.

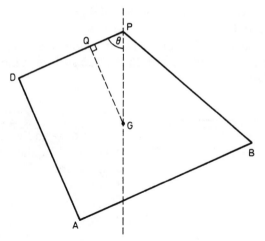

$$GQ = \bar{x} = \frac{13a}{6}, \quad DQ = \bar{y} = \frac{49a}{24}, \qquad \therefore \quad QP = \frac{23a}{24}.$$

Thus $\tan \theta = \dfrac{GQ}{QP} = \dfrac{13}{6} \times \dfrac{24}{23} = \dfrac{52}{23}$ and $\theta \approx 66 \cdot 1°$.

Hence the angle made by DP with the vertical is $66 \cdot 1°$.
Suppose now that the trapezium is in equilibrium with D vertically below P and that a couple of moment M in the sense DAB is required to maintain this position. Taking moments anti-clockwise about P,

$$M - 4W \times \frac{13a}{6} = 0 \qquad \therefore \quad M = \frac{26Wa}{3}.$$

Hence the moment of the required couple is $26Wa/3$.

When a body rests in equilibrium on a horizontal plane, the weight of the body and the force exerted by the plane on the body must act along the same line, namely the vertical line through the centre of gravity.

In the case of a lamina with an edge AB resting on a smooth horizontal plane, the force N exerted by the plane on the lamina is the resultant of normal reactions at the points of contact along AB. Thus N must act through some point on AB. It follows that, if the vertical line through the centre of gravity G passes through a point on the edge AB, then the force N can act to maintain equilibrium. Otherwise equilibrium is not possible and the lamina will topple.

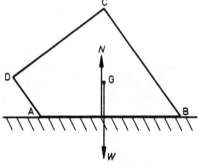

Lamina in equilibrium

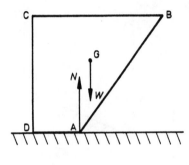

Lamina will topple

Example 4   A uniform solid is formed by joining a hemisphere of radius a to a circular cylinder of radius a and height h, so that the plane face of the hemisphere coincides with a plane face of the cylinder. Show that this solid can rest in equilibrium on a horizontal plane with the curved surface of the cylinder touching the plane if $h^2 \geqslant \frac{1}{2}a^2$.

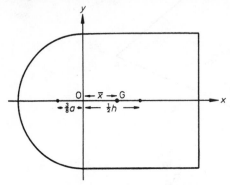

If we take x- and y-axes as shown in the diagram, then the centre of gravity G of the combined solid must lie on the x-axis.

Let w be the weight per unit volume of the solid.

Body	Weight	x-coordinate of centre of gravity
Cylinder	$\pi a^2 h w$	$\frac{1}{2}h$
Hemisphere	$\frac{2}{3}\pi a^3 w$	$-\frac{3}{8}a$
Whole body	$(h + \frac{2}{3}a)\pi a^2 w$	$\bar{x}$

Taking moments about the y-axis,

$$(h + \tfrac{2}{3}a)\pi a^2 w \bar{x} = \pi a^2 h w \times \tfrac{1}{2}h - \tfrac{2}{3}\pi a^3 w \times \tfrac{3}{8}a$$
$$\therefore \qquad (h + \tfrac{2}{3}a)\bar{x} = \tfrac{1}{2}h^2 - \tfrac{1}{4}a^2$$

When this solid is placed with the curved surface of the cylinder touching a horizontal plane, it will rest in equilibrium if the vertical line through G passes through a point of contact between the plane and the solid.

This condition will be satisfied if $\bar{x} \geqslant 0$ i.e. if $h^2 \geqslant \frac{1}{2}a^2$.

For a body to rest in equilibrium on a rough inclined plane the force exerted by the plane on the body must act along a vertical line through the centre of gravity of the body.

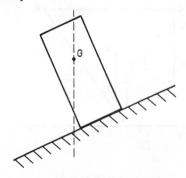

For the block shown in this diagram equilibrium is not possible. Since the vertical line through the centre of gravity G falls outside the base of the block, it will topple.

The reaction R between a body and a rough surface is the resultant of two components, the normal reaction N and a friction force F. According to the laws of friction, if μ is the coefficient of friction between the body and the surface, then $F \leqslant \mu N$. We can also express this condition in terms of λ, the angle of friction, and θ, the angle made by R with the normal to the surface, since $\tan \lambda = \mu$ and $\tan \theta = F/N$.

$$F \leqslant \mu N \quad \Leftrightarrow \quad \tan \theta \leqslant \mu \quad \Leftrightarrow \quad \theta \leqslant \lambda.$$

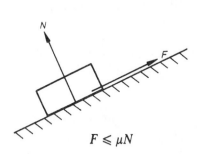

$$F \leqslant \mu N$$

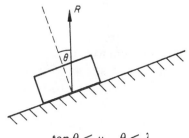

$$\tan \theta \leqslant \mu, \quad \theta \leqslant \lambda$$

Example 5 A uniform solid cube is in equilibrium with one face resting on a rough inclined plane and one pair of opposite faces vertical. The coefficient of friction between the cube and the plane is μ. The angle of inclination of the plane is gradually increased. Show that equilibrium will be broken by sliding rather than toppling if $\mu < 1$.

(1)

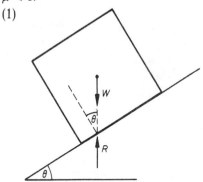

Let θ be the angle of inclination of the plane to the horizontal. When the cube is in equilibrium, as shown in diagram (1), the total reaction R acts vertically. The angle between its line of action and the normal to the plane is θ. When the cube is on the point of sliding, friction is limiting,

$$\therefore \qquad \tan \theta = \mu.$$

(2)

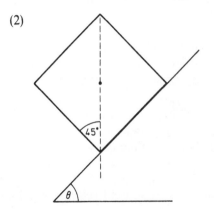

In diagram (2) the cube is on the point of toppling, since the vertical line through its centre of gravity passes through the lower edge of the base. Thus, when the cube is about to topple,

$$\tan \theta = \tan 45° = 1.$$

Hence equilibrium will be broken by sliding if tan θ reaches the value μ before it reaches the value 1, i.e. if $\mu < 1$.

Exercise 10.1

1.   A beam AB of length 4·5 m is supported in a horizontal position by two vertical cables attached to its ends. The tensions in the cables at A and B are 160 N and 200 N respectively. Find the weight of the beam and the distance of its centre of gravity from A.

2.   A uniform rod AB of length 3 m and weight 50 N rests horizontally on smooth supports at A and B. A load of 24 N is attached to the rod at a point C, where $AC = 1$ m. Find the forces exerted on the rod by the supports.

3.   A uniform bar of length 2·8 m and weight 80 N has loads of 20 N and 40 N attached to its ends A and B respectively. If the bar balances in a horizontal position when smoothly supported at C, find the distance of C from A.

4.   A uniform rod $APQB$ of length 2 m rests horizontally on smooth supports at P and Q, where $PQ = 1·2$ m. If the reaction at P is twice the reaction at Q, find the distance AP. Given that when a weight of 5 N is attached to the rod at B the reactions at P and Q are equal, find the weight of the rod.

5.   A uniform plank ABC of weight 400 N is held in a horizontal position by a smooth support at B and a vertical rope attached at C, where $AB = 1$ m and $AC = 5$ m. If the rope is likely to break when the tension in it exceeds 750 N, find
(a) the maximum weight that can be placed on the plank at the mid-point of BC,
(b) the maximum distance that a man of weight 800 N can safely walk from B towards C.

6.   A non-uniform beam $AXYB$ of length 4 m and weight 400 N is maintained in a horizontal position by smooth supports at X and Y, where $AX = YB = 1$ m. A boy of weight 500 N can just walk to the end A of the beam without overturning it. If the boy walks along the beam towards B, find his distance from B when the beam is just about to tip.

7.   A uniform right circular solid cone of weight W is suspended by two vertical strings attached to the ends A and B of a diameter of its base. If the cone hangs in equilibrium with its vertex vertically below A, find the tensions in the strings.

8. $ABCD$ is a uniform rectangular lamina of weight 10 N. A particle of weight W N is attached to the lamina at B. When the system is freely suspended from A it rests in equilibrium with the mid-point of BC vertically below A. Find the value of W.

9.   A uniform wire is bent into the form of a trapezium $ABCD$ in which $\angle ABC = \angle BCD = 90°$, $AB = 6a$, $BC = 4a$ and $CD = 3a$. Find the distances of

the centre of gravity from AB and BC. If the trapezium is freely suspended from A, find the angle which AB makes with the vertical.

10. A uniform triangular lamina ABC has $AB = 4a, BC = 5a, CA = 3a$. The lamina is folded through $180°$ along LN, where L and N are the mid-points of BC and AB respectively, so that the vertex B is at A. Find the coordinates of the centre of mass of the folded lamina relative to AN and AC as x-axis and y-axis respectively. The folded lamina is suspended from C and hangs in equilibrium under gravity. Find the tangent of the angle that CA makes with the vertical.   (C)

11. A uniform wire is bent to form a semi-circular arc together with the diameter AB joining the ends of the arc. If the wire hangs in equilibrium from a smooth pivot at A, find the tangent of the angle that AB makes with the vertical.

12. A uniform wire AB of weight $2W$ is bent into a semi-circular arc. A particle of weight W is attached to the end B and the system is freely suspended from A. Find the tangent of the angle that AB makes with the vertical.

13. Three uniform rods AB, BC, CD, each of length $2a$ and weight W are rigidly joined together to form three sides of a square $ABCD$. If the system hangs freely from a smooth pivot at A, find the angle that AB makes with the vertical. Find also, in terms of W and a, the moment of the couple required to maintain the system in equilibrium with BC horizontal.

14. $ABCD$ is a uniform square lamina of side $6a$ and weight W. P is a point on the diagonal AC, such that $AP = 2PC$. The square having diagonal PC is cut away and the remaining body is freely suspended from B. Find the angle which BA makes with the vertical. Find also the moment of the couple required to maintain the body in equilibrium with BA horizontal.

15. $ABCD$ is a uniform rectangular lamina in which $BC = 2a$. P is the mid-point of BC and R is a point on AB such that $AR = a$ and $RB = ka$. The rectangle $BPQR$ is cut away and the remaining body is placed in a vertical plane with AR resting on a horizontal plane. Find the maximum value of k given that the lamina does not topple about R.

16. A uniform lamina of weight $3W$ in the form of a trapezium $ABCD$ has $\angle ABC = \angle BCD = 90°, AB = BC = a$ and $CD = 2a$. The lamina is placed in a vertical plane with AB resting on a horizontal plane. Find, in terms of W, the greatest weight that can be attached to the lamina at D without causing it to topple about A.

17. A solid hemisphere of radius a and a solid right circular cone of height h and base radius a are made from the same uniform material and are joined together with their plane faces completely in contact. O is the centre of the common base. Find the position of the centre of gravity of the whole body.

(a) The body is suspended freely from a point A on the edge of the common base and hangs in equilibrium under gravity. If $h = 3a$, find, correct to the nearest degree, the acute angle made by AO with the vertical.

(b) The body is found to rest in equilibrium when it is placed on a horizontal table with *any* point of its hemispherical surface in contact with the table. Find h in terms of a.   (O&C)

18. A uniform thin hemispherical bowl rests in equilibrium with its axis of symmetry horizontal and its curved surface on a rough inclined plane. Find the angle between the plane and the horizontal. Find also the least possible value of the coefficient of friction between the bowl and the plane.

19. A uniform solid hemisphere rests in equilibrium with its curved surface on a rough plane inclined at an angle α to the horizontal, where $\sin \alpha = 0{\cdot}3$. Find the angle between the plane face of the hemisphere and the vertical.

20. A uniform right circular solid cone of radius a and height $3a$ rests in equilibrium with its base in contact with a rough inclined plane. The angle of inclination of the plane is then increased steadily.

(a) Assuming that the cone does not slide down the plane, find the angle of inclination of the plane to the horizontal when the cone is about to topple.

(b) If the coefficient of friction between the cone and the plane is $\frac{1}{2}$, find the angle of inclination of the plane to the horizontal when the cone is about to slide.

21. A uniform solid cylinder of radius a and height h is placed with one plane face resting on a rough inclined plane. The angle of inclination of the plane is then gradually increased. Show that the cylinder will slide before it topples if the coefficient of friction between the cylinder and the plane is less than $\dfrac{2a}{h}$.

10.2 Three force problems

When a body is in equilibrium under the action of *three forces*, the vector sum of these forces must be zero. Hence three non-parallel forces in equilibrium can be represented in magnitude and direction by the sides of a triangle. We also know that the sum of the moments of coplanar forces in equilibrium about any point in their plane is zero.

Thus one approach to three force problems is to

(i) take moments about any suitable point, and

(ii) use a triangle of forces.

Example 1   A uniform rod AB of mass m, which is smoothly hinged at A, is maintained in equilibrium by a horizontal force P acting at B. Given that the rod is inclined at $30°$ to the horizontal with B below A, find (a) an expression for P, (b) the magnitude and direction of the reaction at the hinge.

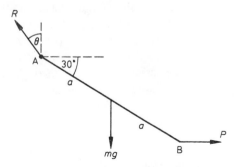

[Note that the reaction at a *smooth hinge* is a single force which may act in any direction. The system of reactions in a hinge which is *not smooth* may reduce to a single force together with a couple.]

Let the length of the rod be $2a$ and let the reaction at the hinge be of magnitude R acting at an angle θ to the vertical.

(a) The weight of the rod is mg and acts through the mid-point of the rod. Thus taking moments anti-clockwise about A, we have

$$P \times 2a \sin 30° - mg \times a\cos 30° = 0$$

$$\therefore \qquad\qquad Pa - \frac{\sqrt{3}}{2}mga = 0$$

Hence $P = \dfrac{\sqrt{3}}{2}mg.$

(b)

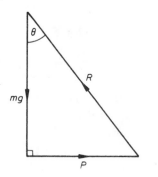

Using the triangle of forces,

$$R = \sqrt{\{(mg)^2 + P^2\}} = mg\sqrt{(1 + \tfrac{3}{4})}$$
$$= \frac{\sqrt{7}}{2}mg$$

$$\tan\theta = \frac{P}{mg} = \frac{\sqrt{3}}{2} \qquad \therefore \quad \theta \approx 40.9°$$

Hence the reaction at the hinge has magnitude $\dfrac{\sqrt{7}}{2}mg$ and makes an angle $\tan^{-1}\dfrac{\sqrt{3}}{2} \approx 40.9°$ with the vertical.

We now establish a property of three force systems which is a useful aid to problem solving. Suppose that a rigid body is in equilibrium under the action of three coplanar forces F_1, F_2 and F_3. Then either all three forces are parallel or the lines of action of two of them meet.

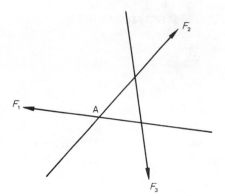

If F_1 and F_2 act along lines which intersect at a point A, then the moments of F_1 and F_2 about A are zero. Since F_1, F_2 and F_3 are in equilibrium, the moment of F_3 about A must also be zero. Hence the line of action of F_3 passes through A. We may deduce the following general principle.

If a rigid body is in equilibrium under the action of three coplanar forces, then the lines of action of the forces are either parallel or concurrent.

Example 2 A uniform pole AB of length 5 m is smoothly hinged at A and supported at B by a light elastic string BC of natural length 3 m and modulus 60 N. The end C of the string is fixed 3 m vertically above A. Given that the system is in equilibrium with BC horizontal, find in newtons the tension T in the string, the weight W of the pole and magnitude R of the reaction at A.

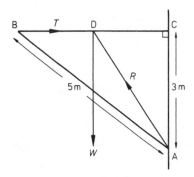

The lines of action of T and W meet at D, the mid-point of BC,

∴   the third force R must also act through D.

By Pythagoras' theorem in $\triangle ABC$,
$$BC = 4\,\text{m},$$

∴   the extension in the elastic string
$$= (4 - 3)\,\text{m} = 1\,\text{m}.$$

By Hooke's law, $T = \dfrac{\lambda x}{l}$

where $\lambda = 60$, $l = 3$ and $x = 1$,

∴ $T = \dfrac{60 \times 1}{3} = 20.$

Hence the tension in the elastic string is 20 N.

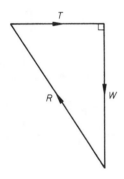

Triangle of forces

Comparing the diagrams we see that the triangle of forces is similar to $\triangle ADC$. By Pythagoras' theorem in $\triangle ADC$,
$$AD = \sqrt{(AC^2 + DC^2)} = \sqrt{(3^2 + 2^2)}\,\mathrm{m}$$
$$= \sqrt{13}\,\mathrm{m},$$

$$\therefore \quad \frac{T}{2} = \frac{W}{3} = \frac{R}{\sqrt{13}}$$

$$\therefore \quad W = \frac{3}{2}T = 30$$

and $\quad R = \frac{\sqrt{13}}{2}T = 10\sqrt{13} \approx 36{\cdot}1.$

Hence the weight of the pole is $30\,\mathrm{N}$ and the magnitude of the reaction at A is $36{\cdot}1\,\mathrm{N}$.

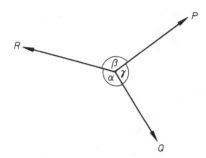

When solving three force problems in which angles rather than lengths are known, *Lami's theorem* may be useful. It states that for forces P, Q and R in equilibrium, as shown in the diagram.

$$\frac{P}{\sin \alpha} = \frac{Q}{\sin \beta} = \frac{R}{\sin \gamma}$$

Example 3 A uniform rod AB of length $5a$ and weight W rests with the end A on a smooth plane inclined at an angle α to the horizontal, where $\sin \alpha = 3/5$. It is maintained in equilibrium by a smooth support at C. If the rod makes an angle β with the horizontal, where $\sin \beta = 7/25$, find

(a) the magnitudes of the reactions at A and C,
(b) the distance AC.

The reaction at A is perpendicular to the inclined plane and the reaction at C is perpendicular to the rod. Let their magnitudes be N_1 and N_2 respectively. Since the forces N_1, N_2 and W are in equilibrium, their lines of action are concurrent.

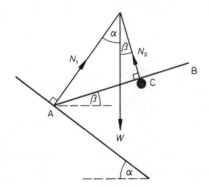

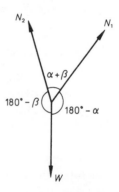

(a) By Lami's theorem, $\dfrac{N_1}{\sin(180° - \beta)} = \dfrac{N_2}{\sin(180° - \alpha)} = \dfrac{W}{\sin(\alpha + \beta)}$

$\therefore \quad \dfrac{N_1}{\sin \beta} = \dfrac{N_2}{\sin \alpha} = \dfrac{W}{\sin(\alpha + \beta)}$ \qquad (1)

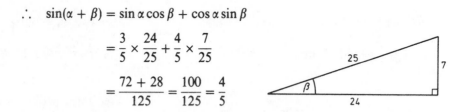

$$\sin \alpha = \frac{3}{5} \Rightarrow \cos \alpha = \frac{4}{5}$$

$$\sin \beta = \frac{7}{25} \Rightarrow \cos \beta = \frac{24}{25}$$

$\therefore \quad \sin(\alpha + \beta) = \sin \alpha \cos \beta + \cos \alpha \sin \beta$

$$= \frac{3}{5} \times \frac{24}{25} + \frac{4}{5} \times \frac{7}{25}$$

$$= \frac{72 + 28}{125} = \frac{100}{125} = \frac{4}{5}$$

Substituting these values in equation (1),

$$\frac{25}{7}N_1 = \frac{5}{3}N_2 = \frac{5}{4}W$$

$\therefore \quad N_1 = \dfrac{7}{25} \times \dfrac{5}{4}W = \dfrac{7}{20}W$ and $N_2 = \dfrac{3}{5} \times \dfrac{5}{4}W = \dfrac{3}{4}W$

Hence the magnitudes of the reactions at A and C are $7W/20$ and $3W/4$ respectively.

(b) The distance of the centre of gravity of the rod from A is $5a/2$. Let the distance AC be x.

Taking moments anti-clockwise about A,

$$N_1 \times 0 + N_2 \times x - W \times \frac{5}{2}a \cos \beta = 0$$

$\therefore \qquad\qquad \dfrac{3}{4}Wx - \dfrac{5}{2} \times \dfrac{24}{25}Wa = 0$

$\therefore \quad x = \dfrac{4}{3} \times \dfrac{5}{2} \times \dfrac{24}{25}a = \dfrac{16}{5}a$

Hence the distance AC is $16a/5$.

In problems involving contact between rough surfaces the reaction at any point of contact can be treated as the resultant of the normal reaction and a frictional force or as a single force. For instance, a problem concerning a ladder resting on a rough horizontal floor and against a rough vertical wall may be solved using diagram (a) and the general methods to be described in §10.3. Alternatively, as indicated in diagram (b), the set of forces on the ladder can be reduced to a three force system by using the total reactions at the points of contact with the floor and the wall.

(a)

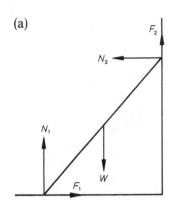

(b)

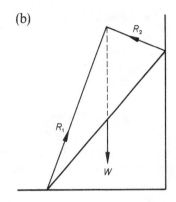

When using this latter approach, it is helpful to remember that if θ is the angle between the total reaction and the normal to the surfaces in contact, then

$$\tan \theta \leqslant \mu \quad \text{and} \quad \theta \leqslant \lambda,$$

where μ is the coefficient of friction and λ is the angle of friction.

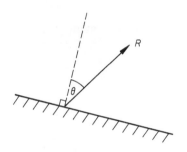

Example 4   A uniform rod AB of length $1 \cdot 7$ m is placed with the end A against a smooth vertical wall and the end B on rough horizontal ground at a distance of $0 \cdot 8$ m from the wall. If the coefficient of friction between the rod and the ground is μ, find the least value of μ for which equilibrium is possible.

If the rod is in equilibrium under the action of its weight W, the normal reaction N at A and the reaction R at B, then the lines of action of these three forces must be concurrent. Let C be their point of intersection and let θ be the angle the reaction R makes with the vertical.

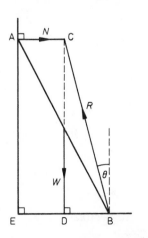

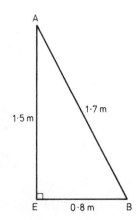

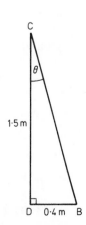

By Pythagoras' theorem in $\triangle ABE$, $AE^2 + EB^2 = AB^2$

$\therefore$ $AE = \sqrt{\{(1\cdot7)^2 - (0.8)^2\}}\,\text{m} = 1\cdot5\,\text{m}.$

Since the weight of the rod acts vertically through its mid-point, D must be the mid-point of EB,

$\therefore$ using $\triangle BCD$, $\tan\theta = \dfrac{0\cdot4}{1\cdot5} = \dfrac{4}{15}.$

Equilibrium is possible provided that $\tan\theta \leqslant \mu$.
Hence the least possible value of μ is 4/15.

Example 5   A uniform ladder AB of weight W rests in limiting equilibrium with the end A on rough horizontal ground and the end B against a rough vertical wall. If the coefficient of friction at each end of the ladder is 5/12, find the magnitudes of the reactions at A and B.

Since the ladder is in limiting equilibrium, the reaction R_1 at A acts at an angle λ to the vertical and the reaction R_2 at B acts at an angle λ to the horizontal, where $\tan\lambda = 5/12$. If the lines of action of R_1 and R_2 meets at C, then the weight of the ladder also acts through C and $\angle ACB = \lambda + (90° - \lambda) = 90°$.

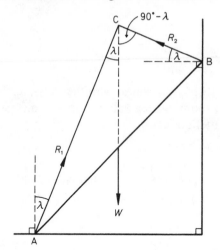
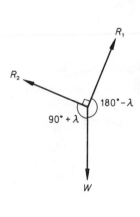

By Lami's theorem, $\dfrac{R_1}{\sin(90° + \lambda)} = \dfrac{R_2}{\sin(180° - \lambda)} = \dfrac{W}{\sin 90°}$

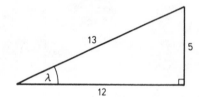

$\therefore$ $\dfrac{R_1}{\cos\lambda} = \dfrac{R_2}{\sin\lambda} = W$

Since $\tan\lambda = \frac{5}{12}$,

$\cos\lambda = \frac{12}{13}$ and $\sin\lambda = \frac{5}{13}$,

$\therefore$ $R_1 = W\cos\lambda = \frac{12}{13}W$ and $R_2 = W\sin\lambda = \frac{5}{13}W.$

Hence the reactions at A and B are $12W/13$ and $5W/13$ respectively.

Exercise 10.2

[Take g as $10\,\mathrm{m\,s^{-2}}$.]

1.   A uniform rod AB of weight $20\,\mathrm{N}$ is smoothly hinged at B and maintained in equilibrium by a horizontal force of $P\,\mathrm{N}$ acting at A. If the rod is inclined at $45°$ to the horizontal with A above B, find (a) the value of P, (b) the magnitude and direction of the reaction at the hinge.

2.   A non-uniform bar AB of length $2a$ and mass m is maintained in a horizontal position by two strings AC and BC attached to a fixed point C above the bar. If $\angle CAB = 60°$ and $\angle ABC = 30°$, find expressions for the tensions in the strings. Find also the distance of the centre of gravity of the bar from A.

3.   A uniform rod AB of length $40\,\mathrm{cm}$ and weight $8\,\mathrm{N}$ rests on a rough peg at C, where $AC = 15\,\mathrm{cm}$, and against a smooth vertical wall at A. If the rod is in equilibrium at an angle α to the horizontal, where $\sin \alpha = 4/5$, find the magnitudes of the reactions at A and at C.

4.   A uniform bar AB of length $2\,\mathrm{m}$ and mass $3\,\mathrm{kg}$ rests on a smooth peg at X, where $AX = 0{\cdot}5\,\mathrm{m}$ and against a rough vertical wall at A. If the bar is in equilibrium at $60°$ to the horizontal, find the magnitude and direction of the force exerted by the wall on the bar.

5.   A sphere of radius $40\,\mathrm{cm}$ and weight $30\,\mathrm{N}$ rests in equilibrium on a smooth plane inclined at an angle α to the horizontal, where $\tan \alpha = 8/15$. A horizontal string joins a point on the sphere to a fixed point on the plane. Find the length of the string and the tension in the string.

6.   A rod AB of length $40\,\mathrm{cm}$, mass $6\,\mathrm{kg}$ and centre of mass G, is suspended by a light inextensible string AXB of length $80\,\mathrm{cm}$, which passes over a smooth peg at X. Find the tension in the string and the angle the rod makes with the vertical when it hangs in equilibrium if (a) $AG = GB$, (b) $AG:GB = 3:5$.

7.   A uniform rod of weight W is in equilibrium with one end resting against a smooth vertical plane and the other end against a smooth plane inclined at an angle α to the horizontal, where $\tan \alpha = 5/12$. The line of intersection of the planes is horizontal. If the rod makes an angle θ with the vertical, find $\tan \theta$. Find also the magnitudes of the reactions at the vertical and inclined planes.

8.   A non-uniform rod AB of weight $3W$ rests with the end A on a smooth plane inclined at $30°$ to the horizontal. It is maintained in equilibrium at $30°$ to the horizontal by a smooth peg at C, where $AC = 3a$. Find (a) the magnitudes of the reactions at A and C, (b) the distance of the centre of gravity of the rod from A.

9.   A uniform rod AB of length $1\,\mathrm{m}$ is smoothly hinged at A and the end B is attached by means of a light elastic string of natural length $1\,\mathrm{m}$, modulus $20\,\mathrm{N}$ to a point C which is $1\,\mathrm{m}$ vertically above A. Given that the tension in the string is $12\,\mathrm{N}$,

find (a) the weight of the rod, (b) the magnitude and direction of the reaction at the hinge.

10. A uniform rod AB of weight $4W$ rests in equilibrium with the end A against a smooth vertical wall. A light elastic string XY of natural length 24 cm, modulus $15W$ is attached to a point X vertically above A and a point Y on the rod. Given that $XY = 32$ cm and $\angle XYB = 90°$, find the tension in the string and the length of the rod.

11. A smooth hemispherical bowl of radius $5\sqrt{5}$ cm is fixed with its rim horizontal. A uniform rod AB is in equilibrium with the end A resting inside the bowl and a point C of the rod against the rim, where $AC = 20$ cm. If the rod is inclined at an angle α to the horizontal, find $\tan \alpha$. Find also the length of the rod.

12. A uniform ladder of length 6·5 m rests with one end against a smooth vertical wall and the other end on rough horizontal ground at a distance of 2·5 m from the wall. If the foot of the ladder is about to slip, find the coefficient of friction between the ladder and the ground.

13. A uniform pole of length $2a$ and mass m rests in equilibrium at an angle α to the horizontal, with one end against a smooth vertical wall and the other end on rough horizontal ground. Find expressions for (a) the force exerted on the pole by the wall, (b) the least possible value of the coefficient of friction between the pole and the ground.

14. A uniform ladder of weight W and length $2l$ rests with its upper end against a smooth vertical wall. Its lower end stands on rough horizontal ground, and the coefficient of friction between the ladder and the ground is $\frac{1}{2}$. The ladder is in limiting equilibrium. Find the angle the ladder makes with the horizontal. Find also the reaction at the wall. A man of weight W climbs the ladder. Find how far up it he can go before the ladder will slip. Find also how far up the ladder he can go when a load of weight W is placed on the foot of the ladder.   (L)

15. A uniform rod AB of length a and weight W has a light ring attached to the end A. The ring is free to slide along a straight wire inclined at 30° to the horizontal. The rod is maintained in equilibrium by a light inextensible string of length a attached to the end B. The other end of the string is attached to the wire at a fixed point C above A. (a) If the wire is smooth, find the angle θ which the string makes with the vertical. (b) If the string is vertical, find the least value of the coefficient of friction between the ring and the wire.

16. A heavy uniform rod of length $2a$ rests in equilibrium against a small smooth horizontal peg with one end of the rod on a rough horizontal floor. If the height of the peg above the floor is b and friction is limiting when the rod makes an angle $\dfrac{\pi}{6}$ with the floor, show that the coefficient of friction between the floor and the rod is

$$\frac{\sqrt{3}a}{(8b - 3a)}.$$ (O)

17. A uniform rod AB of length $10a$ rests in limiting equilibrium with the end A on horizontal ground and the end B against a vertical wall. The coefficient of friction at each end of the rod is μ. Given that A is at a distance $6a$ from the wall, find the value of μ.

18. (a)

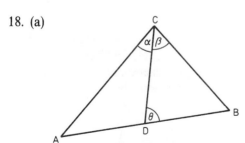

In the given diagram D is the mid-point of AB. Using the sine rule or otherwise prove that

$$2 \cot \theta = \cot \alpha - \cot \beta.$$

(b) A uniform ladder rests at an angle θ to the vertical, with one end on horizontal ground and the other end against a vertical wall. The coefficients of friction between the ladder and the ground and between the ladder and the wall are μ_1 and μ_2 respectively. Given that the ladder is on the point of slipping, use part (a) to prove that $\tan \theta = 2\mu_1/(1 - \mu_1\mu_2)$.

10.3 General conditions for equilibrium

We have already established that if a body is in equilibrium under the action of a set of coplanar forces, then the sum of their components in any direction is zero and the sum of their moments about any point is zero. In this section we consider sets of conditions that are sufficient to ensure equilibrium.

Suppose that a system of coplanar forces is such that
(i)   the sum of the components in a direction d_1 is zero,
(ii) the sum of the components in a direction d_2, not parallel to d_1, is zero, and
(iii) the sum of the moments about a point A in the plane is zero.
This system of forces is not equivalent to a single force, because no force can have zero components in two directions. The system does not reduce to a couple, because a couple has the same non-zero moment about every point in its plane. Thus, if a set of forces acting on a rigid body satisfies conditions (i), (ii) and (iii), it follows that the body is in equilibrium.

We can use this set of equilibrium conditions to solve problems involving forces in a *vertical plane* by
(i)   resolving horizontally,
(ii) resolving vertically, and
(iii) taking moments about a suitable point.
In this way we obtain up to three equations which we then solve to find any unknown quantities.

Example 1   A uniform rod AB of weight 15 N and length 4 m is smoothly hinged at A and has a particle of weight 30 N attached to it at B. A light inextensible string, attached to the rod at a point C, where $AC = 2.5$ m, and to a point D vertically above A, keeps the rod in a horizontal position. If the angle between the rod and the string is 30°, find (a) the tension in the string, (b) the magnitude and direction of the reaction at the hinge.

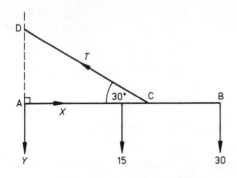

Let the tension in the string be T N and let the horizontal and vertical components of the reaction at the hinge be X N and Y N respectively.

(a) Taking moments anti-clockwise about A,

$$T \times 2.5 \sin 30° - 15 \times 2 - 30 \times 40 = 0$$

i.e. $$T \times \tfrac{5}{2} \times \tfrac{1}{2} - 30 - 120 = 0$$

$$\therefore \quad T = 150 \times \tfrac{4}{5} = 120.$$

Hence the tension in the string is 120 N

(b) Resolving horizontally and vertically,

$$\rightarrow \qquad\qquad\qquad X - T\cos 30° = 0 \qquad\qquad (1)$$
$$\downarrow \qquad\qquad Y + 15 + 30 - T\sin 30° = 0 \qquad\qquad (2)$$

From (1), $\quad X = 120 \times \dfrac{\sqrt{3}}{2} = 60\sqrt{3}$

From (2), $\quad Y = 120 \times \tfrac{1}{2} - 45 = 15$

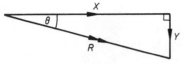

If the resultant reaction R acts at an angle θ to the horizontal, then

$$R^2 = X^2 + Y^2, \tan\theta = \frac{Y}{X}.$$

$$\therefore \quad R = \sqrt{\{(60\sqrt{3})^2 + 15^2\}} = 15\sqrt{\{(4\sqrt{3})^2 + 1^2\}} = 15\sqrt{(48 + 1)} = 105,$$

$$\tan\theta = \frac{15}{60\sqrt{3}} = \frac{1}{4\sqrt{3}} \quad \text{i.e.} \quad \theta \approx 8.2°.$$

Hence the reaction at the hinge has magnitude 105 N and acts at 8·2° to the horizontal.

When a rigid body is kept in equilibrium by frictional forces, then at each point of contact with a rough surface the frictional force F acts along the surface, opposing any tendency to slide. It also satisfies the condition $F \leqslant \mu N$, where N is the normal reaction and μ is the coefficient of friction. If the body is just about to slip, then friction is limiting at *every* point of contact and in each case $F = \mu N$.

Example 2 A uniform solid hemisphere rests in limiting equilibrium with its curved surface in contact with a horizontal floor and a vertical wall. The coefficient of friction at the floor is $\frac{1}{4}$ and at the wall is $\frac{1}{2}$. If θ is the angle of inclination of the plane face of the hemisphere to the horizontal, find $\sin \theta$.

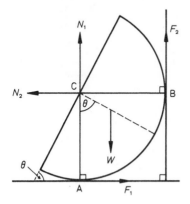

Let the hemisphere have centre C and radius a. Let the forces on it be as shown in the diagram. Since the hemisphere is in limiting equilibrium, friction must be limiting at both A and B,

$$\therefore \quad F_1 = \tfrac{1}{4}N_1, \quad F_2 = \tfrac{1}{2}N_2.$$

Resolving horizontally and vertically,

$$\rightarrow \qquad\qquad\qquad F_1 - N_2 = 0 \qquad\qquad\qquad (1)$$
$$\uparrow \qquad\qquad\qquad N_1 + F_2 - W = 0 \qquad\qquad\qquad (2)$$

Substituting for F_1 in (1):

$$\tfrac{1}{4}N_1 - N_2 = 0 \qquad \therefore \quad N_1 = 4N_2$$

Substituting for N_1 and F_2 in (2):

$$4N_2 + \tfrac{1}{2}N_2 - W = 0 \qquad \therefore \quad N_2 = \tfrac{2}{9}W$$

Hence $F_1 = N_2 = \tfrac{2}{9}W$ and $F_2 = \tfrac{1}{2}N_2 = \tfrac{1}{9}W$.

The centre of gravity of the hemisphere is on its axis of symmetry at a distance $\tfrac{3}{8}a$ from C.

Thus, taking moments clockwise about C,

$$W \times \tfrac{3}{8}a \sin \theta - F_1 \times a - F_2 \times a = 0$$
$$\therefore \qquad\qquad \tfrac{3}{8}aW \sin \theta - \tfrac{2}{9}aW - \tfrac{1}{9}aW = 0$$

Hence $\tfrac{3}{8} \sin \theta - \tfrac{3}{9} = 0$ i.e. $\sin \theta = \tfrac{8}{9}$.

Example 3 A uniform ladder AB of length $2a$ and weight W rests with the end A on horizontal ground and the end B against a vertical wall. The coefficients of friction at A and B are $\frac{2}{3}$ and $\frac{1}{2}$ respectively. The ladder makes an angle α with the horizontal, where $\tan \alpha = \frac{5}{4}$. If a man of weight W starts to climb the ladder, find his distance from A when the ladder begins to slip.

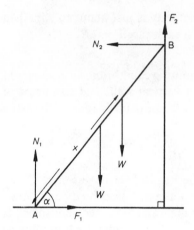

Let the reactions at A and B when the ladder is about to slip be as shown in the diagram. Since friction must be limiting at both A and B,

$$F_1 = \tfrac{2}{5}N_1, \quad F_2 = \tfrac{1}{2}N_2.$$

Resolving horizontally and vertically,

$$\rightarrow \qquad F_1 - N_2 = 0 \qquad (1)$$
$$\uparrow \qquad N_1 + F_2 - 2W = 0 \qquad (2)$$

Substituting for F_1 in (1),

$$\tfrac{2}{5}N_1 - N_2 = 0 \qquad \therefore \quad N_1 = \tfrac{5}{2}N_2$$

Substituting for N_1 and F_2 in (2),

$$\tfrac{5}{2}N_2 + \tfrac{1}{2}N_2 - 2W = 0 \qquad \therefore \quad N_2 = \tfrac{2}{3}W$$

Hence $F_2 = \tfrac{1}{2}N_2 = \tfrac{1}{3}W$

Let the man be a distance x from A when the ladder begins to slip. Taking moments clockwise about A,

$$W \times x \cos \alpha + W \times a \cos \alpha - F_2 \times 2a \cos \alpha - N_2 \times 2a \sin \alpha = 0$$

Dividing by $\cos \alpha$,

$$Wx + Wa - 2F_2 a - 2N_2 a \tan \alpha = 0$$
$$\therefore \quad Wx + Wa - \tfrac{2}{3}Wa - \tfrac{4}{3}Wa \times \tfrac{5}{4} = 0$$
$$\therefore \quad x = \tfrac{5}{3}a + \tfrac{2}{3}a - a = \tfrac{4}{3}a.$$

Hence the man is at a distance of $4a/3$ from A when the ladder begins to slip.

The set of conditions discussed earlier, for the equilibrium of a rigid body under the action of coplanar forces, involved the sums of components in two directions and the sum of moments about one point. We now consider whether any other combinations of similar conditions will also ensure equilibrium.

To be certain that a set of forces is not equivalent to a couple, we need to know that the system has zero moment about at least one point. A system with zero moments about two points A and B may have a resultant whose line of action passes through A and B. We can rule out this possibility if we find that the components of the forces in some direction, not perpendicular to AB, have zero sum or that the system has zero moment about a third point not on AB.

We have then three sets of equilibrium conditions. A system of coplanar forces must be in equilibrium if

  (a) the sums of the components in two non-parallel directions are each zero, and
       the sum of the moments about one point is zero;
or (b) the sums of the moments about two points A and B are each zero, and the sum
       of the components in a direction, not perpendicular to AB, is zero;
or (c) the sums of the moments about three points, not in a straight line, are each
       zero.
   Thus when tackling problems we may
  (a) resolve in two directions and take moments about one point;
or (b) take moments about two points A and B then resolve in a direction not
       perpendicular to AB;
or (c) take moments about three points which are not collinear.
Since each method involves putting three different restrictions on the system of
forces concerned, we will obtain three *independent* equations connecting any unknown quantities i.e. three equations each giving information which could not be
obtained from the other two. [Note that since these three equations ensure the
equilibrium of the system, no new information can be gained from further equations
formed by resolving or taking moments.]
   The following examples show that, by careful choice of the points about which we
take moments and of the directions in which we resolve, we may
(1) avoid equations involving quantities that we do not need to find,
(2) form equations containing as few unknowns as possible.

Example 4   A uniform rod AB of mass 6 kg rests on a smooth peg at a point C. The
rod is kept in equilibrium at an angle α to the horizontal, where $\tan \alpha = 5/12$, by a
horizontal force of P newtons acting at the upper end B of the rod. Find the value of
P.
[Take g as $10 \, \text{m s}^{-2}$.]

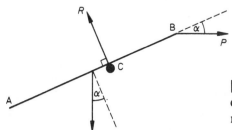

[We try to avoid equations involving
distances or the reaction at C, as we do
not need to find these quantities.]

Resolving along the rod in the direction AB,

$$P \cos \alpha - 6g \sin \alpha = 0$$

$$\therefore \quad P = 6g \tan \alpha = 6 \times 10 \times \tfrac{5}{12} = 25.$$

Example 5   A uniform bar AB of weight W and length $4a$ rests on a rough peg at a
point C, where $AC = a$. The bar is maintained in equilibrium, with A above B, by a
force of magnitude $\tfrac{1}{2}W$ acting at A in a direction perpendicular to the bar. Find the

angle α, which the bar makes with the horizontal. Given that the bar is about to slip, find the coefficient of friction μ between the bar and the peg.

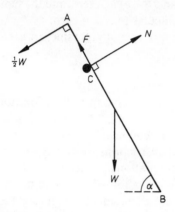

[In this example we try to form equations which simplify the working as much as possible.]

Taking moments clockwise about C,

$$W \times a \cos \alpha - \tfrac{1}{2}W \times a = 0 \qquad \therefore \cos \alpha = \tfrac{1}{2}$$

Hence
$$\alpha = 60°.$$

Let F be the frictional force at C and let N be the normal reaction. Taking moments clockwise about the mid-point of AB,

$$N \times a - \tfrac{1}{2}W \times 2a = 0 \qquad \therefore \quad N = W$$

Resolving along the bar in the direction BA,

$$F - W \sin \alpha = 0 \qquad \therefore \quad F = \frac{\sqrt{3}}{2}W$$

Since the bar is about to slip, $F = \mu N$.

Hence $\quad \mu = \dfrac{F}{N} = \dfrac{\sqrt{3}}{2}.$

Exercise 10.3

[Take g as $10 \, \mathrm{m \, s^{-2}}$.]

1. A uniform rod AB of weight 20 N and length 2 m is freely hinged at A. The rod is held in equilibrium at $30°$ to the horizontal, with B higher than A, by a light inextensible string of length 1·25 m. The string joins a point C on the rod to a fixed point D at a distance of 1·25 m vertically above A. If a particle of weight 5 N is suspended from B, find (a) the tension in the string, (b) the horizontal and vertical components of the reaction at A.

2. A uniform rod AB of mass 6 kg and length 3 m is freely hinged at A. A load of mass 2 kg is attached to the rod at B. The rod is kept in equilibrium by a light inextensible string CD of length 1·5 m, which is attached to a point C on the rod and

to a fixed point D on the same horizontal level as A. Given that $AC = 2\,\text{m}$ and $AD = 2\cdot5\,\text{m}$, find (a) the tension in the string, (b) the magnitude and direction of the reaction at the hinge.

3.   A uniform square lamina $ABCD$ of mass $6\,\text{kg}$ is hinged at A so that it is free to move in a vertical plane. It is maintained in equilibrium, with B vertically below A, by a horizontal force acting at C and a vertical force acting at D each of magnitude P newtons. Find (a) the value of P, (b) the magnitude and direction of the force exerted by the hinge on the lamina.

4.   A uniform rod AB of weight $16\,\text{N}$ is freely hinged at A. It is kept in equilibrium at an angle of $30°$ to the horizontal, with B lower than A, by a force acting at B. Find the magnitude and direction of the least force required at B to maintain equilibrium. Find also the corresponding horizontal and vertical components of the reaction at A.

5.   A uniform rod AB of length $3\,\text{m}$ and weight $40\,\text{N}$ rests in equilibrium with the lower end A on a smooth plane inclined at an angle α to the horizontal, where $\tan\alpha = 3/4$, and a point C of the rod against a smooth peg. If the rod makes an angle θ with the horizontal, where $\tan\theta = 7/24$, find (a) the magnitudes of the reactions at A and C, (b) the distance AC.

6.   A uniform rod AB of mass $13\,\text{kg}$ is in limiting equilibrium with its lower end A on a rough horizontal plane and its upper end B attached to a light inextensible string inclined at an angle θ to the upward vertical, where $\tan\theta = 12/5$. The string passes over a smooth fixed pulley at a point vertically above A and supports at its other end a mass of $6\cdot5\,\text{kg}$. Find (a) the coefficient of friction between the rod and the plane, (b) the angle the rod makes with the horizontal.

7.   A smooth hemisphere of radius $60\,\text{cm}$ is fixed with its plane face on a rough horizontal floor. A uniform rod AB of length $1\,\text{m}$ and weight $10\,\text{N}$ rests in equilibrium in a vertical plane with the end A on the floor and a point C of the rod in contact with the hemisphere, where $AC = 80\,\text{cm}$. Given that the rod is on the point of slipping, find the reaction at C and the coefficient of friction between the rod and the floor.

8.   A uniform ladder AB of length $5\,\text{m}$ and mass $12\,\text{kg}$ rests with the end A on rough horizontal ground and the end B in contact with a smooth vertical wall. The foot of the ladder is at a distance of $1\cdot4\,\text{m}$ from the wall. Find the magnitudes of the reactions at A and B. If the ladder is about to slip, find the coefficient of friction between the ladder and the ground.

9.   A uniform beam AB of length $2a$ and weight W rests with its end A against a smooth vertical wall and B on a rough horizontal plane. The vertical plane through AB is perpendicular to the wall. When it makes an angle of α with the wall the beam is on the point of slipping. Find the coefficient of friction between the beam and the horizontal plane. Find, also, what horizontal force applied to the mid-point of the

beam (in the vertical plane through AB) will just cause the beam to slip at B towards the wall.   (SU)

10. A thin uniform hemispherical bowl, of weight W and radius a, rests in limiting equilibrium with its plane face at an angle θ to the horizontal. Its curved surface is in contact with a rough horizontal floor and a rough vertical wall. If the coefficient of friction at each point of contact is $\frac{1}{3}$, find the magnitudes of the frictional forces at the floor and the wall. Find also the value of $\sin \theta$.

11. A uniform solid hemisphere rests in limiting equilibrium with its plane face at an angle α to the horizontal, where $\sin \alpha = 8/13$. Its curved surface is in contact with rough horizontal ground and a rough vertical wall. If the coefficient of friction at both points of contact is μ, find the value of μ.

12. A uniform rod AB of weight W and length $4a$ rests with its end A on a rough horizontal plane and a point C of the rod, where $AC = 3a$, in contact with a smooth peg. Given that the rod makes an angle θ with the horizontal, where $\sin \theta = 3/5$, find the magnitude of the reaction at C and the horizontal and vertical components of the reaction at A. If μ is the coefficient of friction between the rod and the horizontal plane, show that $\mu \geqslant 24/43$.

13. A uniform ladder of weight W rests at $60°$ to the horizontal with its foot on rough horizontal ground and the other end against a smooth vertical wall. If the ladder is just about to slip when a man of weight $2W$ stands at the top, find the coefficient of friction between the ladder and the ground. Find the frictional force between the ladder and the ground when the man is standing at the mid-point of the ladder.

14. A uniform ladder of length $2a$ and weight W rests against a smooth vertical wall and has its foot on rough horizontal ground. The coefficient of friction between the ladder and the ground is $\frac{1}{2}$. If the ladder is placed at an angle α to the horizontal, where $\tan \alpha = \frac{3}{2}$, find the distance that a man of weight $3W$ can climb up the ladder before it slips.

15. A uniform pole AB of length 8 m and mass 60 kg rests in limiting equilibrium with the end A on horizontal ground and the end B against a vertical wall. If the coefficient of friction at each end of the pole is $\frac{1}{3}$, find the angle the pole makes with the horizontal. The pole is now placed at an angle α to the horizontal, where $\tan \alpha = 2$, and a body of mass m kg is attached to the pole at B without causing the pole to slip. Find the maximum value of m and the magnitude of the corresponding normal reaction at A.

16. A uniform circular hoop of weight 15 N hangs over a rough horizontal peg A. A horizontal force P N, acting in the plane of the hoop, is applied at the other end B of the diameter through A. If the hoop is on the point of slipping when AB is inclined at

an angle α to the downward vertical, where $\tan \alpha = 4/3$, find the value of P and the coefficient of friction between the hoop and the peg.

17. A uniform rod AB, of weight W and length $6a$, rests with its lower end A on a smooth horizontal plane and a point C of the rod against a smooth peg, where $AC = 4a$. The rod is kept in equilibrium at an angle α to the horizontal by a force of magnitude $\frac{1}{4}W$ acting along the rod. Find the magnitude of the reaction at A and the value of $\sin \alpha$.

18. A uniform ladder, of weight W and length l, rests in a vertical plane with one end against a smooth vertical wall, the wall being perpendicular to the vertical plane through the ladder. The other end of the ladder rests on horizontal ground, the coefficient of friction between the ladder and the ground being 1/4. The ladder is inclined at an angle θ to the horizontal, where $\tan \theta = 24/7$. A man of weight $10W$ climbs up the ladder. Show that the man can reach a height of $6l/7$ above the ground before the ladder begins to slip and calculate the force exerted by the ladder on the wall at this instant. (L)

19. A uniform ladder of length 7 m rests against a vertical wall with which it makes an angle of $45°$, the coefficients of friction between the ladder and the wall and the ladder and the (horizontal) ground being $\frac{1}{3}$ and $\frac{1}{2}$ respectively. A boy whose weight is one half that of the ladder slowly ascends the ladder. How far along the ladder will he be when the ladder slips? [Assume the ladder is a uniform rod which is perpendicular to the line of intersection of the wall and ground.] (O&C)

20. A uniform circular disc, of radius a and weight w, stands in a vertical plane upon a rough horizontal floor with the point P of its circumference in contact with an equally rough vertical wall and its plane at right angles to that of the wall. A particle of equal weight w is attached to a point Q of the disc between its centre O and P so that the disc is on the point of slipping. Draw a good diagram indicating clearly the normal reactions and the friction forces acting on the disc. Show that

$$OQ = \frac{2a\mu(1 + \mu)}{1 + \mu^2},$$

where μ is the coefficient of friction. (W)

10.4 Rigid body systems

When two or more rigid bodies are in equilibrium under the action of a set of coplanar forces, then the whole system can be treated as a single body in equilibrium under the action of the external forces. Each separate body in the system is in equilibrium under the action of a set of forces which includes both the external forces on the body and the forces exerted on it by the other bodies in the system.

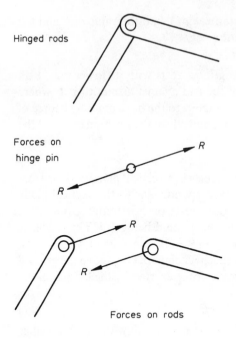

Hinged rods

Forces on
hinge pin

Forces on rods

We first consider two rods connected by
a smooth light hinge. Each rod exerts a
force on the hinge and, according to
Newton's third law, the hinge exerts an
equal and opposite force on the rod.
Thus, provided no external force acts on
the hinge, the effect of the hinge is to set
up equal and opposite forces on the two
rods.

Example 1 Two equal uniform rods *AB* and *BC*, each of length 2*a* and weight *W*,
are freely hinged together at *B* and hang freely from the point *A*. Equilibrium is
maintained by a horizontal force *P* acting at *C*. Given that *BC* makes an angle α
with the downward vertical, where $\tan \alpha = 4/3$, find the value of *P* and the horizontal
and vertical components of the force exerted by the rod *AB* on the rod *BC*. Find also
the angle made by *AB* with the vertical.

Let the horizontal and vertical components of the reaction at *B* be *X* and *Y*
respectively and let θ be the angle *AB* makes with the vertical.

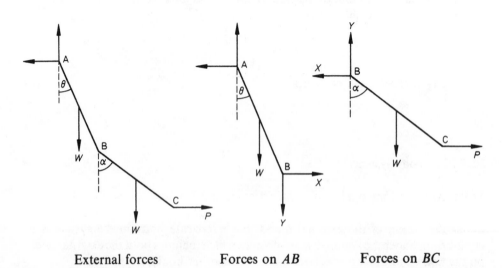

External forces   Forces on *AB*   Forces on *BC*

Consider first the forces on the rod BC.
Taking moments about B,

$$P \times 2a\cos\alpha - W \times a\sin\alpha = 0$$
$$\therefore \quad P = \tfrac{1}{2}W\tan\alpha = \tfrac{2}{3}W.$$

Resolving horizontally and vertically,

$$\leftarrow \qquad X - P = 0 \qquad \therefore \quad X = P = \tfrac{2}{3}W$$
$$\uparrow \qquad Y - W = 0 \qquad \therefore \quad Y = W$$

Hence the horizontal and vertical components of the force exerted by the rod AB on the rod BC are $\tfrac{2}{3}W$ and W respectively.
Consider now the forces on the rod AB.
Taking moments about A,

$$W \times a\sin\theta + Y \times 2a\sin\theta - X \times 2a\cos\theta = 0$$
$$\therefore \qquad Wa\sin\theta + 2Wa\sin\theta - \tfrac{4}{3}Wa\cos\theta = 0$$

$$\therefore \quad 3Wa\sin\theta = \tfrac{4}{3}Wa\cos\theta$$
$$\therefore \quad \tan\theta = \tfrac{4}{9} \quad \text{and} \quad \theta \approx 24°.$$

Hence AB makes an angle of $24°$ with the vertical.

Example 2 Two uniform rods AB and BC, each of length $2a$, have weights $2W$ and W respectively. The rods are freely jointed at B and rest in a vertical plane with A and C on a rough horizontal plane, the coefficient of friction at both points of contact being $\tfrac{1}{2}$. A particle of weight $2W$ is attached to a point P of the rod AB, where $AP = \tfrac{1}{2}a$. Given that the rods are inclined at an angle θ to the vertical, find the maximum value of θ for which equilibrium is possible.

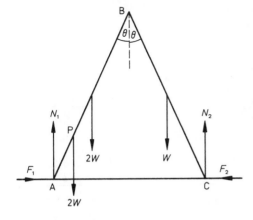

Let the reactions at A and C be as shown in the diagram.

Consider first the forces on the whole system.
Resolving horizontally and vertically,

$$\rightarrow \qquad F_1 - F_2 = 0 \qquad (1)$$
$$\uparrow \qquad N_1 + N_2 - 5W = 0 \qquad (2)$$

Taking moments about A,

$$N_2 \times 4a\sin\theta - W \times 3a\sin\theta - 2W \times a\sin\theta - 2W \times \tfrac{1}{2}a\sin\theta = 0$$
$$\therefore \quad 4N_2 - 3W - 2W - W = 0 \quad \text{giving} \quad N_2 = \tfrac{3}{2}W.$$
From (2), $\qquad\qquad N_1 = 5W - N_2 = \tfrac{7}{2}W.$

Using the laws of friction, $F_1 \leqslant \mu N_1$ and $F_2 \leqslant \mu N_2$
Since $\mu = \frac{1}{2}$, $F_1 \leqslant \frac{1}{2}W$ and $F_2 \leqslant \frac{3}{4}W$
However, using (1), we may write $F_1 = F_2 = F$
$\therefore$ in any equilibrium position, $F \leqslant \frac{3}{4}W$ (3)
Taking moments about B for the forces on rod BC,

$$\circlearrowright \quad N_2 \times 2a\sin\theta - W \times a\sin\theta - F_2 \times 2a\cos\theta = 0$$
$$\therefore \qquad\qquad 3\,Wa\sin\theta - Wa\sin\theta - 2Fa\cos\theta = 0$$
$$\therefore \qquad\qquad 2Wa\sin\theta = 2Fa\cos\theta$$

Thus $\tan\theta = F/W$
$\therefore$ using (3), $\tan\theta \leqslant 3/4$

Hence the maximum value of θ for which equilibrium is possible is $\tan^{-1}(3/4) \approx 36.9°$.

[Note that when θ takes this maximum value, slipping is about to occur at C.]

We now consider problems concerning two bodies in contact. By Newton's third law, the forces exerted by each body on the other are equal and opposite. Thus, as in the case of jointed bodies, unknown quantities can be found by resolving and taking moments, considering either the external forces acting on the system as a whole, or both internal and external forces acting on each body separately. In any given problem we try to simplify the working by avoiding equations involving quantities that we do not need to find.

Example 3   A uniform cube of side $12a$ and weight $3W$ rests on a rough horizontal table. A uniform rod AB of length $20a$ and weight $5W$ is freely hinged at A to a fixed point on the table. A point C of the rod rests against the mid-point of one edge of the cube, this edge being perpendicular to the vertical plane containing the rod. When the rod is at an angle α to the horizontal, where $\sin\alpha = 4/5$, the cube is on the point of sliding across the table without toppling. If the coefficient of friction at C is $\frac{1}{2}$, find the coefficient of friction between the cube and the table.

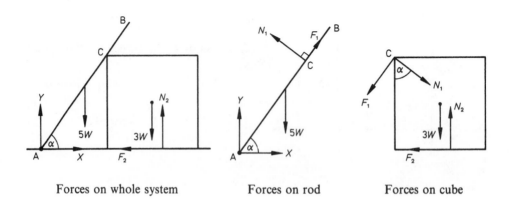

Forces on whole system   Forces on rod   Forces on cube

Let F_1, N_1 and F_2, N_2 be the frictional forces and normal reactions at C and the base of the cube respectively. Consider first the forces on the rod.

Taking moments about A,

$$N_1 \times 12a \operatorname{cosec} \alpha - 5W \times 10a \cos \alpha = 0$$

Using a right-angled triangle,

if $\sin \alpha = \frac{4}{5}$, then $\operatorname{cosec} \alpha = \frac{5}{4}, \cos \alpha = \frac{3}{5}$

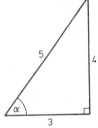

$$\therefore \quad N_1 \times 12a \times \tfrac{5}{4} - 5W \times 10a \times \tfrac{3}{5} = 0$$

Hence $N_1 = 2W$.
Since the cube is about to slide, $F_1 = \frac{1}{2}N_1 = W$.
Consider now the forces on the cube.
Resolving horizontally and vertically,

$$\leftarrow \qquad F_2 + F_1 \cos \alpha - N_1 \sin \alpha = 0 \qquad\qquad (1)$$
$$\uparrow \qquad N_2 - 3W - F_1 \sin \alpha - N_1 \cos \alpha = 0 \qquad (2)$$

From (1), $\qquad F_2 + \tfrac{3}{5}W - \tfrac{8}{5}W = 0 \qquad \therefore \quad F_2 = W$

From (2), $\qquad N_2 - 3W - \tfrac{4}{5}W - \tfrac{6}{5}W = 0 \qquad \therefore \quad N_2 = 5W$

Since the cube is on the point of sliding, the coefficient of friction between the cube and the table is given by F_2/N_2 and is equal to $1/5$.

Exercise 10.4

1. Two uniform rods AB and BC, of weights 5 N and 10 N respectively, are freely hinged at B and hang freely from a fixed hinge at A. The system is kept in equilibrium by a horizontal force of magnitude 5 N acting at C. Find (a) the magnitudes of the reactions at the hinges A and B, (b) the angles the rods AB and BC make with the vertical.

2. Two equal uniform rods, each of weight W, are freely jointed at B and hang freely from a hinge at A. The end C is attached by means of a light inextensible string to a point D on the same horizontal level as A. When the system is in equilibrium the rod AB is inclined at $45°$ to the vertical and the rod BC is horizontal. Find the tension in the string and the angle it makes with the vertical.

3. Two uniform rods AB and BC, each of length $2a$, have weights W and $3W$ respectively. The rods are smoothly jointed at B. The ends A and C of the rods are smoothly hinged to fixed points at the same horizontal level and a distance $2a$ apart. If the system is in equilibrium with B below AC, find the horizontal and vertical components of the reaction at B.

4. Two equal uniform rods, AB and AC, each of length $2a$ and weight W, are freely jointed at A. The end C is freely hinged to a point on a rough horizontal plane, the end B rests on the plane and is about to slip, and both rods are in a vertical plane. If the coefficient of friction between B and the plane is μ and the angle ABC is θ, (i) prove that $\mu = \frac{1}{2}\cot\theta$, (ii) find, in terms of μ, the magnitude and direction of the reaction at the hinge at C, (iii) find the magnitude of the reaction at the joint A.

(SU)

5. Two uniform rods AB and BC, freely jointed together at B, are of equal length, but have weights $4W$ and W respectively. The end A is freely hinged to a fixed point on a rough vertical wall and the end C rests against the wall at a point vertically below A. The system rests in limiting equilibrium with each rod inclined at an angle α to the vertical, where $\tan \alpha = 2$. Find (a) the coefficient of friction between the rod BC and the wall, (b) the horizontal and vertical components of the reaction of AB on BC.

6. Two uniform rods AB and AC, of length $2a$, but of weights $2W$ and W respectively, are smoothly jointed at A. The rods rest in a vertical plane with B and C on a rough horizontal plane, the coefficient of friction between the rods and the plane being 0.4. Given that the system is in limiting equilibrium, determine whether slipping is about to occur at B or at C and find angle BAC.

7. Two equal uniform rods, AB and BC, each of mass $4m$, are smoothly hinged together at B and stand in a vertical plane with A and C on a rough horizontal floor. The angle ABC is 2α where $\tan \alpha = \frac{1}{2}$, and the coefficient of friction at both A and C is μ. A mass m is fixed to the mid-point of AB. Show that equilibrium is possible provided that $\mu \geqslant 9/34$. What happens if $\mu = \frac{1}{4}$?

8. Two smooth uniform spheres of weights W and $2W$ are each suspended from a fixed point O by a light inextensible string and rest against each other. The angle between the strings is $90°$ and the string supporting the heavier sphere makes an angle α with the vertical, where $\tan \alpha = \frac{3}{4}$. Find (a) the tensions in the strings, (b) the angle of inclination to the horizontal of the line joining the centres of the spheres.

9. A uniform rod AB of length $4a$ and weight W is freely hinged at A. A second uniform rod CD of length $5a$ and weight $2W$ is freely hinged at C, which lies at a distance $4a\sqrt{3}$ from A in the same horizontal plane. The rods rest in equilibrium in a vertical plane with the rod CD in contact with the end B of the rod AB. If the rods are on the point of slipping when $BC = 4a$, find the coefficient of friction between the rods.

10. Two uniform circular cylinders rest in contact on a horizontal table. A third cylinder is supported by the first two. The cylinders are identical and their axes are horizontal and parallel. The coefficient of friction between any pair of cylinders and between the lower cylinders and the table is μ. Find the least value of μ for which equilibrium is possible.

11. A uniform rod OA of weight W and length $2a$ is pivoted smoothly to a fixed point at the end O. A light inextensible string, also of length $2a$, has one end attached to the end A of the rod, its other end being attached to a small heavy ring of weight $\frac{1}{2}W$ which is threaded on to a fixed rough straight horizontal wire passing through O. The system is in equilibrium with the string taut and the rod making an angle α with the downward vertical at O. By taking moments about O for the rod and ring

together, or otherwise, find the normal component R of the reaction exerted by the wire on the ring. Find also the frictional force F on the ring. The equilibrium is limiting when $\alpha = 60°$. Determine the coefficient of friction between the wire and the ring. (O&C)

12. Two uniform rods AB, AC, each of weight W and length $2a$, are smoothly jointed at A. The rods rest on a smooth circular cylinder of radius a with their plane perpendicular to the axis of the cylinder which is horizontal. When the rods are in equilibrium in a vertical plane with A vertically above the axis of the cylinder, angle $BAC = 2\theta$. Show that the force exerted by the cylinder on each rod is of magnitude $W \csc \theta$. Show also that $\sin^3 \theta = \cos \theta$. Hence show that there is only one such position of equilibrium. (O&C)

13.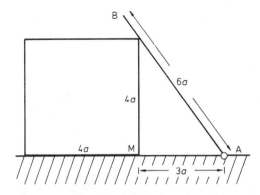

A uniform cube, of edge $4a$ and weight W, rests on a smooth horizontal surface (see diagram). A uniform smooth rod AB, of length $6a$ and weight w, has one end freely hinged to a point A of the surface. The rod rests against the mid-point of a horizontal edge of the top face of the cube. The rod is in a vertical plane through the centre of the cube. A light inelastic string of length $3a$ joins A to the mid-point M of the horizontal edge of the cube nearest to A. The system is in equilibrium. (i) Find the magnitude of the reaction between the rod and the cube. (ii) Find the magnitude of the reaction between the cube and the horizontal surface. (iii) Find the tension in the string AM. (iv) Show that $18w \leqslant 125W$. (C)

10.5 Light frameworks

The expression *light framework* is used to describe a system of rods whose weights are negligible compared with the other forces involved. It is also assumed that the rods are smoothly jointed together at their ends.

Let us consider the two resultant forces acting at the ends of a typical light rod AB in such a framework. If the rod is in equilibrium these forces must be equal and opposite. By taking moments about A and B we also find that both forces act along AB.

Forces on a rod in tension

Forces exerted by a rod in tension

Forces on a rod in thrust

Forces exerted by a rod in thrust

As shown in the diagrams above, a rod may either be in *tension* or in *thrust* i.e. under *compression*. It follows from Newton's third law that at each end of the rod, the force exerted by the rod on the joint is equal and opposite to the force exerted by the joint on the rod.

Elementary problems about light frameworks can be solved by considering the equilibrium of the external forces on the framework and the equilibrium of the forces at each joint. In general, unknown forces at joints are found by resolving in suitable directions. However, when dealing with three forces at a joint it is sometimes quicker to use a triangle of forces.

Whatever method is chosen, it is important to draw a large clear diagram showing the forces acting at each joint. Sometimes it is difficult to decide whether a particular rod is in tension or in thrust. In this case we may choose to indicate one type of stress in the diagram, but if calculation leads to a negative value for this stress, we deduce that it is of the other type.

Example 1

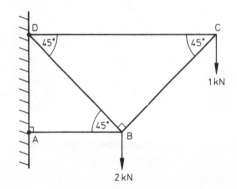

The diagram shows a framework of four smoothly jointed light rods. The framework is freely hinged at A and D to a vertical wall. Loads of 2 kN and 1 kN are hung from B and C respectively. Find the magnitudes of the reactions at A and B. Find also the stresses in the rods, stating whether they are tensions or thrusts.

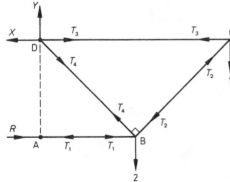

Let the stresses in the rods be thrusts T_1, T_2 and tensions T_3, T_4 as shown. Let the magnitude of the reaction at A be R and let the horizontal and vertical components of the reaction at D be X and Y respectively.

Since there are only two forces acting at A, the reaction R must be a horizontal force such that

$$R - T_1 = 0 \tag{1}$$

Consider now the forces on the whole framework.
Let $AB = AD = a$, then taking moments about D,

$$R \times a - 2 \times a - 1 \times 2a = 0 \qquad \therefore \quad R = 4$$

Hence the magnitude of the reaction at A is $4\,\mathrm{kN}$.
Resolving horizontally and vertically,

$$\leftarrow \qquad X - R = 0 \qquad\qquad \therefore \quad X = R = 4$$
$$\uparrow \qquad Y - 2 - 1 = 0 \qquad\qquad \therefore \quad Y = 3$$

Hence the magnitude of the reaction at D

$$= \sqrt{(X^2 + Y^2)}\,\mathrm{kN} = \sqrt{(4^2 + 3^2)}\,\mathrm{kN} = 5\,\mathrm{kN}$$

From (1), $T_1 = R = 4$.
Using the triangle of forces for the joint C,

$$T_2 = \sqrt{2}, \quad T_3 = 1.$$

Resolving the forces at B in the direction BD,

$$\nwarrow \quad T_4 - 2\cos 45° - T_1 \cos 45° = 0$$

$$\therefore \quad T_4 = 2 \times \frac{1}{\sqrt{2}} + 4 \times \frac{1}{\sqrt{2}} = 3\sqrt{2}$$

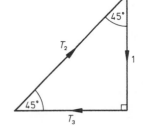

Hence the stresses in AB and BC are thrusts of magnitude $4\,\mathrm{kN}$ and $\sqrt{2}\,\mathrm{kN}$ respectively. The stresses in BD and CD are tensions of magnitude $3\sqrt{2}\,\mathrm{kN}$ and $1\,\mathrm{kN}$ respectively.

Exercise 10.5

In questions 1 to 8 each diagram shows a light framework consisting of smooth jointed rods. The large dots represent points at which the framework is smoothly hinged to a fixed point. External forces acting at other points are indicated by arrows and given in kilonewtons. Find the stresses in the rods, stating whether they are tensions or thrusts.

1.

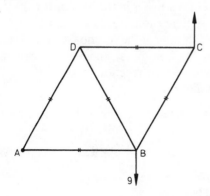

2.

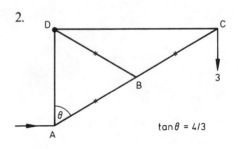

$\tan \theta = 4/3$

3.

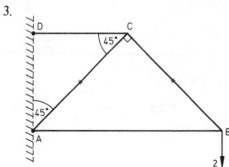

4.

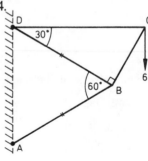

5.

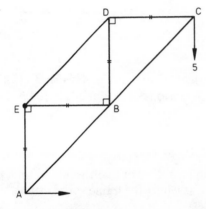

6.

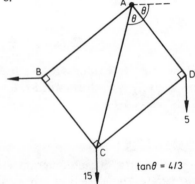

$\tan \theta = 4/3$

7.

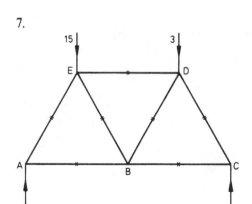

8.

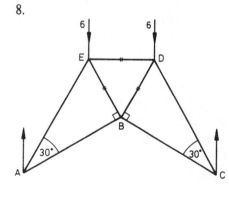

9.

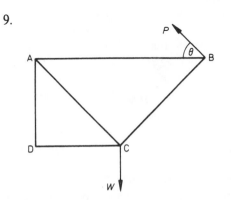

The diagram represents a framework of five smoothly jointed light rods with $AB = \sqrt{2}BC = \sqrt{2}CA = 2CD = 2DA$. The framework is freely hinged to a support at D. A weight W is hung from C and the framework is supported with CD horizontal by a force P at B making an angle θ with the horizontal.

If the magnitude of the stress in CA is twice the magnitude of the stress in BC, find P and the stresses in the rods, specifying whether they are tensions or thrusts. (O)

10.

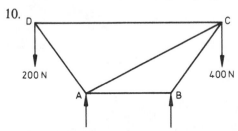

The diagram shows a smoothly jointed framework consisting of five light rigid rods with $AB = BC = AD = 5$ metres and $DC = 11$ metres. The framework is simply supported at A and B and is in equilibrium in a vertical plane with AB and DC horizontal and with loads of 400 N and 200 N at C and D respectively.
(i) Show that the magnitude of the force supporting the framework at B is 520 N.
(ii) Find the magnitude of the force acting in each member of the framework.
(iii) State which members of the framework are in tension. (AEB 1978)

Exercise 10.6 (miscellaneous)

[Take g as $10\,\mathrm{m\,s^{-2}}$.]

1. A uniform plank $ABCD$ of length $6a$ and weight W rests on two supports B and C; $AB = BC = CD = 2a$. A man of weight $4W$ wishes to stand on the plank at A, for

which purpose he places a counter-balancing weight Y at a point P between C and D at a distance x from D. Show that the least value of Y required is $7Wa/(4a - x)$. Show that, if the board is also to be in equilibrium when he is not standing on it, then the greatest value of Y that may be used is $Wa/(2a - x)$.   (JMB)

2.   A uniform lamina $ABCD$ is in the form of a trapezium in which $DC = AD = a$, $AB = 2a$ and $\angle BAD = \angle CDA = 90°$. When the lamina is freely suspended from a point E in BC the edge AB is vertical. Show that $BE:EC = 4:5$. Find the tangent of the angle which AB makes with the vertical when the lamina is freely suspended from B. The lamina is suspended by two vertical strings attached at C and D. Find the ratio of the tensions in the strings if CD is horizontal.   (L)

3.   Three equal uniform rods AB, BC, CA, each of weight w, are joined together to form a triangle ABC. A particle of weight W is attached to B and the system is suspended freely from the point A. In equilibrium the rod AB makes an angle θ with the vertical. Prove that $\tan \theta = \sqrt{3}w/(2W + 3w)$.   (O)

4.   A uniform thin sheet of cardboard of weight W is in the form of a square $ABCD$ of side $6a$. A cut is made along DO, where O is the point of intersection of the diagonals, and the triangular portion AOD is folded over along AO and stuck to the portion AOB with which it now coincides. Find the distances of the centre of gravity of the resulting object from AB and from BC and show that the centre of gravity lies on BD. If this object hangs freely from A, find the angle which BO makes with the horizontal. A particle of weight w is now attached to the object at D so that, in equilibrium, BO is horizontal. Find w.   (L)

5.   A uniform right circular solid cone of radius r and height h rests with its base on a rough plane which is initially horizontal. The inclination of the plane to the horizontal is gradually increased. Show that the cone will slide before it topples if the coefficient of friction between the plane and the cone is less than $4r/h$.   (O)

6.   If three non-parallel coplanar forces are in equilibrium, show that they must be concurrent.
    A uniform rod AB of length $2a$ and weight W has one end A in contact with a vertical wall and to the other end B is attached one end of a light string. The other end of the string is attached to the wall at C, the point at a height $2a$ vertically above A. The rod makes an angle α $(0° < \alpha < 90°)$ with the downward vertical. Show that equilibrium is impossible if the wall is smooth. If $\alpha = 60°$ and the rod is in equilibrium, show that the least possible value of the coefficient of friction between the rod and the wall is $1/\sqrt{3}$.   (L)

7.   A uniform rectangular lamina $ABCD$ of mass $1\,\text{kg}$ has $AB = 0.8\,\text{m}$ and $AD = 0.6\,\text{m}$. The lamina is smoothly pivoted at A. It is kept in equilibrium in a vertical plane with the diagonal AC horizontal and with B as the lowest point by a force P acting at right angles to CD. Find the magnitude of P and the magnitude and direction of the force exerted on the lamina by the pivot if (a) the force P acts through

the mid-point of CD, (b) the force P acts at C. Find also the magnitude and the line of action of P when the force exerted by the pivot acts in the direction BA. (L)

8. A uniform rod AB, of length $2l$ and weight W, is smoothly hinged to a vertical wall at A. It is held at rest in a horizontal position by a light inextensible string attached at B and to a point C which is vertically above and at a distance l from A. Calculate the tension in the string and show that the reaction at A is equal in magnitude to the tension. When a load of weight $4W$ is attached to the rod at a point D the horizontal and vertical components of the reaction at A are equal in magnitude. Find AD. (L)

9. A thin uniform rod AB of length $3\,$m and mass $5\,$kg is freely pivoted to a fixed point A. A light elastic string BC of modulus $30\,$N has one end attached to B and its other end C fixed to a point at the same level as A, where $AC = 5\,$m. When the system is in equilibrium $BC = 4\,$m. Calculate (a) the tension in the string. (b) the natural length of the string. (c) the resultant force, in magnitude and direction, exerted on the rod at A. (L)

10.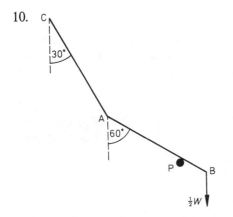

The diagram shows a uniform rod AB, of length $4c$ and weight W, resting on a rough fixed peg P, where $AP = 3c$. A particle of weight $\frac{1}{2}W$ hangs from B. One end of a light string is tied at A and the other end is tied at a fixed point C. The rod and the string are in the same vertical plane and are inclined at angles of $60°$ and $30°$ respectively to the vertical. (i) Show that the tension in the string is $\frac{1}{6}W\sqrt{3}$. (ii) Given that equilibrium is limiting, calculate the coefficient of friction between the peg and the rod. (iii) Given that $AC = 4c$ and that the string is elastic with modulus of elasticity $W\sqrt{3}$, calculate the natural length of the string. (AEB 1979)

11. A uniform square lamina $ABCD$ of weight W and side $2a$ rests in a vertical plane with the vertex A in contact with a rough horizontal plane. The lamina is kept in equilibrium by a force P acting at the vertex C in the direction of DC produced. Given that the height of the vertex D above the horizontal plane is $6a/5$, show that $P = W/10$. Find the coefficient of friction between the lamina and the plane if the lamina is in limiting equilibrium. (L)

12. A uniform rod AB, of weight W and length $2l$, rests in equilibrium with the end A on rough horizontal ground and with the end B in contact with a smooth vertical wall, which is perpendicular to the vertical plane containing the rod. If AB makes an angle α with the horizontal, where $\tan \alpha = 4/3$, find the least possible value of μ, the coefficient of friction between the rod and the ground, for equilibrium to be

preserved. If $\mu = \frac{1}{2}$, find the distance from A to the highest point of the rod at which a load of weight W can be attached without equilibrium being disturbed.   (L)

13. Prove that the position of the centre of gravity of a uniform solid hemisphere of radius a is distant $\frac{3}{8}a$ from the centre of its plane face.

A uniform solid hemisphere rests with its curved surface on a rough horizontal surface and also against a rough vertical surface. The coefficient of friction at both points of contact is $\frac{1}{4}$. If the hemisphere is just about to slip, show that its top surface is inclined at an angle of just under $52°$ to the horizontal.   (SU)

14. A uniform bar, of length $3a$ and mass m, rests in limiting equilibrium at an angle α to the horizontal with one end A on rough horizontal ground and the other end B against a smooth vertical wall. A horizontal force P is now applied to the bar at a point C, where $AC = a$. Find in terms of m, α and g, the value of P which will just cause the bar to slip towards the wall and the corresponding reaction between the bar and the wall.

15.

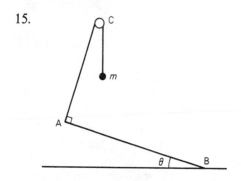

AB is a uniform rod of mass M. The end B rests on a rough horizontal table (coefficient of friction μ), and a light inextensible string is attached to the end A, passes over a smooth pulley at C and carries a mass m at its other end. The system rests in equilibrium with the string at right angles to AB. Find an expression for θ in terms of M and m and show that equilibrium is not possible

unless $2m < M$. Show also that $\quad \mu \geqslant \dfrac{m\sqrt{(M^2 - 4m^2)}}{M^2 - 2m^2}$.   (SU)

16. A hemisphere of radius a, whose curved surface is smooth, is fixed with its flat base on a rough horizontal table. A uniform rod AB of length $4a$ and weight W rests in equilibrium against the hemisphere, its point of contact with the hemisphere lying between A and B. The end A of the rod is in contact with the table and AB makes an acute angle θ with the horizontal. Prove that the frictional force F at A has magnitude $2W\sin^2 \theta$ and find the normal reaction R at A. If the coefficient of friction between the end A and the table is $\frac{1}{2}$, prove that $3\tan^2 \theta + 2\tan \theta - 1 \leqslant 0$ and deduce the maximum value of θ consistent with equilibrium.   (O&C)

17. $ABCD$ is a rectangular lamina, freely pivoted at a point X on AB. The length of AB is $2a$ and of BC is a. Forces $3W, 5W, 2W$ and $7W$ act along the sides AB, BC, DC and AD respectively in the directions indicated by the order of the letters. Find the position of X so that the lamina is in equilibrium and, in this case, determine the reaction of the pivot on the lamina in magnitude and direction. If, instead, the lamina is pivoted at a point Y on CD and is in equilibrium, deduce from your results the position of Y.   (O&C)

18. Explain, with the aid of a diagram, the meaning of the expression coefficient of friction.

A straight uniform rod AB of weight W rests in limiting equilibrium with the end A on horizontal ground and the end B against a vertical wall. The vertical plane containing AB is perpendicular to the wall. The coefficient of friction between the rod and the ground is 4/5. The coefficient of friction between the rod and the wall is 3/5. Given that the inclination of AB to the horizontal is α, calculate (i) the normal reactions at A and B in terms of W, (ii) the numerical value of $\tan \alpha$. (AEB 1980)

19. A uniform right circular heavy cylinder, of height h and radius a, rests with one plane face upon a rough horizontal plane. A gradually increasing horizontal force is applied to a point on the edge of the upper face, and the force passes through the axis of the cylinder. Show that the cylinder will slide before it topples if $\mu h < a$, where μ is the coefficient of friction between the cylinder and the horizontal plane. (O)

20. A uniform solid hemisphere of radius a has mass M. A concentric hemisphere of mass $M/8$ is removed. Show that the centre of mass of the remainder is at a distance $45a/112$ from the centre O of the plane base. A particle of mass M is attached to a point X on the outer edge of the plane base of the remainder. Find, relative to OX and the axis of symmetry of the hemisphere as axes, the coordinates of the centre of mass G of the combined solid (i.e. remainder together with attached mass). The combined solid is placed with its curved surface on a horizontal plane and rests in equilibrium. Find the tangent of the angle between the plane base of the solid and the horizontal. (C)

21. Prove by integration that the centre of mass of a uniform solid right circular cone of height h and base radius r is at a distance $\frac{3}{4}h$ from the vertex. Such a cone is joined to a uniform solid right circular cylinder, of the same material, with base radius r and height l, so that the plane base of the cone coincides with a plane face of the cylinder. Find the centre of mass of the solid thus formed. Show that, if $6l^2 \geqslant h^2$, this solid can rest in equilibrium on a horizontal plane, with the curved surface of the cylinder touching the plane. Given that $l = h$, show that the solid can rest in equilibrium with its conical surface touching the plane provided that $r \geqslant \frac{1}{4}h\sqrt{5}$. (JMB)

22. A toy consists of a solid hemisphere of radius a to which is glued a solid circular cylinder of radius a and height $2a$ so that the plane end of the hemisphere is in complete contact with a plane end of the cylinder. The cylinder is made of uniform material of density ρ, and the hemisphere is made of uniform material of density $k\rho$. The toy is designed so that if placed on a horizontal table with the hemisphere downwards and then tilted to one side, it will return to the vertical position. Show that $k > 8$. The toy is placed on a desk of slope α where $\sin \alpha = 1/8$, sufficiently rough to prevent slipping. It rests in equilibrium with the hemisphere in contact with the desk. Find an expression giving the (acute) angle β made by its axis of symmetry with the vertical. Hence deduce that $k \geqslant 13\frac{1}{2}$. (O&C)

23. Using a diagram, explain the meaning of the term angle of friction. A uniform straight pole AB of length 2·5 metres stands in limiting equilibrium with the end A on horizontal ground and the end B against a vertical wall. The vertical plane containing AB is perpendicular to the wall and A is at a distance 0·7 metres from the wall. The angles of friction between the pole and the ground and between the pole and the wall are equal. Show that the line of action of the resultant force exerted on the pole by the ground at A is perpendicular to the line of action of the resultant force exerted on the pole by the wall at B. Hence, or otherwise, show that the coefficient of friction at A and B is $1/7$. Given that the pole weighs 50 N, find the magnitude of the resultant reactions (i) between the pole and the ground, (ii) between the pole and the wall. (AEB 1978)

24. A uniform rod of weight W rests in contact with two parallel, horizontal, smooth pegs, passing over the higher peg and under the lower one. The lower end of the rod rests on a smooth horizontal plane. A force of magnitude P acts on the upper end of the rod in the direction of the rod and tending to move the rod upwards. The length of the rod is l, and its inclination to the horizontal is θ. If the upper and lower pegs are at distances a and b respectively from the lower end of the rod, prove that, so long as the rod remains in equilibrium, the reaction of the upper peg on the rod is $\dfrac{Wl\cos\theta - 2Pb\cot\theta}{2(a-b)}$. Given that $l > 2a$, determine which of the three forces exerted on the rod by the two pegs and the ground will first become zero as P is gradually increased from zero. (C)

25. A uniform rod AB, of length l and weight W, is smoothly hinged at A. The point C is vertically above A and is such that $AC = l$. An elastic string, of unstretched length $\frac{1}{2}l$, obeys Hooke's law and has modulus W. The ends of the string are attached to B and C so that the rod rests in equilibrium in an inclined position. Show that the tension in the string is $W/3$. Find the magnitude of the couple which when applied to the rod will maintain the system in equilibrium with $AB = BC$. (L)

26. A uniform rod AB of weight W and length $2a$ has the end A freely hinged to a fixed point. The other end B is freely hinged to a uniform rod BC of weight W and length $6a$. The ends A and C are joined by a light inelastic string whose length is such that AB is perpendicular to BC, and the system hangs in equilibrium. Show that AB is inclined at $45°$ to the vertical. Find the tension in AC and the horizontal and vertical components of the reaction on BC at B. (C)

27. Two uniform rods AB and BC of the same thickness and material, and of length 4 metres and 3 metres respectively, are freely hinged together and rest in a vertical plane with the ends A and C on a rough horizontal plane. The system is in limiting equilibrium when the angle ABC is $90°$. Determine how equilibrium will be broken when the angle ABC is slightly increased beyond $90°$ and show that the coefficient of friction between the rods and the ground is $84/163$. (W)

28.

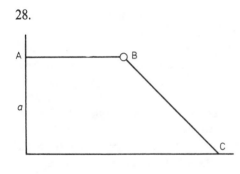

A uniform rod AB of length a and weight W is smoothly jointed at B to a uniform rod BC of length $a\sqrt{2}$ and also of weight W. The system is in equilibrium with C resting on a rough horizontal floor at a distance $2a$ from a rough vertical wall, A resting against the wall, and AB horizontal at a height a above the floor. The plane of the rods is perpendicular to the floor and the wall. (i) Find the frictional force exerted by the wall at A. (ii) Find the vertical and horizontal components of the force exerted on BC at C. (iii) Show that equilibrium is possible only if the coefficient of friction at C is at least $\frac{2}{3}$. (iv) Find the least value of the coefficient of friction at A for equilibrium to be possible. (JMB)

29. Three uniform straight rods, each of weight W, are smoothly jointed together to form an equilateral triangle ABC. The joint B is hinged to a fixed support and the system is free to rotate about B in a vertical plane. The system is held in equilibrium with BC horizontal and A uppermost by a horizontal light string which connects A with a fixed point. Show that the tension in the string is $W\sqrt{3}$ and find the magnitude and direction of the force exerted on the triangle by the support at B. Find the horizontal and vertical components of all the forces which are exerted on the rod AC, and indicate them clearly on your diagram. (JMB)

30. The diagram shows two parallel vertical walls at a distance $3a$ apart, with two

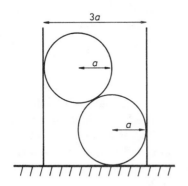

uniform smooth cylinders, each of radius a and weight W. The axes of the cylinders are horizontal and parallel to the walls. Each cylinder is in contact with the other and with one wall; the lower cylinder rests on horizontal ground. Find the magnitudes of the reactions between the two cylinders and between each cylinder and the corresponding wall. (C)

31. A uniform sphere of radius a and weight $W/\sqrt{3}$ rests on a rough horizontal table. A uniform rod AB of weight $2W$ and length $2a$ is freely hinged at A to a fixed point on the table and leans against the sphere so that the centre of the sphere and the rod lie in a vertical plane. The rod makes an angle of $60°$ with the horizontal. Show that the frictional force between the rod and the sphere is $\frac{1}{3}W$. The coefficient of friction at each point of contact is μ. What is the smallest value of μ which makes equilibrium possible? (O&C)

32.

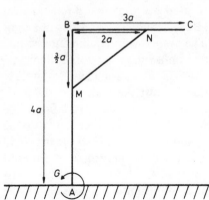

The diagram shows a uniform post AB, of length $4a$ and weight W, smoothly hinged to the ground at A. A horizontal uniform beam BC, of length $3a$ and weight W, is smoothly hinged to AB at B. The beam is supported by a light inelastic rod MN smoothly jointed to AB at M and to BC at N, where $BM = \frac{3}{2}a$ and $BN = 2a$. A weight $3W$ hangs from C, and the system is maintained in equilibrium, with AB vertical, by an external couple of magnitude G applied to AB, as shown.

Find (i) the thrust in the rod MN, (ii) the horizontal and vertical components of the forces on the post AB at A and at B, (iii) the value of G. (C)

33.

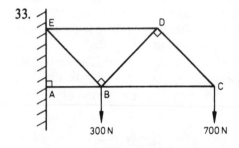

The diagram shows a framework $ABCDE$, consisting of 6 light rigid rods which are smoothly jointed. The framework is smoothly hinged to a vertical wall at A and E and the triangles ABE, BED and BCD are all right-angled and isosceles. When loads of $300\,\mathrm{N}$ and $700\,\mathrm{N}$ are hung from B and C respectively, the framework is in equilibrium in a vertical plane. (i) Explain why the reaction on the hinge at A is horizontal and find its magnitude. (ii) Find the magnitude and the direction of the reaction on the hinge at E. (iii) Find the magnitude of the force acting in each member of the framework and state which rods are in compression. (AEB 1978)

34.

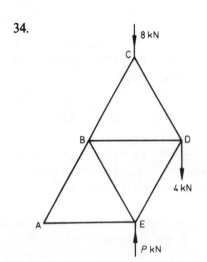

The diagram shows a framework of 7 light equal rods, smoothly jointed at their ends. It is freely hinged to a vertical wall at A. Forces of $8\,\mathrm{kN}$ and $4\,\mathrm{kN}$ are applied at C and D as shown. A force of size $P\,\mathrm{kN}$ is applied vertically upwards at E in order to keep the rod AE in a horizontal position. Calculate (i) the magnitude of P; (ii) the stresses in the rods, stating if they are in tension or under compression; (iii) the magnitude and direction of the reaction of the support at A on the frame. (SU)

11 Vector methods

11.1 Forces and their lines of action

In this chapter we consider the application of vector methods to systems of forces given in vector form, often in terms of unit vectors $\mathbf{i}$, $\mathbf{j}$ and $\mathbf{k}$.

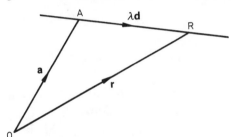

The diagram shows a straight line which passes through a fixed point A with position vector $\mathbf{a}$ and which is parallel to a given vector $\mathbf{d}$. Let $\mathbf{r}$ be the position vector of a point R on the line.

Since $\mathbf{AR}$ is parallel to $\mathbf{d}$, then, for some scalar λ,

$$\mathbf{AR} = \lambda\mathbf{d}$$
$$\therefore \quad \mathbf{r} - \mathbf{a} = \lambda\mathbf{d}$$
i.e. $$\mathbf{r} = \mathbf{a} + \lambda\mathbf{d}$$

Thus every point on the line has a position vector of the form $\mathbf{a} + \lambda\mathbf{d}$. Moreover, each real value of the parameter λ corresponds to some point on the line.

The equation $\mathbf{r} = \mathbf{a} + \lambda\mathbf{d}$ is called the *vector equation* of the line through A parallel to $\mathbf{d}$. The vector $\mathbf{d}$ is a *direction vector* of the line.

Example 1 Find the vector equation of the line which passes through the point with position vector $2\mathbf{i} - \mathbf{j} + 3\mathbf{k}$ and which is parallel to the vector $2\mathbf{j} - \mathbf{k}$.

The vector equation of the given line is

$$\mathbf{r} = 2\mathbf{i} - \mathbf{j} + 3\mathbf{k} + \lambda(2\mathbf{j} - \mathbf{k})$$
i.e. $$\mathbf{r} = 2\mathbf{i} + (2\lambda - 1)\mathbf{j} + (3 - \lambda)\mathbf{k}.$$

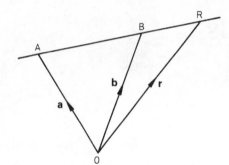

Consider now the line through two points A and B with position vectors **a** and **b** respectively. If a point R, with position vector **r**, lies on this line, then for some scalar λ,

$$AR = \lambda AB$$
$$\therefore \quad \mathbf{r} - \mathbf{a} = \lambda(\mathbf{b} - \mathbf{a})$$
$$\therefore \quad \mathbf{r} = \mathbf{a} + \lambda(\mathbf{b} - \mathbf{a}).$$

Hence the vector equation of the line through A and B is $\mathbf{r} = (1 - \lambda)\mathbf{a} + \lambda\mathbf{b}$.

Example 2   Find the vector equation of the straight line which passes through the points $A(1, 0, -2)$ and $B(2, 3, -1)$.

The position vectors of A and B are $\mathbf{i} - 2\mathbf{k}$ and $2\mathbf{i} + 3\mathbf{j} - \mathbf{k}$ respectively. Hence the vector equation of the line through A and B is

$$\mathbf{r} = (1 - \lambda)(\mathbf{i} - 2\mathbf{k}) + \lambda(2\mathbf{i} + 3\mathbf{j} - \mathbf{k})$$
i.e. $\mathbf{r} = (\lambda + 1)\mathbf{i} + 3\lambda\mathbf{j} + (\lambda - 2)\mathbf{k}.$

Example 3   A force **P** of magnitude 28 N acts at the point A with position vector $2\mathbf{j} + \mathbf{k}$ in the direction of the vector $3\mathbf{i} - 2\mathbf{j} + 6\mathbf{k}$. A second force **Q** of magnitude 27 N also acts at A, but in the direction of the vector $\mathbf{i} - 4\mathbf{j} - 8\mathbf{k}$. Find the magnitude of the resultant of the forces **P** and **Q**. Obtain a vector equation for its line of action.

$$|3\mathbf{i} - 2\mathbf{j} + 6\mathbf{k}| = \sqrt{\{3^2 + (-2)^2 + 6^2\}} = \sqrt{\{9 + 4 + 36\}} = 7$$
$$|\mathbf{i} - 4\mathbf{j} - 8\mathbf{k}| = \sqrt{\{1^2 + (-4)^2 + (-8)^2\}} = \sqrt{\{1 + 16 + 64\}} = 9$$

$\therefore$ the unit vectors in the directions of **P** and **Q** are $\frac{1}{7}(3\mathbf{i} - 2\mathbf{j} + 6\mathbf{k})$ and $\frac{1}{9}(\mathbf{i} - 4\mathbf{j} - 8\mathbf{k})$ respectively.

Thus $\mathbf{P} = 28 \times \frac{1}{7}(3\mathbf{i} - 2\mathbf{j} + 6\mathbf{k}) = 12\mathbf{i} - 8\mathbf{j} + 24\mathbf{k}$
and $\mathbf{Q} = 27 \times \frac{1}{9}(\mathbf{i} - 4\mathbf{j} - 8\mathbf{k}) = 3\mathbf{i} - 12\mathbf{j} - 24\mathbf{k}$
$\therefore$ $\mathbf{P} + \mathbf{Q} = 15\mathbf{i} - 20\mathbf{j} = 5(3\mathbf{i} - 4\mathbf{j})$
$\therefore$ $|\mathbf{P} + \mathbf{Q}| = 5\sqrt{\{3^2 + (-4)^2\}} = 5\sqrt{\{9 + 16\}} = 25$

Hence the resultant of **P** and **Q** acts in the direction of the vector $3\mathbf{i} - 4\mathbf{j}$ and has magnitude 25 N.
Since **P** and **Q** act at A, their resultant must also act at A. Thus a vector equation for its line of action is

$$\mathbf{r} = 2\mathbf{j} + \mathbf{k} + \lambda(3\mathbf{i} - 4\mathbf{j})$$
i.e. $\mathbf{r} = 3\lambda\mathbf{i} + (2 - 4\lambda)\mathbf{j} + \mathbf{k}.$

The approach of Example 3 can also be used to find the magnitude and direction of the resultant of a set of coplanar forces with different points of application. However, to find the line of action of the resultant we must use the principle of moments introduction in §9.1.

[Note that unless otherwise stated we will assume that vector quantities are measured in the appropriate SI units.]

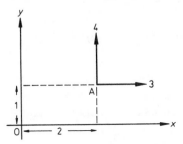

To illustrate how the moments of individual forces are calculated, we suppose that a force $\mathbf{F} = 3\mathbf{i} + 4\mathbf{j}$ acts at the point A with position vector $2\mathbf{i} + \mathbf{j}$.

Taking anti-clockwise moments as positive, the moment of $\mathbf{F}$ about O

$$= \text{(moment about } O \text{ of the force } 3\mathbf{i}) + \text{(moment about } O \text{ of the force } 4\mathbf{j})$$
$$= -(3 \times 1) + (4 \times 2)\,\mathrm{N\,m} = 5\,\mathrm{N\,m}.$$

Example 4   Coplanar forces $\mathbf{F}_1 = 5\mathbf{i} + 2\mathbf{j}$, $\mathbf{F}_2 = 4\mathbf{i} + 4\mathbf{j}$ and $\mathbf{F}_3 = 3\mathbf{i} - \mathbf{j}$ act at points A_1, A_2 and A_3 with position vectors $\mathbf{i} - 3\mathbf{j}, 4\mathbf{i} + 2\mathbf{j}$ and $-2\mathbf{i} + \mathbf{j}$ respectively. Find the magnitude of the resultant of these forces and the Cartesian equation of its line of action.

$$\mathbf{F}_1 + \mathbf{F}_2 + \mathbf{F}_3 = (5 + 4 + 3)\mathbf{i} + (2 + 4 - 1)\mathbf{j} = 12\mathbf{i} + 5\mathbf{j}$$
$$\therefore\ |\mathbf{F}_1 + \mathbf{F}_2 + \mathbf{F}_3| = \sqrt{(12^2 + 5^2)} = \sqrt{(144 + 25)} = 13.$$

Hence the magnitude of the resultant of the three forces is 13 N.

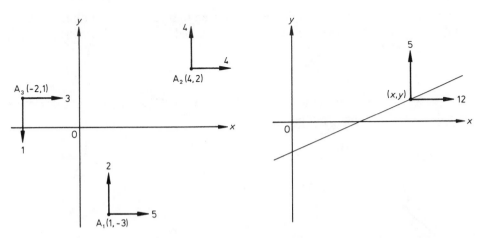

Let the point with position vector $x\mathbf{i} + y\mathbf{j}$ be some point on the line of action of the resultant, then the anti-clockwise moment of the resultant about O is $5x - 12y$.

Taking moments anti-clockwise about O for the original forces,

$$\text{moment of } \mathbf{F}_1 = 5 \times 3 + 2 \times 1 = 17$$
$$\text{moment of } \mathbf{F}_2 = -4 \times 2 + 4 \times 4 = 8$$
$$\text{moment of } \mathbf{F}_3 = -3 \times 1 + 1 \times 2 = -1$$

$\therefore$ using the principle of moments,

$$5x - 12y = 17 + 8 - 1$$

Hence the Cartesian equation of the line of action of the resultant is $5x - 12y = 24$.

Let us consider three points P, Q and R such that R divides PQ in the ratio $\mu:\lambda$. We will observe the convention that (i) if λ and μ have the same sign then R lies between P and Q, and (ii) if λ and μ have opposite signs then R does not lie between P and Q.

(i) 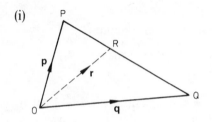   (ii)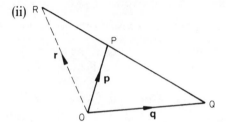

In both cases
$$\lambda\mathbf{PR} = \mu\mathbf{RQ}$$
$\therefore$
$$\lambda(\mathbf{OR} - \mathbf{OP}) = \mu(\mathbf{OQ} - \mathbf{OR})$$
$\therefore$
$$\lambda\mathbf{OR} - \lambda\mathbf{OP} = \mu\mathbf{OQ} - \mu\mathbf{OR}$$
Hence
$$(\lambda + \mu)\mathbf{OR} = \lambda\mathbf{OP} + \mu\mathbf{OQ}$$

This result is called the *ratio theorem* and may also be stated as follows:

> If two forces acting at a point O are represented in magnitude and direction by $\lambda\mathbf{OP}$ and $\mu\mathbf{OQ}$, then their resultant is represented by $(\lambda + \mu)\mathbf{OR}$, where R is the point which divides PQ in the ratio $\mu:\lambda$.

Example 5   Forces represented by $\mathbf{AB}$, $2\mathbf{AC}$ and $4\mathbf{BC}$ act along the sides of a triangle ABC. Find their resultant.

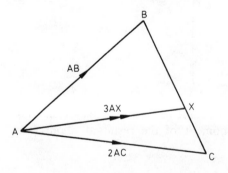   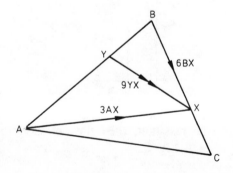

By the ratio theorem, $\mathbf{AB} + 2\mathbf{AC} = 3\mathbf{AX}$,
where X is the point which divides BC in the ratio $2:1$.

Since $BX:XC = 2:1$, we have $BC = \frac{3}{2}BX$,

$\therefore$ $\mathbf{AB} + 2\mathbf{AC} + 4\mathbf{BC} = 3\mathbf{AX} + 6\mathbf{BX}$.

By the ratio theorem, $3\mathbf{AX} + 6\mathbf{BX} = 9\mathbf{YX}$,

where Y is the point which divides AB in the ratio $6:3$ i.e. $2:1$. Hence the resultant of the three forces acts through X and is represented by $9\mathbf{YX}$, where X divides BC in the ratio $2:1$ and Y divides AB in the ratio $2:1$.

Exercise 11.1

1.   Forces of magnitude $10\,\mathrm{N}$ and $5\,\mathrm{N}$ act in the directions of the vectors $3\mathbf{i} - 4\mathbf{j}$ and $4\mathbf{i} + 3\mathbf{j}$ respectively. Express each force as a vector in terms of $\mathbf{i}$ and $\mathbf{j}$. Hence find the resultant of the forces as a vector.

2.   A force $\mathbf{R}$ of magnitude $4\sqrt{2}\,\mathrm{N}$ acting in the direction of the vector $\mathbf{i} - \mathbf{j}$ is the resultant of two forces $\mathbf{P}$ and $\mathbf{Q}$ which act in the directions of the vectors $\mathbf{i} + \mathbf{j}$ and $\mathbf{i} - 7\mathbf{j}$ respectively. Find the magnitudes of $\mathbf{P}$ and $\mathbf{Q}$.

3.   In a parallelogram $OABC$ the position vectors of A and B relative to O are $\mathbf{a} = 4\mathbf{i} + 3\mathbf{j}$ and $\mathbf{b} = 3\mathbf{j} + 3\mathbf{k}$ respectively. Forces of magnitude $20\,\mathrm{N}, 9\sqrt{2}\,\mathrm{N}$ and $5\,\mathrm{N}$ act along OA, OB and OC respectively. Find the magnitude of their resultant.

4.   In each of the following cases obtain a vector equation for the line of action of the resultant of forces $\mathbf{F}_1$, $\mathbf{F}_2$ and $\mathbf{F}_3$ acting at a point with position vector $\mathbf{a}$.
(a) $\mathbf{F}_1 = 2\mathbf{i} - 3\mathbf{j}, \mathbf{F}_2 = \mathbf{i} + 5\mathbf{j}, \mathbf{F}_3 = -\mathbf{i} + 2\mathbf{j}; \mathbf{a} = \mathbf{i} + \mathbf{j}$.
(b) $\mathbf{F}_1 = -3\mathbf{i} + 2\mathbf{k}, \mathbf{F}_2 = \mathbf{i} + \mathbf{j} + \mathbf{k}, \mathbf{F}_3 = 4\mathbf{j}; \mathbf{a} = 2\mathbf{j} - \mathbf{k}$.
(c) $\mathbf{F}_1 = \mathbf{i} - 5\mathbf{j} + 8\mathbf{k}, \mathbf{F}_2 = 2\mathbf{i} - \mathbf{j}, \mathbf{F}_3 = -3\mathbf{i} + \mathbf{k}; \mathbf{a} = 3\mathbf{i}$.

5.   Forces $\mathbf{P} = 3\mathbf{i} + \mathbf{j} - 2\mathbf{k}$ and $\mathbf{Q} = \mathbf{i} - \mathbf{j} + 3\mathbf{k}$ act through points with position vectors $2\mathbf{i} - \mathbf{j}$ and $9\mathbf{i} - \mathbf{k}$ respectively. Write down vector equations for the lines of action of $\mathbf{P}$ and $\mathbf{Q}$. Hence find the position vector of the point through which both forces act. Find also a vector equation for the line of action of the resultant of $\mathbf{P}$ and $\mathbf{Q}$.

6.   Forces $\mathbf{F}_1 = \mathbf{i} + 7\mathbf{j} + 4\mathbf{k}$ and $\mathbf{F}_2 = 5\mathbf{i} + 3\mathbf{j} - 4\mathbf{k}$ act through the origin O. A third force $\mathbf{F}_3 = \mathbf{i} - 4\mathbf{j} + 6\mathbf{k}$ acts through the point A with position vector $\mathbf{a} = 3\mathbf{i} + 5\mathbf{j}$. Show that the resultant of $\mathbf{F}_1$ and $\mathbf{F}_2$ also acts through A. Find the magnitude of the resultant of all three forces and obtain a vector equation for its line of action.

7.   Coplanar forces $\mathbf{F}_1 = \mathbf{i} - 2\mathbf{j}, \mathbf{F}_2 = 3\mathbf{i} + 4\mathbf{j}, \mathbf{F}_3 = -5\mathbf{i} + \mathbf{j}$ act at points A_1, A_2, A_3 with position vectors $4\mathbf{i} + 5\mathbf{j}, 3\mathbf{i} - 2\mathbf{j}, \mathbf{i} + 4\mathbf{j}$ respectively. Find the Cartesian equation of the line of action of the resultant of these forces.

8. Coplanar forces $F_1 = 6i + 2j, F_2 = -i + 7j, F_3 = 4i - 3j$ act at points $A_1, A_2,$ A_3 with position vectors $i - j, 4j, 2i + 3j$ respectively. Find the magnitude of the resultant and the tangent of the angle it makes with the vector i. Find also the Cartesian equation of its line of action.

9. The following sets of forces act along the edges of a triangle ABC. In each case find the resultant force, using a clear diagram to illustrate your answer.
(a) $2AB, 3AC, 6BC,$ (b) $CB, 3AB, 5CA,$
(c) $2BC, BA, 2AC,$ (d) $6AB, 4CA, 3CB.$

10. Three forces acting at a point P are represented by PA, PB and PC. Show that their resultant is given by $3PG$, where G is the centroid of triangle ABC.

11. Forces represented by $3AB, 2CB, 4CD$ and $6AD$ act along the sides of a square $ABCD$. Show that their resultant is $15XY$, where X divides AC in the ratio $2:3$ and Y divides BD in the ratio $2:1$.

12. Three forces represented by PQ, QR and RP act along the sides of a triangle PQR. Show that these forces are equivalent to a couple whose moment is represented by twice the area of the triangle.

11.2 Use of vectors in kinematics and dynamics

Suppose that a particle P moving with constant velocity v has position vector r_0 initially and position vector r at time t.

It follows that $$r = r_0 + tv.$$

This equation gives the position vector of P at any instant and can be taken as the vector equation of the straight line path of the particle.

The next example shows the use of such equations in a problem concerning the *relative motion* of two ships.

Example 1   At noon ships A and B have position vectors $3i + 2j$ and $i - 4j$ respectively and constant velocities $4i + 3j$ and $3i + 5j$ respectively, where distances are measured in kilometres and times in hours. Find vectors to represent (a) the velocity of A relative to B, (b) the displacement of A relative to B, t hours after noon. Find also the least distance between the ships.

(a) The velocity of A relative to B

$= $ (velocity of A) $-$ (velocity of B)
$= (4i + 3j) - (3i + 5j) = i - 2j.$

(b) The position vector of A after t hours is given by

$$r_A = 3i + 2j + t(4i + 3j)$$

The position vector of B after t hours is given by

$$\mathbf{r}_B = \mathbf{i} - 4\mathbf{j} + t(3\mathbf{i} + 5\mathbf{j})$$

∴   the displacement of A relative to B after t hours is

$$\mathbf{r}_A - \mathbf{r}_B = 2\mathbf{i} + 6\mathbf{j} + t(\mathbf{i} - 2\mathbf{j})$$

i.e. $\mathbf{r}_A - \mathbf{r}_B = (2 + t)\mathbf{i} + (6 - 2t)\mathbf{j}$.

The distance between the ships

$$
\begin{aligned}
= |\mathbf{r}_A - \mathbf{r}_B| &= \sqrt{\{(2 + t)^2 + (6 - 2t)^2\}} \\
&= \sqrt{\{4 + 4t + t^2 + 36 - 24t + 4t^2\}} \\
&= \sqrt{\{5t^2 - 20t + 40\}} \\
&= \sqrt{\{5(t - 2)^2 + 20\}}
\end{aligned}
$$

Since $(t - 2)^2$ is never negative, this expression takes its least value when $t = 2$. Hence the least distance between the ships is $\sqrt{20}$ km i.e. $5\sqrt{2}$ km.

[Note that the least distance can also be found by writing

$$f(t) = 5t^2 - 20t + 40$$

Differentiating, $f'(t) = 10t - 20, \quad f''(t) = 10$

∴ $f'(t) = 0 \iff 10t - 20 = 0 \iff t = 2$.

Since $f(2) = 20$ and $f''(2) > 0$, the function $f(t)$ has a minimum value of 20.]

In general, if a moving particle P has position vector $\mathbf{r}$ at time t, then its velocity $\mathbf{v}$ and acceleration $\mathbf{a}$ are given by

$$\mathbf{v} = \frac{d\mathbf{r}}{dt} \quad \text{and} \quad \mathbf{a} = \frac{d\mathbf{v}}{dt} = \frac{d^2\mathbf{r}}{dt^2}$$

or, using a dot to indicate differentiation with respect to time,

$$\mathbf{v} = \dot{\mathbf{r}} \quad \text{and} \quad \mathbf{a} = \ddot{\mathbf{r}}.$$

Example 2   A particle P has position vector $\mathbf{r}$ at time t and moves in a circle with constant angular velocity ω. The centre of the circle is the point C with position vector $\mathbf{c} = 2\mathbf{i} + 3\mathbf{j}$, and when $t = 0$, $\mathbf{CP} = 5\mathbf{i}$. Find an expression for $\mathbf{r}$ and hence for the velocity $\mathbf{v}$ of the particle at time t. Find also the time at which P first moves parallel to the vector $\sqrt{3}\mathbf{i} - \mathbf{j}$.

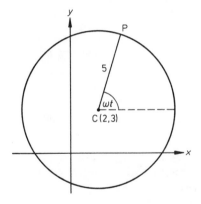

Since P moves on a circle with centre C, the vector $\mathbf{CP}$ has constant magnitude and rotates with constant angular velocity ω. Initially $\mathbf{CP} = 5\mathbf{i}$ and $|\mathbf{CP}| = |5\mathbf{i}| = 5$. Thus, at time t, the vector **CP** has magnitude 5 units and makes an angle ωt with the direction of **i**. It follows that

$$\mathbf{CP} = 5\cos\omega t\mathbf{i} + 5\sin\omega t\mathbf{j}$$
$$\therefore \quad \mathbf{r} - \mathbf{c} = 5\cos\omega t\mathbf{i} + 5\sin\omega t\mathbf{j}$$
$$\therefore \quad \mathbf{r} = 2\mathbf{i} + 3\mathbf{j} + 5\cos\omega t\mathbf{i} + 5\sin\omega t\mathbf{j}$$

Differentiating with respect to t,

$$\mathbf{v} = \dot{\mathbf{r}} = -5\omega\sin\omega t\mathbf{i} + 5\omega\cos\omega t\mathbf{j}.$$

Thus when P is moving parallel to the vector $\sqrt{3}\mathbf{i} - \mathbf{j}$ there is a scalar λ such that

$$-5\omega\sin\omega t\mathbf{i} + 5\omega\cos\omega t\mathbf{j} = \lambda(\sqrt{3}\mathbf{i} - \mathbf{j})$$

i.e. $\quad -5\omega\sin\omega t = \lambda\sqrt{3}$ and $\quad 5\omega\cos\omega t = -\lambda$

$$\therefore \quad \tan\omega t = \frac{\sin\omega t}{\cos\omega t} = \sqrt{3}$$

Hence P first moves parallel to the vector $\sqrt{3}\mathbf{i} - \mathbf{j}$ when $\omega t = \pi/3$ i.e. when $t = \pi/3\omega$.

[Note that at this instant P is not moving in the direction of the vector $\sqrt{3}\mathbf{i} - \mathbf{j}$, but in the opposite direction.]

In problems concerning the forces on moving objects *Newton's second law* is useful. It states that if a particle of mass m moves under the action of a force **F** with acceleration **a**, then

$$\mathbf{F} = m\mathbf{a}.$$

Example 3   A particle of mass 3 kg moves so that its position vector after t seconds is $\mathbf{r} = 8t\mathbf{i} - 5\mathbf{j} + 2t^3\mathbf{k}$. Find (a) the speed of the particle when $t = 1$, (b) the force acting on the particle when $t = 3$.

Let **v** and **a** be the velocity and acceleration of the particle after t seconds, then

$$\mathbf{v} = \dot{\mathbf{r}} = 8\mathbf{i} + 6t^2\mathbf{k}$$
and $\quad \mathbf{a} = \ddot{\mathbf{r}} = 12t\mathbf{k}.$

(a) When $t = 1$, $\mathbf{v} = 8\mathbf{i} + 6\mathbf{k}$

$$\therefore \quad v = |8\mathbf{i} + 6\mathbf{k}| = \sqrt{(8^2 + 6^2)} = 10.$$

Hence, when $t = 1$, the speed of the particle is $10\,\mathrm{m\,s^{-1}}$.

(b) Let **F** be the force on the particle after t seconds, then by Newton's second law,

$$\mathbf{F} = 3\mathbf{a}.$$

When $t = 3$, $\mathbf{a} = 36\mathbf{k}$ $\qquad \therefore \quad \mathbf{F} = 108\mathbf{k}.$

Hence, when $t = 3$, the force acting on the particle is $108\mathbf{k}$ (in newtons).

Example 4   A particle of unit mass is acted upon at time t by a force **F**, where $\mathbf{F} = 4\mathbf{i} - 6t\mathbf{j}$. At time $t = 0$ the particle is at the point with position vector $\mathbf{i} + \mathbf{j}$ and its velocity is $5\mathbf{i}$. Find the position vector of the particle at time $t = 2$.

Let **r**, **v** and **a** be the position vector, velocity and acceleration of the particle at time t.

By Newton's second law, $\quad \mathbf{F} = m\mathbf{a}$.

Since the particle has unit mass, $\quad \mathbf{F} = \mathbf{a}$.

$$\therefore \qquad \mathbf{a} = \frac{d\mathbf{v}}{dt} = 4\mathbf{i} - 6t\mathbf{j}$$

Integrating, $\qquad \mathbf{v} = 4t\mathbf{i} - 3t^2\mathbf{j} + \mathbf{c},$

where **c** is a constant vector.

When $t = 0$, $\mathbf{v} = 5\mathbf{i},$ $\qquad \therefore \quad \mathbf{c} = 5\mathbf{i}$

$$\therefore \qquad \mathbf{v} = \frac{d\mathbf{r}}{dt} = (4t + 5)\mathbf{i} - 3t^2\mathbf{j}$$

Integrating, $\qquad \mathbf{r} = (2t^2 + 5t)\mathbf{i} - t^3\mathbf{j} + \mathbf{d},$

where **d** is a constant vector.

When $t = 0$, $\mathbf{r} = \mathbf{i} + \mathbf{j},$ $\qquad \therefore \quad \mathbf{d} = \mathbf{i} + \mathbf{j}$

$\therefore \quad \mathbf{r} = (2t^2 + 5t + 1)\mathbf{i} + (1 - t^3)\mathbf{j}$

Hence, when $t = 2$, the position vector of the particle is

$$\mathbf{r} = (8 + 10 + 1)\mathbf{i} + (1 - 8)\mathbf{j} = 19\mathbf{i} - 7\mathbf{j}.$$

Exercise 11.2

1. Particles A and B are moving with constant velocities $5\mathbf{i} + 2\mathbf{j}$ and $2\mathbf{i} + \mathbf{j}$ respectively. Initially the particle A has position vector $3\mathbf{i} + 4\mathbf{j}$ and the particle B has position vector $5\mathbf{i} + 8\mathbf{j}$. Write down expressions for $\mathbf{r}_A$ and $\mathbf{r}_B$, the position vectors of the particles at time t. Find the vector **AB** at time t. Hence find the minimum distance between the particles.

2. Particles P and Q are moving with constant velocities $3\mathbf{i} - 2\mathbf{j}$ and $-\mathbf{i} + 4\mathbf{j}$ respectively. Initially the particle P has position vector $\mathbf{i} + 5\mathbf{j}$ and the particle Q has position vector $3\mathbf{i} + 2\mathbf{j}$. Find the velocity of P relative to Q and the displacement of P relative to Q at time t. Show that the particles collide and state the value of t when the collision occurs.

3. At noon ships A and B have position vectors $10\mathbf{i} + 3\mathbf{j}$ and $12\mathbf{i} - 15\mathbf{j}$ respectively. Both ships move with constant velocity, the velocity of A being $3\mathbf{i} + 8\mathbf{j}$ and the velocity of B relative to A being $-5\mathbf{i} + 4\mathbf{j}$. The unit of distance is the kilometre and the unit of time is the hour. Find an expression for the vector **AB**, t hours after noon. Hence find the shortest distance between the ships. Find also the position vectors of the ships A and B when they are closest together.

4. A particle P is moving with constant angular velocity ω on a circle of radius 8 units, with centre at the origin. Given that initially P has position vector $8\mathbf{i}$, find its position vector **r** at time t. Hence show that $\ddot{\mathbf{r}} = -\omega^2\mathbf{r}$.

5. A particle P moves so that its position vector at time t is given by $\mathbf{r} = \mathbf{i} - 2\mathbf{j} + 3(\mathbf{i}\sin 2t + \mathbf{j}\cos 2t)$. Show that P is moving on a circle, stating the position vector of the centre of the circle and its radius. Find also the speed at which P is moving.

6. Two particles A and B are moving such that, at time t, their position vectors are $\mathbf{r}_A = 3(1 + \cos t)\mathbf{i} + (2\sin t)\mathbf{j}$ and $\mathbf{r}_B = (5 - 6t)\mathbf{i} + (3 + 4t)\mathbf{j}$. Find the value of t when the particles are first moving (a) in the same direction, (b) in opposite directions.

7.   The position vector of a particle P at time t is $\mathbf{r} = (1 - t^2)\mathbf{i} + (3t - 5t^2)\mathbf{j}$. Find the time at which P is moving (a) directly towards the origin, (b) directly away from the origin.

8.   A particle of mass m moves so that its position vector at time t is $\mathbf{r}$. Find its velocity $\mathbf{v}$ and the force $\mathbf{F}$ acting on it, given that
(a) $\mathbf{r} = 4t^2\mathbf{i} + (3t^3 - 2t)\mathbf{j}$,   (b) $\mathbf{r} = 5\mathbf{i} - 2t^3\mathbf{j} + (t^2 - 1)\mathbf{k}$,
(c) $\mathbf{r} = (2t - t^2)\mathbf{i} + (3\sin 2t)\mathbf{j}$,   (d) $\mathbf{r} = (te^{-t})\mathbf{i} - 2t\mathbf{j}$.

9.   A particle of mass $5\,\mathrm{kg}$ moves so that its position vector after t seconds is $\mathbf{r} = (\cos 2t)\mathbf{i} + (4\sin 2t + 3)\mathbf{j}$. Find (a) the speed of the particle when $t = \pi/3$, (b) the force acting on the particle when $t = \pi/2$.

10. A particle of mass $2\,\mathrm{kg}$ starts from rest at the origin and moves under the action of the force $\mathbf{F}$, where $\mathbf{F} = 8\mathbf{i} + 20\mathbf{j}$. Find the velocity and the position vector of the particle after 3 seconds.

11. A particle of unit mass starts from rest at the point with position vector $2\mathbf{i} - 3\mathbf{j}$. At time t the force acting on the particle is $12t\mathbf{i} - 16\mathbf{j}$. Find the speed of the particle and its position vector at time $t = 2$.

12. A particle of mass $3\,\mathrm{kg}$ is acted upon at time t by a force $\mathbf{F}$, where $\mathbf{F} = 6\mathbf{i} - 36t^2\mathbf{j} + 54t\mathbf{k}$. At time $t = 0$ the particle is at the point with position vector $\mathbf{i} - 5\mathbf{j} - \mathbf{k}$ and its velocity is $3(\mathbf{i} + \mathbf{j})$. Find the position vector of the particle at time $t = 1$.

13. A particle of mass $2\,\mathrm{kg}$ moves from rest at the origin under the action of two forces. One force $\mathbf{P}$ has magnitude $22\,\mathrm{N}$ and acts in the direction of the vector $2\mathbf{i} - 6\mathbf{j} + 9\mathbf{k}$. The other force $\mathbf{Q}$ has magnitude $30\,\mathrm{N}$ and acts in the direction of the vector $4\mathbf{j} - 3\mathbf{k}$. Find the acceleration of the particle and the distance it travels in the first 3 seconds of its motion.

14. A particle P is projected vertically upwards from a point O with a speed of $16\,\mathrm{m\,s^{-1}}$. At the same instant a second particle Q is projected horizontally from a point A, $25\,\mathrm{m}$ vertically above O, with speed $12\,\mathrm{m\,s^{-1}}$. Using $\mathbf{i}$ and $\mathbf{j}$ as unit vectors in the horizontal and upward vertical directions respectively, find expressions for the position vectors of P and Q with respect to O at time t after projection. Hence find the least distance between the particles.

[Take g as $10\,\mathrm{m\,s^{-2}}$.]

11.3 Scalar product and its applications

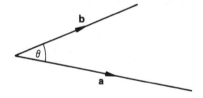

The *scalar product* (or dot product) of two vectors **a** and **b** is defined as the scalar $ab\cos\theta$, where θ is the angle between **a** and **b**.

The scalar product is denoted by **a.b**, which is read "**a** dot **b**".

Thus
$$\mathbf{a.b} = ab\cos\theta$$

The scalar product **a.a** is sometimes written as $\mathbf{a}^2$.

[Note that although a product of three real numbers a, b, c can be evaluated by writing $abc = (ab)c$, it is not possible to define a scalar product of three vectors in a similar way. Since **a.b** is a scalar, the expressions $(\mathbf{a.b}).\mathbf{c}$ and $\mathbf{a.b.c}$ are meaningless. Similarly, since **a.a** is a scalar, the expression $\mathbf{a}^3$ cannot be defined as $(\mathbf{a.a}).\mathbf{a}$.]

The definition of the scalar product gives rise to various useful properties.

(4) For any vector **a**, $\mathbf{a.a} = a^2\cos 0° = a^2$.

(5) If non-zero vectors **a** and **b** are perpendicular, then

$$\mathbf{a.b} = ab\cos 90° = 0.$$

Conversely, if non-zero vectors **a** and **b** are such that $\mathbf{a.b} = 0$, then **a** is perpendicular to **b**.

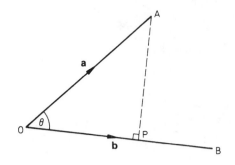

The diagram shows two vectors **a** and **b** represented by line segments $\overrightarrow{OA}$ and $\overrightarrow{OB}$ respectively. If the vector **a** is resolved along and perpendicular to **b**, then its component in the direction of **b** is $a\cos\theta$.

Thus the component of **a** in the direction of **b** is $\dfrac{\mathbf{a.b}}{b}$ or $\mathbf{a}.\hat{\mathbf{b}}$, where $\hat{\mathbf{b}}$ is the unit vector in the direction of **b**.

In geometrical work the quantity $\mathbf{a}.\hat{\mathbf{b}}$ is called the *projection* of **a** on **b**. In the diagram the length of this projection is represented by the distance OP.

Example 1   The points A and B have position vectors $\mathbf{a}$ and $\mathbf{b}$ with respect to an origin O. Show that the area of triangle OAB is given by $\frac{1}{2}\sqrt{\{a^2b^2 - (\mathbf{a}.\mathbf{b})^2\}}$.

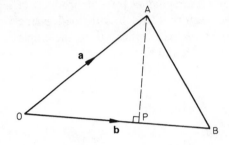

The projection of $\mathbf{a}$ on $\mathbf{b}$ is

$$(\mathbf{a}.\mathbf{b})/b,$$

$\therefore$ if P is the foot of the perpendicular from A to OB,

$$OP^2 = (\mathbf{a}.\mathbf{b})^2/b^2$$

Using Pythagoras' theorem in $\triangle OAP$, $OP^2 + AP^2 = OA^2$

$$\therefore \quad AP^2 = OA^2 - OP^2 = a^2 - \frac{(\mathbf{a}.\mathbf{b})^2}{b^2}$$

Hence the area of $\triangle OAB = \frac{1}{2} \times OB \times AP$

$$= \frac{1}{2}\sqrt{\left\{b^2 \times \left(a^2 - \frac{(\mathbf{a}.\mathbf{b})^2}{b^2}\right)\right\}} = \frac{1}{2}\sqrt{\{a^2b^2 - (\mathbf{a}.\mathbf{b})^2\}}.$$

When considering the unit vectors $\mathbf{i}, \mathbf{j}$ and $\mathbf{k}$ the definition of scalar product leads to the results

$$\mathbf{i}.\mathbf{i} = \mathbf{j}.\mathbf{j} = \mathbf{k}.\mathbf{k} = 1, \quad \mathbf{i}.\mathbf{j} = \mathbf{j}.\mathbf{k} = \mathbf{k}.\mathbf{i} = 0$$

Thus for vectors $\mathbf{a} = a_1\mathbf{i} + a_2\mathbf{j} + a_3\mathbf{k}$ and $\mathbf{b} = b_1\mathbf{i} + b_2\mathbf{j} + b_3\mathbf{k}$,

$$\begin{aligned}
\mathbf{a}.\mathbf{b} &= (a_1\mathbf{i} + a_2\mathbf{j} + a_3\mathbf{k}).(b_1\mathbf{i} + b_2\mathbf{j} + b_3\mathbf{k}) \\
&= a_1b_1\mathbf{i}.\mathbf{i} + a_1b_2\mathbf{i}.\mathbf{j} + a_1b_3\mathbf{i}.\mathbf{k} \\
&\quad + a_2b_1\mathbf{j}.\mathbf{i} + a_2b_2\mathbf{j}.\mathbf{j} + a_2b_3\mathbf{j}.\mathbf{k} \\
&\quad + a_3b_1\mathbf{k}.\mathbf{i} + a_3b_2\mathbf{k}.\mathbf{j} + a_3b_3\mathbf{k}.\mathbf{k}
\end{aligned}$$

$\therefore$

$$\boxed{\mathbf{a}.\mathbf{b} = a_1b_1 + a_2b_2 + a_3b_3}$$

Example 2   Find the component of the force $\mathbf{F} = 2\mathbf{i} + 13\mathbf{j} - 8\mathbf{k}$ in the direction of the vector $\mathbf{d} = 2\mathbf{i} - 6\mathbf{j} + 3\mathbf{k}$. Hence resolve $\mathbf{F}$ into component forces parallel and perpendicular to $\mathbf{d}$.

Let $\hat{\mathbf{d}}$ be the unit vector in the direction of $\mathbf{d}$.

$$d = |2\mathbf{i} - 6\mathbf{j} + 3\mathbf{k}| = \sqrt{\{2^2 + (-6)^2 + 3^2\}} = \sqrt{\{4 + 36 + 9\}} = 7$$

$$\therefore \quad \hat{\mathbf{d}} = \frac{\mathbf{d}}{d} = \tfrac{2}{7}\mathbf{i} - \tfrac{6}{7}\mathbf{j} + \tfrac{3}{7}\mathbf{k}$$

Hence the component of $\mathbf{F}$ in the direction of $\mathbf{d}$

$$= \mathbf{F}.\hat{\mathbf{d}} = (2\mathbf{i} + 13\mathbf{j} - 8\mathbf{k}).(\tfrac{2}{7}\mathbf{i} - \tfrac{6}{7}\mathbf{j} + \tfrac{3}{7}\mathbf{k})$$

$$= \tfrac{4}{7} - \tfrac{78}{7} - \tfrac{24}{7} = -\tfrac{98}{7} = -14.$$

Resolving **F** parallel and perpendicular to **d**, the component force parallel to **d**

$$= (\mathbf{F} \cdot \hat{\mathbf{d}})\hat{\mathbf{d}} = -14(\tfrac{2}{7}\mathbf{i} - \tfrac{6}{7}\mathbf{j} + \tfrac{3}{7}\mathbf{k}) = -4\mathbf{i} + 12\mathbf{j} - 6\mathbf{k}.$$

Thus the component force perpendicular to **d**

$$= (2\mathbf{i} + 13\mathbf{j} - 8\mathbf{k}) - (-4\mathbf{i} + 12\mathbf{j} - 6\mathbf{k}) = 6\mathbf{i} + \mathbf{j} - 2\mathbf{k}.$$

If the angle between **a** and **b** is θ, then $\mathbf{a} \cdot \mathbf{b} = ab \cos \theta$.

Thus
$$\cos \theta = \frac{\mathbf{a} \cdot \mathbf{b}}{ab} = \frac{a_1 b_1 + a_2 b_2 + a_3 b_3}{ab}$$

It follows that non-zero vectors **a** and **b** are perpendicular if and only if

$$a_1 b_1 + a_2 b_2 + a_3 b_3 = 0.$$

Example 3   Find the angle θ between the vectors $\mathbf{a} = 4\mathbf{i} + 5\mathbf{j} + 3\mathbf{k}$ and $\mathbf{b} = 3\mathbf{i} - 5\mathbf{j} - 4\mathbf{k}$.

$$\mathbf{a} \cdot \mathbf{b} = 4 \times 3 + 5 \times (-5) + 3 \times (-4) = 12 - 25 - 12 = -25$$
$$a = \sqrt{\{4^2 + 5^2 + 3^2\}} = \sqrt{\{16 + 25 + 9\}} = \sqrt{50}$$
$$b = \sqrt{\{3^2 + (-5)^2 + (-4)^2\}} = \sqrt{\{9 + 25 + 16\}} = \sqrt{50}$$
$$\therefore \quad \cos \theta = \frac{\mathbf{a} \cdot \mathbf{b}}{ab} = \frac{-25}{\sqrt{50} \times \sqrt{50}} = -\frac{25}{50} = -\frac{1}{2}$$

Hence the angle between the vectors is $120°$.

We next show that the *work done by a force* can be expressed as a scalar product. We recall that if the point of application of a constant force **F** moves a distance s in a direction which makes an angle θ with the direction of **F**, then the work done by the force is $Fs \cos \theta$.

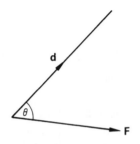

If we now suppose that the point of application of a constant force **F** is given a displacement **d**, where the angle between the vectors **F** and **d** is θ, then,

work done by $\mathbf{F} = Fd \cos \theta = \mathbf{F} \cdot \mathbf{d}$.

[We will assume that forces, displacements and work are measured in newtons, metres and joules respectively.]

Example 4   A constant force $\mathbf{F} = 3\mathbf{i} - 4\mathbf{j} - 2\mathbf{k}$ acts on a particle. Find the work done by $\mathbf{F}$ when the particle moves from the point with position vector $\mathbf{i} + 3\mathbf{j} - \mathbf{k}$ to the point with position vector $4\mathbf{i} + 2\mathbf{j} + 3\mathbf{k}$.

The displacement of the particle

$$= (4\mathbf{i} + 2\mathbf{j} + 2\mathbf{k}) - (\mathbf{i} + 3\mathbf{j} - \mathbf{k}) = 3\mathbf{i} - \mathbf{j} + 4\mathbf{k}$$

$\therefore$ the work done by $\mathbf{F}$

$$= (3\mathbf{i} - 4\mathbf{j} - 2\mathbf{k}).(3\mathbf{i} - \mathbf{j} + 4\mathbf{k}) = 9 + 4 - 8 = 5.$$

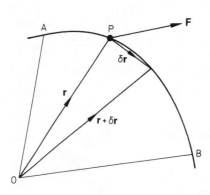

Consider now a variable force $\mathbf{F}$ acting on a particle P as it moves along a curve from a point A to a point B. If the path from A to B is regarded as a series of small displacements, then the work done by $\mathbf{F}$ in a typical displacement $\delta\mathbf{r}$ is approximately equal to $\mathbf{F}.\delta\mathbf{r}$.

$\therefore$ total work done by $\mathbf{F}$

$$\approx \sum_A^B \mathbf{F}.\delta\mathbf{r}$$

Letting $\delta\mathbf{r} \rightarrow 0$, we deduce that as the particle moves from A to B,

$$\text{the work done by } \mathbf{F} \text{ is} \int_A^B \mathbf{F}.d\mathbf{r} \tag{1}$$

If $\mathbf{F}$ and $\mathbf{r}$ are given as functions of the time t, then we write

$$\int_A^B \mathbf{F}.d\mathbf{r} = \int_{t_1}^{t_2} \mathbf{F}.\frac{d\mathbf{r}}{dt} dt = \int_{t_1}^{t_2} \mathbf{F}.\mathbf{v}\, dt \tag{2}$$

where t_1 and t_2 are the times at which the particle passes through A and B respectively.

Example 5   A particle moves along a curve so that its position vector at time t is given by $\mathbf{r} = t^3\mathbf{i} + 2t\mathbf{j}$. If one of the forces acting on the particle is a force $\mathbf{F}$, where $\mathbf{F} = 2\mathbf{i} - t\mathbf{j}$ at time t, find the work done by $\mathbf{F}$ in the interval from $t = 0$ to $t = 3$.

$$\mathbf{r} = t^3\mathbf{i} + 2t\mathbf{j} \Rightarrow \frac{d\mathbf{r}}{dt} = 3t^2\mathbf{i} + 2\mathbf{j}$$

$\therefore$ the work done by **F** from $t = 0$ to $t = 3$

$$= \int_0^3 \mathbf{F} . \frac{d\mathbf{r}}{dt} \, dt$$

$$= \int_0^3 (2\mathbf{i} - t\mathbf{j}) . (3t^2\mathbf{i} + 2\mathbf{j}) \, dt$$

$$= \int_0^3 (6t^2 - 2t) \, dt$$

$$= \left[2t^3 - t^2 \right]_0^3 = 54 - 9 = 45.$$

If a particle of mass m is moving with velocity **v** at time t, then its *kinetic energy* at that instant is $\frac{1}{2}mv^2$. We can establish the relationship between work and kinetic energy by considering the motion of this particle along a curved path AB. We will assume that the particle passes through A at time t_1 with velocity $\mathbf{v}_1$ and through B at time t_2 with velocity $\mathbf{v}_2$. If **F** is the resultant force acting on the particle at time t and W is the work done by **F** in the interval $t_1 \leqslant t \leqslant t_2$, then using our earlier results (1) and (2),

$$W = \int_A^B \mathbf{F} . d\mathbf{r} = \int_{t_1}^{t_2} \mathbf{F} . \mathbf{v} \, dt.$$

Using Newton's second law, $\mathbf{F} = m\mathbf{a} = m\dfrac{d\mathbf{v}}{dt}$

$\therefore$

$$W = \int_{t_1}^{t_2} m \frac{d\mathbf{v}}{dt} . \mathbf{v} \, dt$$

But, using the product rule proved in Exercise 7.5 question 25,

$$\frac{d}{dt}(v^2) = \frac{d}{dt}(\mathbf{v} . \mathbf{v}) = \mathbf{v} . \frac{d\mathbf{v}}{dt} + \frac{d\mathbf{v}}{dt} . \mathbf{v} = 2\frac{d\mathbf{v}}{dt} . \mathbf{v}$$

$\therefore$

$$\int \frac{d\mathbf{v}}{dt} . \mathbf{v} \, dt = \tfrac{1}{2}v^2 + \text{constant}.$$

Hence

$$W = \left[\tfrac{1}{2}mv^2 \right]_{t_1}^{t_2} = \tfrac{1}{2}mv_2^2 - \tfrac{1}{2}mv_1^2$$

Thus

> work done by **F** = K.E. at B − K.E. at A

Example 6   A particle of mass $10 \, \text{kg}$ moves under the action of a force **F**, so that its position vector after t seconds is given by $\mathbf{r} = 3t\mathbf{i} - \mathbf{j} + t^2\mathbf{k}$. Find the work done by **F** in the interval $1 \leqslant t \leqslant 5$.

$$\mathbf{r} = 3t\mathbf{i} - \mathbf{j} + t^2\mathbf{k} \quad \Rightarrow \quad \mathbf{v} = \frac{d\mathbf{r}}{dt} = 3\mathbf{i} + 2t\mathbf{k}$$

$$\Rightarrow \quad v^2 = 3^2 + (2t)^2 = 9 + 4t^2$$

$\therefore$ when $t = 1$, $v^2 = 13$ and when $t = 5$, $v^2 = 109$.

Work done by $\mathbf{F}$ = (K.E. when $t = 5$) − (K.E. when $t = 1$)

$= \frac{1}{2} \times 10 \times 109 - \frac{1}{2} \times 10 \times 13 \, \mathrm{J}$

$= 480 \, \mathrm{J}.$

The *power* of a force is the rate at which it does work. Let us suppose that at time t a force $\mathbf{F}$ acts at a point with position vector $\mathbf{r}$. If the point of application of $\mathbf{F}$ is given a displacement $\delta \mathbf{r}$ in a small interval of time δt, then the work done is approximately $\mathbf{F} . \delta \mathbf{r}$ and the average rate of working is $(\mathbf{F} . \delta \mathbf{r})/\delta t$.

∴   the power of the force $\mathbf{F}$ at time t

$$= \lim_{\delta t \to 0} \frac{\mathbf{F} . \delta \mathbf{r}}{\delta t} = \lim_{\delta t \to 0} \mathbf{F} . \frac{\delta \mathbf{r}}{\delta t} = \mathbf{F} . \frac{d\mathbf{r}}{dt}.$$

Hence if the point of application of a force $\mathbf{F}$ is moving with velocity $\mathbf{v}$, then

> the power of $\mathbf{F}$ is $\mathbf{F} . \mathbf{v}$.

Example 7   At time t a particle of unit mass is moving with velocity $\mathbf{v}$ under the action of a force $\mathbf{F} = 4t\mathbf{i} + 3\mathbf{k}$. Given that when $t = 0$, $\mathbf{v} = \mathbf{i} + 2\mathbf{j}$, find an expression for the velocity $\mathbf{v}$ at time t. Hence find an expression for the power of $\mathbf{F}$ at time t.

By Newton's second law, $\mathbf{F} = m\mathbf{a}$.

Since $\mathbf{F} = 4t\mathbf{i} + 3\mathbf{k}$, $m = 1$ and $\mathbf{a} = \dfrac{d\mathbf{v}}{dt}$,

we have $\dfrac{d\mathbf{v}}{dt} = 4t\mathbf{i} + 3\mathbf{k},$

Integrating, $\mathbf{v} = 2t^2\mathbf{i} + 3t\mathbf{k} + \mathbf{c},$

where $\mathbf{c}$ is a constant vector.

But when $t = 0$, $\mathbf{v} = \mathbf{i} + 2\mathbf{j}$ ∴ $\mathbf{c} = \mathbf{i} + 2\mathbf{j}$.

Hence $\mathbf{v} = (2t^2 + 1)\mathbf{i} + 2\mathbf{j} + 3t\mathbf{k}.$

The power of $\mathbf{F}$ at time t = $\mathbf{F} . \mathbf{v}$

$= (4t\mathbf{i} + 3\mathbf{k}).(\{2t^2 + 1\}\mathbf{i} + 2\mathbf{j} + 3t\mathbf{k})$

$= 4t(2t^2 + 1) + 3 \times 3t$

$= 8t^3 + 4t + 9t = 8t^3 + 13t.$

Exercise 11.3

1.   Two particles A and B are moving with constant velocities $8\mathbf{i} + \mathbf{j} − 4\mathbf{k}$ and $4\mathbf{i} − 2\mathbf{j} − 4\mathbf{k}$ respectively. Find the angle between the paths of the particles. Find also the speed of A relative to B.

2.   Two forces $F_1 = 4j - 5k$ and $F_2 = 2i - 5j - k$ act on a particle. Find the magnitude of the resultant force acting on the particle and the angle the resultant makes with the force F_1.

3.   Find the component of the force F in the direction of the vector d if
(a) $F = 3i - 4j + 4k, d = 6i - 2j - 3k$,
(b) $F = i + 5j - 3k, d = 2i - j + 2k$,
(c) $F = 7i - j - 4k, d = 3i - 5j + 4k$,
(d) $F = 3i + 5j - k, d = 4i - 4j + 7k$.

4.   Resolve the force F into component forces parallel and perpendicular to the vector d if
(a) $F = 11i + 4j - 2k, d = 4i - 3k$,
(b) $F = 5i - 22j + 19k, d = -5j + 12k$,
(c) $F = 18i + 35j - 21k, d = 2i - 6j + 9k$,
(d) $F = 3i - 4j + 10k, d = 4i - 8j + k$.

5.   Find the work done when the point of application of a force F moves through a displacement d, given that
(a) $F = 3i - 7j + 6k, d = 5i + j - k$,
(b) $F = -2i + 3j - 8k, d = 6i - 4j - 3k$,
(c) $F = 15i + 7k, d = 10j + 3k$,
(d) $F = 3i - 9j - 4k, d = i + 2j - k$.

6.   At time t a particle of mass m is moving with position vector r and velocity v under the action of a force F. In each of the following cases find an expression for v and hence determine the work done by F in the given interval of time.
(a) $r = 3ti + t^2j, 0 \leqslant t \leqslant 2$,
(b) $r = 5i - t^2j + 3tk, 2 \leqslant t \leqslant 4$,
(c) $r = t^3i - 4tj + 3k, 1 \leqslant t \leqslant 3$,
(d) $r = ti - j + (t^2 - 7t)k, 2 \leqslant t \leqslant 5$.

7.   At time t a particle of mass m is moving with position vector r and velocity v under the action of a force F. Find expressions for F, v and the power of F at time t, given that
(a) $r = 2t^2i - 5tk$,
(b) $r = i + t^3j - 3t^2k$,
(c) $r = ti - e^{-t}j$,
(d) $r = \sin tj + 3\cos tk$.

8.   A particle of unit mass is moving under the action of a constant force $F = i - 3j + 4k$. Find the work done by F when the particle moves from the point A with position vector $5j + 2k$ to the point B with position vector $3i + k$. If the speed of the particle at A is $6\,\text{m s}^{-1}$, find the speed of the particle at B.

9.   A particle of mass $3\,\text{kg}$ moves under the action of a constant force F with acceleration $a = 3i + 2k$. Find the work done by F as the particle moves from the point A with position vector $4i - 9j + 21k$ to the point B with position vector $10i + 15j - 7k$. If the particle passes through A with velocity $12j - 16k$ and through

B with velocity $\lambda(\mathbf{i} + 2\mathbf{j} - 2\mathbf{k})$, find the value of λ and the power of $\mathbf{F}$ at the points A and B.

10. A particle of unit mass is acted upon at time t by a force $\mathbf{F} = 2t\mathbf{i} - 3\mathbf{j}$. Given that the initial velocity of the particle is $\mathbf{j} + \mathbf{k}$, find an expression for its velocity $\mathbf{v}$ at time t. Hence find the work done by $\mathbf{F}$ in the interval $0 \leqslant t \leqslant 2$ and the power of $\mathbf{F}$ when $t = 2$.

11. A particle of mass 2 kg is acted upon at time t by a force $\mathbf{F} = 8\mathbf{i} - 4\cos t\mathbf{j} + 2t\mathbf{k}$. When $t = 0$ the velocity of the particle is $6\mathbf{i}$. Find expressions for the velocity of the particle and the power of $\mathbf{F}$ at time t.

12. A particle moves along a curve so that its position vector at time t is $\mathbf{r} = (3t - 2)\mathbf{i} + t^4\mathbf{j}$. If one of the forces acting on the particle is $\mathbf{F} = 5t^2\mathbf{i} - \mathbf{j}$, find by integration the work done by $\mathbf{F}$ in the interval $0 \leqslant t \leqslant 2$.

13. A particle moves along a curve with velocity $\mathbf{v} = \mathbf{i} + 10t^2\mathbf{j} - 3t\mathbf{k}$ at time t. If one of the forces acting on the particle is $\mathbf{F} = 2t\mathbf{i} + t^2\mathbf{j} - 2t\mathbf{k}$, find the power of $\mathbf{F}$ in terms of t. Hence find the work done by $\mathbf{F}$ in the interval from $t = 1$ to $t = 3$.

14. A particle moves on a curve with vector equation $\mathbf{r} = (\lambda - 12)\mathbf{i} - \lambda^2\mathbf{j} + \mathbf{k}$, where λ is a parameter. One of the forces acting on the particle is a variable force $\mathbf{F}$. Write down, in the form of a definite integral, an expression for the work done by $\mathbf{F}$ as the particle moves from the point where $\lambda = 1$ to the point where $\lambda = 2$. Evaluate this integral given that $\mathbf{F} = -4\mathbf{r}$.

Exercise 11.4 (miscellaneous)

1. (i) The force $\mathbf{F}_1$, of magnitude 26 N, acts at the origin in the direction of the vector $(3\mathbf{i} + 4\mathbf{j} + 12\mathbf{k})$. A second force $\mathbf{F}_2$, of magnitude 30 N, also acts at the origin, but in the direction of the vector $(6\mathbf{j} - 8\mathbf{k})$. Calculate the magnitude and the direction of the resultant of the forces $\mathbf{F}_1$ and $\mathbf{F}_2$. Calculate also the cosine of the angle between $\mathbf{F}_1$ and $\mathbf{F}_2$.
   (ii) A particle of mass 2 kg starts from rest at the origin and the force $\mathbf{F}_3$, where $\mathbf{F}_3 = (6\mathbf{i} + 26\mathbf{j})$ N, acts on it as it moves. Find the position vector of the particle 2 seconds later.   (L)

2. The force acting at time t ($0 \leqslant t < 2$) on a particle of unit mass is $24t^2\mathbf{i} + 6\mathbf{j}$. At time $t = 0$ the particle is at rest at the point with position vector $-2\mathbf{i} + 3\mathbf{j}$. Find the position vector of the particle at time $t = T$ ($0 \leqslant T < 2$). For time $t \geqslant 2$ the force acting on the particle is $6\mathbf{j}$. Find the position vector of the particle at time $t = 3$.
   (L)

3. State the centre and radius of the circle which has vector equation $\mathbf{r} = 6\mathbf{i} + 8\mathbf{j} + 6(\mathbf{i}\cos\theta + \mathbf{j}\sin\theta)$. A particle P of mass 2 kg moves on this circle with

constant angular velocity $\pi/12$ radians per second. Write down the position vector of P at time t given that, at $t = 0$, P is at the point corresponding to $\theta = 0$. Calculate the components parallel to $\mathbf{i}$ and $\mathbf{j}$ of the resultant vector force on the particle when $t = 4$. Find the position vector of the particle when $t = 8$ given that the forces on the particle cease to act when $t = 4$. (L)

4. The position vector, relative to the origin O, of an object of mass m moving in a horizontal plane in which $\mathbf{i}$ and $\mathbf{j}$ are perpendicular unit vectors is given by

$$\mathbf{r} = \frac{\cos\theta}{1 + \cos\theta}\mathbf{i} + \frac{\sin\theta}{1 + \cos\theta}\mathbf{j}, \quad -\pi < \theta < \pi.$$

Obtain an expression for r, the magnitude of $\mathbf{r}$. Given that $r^2\dfrac{d\theta}{dt} = h$ where h is constant, show that the velocity of the object is $-h\sin\theta\mathbf{i} + h(1 + \cos\theta)\mathbf{j}$. Show that the force acting on the object is of magnitude mh^2/r^2, and find the direction of this force. (JMB)

5. A particle is projected from the origin O with initial velocity $u\mathbf{i} + v\mathbf{j}$, where $\mathbf{i}$ and $\mathbf{j}$ are unit vectors in the horizontal and upward vertical directions respectively, and moves freely under gravity. Show that its velocity and position vector with respect to O, at time t after projection, are given by $\dot{\mathbf{r}} = u\mathbf{i} + (v - gt)\mathbf{j}$ and $\mathbf{r} = ut\mathbf{i} + (vt - \frac{1}{2}gt^2)\mathbf{j}$ respectively.

For the remainder of this question components of velocities are measured in $\mathrm{m\,s^{-1}}$ and components of displacements in m. Take g as $10\,\mathrm{m\,s^{-2}}$.

Two particles, A and B, are projected simultaneously from the origin with velocities $-30\mathbf{i} + 90\mathbf{j}$ and $30\mathbf{i} + 110\mathbf{j}$ respectively. Both particles impinge on a plane which contains the origin, meeting the plane on a line of greatest slope which has the equation $\mathbf{r} = \lambda(3\mathbf{i} + \mathbf{j})$, where λ is a scalar. Show that the times of flight of A and B are equal and that the distance between the points of impact is $400\sqrt{10}\,\mathrm{m}$. Find the cosine of the acute angle between the direction of motion of A at the instant of impact and the line of greatest slope of the plane. (JMB)

6. At noon two ships A and B have the following position and velocity vectors:

	Position vector	Velocity vector
Ship A	$10\mathbf{i} + 5\mathbf{j}$	$-2\mathbf{i} + 4\mathbf{j}$
Ship B	$2\mathbf{i} - \mathbf{j}$	$2\mathbf{i} + 7\mathbf{j}$

where $\mathbf{i}$ and $\mathbf{j}$ are unit vectors in the directions East and North respectively, and where the speeds are measured in kilometres per hour and the distances in kilometres. If they continue on their respective courses, (i) find the position vector of A after a time t hours; (ii) show that they will collide, and give the time of the collision; (iii) determine how far ship A will have travelled between noon and the collision. (SU)

7. A ship A is travelling on a course of $060°$ at a speed of $30\sqrt{3}\,\mathrm{km/h}$ and a ship B is travelling on a course of $030°$ at $20\,\mathrm{km/h}$. At noon B is $260\,\mathrm{km}$ due east of A.

Using unit base vectors **i** and **j** pointing east and north respectively find $\overrightarrow{AB}$ in terms of **i**, **j** and t at time t hours in the afternoon. Hence, or otherwise, calculate the least distance between A and B, to the nearest kilometre, and the time at which they are nearest to one another.   (L)

8.   An aeroplane A moves in space with a variable velocity **v** and is attacked by a guided missile B which moves with constant speed u, where $u > |v|$. The guidance system of B is such that, if from any instant the velocity of A stayed constant, B would hit A without having to change direction. Show that the velocity of A relative to B is

$$\left[\frac{\mathbf{r}.\mathbf{v} - \sqrt{\{(\mathbf{r}.\mathbf{v})^2 + (u^2 - v^2)\mathbf{r}^2\}}}{\mathbf{r}^2}\right]\mathbf{r},$$

where **r** is the position vector of A relative to B.   (O)

9.   At time t a particle is in motion with velocity **v** and is being acted upon by a variable force **F**. Write down expressions for (i) the power at time t, (ii) the work done by **F** during the time interval $0 \leqslant t \leqslant T$.

   The particle, of mass m, moves in a plane where **i** and **j** are perpendicular unit vectors so that its position vector at time t is given by $\mathbf{r} = 2a\cos 2t\mathbf{i} + a\sin 2t\mathbf{j}$, where a is a positive constant. Derive expressions for the velocity **v** and the force **F** at time t. Obtain an expression in terms of t for the power at time t and show that the work done by **F** during the interval $0 \leqslant t \leqslant T$ is $3ma^2(1 - \cos 4T)$. If T varies, find the maximum value of the work done by **F** and determine also the smallest value of T for which this maximum value is reached.   (JMB)

10. A smooth fixed wire is in the shape of the curve given by

$$\mathbf{r} = a(\theta - \sin\theta)\mathbf{i} + a(1 + \cos\theta)\mathbf{j}, \ 0 \leqslant \theta \leqslant 2\pi,$$

where **i**, **j** are unit vectors in the horizontal and upward vertical directions respectively. A particle threaded on the wire is released from rest at the point A ($\theta = 0$). Write down, in terms of θ and its derivative, an equation expressing the conservation of energy during the motion. Show that the time taken for the particle to reach B ($\theta = 2\pi$) is $2\pi\sqrt{(a/g)}$.   (JMB)

12 Impulse and momentum

12.1 The impulse of a force

When a constant force $\mathbf{F}$ acts for a time t, then the *impulse* of the force is defined as the vector quantity $\mathbf{F}t$.

The SI unit of impulse is the newton second (N s).

Example 1 A force $\mathbf{F} = 4\mathbf{i} - 3\mathbf{j}$ acts on a particle for 3 seconds. Find the magnitude of the impulse of the force.

If the impulse of the force is $\mathbf{I}$, then

$$\mathbf{I} = (4\mathbf{i} - 3\mathbf{j}) \times 3$$
$$\therefore \quad |\mathbf{I}| = 3|4\mathbf{i} - 3\mathbf{j}| = 3\sqrt{(4^2 + 3^2)} = 15.$$

Hence the magnitude of the impulse is 15 N s.

When a variable force $\mathbf{F}$ acts from time t_1 to time t_2, then the impulse of the force is defined as $\displaystyle\int_{t_1}^{t_2} \mathbf{F}\, dt$.

Example 2 A particle is moving under the action of a force $\mathbf{F} = 2\mathbf{i} - 3t^2\mathbf{j} + 4t\mathbf{k}$ at the time t. Find the impulse given to the particle in the interval $1 \leqslant t \leqslant 2$.

$$\text{Impulse} = \int_1^2 (2\mathbf{i} - 3t^2\mathbf{j} + 4t\mathbf{k})\, dt$$

$$= \left[2t\mathbf{i} - t^3\mathbf{j} + 2t^2\mathbf{k} \right]_1^2$$
$$= (4\mathbf{i} - 8\mathbf{j} + 8\mathbf{k}) - (2\mathbf{i} - \mathbf{j} + 2\mathbf{k})$$
$$= 2\mathbf{i} - 7\mathbf{j} + 6\mathbf{k}.$$

In some circumstances it is difficult to determine the exact nature of the forces involved. For example, in collisions between moving objects comparatively large

243

unknown forces act for very short intervals of time. We will now show that the impulse of such a force can be found by considering the effect it produces.

Suppose that at time t a particle of mass m is moving with velocity $\mathbf{v}$ under the action of a force $\mathbf{F}$. Let $\mathbf{I}$ be the impulse given to the particle by $\mathbf{F}$ in the interval $t_1 \leqslant t \leqslant t_2$. Whether $\mathbf{F}$ is constant or variable,

$$\mathbf{I} = \int_{t_1}^{t_2} \mathbf{F}\, dt$$

Using Newton's second law in its original form,

$$\mathbf{F} = \frac{d(m\mathbf{v})}{dt},$$

where $m\mathbf{v}$ is the *momentum* of the particle.

$\therefore$

$$\mathbf{I} = \int_{t_1}^{t_2} \frac{d(m\mathbf{v})}{dt}\, dt$$

$$\mathbf{I} = \left[\, m\mathbf{v}\, \right]_{t_1}^{t_2}$$

$$\mathbf{I} = (m\mathbf{v})_{at\, t_2} - (m\mathbf{v})_{at\, t_1}$$

i.e.

$$\boxed{\text{impulse} = \text{change in momentum}}$$

[Because of the relationship between impulse and momentum, both quantities are usually measured in newton seconds. An alternative unit of momentum is the kilogramme metre per second. However, since $1\,\mathrm{N} = 1\,\mathrm{kg\,m\,s^{-2}}$, it follows that $1\,\mathrm{N\,s} = 1\,\mathrm{kg\,m\,s^{-1}}$.]

Example 3   A truck of mass $1400\,\mathrm{kg}$ moving along a straight horizontal track at $2\,\mathrm{m\,s^{-1}}$ runs into fixed buffers and rebounds at a speed of $1\,\mathrm{m\,s^{-1}}$. If the truck and the buffers are in contact for $1\cdot2\,\mathrm{s}$, find the average force exerted by the buffers on the truck.

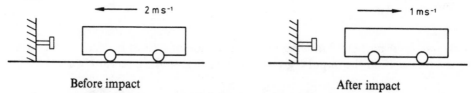

Before impact   After impact

Let the direction away from the buffers be positive and let F N be the average force exerted by the buffers.

Impulse = change in momentum
$\therefore$ $F \times 1\cdot2 = 1400 \times 1 - 1400 \times (-2)$

$\therefore$ $$F = \frac{1400 \times 3}{1\cdot2} = 3500$$

Hence the average force exerted by the buffers is $3500\,\mathrm{N}$.

Example 4   A particle of mass 5 kg is moving with velocity $3\mathbf{i} - 7\mathbf{j}$ when it is given an impulse $\mathbf{I} = -7\mathbf{i} + 16\mathbf{j}$. If the velocity of the particle after the impulse is $\mathbf{v}$, find $\mathbf{v}$. Find also the change in kinetic energy.

Impulse = change in momentum

$\therefore$ $-7\mathbf{i} + 16\mathbf{j} = 5\mathbf{v} - 5(3\mathbf{i} - 7\mathbf{j})$

$\therefore$ $5\mathbf{v} = -7\mathbf{i} + 16\mathbf{j} + 15\mathbf{i} - 35\mathbf{j}$

i.e. $\mathbf{v} = \frac{1}{5}(8\mathbf{i} - 19\mathbf{j})$

Initial speed $= \sqrt{(3^2 + 7^2)} = \sqrt{(9 + 49)} = \sqrt{58}$

New speed $= \frac{1}{5}\sqrt{(8^2 + 19^2)} = \frac{1}{5}\sqrt{(64 + 361)} = \frac{1}{5}\sqrt{425} = \sqrt{17}$.

$\therefore$ there is a loss in kinetic energy of

$$(\tfrac{1}{2} \times 5 \times 58 - \tfrac{1}{2} \times 5 \times 17)\,\mathrm{J} \quad \text{i.e.} \quad 102{\cdot}5\,\mathrm{J}.$$

Example 5   A ball of mass $0{\cdot}25$ kg strikes a wall at a speed of $16\,\mathrm{m\,s^{-1}}$ and rebounds with a speed of $10\,\mathrm{m\,s^{-1}}$. If the angle between the velocities of the ball before and after impact is α, where $\tan\alpha = \frac{3}{4}$, find the magnitude of the impulse exerted by the wall on the ball.

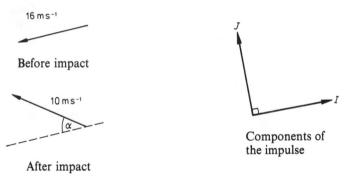

Resolving parallel and perpendicular to the initial velocity of the ball,

↗
↖

$I = 0{\cdot}25(-10\cos\alpha) - 0{\cdot}25(-16)$

$J = 0{\cdot}25(10\sin\alpha)$

Using a right-angled triangle,

$\sin\alpha = \frac{3}{5}, \quad \cos\alpha = \frac{4}{5}$.

$\therefore$ $I = 0{\cdot}25(-8) - 0{\cdot}25(-16) = 2$

$J = 0{\cdot}25 \times 6 = 1{\cdot}5$

Hence the magnitude of the impulse exerted by the wall

$= \sqrt{(2^2 + 1{\cdot}5^2)}\,\mathrm{N\,s} = 2{\cdot}5\,\mathrm{N\,s}.$

When a jet of water is directed at a wall, the reaction of the wall on the water produces a *continuous change in momentum*. Provided that the water is being delivered at a steady rate and with constant velocity, the force exerted by the wall can be determined by considering the momentum lost by the water each second.

Example 6   A hose delivers water horizontally at a rate of 20 kg per second with a speed of 25 m s^{-1}. The water strikes a vertical wall and does not rebound. Find the force exerted on the wall.

Let F N be the force exerted on the wall, then the force exerted by the wall is also F N,
∴   impulse exerted in 1 second = $F \times 1$ N s = F N s.
Mass of water delivered in 1 second = 20 kg
∴   loss of momentum in 1 second = 20 × 25 N s = 500 N s
However,   impulse = change in momentum,
∴ $F = 500$
Hence the force exerted on the wall is 500 N.

An instantaneous impulse acting along a string is called an *impulsive tension*. It may produce changes in momentum in the direction of the string, but has no effect perpendicular to the string. In particular, if a stationary particle is jerked into motion by the sudden tightening of a string attached to it, then the initial velocity of the particle will be in the direction of the string.

Example 7   One end of a light inextensible string of length 2 m is fixed at a point A on a smooth horizontal plane. The other end is attached to a particle of mass 2 kg. The particle is placed at a point B on the plane, where $AB = \sqrt{3}$ m, then projected horizontally with speed 6 m s^{-1} in a direction perpendicular to AB. Find the speed of the particle immediately after the string has become taut. Find also the impulsive tension in the string.

If C is the point on the path of the particle at which the string first becomes taut, $\angle CAB = \cos^{-1}(\sqrt{3}/2) = 30°$.

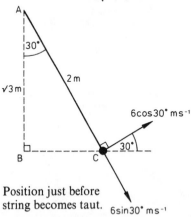

As shown in the diagram, just before the string tightens the velocity of the particle has components $6\sin 30°$ m s^{-1} along AC and $6\cos 30°$ m s^{-1} perpendicular to AC. When the string becomes taut the particle loses its momentum in the direction of AC, but its momentum perpendicular to AC is unchanged.

Position just before string becomes taut.

Hence just after the string has become taut, the speed of the particle is $6\cos 30°$ m s^{-1} i.e. $3\sqrt{3}$ m s^{-1}.
The loss of momentum along AC is produced by the impulsive tension in the string,

∴   impulsive tension = $2 \times 6\sin 30°$ N s = 6 N s.

In problems which involve systems of two or more particles the impulse-momentum relationship can be used both for the system as a whole and for particles taken separately. When considering the impulse given to the whole system, we will see that internal impulses occur in equal and opposite pairs and cancel each other out. Thus we may write:

sum of external impulses = total change in momentum.

The next example concerns two particles connected by a light inextensible string. In this case the impulsive tensions acting on the particles are equal and opposite, so they can be disregarded when dealing with the system as a whole.

Example 8   Particles A and B, of masses 1 kg and 2 kg respectively, are connected by a light inextensible string. The particles are at rest on a smooth horizontal plane with the string taut. A horizontal impulse of magnitude 12 N s is applied to particle B in a direction inclined at $45°$ to the direction of AB. Find the velocities with which A and B start to move. Find also the impulsive tension in the string.

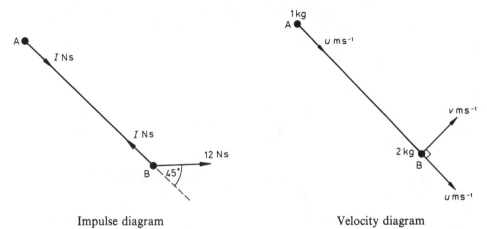

Impulse diagram   Velocity diagram

Let the initial velocity of B have components u and v along and perpendicular to AB respectively. Since the string is taut, A will start to move with speed u along AB.

For A and B together,   impulse = change in momentum,
∴   resolving along and perpendicular to AB,

↘ $12 \cos 45° = 1 \times u + 2 \times u$
↗ $12 \sin 45° = 2 \times v$

∴ $u = 2\sqrt{2}$ and $v = 3\sqrt{2}$

Thus the initial velocity of A is $2\sqrt{2}\,\mathrm{m\,s^{-1}}$ along AB.

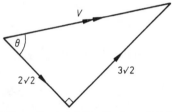

If the initial velocity of B is $V\mathrm{m\,s^{-1}}$ at an angle θ to AB, then

$$V = \sqrt{\{(2\sqrt{2})^2 + (3\sqrt{2})^2\}} = \sqrt{26}$$
$$\theta = \tan^{-1}(3/2) \approx 56\cdot3°$$

Thus the initial velocity of B is $\sqrt{26}\,\mathrm{m\,s^{-1}}$ at an angle of $56\cdot3°$ to AB.

Let I N s be the impulsive tension in the string, then considering the motion of A,

$$I = 1 \times 2\sqrt{2}.$$

Hence the impulsive tension in the string is $2\sqrt{2}$ N s.

Exercise 12.1

1.   When a constant force **F** acts for time t, the impulse of the force is **I**.
(a) If $\mathbf{F} = 2\mathbf{i} - 7\mathbf{j}$ and $t = 4$, find **I**.
(b) If $\mathbf{I} = 6\mathbf{i} - 2\mathbf{j} + 3\mathbf{k}$ and $t = 3$, find **F**.
(c) If $\mathbf{F} = -12\mathbf{i} + 5\mathbf{j}$ and $t = 5$, find $|\mathbf{I}|$.
(d) If $\mathbf{I} = 6\mathbf{i} + 12\mathbf{j} - 4\mathbf{k}$ and $t = 3.5$, find $|\mathbf{F}|$.

2.   Find the impulse of the variable force **F** in the stated interval of time.
(a) $\mathbf{F} = 5t\mathbf{i} + 3\mathbf{j}, 0 \leqslant t \leqslant 2$.
(b) $\mathbf{F} = \mathbf{i} - 6t^2\mathbf{j} + 2t\mathbf{k}, 1 \leqslant t \leqslant 3$.
(c) $\mathbf{F} = \cos 2t\mathbf{i} + 3\sin 2t\mathbf{j}, 0 \leqslant t \leqslant \frac{1}{2}\pi$.

3.   Find the momentum of
(a) a man of mass 80 kg running at $6 \, \mathrm{m \, s^{-1}}$,
(b) a car of mass 1200 kg travelling at $25 \, \mathrm{m \, s^{-1}}$,
(c) a bullet of mass 15 g moving at $800 \, \mathrm{m \, s^{-1}}$.

4.   A particle of mass m moves so that its position vector at time t is **r**. Find, as a vector, the momentum of the particle at time T if
(a) $\mathbf{r} = 3\mathbf{i} + t^2\mathbf{j}, m = 2, T = 3$;
(b) $\mathbf{r} = -4t\mathbf{i} + t^3\mathbf{k}, m = 0.5, T = 2$;
(c) $\mathbf{r} = 5\cos 3t\mathbf{i} + 2\mathbf{j} + 5\sin 3t\mathbf{k}, m = 4, T = \pi$.

5.   A stone of mass 3 kg is falling at a speed of $18 \, \mathrm{m \, s^{-1}}$ when it hits the ground. If the stone is brought to rest by the impact, find the impulse exerted by the ground.

6.   A ball of mass 0·2 kg strikes a wall when moving horizontally at $12 \, \mathrm{m \, s^{-1}}$. If the ball rebounds horizontally at $8 \, \mathrm{m \, s^{-1}}$, find the impulse exerted by the wall.

7.   A bullet of mass 0·03 kg is fired into a fixed block of wood at a speed of $400 \, \mathrm{m \, s^{-1}}$. If the bullet is brought to rest in 0·02 s, find the average resistance exerted by the wood.

8.   A particle of mass 5 kg is moving under the action of a constant force of magnitude 8 N. Initially the speed of the particle is $12 \, \mathrm{m \, s^{-1}}$. Find its speed after 3 seconds if the force (a) acts in the direction of motion, (b) directly opposes motion.

9.   A particle of mass 2 kg is projected across a rough horizontal plane with a speed of $21 \, \mathrm{m \, s^{-1}}$. Find the time in which the particle comes to rest, given that the coefficient of friction is 2/7.

10. A particle of mass 0.5 kg is moving with velocity $\mathbf{u} = 6\mathbf{i} - 7\mathbf{j}$ when it is given an impulse $\mathbf{I} = 3\mathbf{i} + 11\mathbf{j}$. Find the new velocity of the particle and the average force required to bring it to rest in a further 3 seconds.

11. A particle of mass 0.8 kg is moving with velocity $4\mathbf{i} + 7\mathbf{j}$ when it strikes a fixed obstacle and rebounds with velocity $-6\mathbf{i} + 2\mathbf{j}$. Find the impulse exerted by the particle on the obstacle. Find also the kinetic energy lost by the particle in the collision.

12. A particle of mass 3 kg is moving with speed $6 \, \mathrm{m \, s}^{-1}$ when it receives an impulse of magnitude 24 N s. Find the speed of the particle immediately after the impulse and the change in the kinetic energy of the particle if the direction of the impulse and the original direction of motion are (a) the same, (b) opposite, (c) perpendicular.

13. A ball of mass 0.2 kg strikes a wall at a speed of $12 \, \mathrm{m \, s}^{-1}$ and rebounds with a speed of $3.5 \, \mathrm{m \, s}^{-1}$. If its path is diverted through $90°$ by the impact, find the magnitude of the impulse exerted on the wall.

14. An object of mass 4 kg strikes a barrier at a speed of $10 \, \mathrm{m \, s}^{-1}$ and rebounds at a speed of $5 \, \mathrm{m \, s}^{-1}$. If the angle between the velocities of the object before and after impact is $60°$, find the magnitude of the impulse exerted on the barrier.

15. A hose is discharging water at the rate of 50 litres per second. The jet of water is travelling horizontally with a speed of $12 \, \mathrm{m \, s}^{-1}$ when it strikes a vertical wall. Assuming that the water does not rebound, find the force exerted on the wall. [Take the mass of 1 litre of water to be 1 kg.]

16. A stream of water falling vertically from a pipe at the rate of 75 kg per second exerts a force of 900 N on the ground below. Assuming that the ground destroys the momentum of the water, find the speed at which the water hits the ground.

17. In a factory small screws are falling vertically onto a conveyor belt without bouncing at a rate of 48 kg per minute. Just before impact the screws are travelling at $2 \, \mathrm{m \, s}^{-1}$. If the conveyor belt moves horizontally at $1.5 \, \mathrm{m \, s}^{-1}$, find the magnitude and direction of the average force it exerts on the screws.

18. One end of a light inextensible string of length $\sqrt{3}$ m is fixed at a point A on a smooth horizontal plane. The other end is attached to a particle of mass 3 kg. The particle is placed at a point B on the plane, where $AB = 1$ m, then projected horizontally with speed $4 \, \mathrm{m \, s}^{-1}$. Find the speed of the particle immediately after the string has become taut and the impulsive tension in the string, given that the angle between the initial velocity of the particle and the direction BA is (a) $60°$, (b) $90°$.

19. Particles A and B, of masses 3 kg and 2 kg respectively, are connected by a light inextensible string. The particles are at rest on a smooth horizontal plane with the string taut. A horizontal impulse of magnitude 12.5 N s is applied to particle B in a direction inclined at an angle α to the direction of AB, where $\tan \alpha = 4/3$. Find the

velocities with which A and B start to move. Find also the impulsive tension in the string.

20. Particles A and B, both of mass m, are connected by a light inextensible string. A particle C of mass $2m$ is attached to the mid-point of the string. The particles are at rest on a smooth horizontal plane with the string taut and with AC at right angles to BC. A horizontal impulse of magnitude $12m$ is applied to C in a direction inclined at an angle α to AC, such that both parts of the string remain taut. Find the speeds with which the particles begin to move if (a) $\alpha = 45°$, (b) $\alpha = 60°$.

12.2 Conservation of momentum

When two particles collide they exert equal and opposite impulses on each other. Therefore the changes in the momentum of the particles are also equal and opposite. It follows that the total momentum of the two particles together remains unchanged. A similar argument can be used in any situation in which equal and opposite impulses act on two bodies, e.g. when a bullet is fired from a gun or when a light inextensible string connecting two particles suddenly becomes taut.

These examples are special cases of a more general result called the *principle of conservation of linear momentum*.

> If no external force acts on a system of particles in a particular direction, then there can be no change in the total momentum of the system in that direction.

Example 1   Two particles A and B, of masses $3\,\text{kg}$ and $2\,\text{kg}$ respectively, are travelling in opposite directions along the same straight line when they collide. Just before the impact A is moving with speed $8\,\text{m s}^{-1}$ and B with speed $5\,\text{m s}^{-1}$. After the impact the speeds of A and B are $2\,\text{m s}^{-1}$ and $v\,\text{m s}^{-1}$ respectively. Find the value of v given that after the impact A and B are travelling in (a) the same direction, (b) opposite directions.

(a)

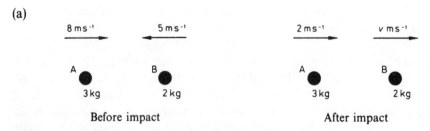

Before impact	After impact

Momentum before impact = momentum after impact
∴   taking the direction of motion of A as positive,

$$3 \times 8 + 2 \times (-5) = 3 \times 2 + 2 \times v$$
i.e. $$14 = 6 + 2v$$
Thus $$v = 4$$

(b)

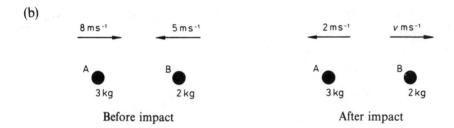

Before impact   After impact

Momentum before impact = momentum after impact
∴ $3 \times 8 + 2 \times (-5) = 3 \times (-2) + 2 \times v$
i.e. $14 = -6 + 2v$
Thus $v = 10.$

Example 2   A bullet of mass 0·02 kg is fired from a gun of mass 6 kg with a speed of 450 m s⁻¹. Find the speed of the gun's recoil. Find also the constant force required to bring the gun to rest in 0·5 seconds.

Let v m s⁻¹ be the speed of the gun and let F N be the force required to bring the gun to rest in 0·5 seconds.

     Momentum after firing = momentum before firing
∴ $6 \times v + 0.02 \times (-450) = 0$
i.e. $6v - 9 = 0$
                     $v = 1.5$

Hence the speed of the gun's recoil is 1·5 m s⁻¹.
As the gun is brought to rest,

     impulse = change in momentum
∴ $F \times 0.5 = 6 \times 1.5$
i.e. $F = 18$

Hence the constant force required is 18 N.

Example 3   A particle A of mass 5 kg slides from rest down a smooth plane inclined at an angle α to the horizontal, where $\sin \alpha = 1/6$. After 3 s it collides with a particle B of mass 1 kg which is sliding down the plane at 2·5 m s⁻¹. If the two particles coalesce, find their common speed immediately after impact.

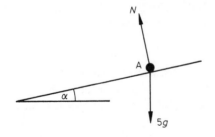

The change in the momentum of A is equal to the impulse received.
∴   just before the collision the momentum of A down the plane

$$= 5g \sin \alpha \times 3 \,\text{N s}$$
$$= 5 \times 9.8 \times \tfrac{1}{6} \times 3 \,\text{N s}$$
$$= 24.5 \,\text{N s}$$

Momentum is conserved in the collision between A and B. Thus if $v\,\text{m}\,\text{s}^{-1}$ is their common speed after impact,

$$24{\cdot}5 + 1 \times 2{\cdot}5 = (5 + 1)v$$
$$\therefore \qquad\qquad v = 4{\cdot}5$$

Hence the common speed of the particles after impact is $4{\cdot}5\,\text{m}\,\text{s}^{-1}$.

Exercise 12.2

1.   A railway truck of mass $12\,000\,\text{kg}$ is moving along a straight level track at $7\,\text{m}\,\text{s}^{-1}$ when it collides with another truck of mass $8000\,\text{kg}$ moving in the same direction at $2\,\text{m}\,\text{s}^{-1}$. After the collision the trucks move on together. Find the common speed of the trucks after impact.

2.   A bullet of mass $0{\cdot}04\,\text{kg}$ is fired horizontally into a block of wood of mass $1{\cdot}4\,\text{kg}$ which rests on a smooth horizontal surface. The bullet becomes embedded in the block and after impact they move on together at a speed of $20\,\text{m}\,\text{s}^{-1}$. Find the speed at which the bullet is fired.

3.   Two particles, A of mass $5\,\text{kg}$ and B of mass $2\,\text{kg}$, are moving horizontally along the same straight line when they collide. Both come to rest instantaneously. If the velocity of A was $3\,\text{m}\,\text{s}^{-1}$ just before the impact, find the velocity of B and the kinetic energy lost in the impact.

4.   A gun of mass $4\,\text{kg}$ fires a bullet of mass $20\,\text{g}$ at a speed of $500\,\text{m}\,\text{s}^{-1}$. Find the speed of the gun's recoil and the energy of the explosion in the gun.

5.   Two particles A and B, of mass $3\,\text{kg}$ and $5\,\text{kg}$ respectively, collide. Just before impact A is moving with speed $8\,\text{m}\,\text{s}^{-1}$ and B is moving with speed $4\,\text{m}\,\text{s}^{-1}$ in the opposite direction. Immediately after the impact A rebounds with speed $7\,\text{m}\,\text{s}^{-1}$. Find the speed of B immediately after impact.

6.   Two particles X and Y, of mass $4\,\text{kg}$ and $3\,\text{kg}$ respectively, collide. Just before impact X is moving with speed $13\,\text{m}\,\text{s}^{-1}$ and Y is moving with speed $5\,\text{m}\,\text{s}^{-1}$ in the opposite direction. Immediately after the impact X moves on, with no change in direction, at $4\,\text{m}\,\text{s}^{-1}$. Find the speed of Y immediately after impact.

7.   A particle of mass m and velocity $4\mathbf{i} + \mathbf{j}$ collides with a particle of mass $2m$ and velocity $\mathbf{i} - 8\mathbf{j}$. If the particles coalesce on impact, find their common velocity just after the collision.

8.   Two particles, A of mass $3m$ and B of mass $2m$, are moving with velocities $4\mathbf{i} - 6\mathbf{j}$ and $2\mathbf{i} + 7\mathbf{j}$ respectively when they collide. Immediately after the impact A moves on in the same direction as before, but with half its original speed. Find the velocity of B just after the collision.

9. A particle of mass 2 kg moving with speed $10\,\mathrm{m\,s}^{-1}$ collides with a stationary particle of mass 7 kg. Immediately after impact the particles move with the same speed but in opposite directions. Find the kinetic energy lost in the collision.

10. Two particles, of masses $3m$ and $2m$ moving in opposite directions with speeds u and $4u$ respectively, collide. Given that no kinetic energy is lost in the collision, find the speeds of the particles immediately after impact.

11. Three trucks A, B and C, each of mass 2 tonnes, are moving on a straight horizontal track in the same direction with speeds of 10, 5 and $3\,\mathrm{m\,s}^{-1}$ respectively. When any two trucks collide, they become coupled. Thus after two collisions the three trucks move on with a common speed. Find this speed and find also the total loss of kinetic energy in the collisions.

12. A truck A of mass 3000 kg moving at $4\,\mathrm{m\,s}^{-1}$ collides with a truck B of mass 2000 kg moving at $2\,\mathrm{m\,s}^{-1}$ in the same direction. If after impact truck A continues to move in the same direction but at a speed of $3\,\mathrm{m\,s}^{-1}$, find the new speed of truck B. If the trucks are in contact for 1·5 s, find the average force each exerts on the other.

13. A van of mass 1800 kg begins to tow a stationary car of mass 1200 kg. Just before the tow-rope tightens, the van is moving at a speed of $1\,\mathrm{m\,s}^{-1}$. Find the common speed of the vehicles just after the rope tightens. Find also the impulsive tension in the rope.

14. A bullet of mass 0·03 kg is fired from a gun with a horizontal velocity of $600\,\mathrm{m\,s}^{-1}$. If the gun is then brought to rest in 1·2 s by a horizontal force which rises uniformly from zero to $P\,\mathrm{N}$ and then falls uniformly to zero, find the value of P.

15. A particle of mass 2 kg slides from rest down a smooth plane inclined at an angle of 30° to the horizontal. After 5 seconds it collides with a particle of mass 3 kg which is sliding down the plane at a speed of $7\,\mathrm{m\,s}^{-1}$. If the two particles coalesce on impact find their common velocity (a) just after the collision, (b) 2 seconds after the collision.

16. Two small beads A and B, each of mass m, are threaded on a smooth straight wire inclined at an angle α to the horizontal. Bead A is released from rest and begins to slide down the wire. At same instant bead B is projected up the wire towards A with speed u. After a time t the two beads collide and are brought to rest by the impact. Find an expression for t in terms of u, g and α.

12.3 Work, energy and momentum

When faced with a problem in particle dynamics, we will now have to decide whether to consider work-energy relationships, impulse-momentum relationships or a combination of both. The two fundamental equations are:

> Work done = change in kinetic energy
> Impulse = change in momentum

Example 1 A bullet of mass m is fired horizontally with velocity V into a fixed block of wood and penetrates a distance d into it. If the block exerts a constant resistance R, which stops the bullet in a time T, find expressions for R and T in terms of m, V and d.

Work done against resistance = loss of kinetic energy

$$\therefore \qquad Rd = \tfrac{1}{2}mV^2$$

Hence $$R = mV^2/2d$$

Impulse = change in momentum

$$\therefore \qquad RT = mV$$

Hence $$T = \frac{mV}{R} = mV \times \frac{2d}{mV^2} = \frac{2d}{V}.$$

[Note that as the resistance is constant this problem could also be solved using Newton's second law and the constant acceleration formulae $v^2 = u^2 + 2as$, $v = u + at$.]

Example 2 A pile-driver of mass 3000 kg falls freely from a height of 2·5 m and strikes a pile of mass 1200 kg. After the blow the pile and the driver move on together. If the pile is driven a distance of 0·5 m into the ground, find the speed at which the pile starts to move into the ground and the average resistance of the ground to penetration.

Let $v\,\mathrm{m\,s^{-1}}$ be the downward velocity of the pile-driver just before impact. Using the formula $v^2 = u^2 + 2as$, where $u = 0, a = 9·8, s = 2·5$, we have

$$v^2 = 0 + 2 \times 9·8 \times 2·5 = 49$$
$$v = 7$$

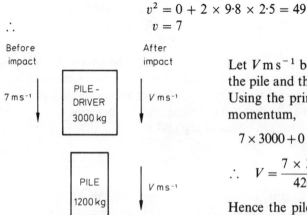

Before impact

7 m s⁻¹

PILE - DRIVER 3000 kg

After impact

V m s⁻¹

PILE 1200 kg

V m s⁻¹

Let $V\,\mathrm{m\,s^{-1}}$ be the common velocity of the pile and the driver after impact. Using the principle of conservation of momentum,

$$7 \times 3000 + 0 \times 1200 = V(3000 + 1200)$$

$$\therefore \quad V = \frac{7 \times 3000}{4200} = 5$$

Hence the pile starts to move into the ground at $5\,\mathrm{m\,s^{-1}}$.

Let R N be the average resistance of the ground, then the resultant force acting on pile and driver together is $(R - 4200g)$ N.

$$\text{Work done} = \text{change in kinetic energy}$$
$\therefore \quad (R - 4200g) \times 0{\cdot}5 = \tfrac{1}{2} \times 4200 \times 5^2$
$\therefore \qquad\qquad R - 4200g = 4200 \times 25$
$\therefore \qquad\qquad\qquad R = 4200(25 + 9{\cdot}8) = 146\,160$

Hence the average resistance of the ground is $146\,160$ N.

When a particle moves in a vertical plane there are changes in its gravitational potential energy. Provided that no force other than gravity is doing work, we may then apply the principle of conservation of mechanical energy in the form:

$$\boxed{\text{K.E.} + \text{P.E.} = \text{constant}}$$

Example 3   A particle A, of mass m, is attached to a fixed point by means of a light inextensible string and hangs in equilibrium. A particle B, of mass $2m$, is travelling horizontally with speed $5u$ when it collides with particle A. Immediately after the impact B continues to move in the same direction but with speed $3u$. If A swings to a height h above its original position before coming instantaneously to rest, find an expression for h in terms of u and g.

Let v be the speed of particle A after impact.

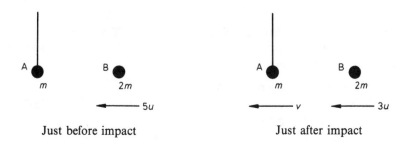

Just before impact   Just after impact

Using the principle of conservation of momentum,

$$m \times 0 + 2m \times 5u = m \times v + 2m \times 3u$$
$$10mu = mv + 6mu$$
$\therefore \qquad\qquad v = 4u$

Hence the speed of A immediately after impact is $4u$.
When A is swinging freely its direction of motion is always at right angles to the string. Thus the tension in the string does no work and mechanical energy is conserved.

P.E. after impact $= 0$,   K.E. after impact $= \tfrac{1}{2}m(4u)^2 = 8mu^2$.
P.E. at height $h = mgh$, K.E. at height $h \;\; = 0$.

$\therefore \qquad 0 + 8mu^2 = mgh + 0$
Hence $\qquad\quad h = 8u^2/g$.

Example 4   Particles A and B, of masses 1 kg and 2 kg respectively, are attached to the ends of a light inextensible string passing over a smooth light pulley. The system is released from rest with both parts of the string taut and vertical. After A has travelled 1·2 m it hits and coalesces with a stationary particle C, of mass 2 kg. Find the new speed of the system and the impulsive tension in the string at the instant when C is picked up.

Taking the initial P.E. of each particle as zero, after the system has travelled 1·2 m the P.E. of A is $1·2g$ J and the P.E. of B is $-1·2 \times 2g$ J i.e. $-2·4g$ J.

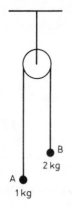

The initial K.E. of the system is zero. If v m s^{-1} is the speed of the particles after they have travelled 1·2 m, the K.E. acquired is $\frac{1}{2}(1 + 2)v^2$ J i.e. $1·5v^2$ J.

Since no external force is doing work, the mechanical energy of the system remains constant.

$\therefore$ $1·5v^2 + (1·2g - 2·4g) = 0$

i.e. $1·5v^2 = 1·2 \times 9·8$

$\therefore$ $v = 2·8$

Thus, just before C is picked up the system is travelling at 2·8 m s^{-1}.
Let V m s^{-1} be the new speed of the system and J N s the impulsive tension in the string when C is picked up.

Impulse $=$ change in momentum

Thus for B: $J = 2 \times 2·8 - 2 \times V$

i.e. $J = 5·6 - 2V$ (1)

For A and C: $J = (1 \times V + 2 \times V) - (1 \times 2·8 + 2 \times 0)$

i.e. $J = 3V - 2·8$ (2)

Subtracting (2) from (1): $0 = 8·4 - 5V$

$\therefore$ $V = 1·68$

Substituting in (1): $J = 5·6 - 2 \times 1·68 = 2·24.$

Hence the new speed of the system is 1·68 m s^{-1} and the impulsive tension in the string is 2·24 N s.

Example 5   A particle P of mass 4 kg is connected to a particle Q of mass 3 kg by means of a light inextensible string which passes over a smooth light pulley. The system is released from rest with both parts of the string taut and vertical. After 3·5 s particle P hits the ground without rebounding. Assuming that particle Q does not hit the pulley, find the further time which elapses before the string is again taut. Find also the speed with which P leaves the ground.

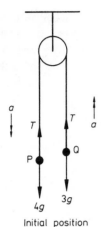

Initial position

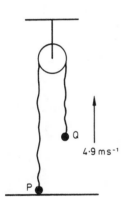

When P hits the ground

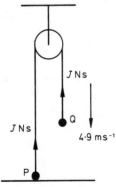

As the string becomes
taut again

Let $a\,\mathrm{m\,s^{-2}}$ be the acceleration of the particles and let $T\,\mathrm{N}$ be the tension in the string.

Using Newton's second law,

for P: $\qquad 4g - T = 4a \qquad (1)$
for Q: $\qquad T - 3g = 3a \qquad (2)$
$(1) + (2)$: $\qquad g = 7a$

$$\therefore \qquad a = \frac{g}{7} = 1{\cdot}4$$

Using the formula $v = u + at$, where $u = 0,\, a = 1{\cdot}4,\, t = 3{\cdot}5,$

$$v = 0 + 1{\cdot}4 \times 3{\cdot}5 = 4{\cdot}9$$

Hence when P hits the ground, Q has an upward velocity of $4{\cdot}9\,\mathrm{m\,s^{-1}}$.

While P is on the ground Q moves freely under gravity. Hence the time which elapses before Q returns to the position where the string slackened is given by the formula $s = ut + \frac{1}{2}at^2$, where $s = 0$, $u = 4{\cdot}9$ and $a = -9{\cdot}8$.

$$\therefore \quad 0 = 4{\cdot}9t - 4{\cdot}9t^2$$
$$\therefore \quad t = 0 \quad \text{or} \quad t = 1.$$

Hence the string is again taut after a further time of 1 s.
Since there is no loss of energy in this time, it follows that as the string tightens Q has a downward velocity of $4.9\,\mathrm{m\,s^{-1}}$.

Let $V\,\mathrm{m\,s^{-1}}$ be the speed with which P is jerked into motion and let $J\,\mathrm{N\,s}$ be the impulsive tension in the string.

$\qquad\qquad\qquad$ Impulse = change in
$\qquad\qquad\qquad\qquad\qquad\qquad$ momentum
Thus for P: $\qquad J = 4V$
and for Q: $\qquad J = 3 \times 4{\cdot}9 - 3V$
Subtracting: $\qquad 0 = 7V - 3 \times 4{\cdot}9$
$\therefore \qquad\qquad V = 2{\cdot}1$

Hence P leaves the ground at a speed of $2{\cdot}1\,\mathrm{m\,s^{-1}}$.

If we look again at the worked examples in this chapter we will see that a collision or the sudden tightening of a string often results in a loss of kinetic energy. This happens because some of the kinetic energy of the bodies involved is converted into other forms such as heat, sound or light. It is therefore important to stress that the principle of conservation of mechanical energy cannot usually be applied to a system when impulsive forces are acting.

Exercise 12.3

1.   A car of mass 1200 kg travelling in a straight line at a speed of $20\,\mathrm{m\,s}^{-1}$ is brought to rest in a distance of 50 m by a constant braking force. Find the magnitude of this force and the time taken to stop the car.

2.   A bullet of mass 25 g is fired horizontally with velocity $600\,\mathrm{m\,s}^{-1}$ into a fixed block of wood and penetrates a distance of 50 cm into it. Find the constant resistance exerted by the wood and the time taken to bring the bullet to rest.

3.   A railway truck of mass 3000 kg moving at $4\,\mathrm{m\,s}^{-1}$ collides with a truck of mass 2000 kg moving in the opposite direction at $1\,\mathrm{m\,s}^{-1}$. If the trucks move on together after the collision, find their common speed just after impact. If a constant retarding force of 400 N acts on the trucks after impact, find the distance they travel before coming to rest.

4.   A particle is projected at a speed of $7\,\mathrm{m\,s}^{-1}$ across a rough horizontal plane. After travelling a distance of 2 m it collides with a stationary particle of equal mass. The two particles coalesce and travel a further distance d m before coming to rest. If the coefficient of friction between the particles and the plane is 5/12, find the value of d.

5.   A stone of mass 5 kg is dropped from a point 10 m above horizontal ground. Find the impulse exerted by the ground on the stone if (a) it comes to rest without rebounding, (b) it rises to a maximum height of 10 cm after impact.

6.   A particle of mass 2 kg is projected vertically upwards from a point A at a speed of $21\,\mathrm{m\,s}^{-1}$. At the same instant a particle of mass 1 kg is dropped from a point 30 m vertically above A. Find the time which elapses before the two particles collide. If the particles coalesce on impact, find the speed at which they pass through A.

7.   A pile-driver of mass 1500 kg falls freely from a height of 1·6 m and strikes a pile of mass 500 kg. After the blow the pile and the driver move on together. If the pile is driven a distance of 0·3 m into the ground, find the speed at which the pile starts to move into the ground and the average resistance of the ground to penetration.

8.   A pile-driver of mass 1200 kg falls freely from a height of 3·6 m and strikes without rebounding a pile of mass 800 kg. The blow drives the pile a distance of 36 cm into the ground. Find the resistance of the ground, assumed to be constant. Find also the time for which the pile is in motion.

9. A particle P is released from rest at a point A on a smooth plane inclined at 30° to the horizontal. When it has reached a point B on the plane, P collides with a particle Q, of equal mass, moving up the plane at $7\,\mathrm{m\,s}^{-1}$. After the collision P moves up the plane coming to rest instantaneously at A. Given that Q is brought to rest by the impact, find the distance AB.

10. A bullet of mass 30 g is fired into a stationary block of wood of mass 5 kg and becomes embedded in it. The block is freely suspended from a fixed point and after impact swings to a height of 40 cm above its initial position. Find, correct to 3 significant figures, the velocity of the bullet just before impact.

11. Two beads, A of mass m and B of mass $2m$, are threaded on a smooth circular wire fixed in a vertical plane. Initially A is at rest at the lowest point O of the wire and B is released from rest at a height h above O. Just before B collides with A it is moving with velocity v and immediately after impact A starts to move with velocity v. Find, in terms of h, the height above O at which each bead first comes to rest.

12. A particle P is attached to one end of a light inextensible string of length 1·25 m, the other end being attached to a fixed point A. The string is taut and inclined at an angle of 60° to the downward vertical when P is released from rest. As P reaches its lowest point B, it strikes a stationary particle Q, of equal mass, which is free to move horizontally. If the speed of Q just after impact is $2\cdot1\,\mathrm{m\,s}^{-1}$, find the maximum height above B to which P rises after the collision.

13. Particles A and B, of masses 1 kg and 3 kg respectively are attached to the ends of a light inextensible string passing over a smooth light pulley. The system is released from rest with both parts of the string taut and vertical. After A has travelled 1·8 m it hits and coalesces with a stationary particle C, of mass 4 kg. Find the new velocity of the system and the impulsive tension in the string at the instant when C is picked up.

14. Particles A and B, of masses 1 kg and 2 kg respectively, are connected by a light inextensible string which passes over a smooth light pulley. The system is released from rest with the string taut and the hanging parts vertical. After 4·5 s A picks up a stationary particle of mass 3 kg. Find the velocity of the system immediately after impact and the further time which elapses before the system first comes instantaneously to rest.

15. A particle A of mass 5 kg is connected to a particle B of mass 2 kg by means of a light inextensible string which passes over a smooth light pulley. The system is released from rest with both parts of the string taut and vertical. After 3·5 s particle A hits the ground without rebounding. Assuming that particle B does not hit the pulley, find the further time which elapses before the string is again taut. Find also the speed with which A leaves the ground.

16. Particles P and Q, of masses m and $2m$ respectively, are connected by a light inextensible string which passes over a smooth light pulley. The system is released from rest with the string taut and both particles at a height h above the ground.

Assuming that Q hits the ground without rebounding and that P does not hit the pulley, find expressions for (a) the greatest height above the ground reached by P, (b) the impulsive tension in the string when Q leaves the ground again.

17. A particle A, of mass 4 kg, rests on a smooth plane inclined at an angle of $30°$ to the horizontal. It is connected by a light inextensible string passing over a smooth pulley fixed at the top of the plane to a particle B, of mass 3 kg, which hangs freely. The system is released from rest with both parts of the string taut. When B has fallen a distance of 6·3 m A picks up a particle C, of mass 3·5 kg, which was previously at rest. Find the velocity of the system immediately after C has been picked up. Find also the loss in kinetic energy as C is picked up, giving your answer correct to 3 significant figures.

18. A pile of mass M is being driven into the ground by a pile-driver of mass m. The pile-driver is released from rest at a height h above the top of the pile and falls freely under gravity on to the top of the pile. The pile-driver rebounds vertically from the top of the pile and, after the first impact, it comes first to rest at a point $\frac{3}{4}h$ below the original point of release. (i) Find the kinetic energy lost by the pile-driver in the first impact. (ii) Find the kinetic energy gained by the pile in the first impact, assuming that the momentum of the system is conserved in the impact. (iii) Given that the pile is driven a distance $\frac{1}{16}h$ into the ground by the first impact, show that the frictional resistance, assumed constant, between the pile and the ground is $(36m^2 + M^2)g/M$.

(C)

19. Two particles, A and B, of masses $2m$ and $3m$ respectively, are attached to the ends of a light inextensible string of length c and are placed close together on a horizontal table. The particle A is projected vertically upwards with speed $\sqrt{(6gc)}$. (i) Show that, at the instant immediately after the string tightens, B is moving with velocity $\frac{4}{5}\sqrt{(gc)}$. (ii) State the impulse of the tension in the string. (iii) Find the height to which A rises above the table before it comes to instantaneous rest. (iv) Calculate the loss in kinetic energy due to the tightening of the string.   (AEB 1979)

20. A cube of mass 100 g and side 14 cm is at rest on a smooth horizontal table. A bullet of mass 20 g is fired with velocity 400 m s^{-1} into the centre of a vertical face of the cube. The bullet travels through the cube in a direction perpendicular to this face and emerges undeflected with velocity 200 m s^{-1}. Find the velocity of the cube as the bullet emerges. Find the kinetic energy gained by the cube and the kinetic energy lost by the bullet. If the cube moves a distance of d cm before the bullet emerges, write down the distance moved by the bullet as it passes through the cube. By considering the work done on the cube and on the bullet, determine the value of d and the magnitude of the constant force exerted by the cube on the bullet.

12.4 Newton's law of restitution

In a collision between two elastic bodies the impulses exerted by each body on the other produce changes in momentum and the bodies bounce away from each other.

If both bodies are moving along the line of action of these impulses at the instant the collision occurs, then the impact is said to be *direct*. Otherwise it is described as *indirect* or *oblique*. Both types of elastic impact were investigated by Sir Isaac Newton and as a result of his experimental work he was able to formulate a law of impact which is known as *Newton's law of restitution* or as *Newton's experimental law*. In its general form the law concerns the indirect impact of two moving bodies. However, we first consider its application to the direct impact of one body with a fixed plane.

Our everyday experience tells us that if several objects made of different materials are dropped from a given height on to horizontal ground, then the various objects will probably rebound to different heights after impact. A lump of plasticine will become flattened and show little tendency to rebound, whereas a "superball" will regain most of its original height. The behaviour of most objects will come somewhere between these two extremes.

Further observation shows that when a body strikes a fixed plane there is a period of time during which the body is compressed and its speed is reduced to zero. This is followed by a period of restitution in which the body regains its original shape and starts to rebound. While the body is being compressed some of its original kinetic energy is stored as elastic potential energy and this is then released as the body rebounds. The remaining kinetic energy is converted into other forms such as heat energy. Thus, the behaviour of a particular body during impact depends on its elasticity.

Experimental evidence suggests that in a series of direct collisions between a given elastic body a fixed plane the ratio of the speed of the body after impact to its speed before impact is approximately constant. Thus, in its simplest form, Newton's law of restitution states that if the speed of the body before impact is u and its speed after impact is v, then

$$v = eu,$$

where e is constant for that particular body. The constant e is known as the *coefficient of restitution* between the body and the plane and its value always lies between 0 and 1. If $e = 0$, collisions between the body and the plane are said to be *inelastic*, but if $e = 1$ they are described as *perfectly elastic*.

Example 1 A ball dropped from a height of 9 m above horizontal ground rebounds to a height of 4 m. Find the coefficient of restitution between the ball and the ground.

Substituting $u = 0, a = g, s = 9$ in the formula $v^2 = u^2 + 2as$,
we have: $v^2 = 0 + 2g \times 9$
∴ $v = 3\sqrt{(2g)}$

Hence the speed of the ball just before impact is $3\sqrt{(2g)} \, \mathrm{m \, s^{-1}}$.
Substituting $v = 0, a = -g, s = 4$ in the formula $v^2 = u^2 + 2as$,
we have: $0 = u^2 - 2g \times 4$
∴ $u = 2\sqrt{(2g)}$

Hence the speed of the ball just after impact is $2\sqrt{(2g)} \, \mathrm{m \, s^{-1}}$.

Thus, if e is the coefficient of restitution,

$$2\sqrt{(2g)} = e \times 3\sqrt{(2g)}$$
$$\therefore \qquad e = \tfrac{2}{3}.$$

When considering indirect impacts between an elastic body and a smooth fixed plane, it is found that Newton's law of restitution can be applied to motion perpendicular to the plane.

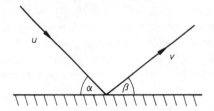

Let us suppose that a body strikes a smooth fixed plane while travelling with speed u in a direction inclined at an angle α to the plane, then rebounds with speed v at an angle β to the plane.

Since the plane is smooth no force acts along the plane and therefore there is no change in the component of velocity along the plane

i.e. $\qquad\qquad\qquad v \cos \beta = u \cos \alpha.$

However, the impulse of the normal reaction of the plane changes the component of velocity perpendicular to the plane in accordance with Newton's law,

i.e. $\qquad\qquad\qquad v \sin \beta = eu \sin \alpha,$

where e is the coefficient of restitution.

Example 2   A particle of mass 2 kg strikes a fixed smooth plane while moving at a speed of $24\,\mathrm{m\,s^{-1}}$ in a direction making an angle of $30°$ with the plane. If the coefficient of restitution between the particle and the plane is $\tfrac{1}{4}$, find the speed at which the particle rebounds. Find also the impulse exerted by the plane on the particle.

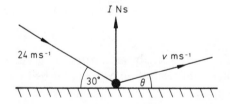

Let the velocity of the particle after impact be $v\,\mathrm{m\,s^{-1}}$ at an angle θ to the plane and let the impulse exerted by the plane be $I\,\mathrm{N\,s}$.

There is no change in velocity parallel to the plane

$$\therefore \quad v \cos \theta = 24 \cos 30° = 12\sqrt{3}.$$

By Newton's law of restitution perpendicular to the plane,

$$v \sin \theta = \tfrac{1}{4} \times 24 \sin 30° = 3$$

Squaring and adding: $v^2 \cos^2 \theta + v^2 \sin^2 \theta = (12\sqrt{3})^2 + 3^2$
$$\therefore \qquad\qquad\qquad v = \sqrt{(432 + 9)} = 21.$$
Hence the speed of the particle after impact is $21\,\mathrm{m\,s^{-1}}$.

Considering the motion of the particle perpendicular to the plane,

impulse = change in momentum

∴ $I = 2 \times v \sin \theta + 2 \times 24 \sin 30° = 30.$

Hence the impulse exerted by the plane is $30\,\text{N s}$.

When applied to the direct impact of two moving bodies, Newton's law of restitution states that the ratio of the relative speed of separation after impact to the relative speed of approach before impact is constant.

Before impact $(u_1 > u_2)$ After impact $(v_1 < v_2)$

Let us suppose that two spheres of masses m_1 and m_2 collide when moving along the same straight line with velocities u_1 and u_2 respectively. Let the velocities of the spheres after impact be v_1 and v_2 respectively. Provided that all velocities are measured in the same direction, as shown in the diagram, the relative speed of approach is $(u_1 - u_2)$ and the relative speed of separation is $(v_2 - v_1)$.

> By Newton's law of restitution
> $$v_1 - v_2 = -e(u_1 - u_2)$$
> where e is the coefficient of restitution.

Assuming that no external impulse acts during the impact, we can also apply the principle of conservation of momentum to give:

$$m_1 u_1 + m_2 u_2 = m_1 v_1 + m_2 v_2$$

Example 3   A sphere A, of mass $2m$ and moving with speed $6u$, collides directly with a sphere B of mass $3m$ moving in the same direction with speed $3u$. After the impact the speed of B is $5u$. Find the coefficient of restitution between the spheres.

Before impact   After impact

6u   3u   v   5u

A (2m)   (3m) B   A (2m)   (3m) B

Let the speed of A after impact be v, as shown in the diagram.

Using the principle of conservation of momentum,

$$2m \times 6u + 3m \times 3u = 2m \times v + 3m \times 5u$$
$$\therefore \quad 12mu + 9mu = 2mv + 15mu$$
$$\therefore \quad v = 3u.$$

Using Newton's law of restitution,

$$v - 5u = -e(6u - 3u)$$
$$\therefore \quad 3u - 5u = -3eu$$
$$\therefore \quad e = \tfrac{2}{3}$$

Hence the coefficient of restitution between the spheres is $\tfrac{2}{3}$.

Example 4 A sphere of mass 5 kg, moving at $8 \, \text{m s}^{-1}$, collides directly with a sphere of mass 3 kg moving in the opposite direction at $7 \, \text{m s}^{-1}$. If the coefficient of restitution between the spheres is 0·6, find their speeds after impact. Find also the magnitude of the impulse exerted on each sphere during the collision.

Before impact		After impact	
$8 \, \text{m s}^{-1}$	$-7 \, \text{m s}^{-1}$	$v_1 \, \text{m s}^{-1}$	$v_2 \, \text{m s}^{-1}$
(5 kg)	(3 kg)	(5 kg)	(3 kg)

Let the velocities of the spheres after impact be $v_1 \, \text{m s}^{-1}$ and $v_2 \, \text{m s}^{-1}$, as shown in the diagram.
Using conservation of momentum,

$$5 \times 8 - 3 \times 7 = 5v_1 + 3v_2$$
$$\therefore \qquad 5v_1 + 3v_2 = 19 \tag{1}$$

Using Newton's law of restitution,

$$v_1 - v_2 = -0 \cdot 6\{8 - (-7)\}$$
$$\therefore \qquad v_1 - v_2 = -9 \tag{2}$$

Adding $3 \times (2)$ to (1): $\qquad 8v_1 = -8$
Hence $\qquad\qquad\qquad\qquad v_1 = -1 \quad \text{and} \quad v_2 = 8.$

Thus after impact the speed of the 5 kg sphere is $1 \, \text{m s}^{-1}$ and the speed of the 3 kg sphere is $8 \, \text{m s}^{-1}$. The directions of both spheres are reversed in the collision.

Considering the motion of the 3 kg sphere,
$$\text{impulse} = \text{change in momentum}$$
$$= 3 \times 8 - 3 \times (-7) \, \text{N s} = 45 \, \text{N s}$$

Hence the magnitude of the impulse exerted on each sphere is 45 N s.

Exercise 12.4

1.   A ball of mass 0.2 kg is dropped from a point 10 m above horizontal ground. If the coefficient of restitution between the ball and the ground is $\frac{1}{2}$, find (a) the height above the ground to which the ball rebounds, (b) the loss of kinetic energy in the impact, (c) the impulse exerted by the ground.

2.   A ball dropped from a height of 8 m above horizontal ground rebounds to a height of 4.5 m. Find the coefficient of restitution between the ball and the ground. If the ball is then dropped from a height of 12.8 m and allowed to bounce twice, find the maximum height it reaches after the second bounce.

3.   A particle is projected vertically upwards with speed $7\,\mathrm{m\,s}^{-1}$ from a point A, which is 2 m above a horizontal plane. After striking this plane the particle first comes instantaneously to rest at A. Find the coefficient of restitution between the particle and the plane.

4.   A particle of mass 3 kg strikes a fixed smooth plane while moving at a speed of $20\,\mathrm{m\,s}^{-1}$ in a direction making an angle α with the plane, where $\sin \alpha = 3/5$. If the coefficient of restitution between the particle and the plane is $2/3$, find the speed at which the particle rebounds. Find also the impulse exerted by the plane on the particle.

5.   A particle strikes a fixed smooth plane while travelling in a direction inclined at $45°$ to the plane. After impact its direction makes an angle of $30°$ with the plane. Find the coefficient of restitution between the particle and the plane. If on another occasion the particle is moving in a direction inclined at $60°$ to the plane, find its direction after impact with the plane.

6.   A particle strikes a smooth fixed plane and rebounds in a direction at right angles to its direction just before impact. If the coefficient of restitution is $\frac{1}{3}$, find the acute angle between the initial direction of motion of the particle and the plane.

7.   A particle is projected with speed $6.5\,\mathrm{m\,s}^{-1}$ at an angle θ to the horizontal, where $\tan \theta = 12/5$, from a point A on a smooth horizontal plane. The particle strikes the plane again at B, then rebounds and strikes the plane for a second time at C. The coefficient of restitution between the particle and the plane is $5/9$. Find the speed and direction with which the particle rebounds from the plane at B. Show that the distance AC is $100/21$ m.

8.   A sphere of mass $4m$ and moving with speed $5u$, collides directly with a sphere of mass $3m$, which is at rest. If the coefficient of restitution between the spheres is 0.4, find their speeds after impact. Find also the loss in kinetic energy due to the impact.

9.   A sphere A, of mass 1 kg and moving with speed $12\,\mathrm{m\,s}^{-1}$, collides directly with a sphere B, of mass 4 kg, moving in the same direction with speed $2\,\mathrm{m\,s}^{-1}$. Given that sphere A is brought to rest by the collision, find the coefficient of restitution between the spheres.

10. A sphere moving with speed $7\,\text{m s}^{-1}$ collides directly with an identical sphere moving in the opposite direction with speed $2\,\text{m s}^{-1}$. Find the speeds of the spheres after impact if the coefficient of restitution is (a) $\frac{1}{3}$, (b) $\frac{2}{3}$. In each case state whether the spheres are travelling in the same direction or in opposite directions.

11. A sphere of mass m moving with speed $9u$ collides directly with a sphere of mass M moving in the same direction with speed $5u$. After impact the spheres move in the same direction with speeds $6u$ and $7u$. Find the coefficient of restitution between the spheres and the ratio $m:M$.

12. Three perfectly elastic particles A, B, C, with masses $4\,\text{kg}, 2\,\text{kg}, 3\,\text{kg}$ respectively, lie at rest in a straight line on a smooth horizontal table. Particle A is projected towards B with speed $15\,\text{m s}^{-1}$ and after A has collided with B, B collides with C. Find the velocities of the particles after the second collision and state whether there will be a third collision.

13. Three identical spheres A, B, C, lie at rest in a straight line on a smooth horizontal table. Particle A is projected towards B with speed u. After the collision between A and B, B moves on to hit C. The coefficient of restitution between any two of the spheres is $\frac{1}{2}$. Find the speeds of the spheres after the second collision and state whether there will be a third collision.

14. A sphere A of mass $2m$, moving on a smooth horizontal floor with speed $5u$, collides directly with a sphere B of mass m, which is at rest. If the coefficient of restitution between the spheres is $4/5$, find the speed of B after impact. Sphere B goes on to strike a vertical wall, which is at right angles to the direction of motion of the spheres. A is then brought to rest by a second collision with B. Find the coefficient of restitution between B and the wall.

15. A small smooth sphere moves on a horizontal table and strikes an identical sphere lying at rest on the table at a distance d from a vertical wall, the impact being along the line of centres and perpendicular to the wall. Prove that the next impact between the spheres will take place at a distance $2de^2/(1 + e^2)$ from the wall, where e is the coefficient of restitution for all impacts involved. (L)

16. The coefficient of restitution between two small, smooth spheres A and B is e. The mass of A is m and of B is em. Show that, if A is at rest and B is projected with velocity u to collide directly with A, B is reduced to rest by the collision. If, instead, B is at rest and A is projected with the same speed to hit B directly, find the velocities of A and B after the collision. Show that the loss of kinetic energy is the same in each collision and is greatest when $e = \frac{1}{2}$. (SU)

17. Two small spheres of masses m and $2m$ are connected by a light inextensible string of length $2a$. When the string is taut and horizontal, its mid-point is fixed and the spheres are released from rest. The coefficient of restitution between the spheres is $\frac{1}{2}$. Show that the first impact brings the heavier sphere to rest, and the second impact brings the lighter sphere to rest. Find the velocity of each sphere immediately after the third impact. (L)

18. Three small smooth spheres A, B, C, of equal radius but of mass $m, 2m$ and m respectively, lie at rest and separated from one another on a smooth horizontal table in the order ABC with their centres in a straight line. Sphere A is projected with speed V directly towards sphere B. The coefficient of restitution at each collision is e, where $0 < e < 1$. Find, in terms of V and e, the speeds of the three spheres (a) after the first collision (between A and B), (b) after the second collision (between B and C). Hence show that there will be at least three collisions if $e^2 - 7e + 1 > 0$.   (O&C)

Exercise 12.5 (miscellaneous)

1.   Two particles of masses $2m$ and $3m$ are moving towards each other with speeds $4u$ and $2u$ respectively. The direction of motion of the heavier particle is reversed by the impact and its speed after impact is u. Find (i) the magnitude of the impulse, (ii) the loss of energy.   (C)

2.   A particle of mass 4 kg moves under the action of a force $\mathbf{F}$ in the interval of time from $t = 0$ to $t = 2$. When $t = 0$ the velocity of the particle is $2\mathbf{i} - 3\mathbf{j}$. Given that $\mathbf{F} = 6t\mathbf{i} + 2\mathbf{j}$, find (a) the impulse of $\mathbf{F}$, (b) the velocity of the particle when $t = 2$, (c) the gain in kinetic energy.

3.   A particle of mass m moves in a horizontal plane Oxy with speed v along the x-axis in the positive direction. It is subjected to a horizontal impulse $\mathbf{I}$ which turns its direction of motion through $30°$ in an anticlockwise sense and reduces its speed to $v/\sqrt{3}$. Find the vector $\mathbf{I}$. At the same instant an impulse $-\mathbf{I}$ is applied to a particle of mass $3m$ which is at rest. Find the magnitude and direction of the resultant velocity of this particle.   (JMB)

4.   A pump raises water from an underground reservoir through a height of 10 m and delivers it at a speed of 9 m s^{-1} through a circular pipe of internal diameter 20 cm. Taking 1 litre of water to have a mass of 1 kg and g to have the value $9 \cdot 8 \text{ m s}^{-2}$ find (i) the mass of water raised per second, correct to 3 sig. fig.; (ii) the kinetic energy imparted to the water each second, correct to 3 sig. fig.; (iii) the effective power of the pump correct to 2 sig. fig.; (iv) the actual power of the pump if it is 70% efficient. If the water hits a vertical wall horizontally and does not rebound calculate the magnitude of the force exerted on the wall, correct to 2 sig. fig.   (SU)

5.   A light inextensible string AB has a particle of mass $2m$ attached at A and a particle of mass m attached at B. The particles are placed on a smooth horizontal table with the string taut. A horizontal impulse is applied to the particle at A of magnitude mu in a direction which makes an angle of $120°$ with AB. (i) Show that B

starts to move along BA with speed $u/6$. (ii) Find the components of the initial velocity of the particle at A along BA and perpendicular to BA and state the magnitude of the impulse of the tension in the string.   (AEB 1977)

6.   A composite particle of mass $m_1 + m_2$ is formed as a result of a head-on collision between two particles of masses m_1, m_2 travelling with speeds u_1, u_2 respectively. Find the speed of the composite particle in terms of m_1, m_2, u_1, u_2. Show that the collision leads to a loss of kinetic energy of amount

$$\frac{1}{2}\left(\frac{m_1 m_2}{m_1 + m_2}\right)(u_1 + u_2)^2. \tag{W}$$

7.   A gun of mass M fires a shell of mass m horizontally. The recoil of the gun is opposed by a constant force F which brings the gun to rest in t seconds. Show that the energy of the explosion is $\dfrac{F^2 t^2 (M + m)}{2Mm}$.   (O)

8.   A particle of mass m is dropped from rest from a point A which is at a height h above a horizontal surface. After hitting the surface the particle rebounds vertically and reaches a maximum height of $\frac{1}{2}h$ above the surface at the point B. Find expressions for the loss of energy and the impulse on the particle at the impact. At the instant of the particle's impact with the surface, a second particle, of mass $4m$, is dropped from rest at A. Show that the two particles collide at B. The two particles coalesce when they collide at B. When the combined particle hits the surface, one-half of its kinetic energy is lost in the impact. Show that, after the impact, the combined particle reaches a greatest height of $41h/100$ above the surface.   (C)

9.   Two beads, one of mass 3 g and the other of mass 2 g, are threaded on a smooth circular wire which is fixed with its plane vertical. The heavier bead is initially at rest at the lowest point L of the wire. The lighter bead is released from rest and is moving with speed $2 \, \text{m s}^{-1}$ when it strikes the other bead. There is no loss of energy in the impact. Find the speed of each bead immediately after impact. In the subsequent motion each bead comes to rest instantaneously before reaching the highest point of the wire. Find, to the nearest millimetre, the height above L at which each bead comes first to rest.   (C)

10.   A pile-driver of mass 2000 kg is raised 1·6 m above a pile of mass 1500 kg and then dropped on to it. After impact the driver and the pile move together and the pile is driven 0·2 m into the ground. Find (i) the velocity of the pile-driver just before it hits the pile, (ii) the common velocity of pile and driver immediately after impact, (iii) the loss of energy on impact, stating the units in which it is measured, (iv) the mean resistance of the ground to penetration.   (AEB 1980)

11.   A particle A of mass $3m$ lies on a smooth horizontal rectangular table at a distance $5a$ from a point C at the edge of the table. The particle is attached to one end of a light inelastic string of length $6a$ which passes over a small smooth pulley at C.

To the other end of the string is attached a particle B of mass $2m$. The horizontal floor is at a depth $4a$ below C. The particle B is released from rest at C and motion takes place in a vertical plane perpendicular to the edge of the table. Show that the speed of the particles immediately after the string becomes taut is $\frac{2}{3}\sqrt{(2ga)}$. Find (i) the magnitude of the impulse which acts on the particle A, (ii) the loss of kinetic energy of the system due to the string becoming taut, (iii) the speed of the particle B just before it hits the floor. (C)

12. Two masses, one $3\,\text{kg}$ and the other $2\,\text{kg}$, are connected by a light inextensible string which passes over a fixed smooth pulley and the system is released from rest. Find the acceleration of the system and show that the tension in the string is $23\cdot52\,\text{N}$. After falling 2 metres the heavier mass strikes a fixed horizontal plane and is brought to rest. If the lighter mass does not reach the pulley, show that after $4/7$ seconds the $3\,\text{kg}$ mass is again in motion. Find the speed with which it begins to ascend and the impulsive tension in the string. (W)

13. Two particles A and B, each of mass m and connected by a light inextensible string of length $4a$, are resting on a smooth horizontal table with $AB = 2a$. A particle C of mass $3m$ is attached to the midpoint of the string and rests on the table so that $AC = BC$. The particles A and B are then simultaneously projected along the table with equal velocities perpendicular to AB and in the sense away from C. Show that, when the string tightens, the initial velocities of the particles A and B are each inclined at angle $\frac{1}{3}\pi$ with the line AB. (O)

14. A particle P of mass $2m$ is connected to a particle Q of mass $3m$ by means of a light inextensible string which passes over a small smooth pulley. The particles are released from rest with the string taut and its hanging parts vertical. (i) Calculate the acceleration of P and the tension in the string. At the instant when P is moving with velocity v it collides and coalesces with a stationary particle of mass $3m$ to form a particle P_1. (ii) Prove that the velocity of P_1 immediately after the collision is $5v/8$. (iii) Calculate the magnitude of the impulse of the tension in the string. (iv) Calculate the loss in kinetic energy of the whole system due to the collision.

The string breaks and particle Q hits a horizontal floor when moving with speed u and bounces to a height $u^2/(6g)$ above the floor. (v) Calculate the coefficient of restitution between Q and the floor. (AEB 1979)

15. A bullet of mass m travelling horizontally with speed u strikes perpendicularly a wooden block of mass M which is free to move horizontally in the line of motion of the bullet. The resistance to penetration is assumed uniform and the bullet comes to rest after penetrating a distance a into the block. Show that the ultimate common velocity of the system is $mu/(m + M)$ and that the total loss of kinetic energy during the penetration is $mMu^2/2(m + M)$. Deduce the value of the resistance and show that (i) the block moves a distance $am/(m + M)$ before the bullet comes to rest relative to the block, (ii) the penetration by the bullet ceases after a time $2a/u$. (W)

16. A particle of mass m is attached to one end of a light inextensible string of length a, the other end being attached to a fixed point O. Initially the string is taut and

makes an angle $\alpha \, (\leqslant 90°)$ with the downward vertical at O. The particle is released and, when it is at its lowest point A, coalesces with a stationary particle of mass m. The combined body next comes to rest with the string making an angle β with the downward vertical at O. Show that $1 - \cos \beta = \frac{1}{4}(1 - \cos \alpha)$.

The motion continues so that each time the body passes through A it coalesces with a stationary particle of mass m. If $\alpha = 90°$, (a) prove that the speed of the body just before passing through A for the fourth time is $\frac{1}{4}\sqrt{(2ag)}$, (b) find the angle (correct to the nearest degree) made by the string with the downward vertical at O when the body next comes to instantaneous rest after passing through A for the fourth time, (c) find the ratio of the tensions in the string just before and just after the body passes through A for the fourth time.   (O&C)

17. Two equal particles are projected at the same instant from points A and B on horizontal ground, the first from A with speed u at an angle of elevation α and the second from B with speed v at an angle of elevation β. They collide directly when they are moving horizontally in opposite directions. Find v in terms of u, α and β, and show that $AB = \dfrac{u^2 \sin \alpha \sin (\alpha + \beta)}{g \sin \beta}$. The particles coalesce on impact. Find, in terms of u, α and β, the speed of the combined particle immediately after the collision. In the case when $\alpha = 30°$ and $\beta = 60°$ find AC, where C is the point where the combined particle returns to the ground.   (JMB)

18. A ball is thrown vertically upwards from the floor with velocity V. It rebounds from the ceiling, which is at height h above the floor, and then rebounds from the floor. After this second rebound, it just reaches the ceiling again. If the coefficient of restitution between the ball and ceiling is e, and between the ball and floor is f, prove that

$$V^2 = \frac{2gh(1 - f^2 + e^2 f^2)}{e^2 f^2}.$$ (SU)

19. A particle of mass m strikes a fixed smooth plane at speed u while moving in a direction inclined at an angle α to the plane, then rebounds at an angle β to the plane. Find expressions for (a) the coefficient of restitution between the particle and the plane, (b) the speed of the particle after impact, (c) the impulse exerted on the plane.

20. A particle of mass m, projected from a point A with speed u at an angle of elevation α, strikes a smooth vertical wall at a point B and after rebounding returns to A. Show that the total time taken to move from A to B and then back to A is $(2u \sin \alpha)/g$. Given that e is the coefficient of restitution between the particle and the wall, find expressions for (a) the loss of kinetic energy on impact, (b) the distance of A from the wall.

21. Two elastic spheres of masses m and M collide directly. Their velocities before impact are $12 \, \text{m/s}$ and $6 \, \text{m/s}$ respectively in the same direction, and after impact they are $5 \, \text{m/s}$ and $8 \, \text{m/s}$ respectively also in the same direction. Find the coefficient of restitution and also the ratio $m:M$. Find also the velocities of the spheres after

impact if they collide directly when travelling in opposite directions, the velocity of the heavier sphere being 4 m/s and that of the lighter sphere 14 m/s.   (L)

22. Three small spheres A, B and C, of equal radii and masses m, $2m$ and $3m$ respectively, are placed with their centres in a straight line on a smooth horizontal table with B between A and C. The sphere A is given a velocity $5u$ in the direction $\overrightarrow{AB}$ and, as a result of the ensuing collision between A and B, B moves towards C with speed $3u$. Calculate (i) the magnitude and the sense of the velocity of A after the collision, (ii) the coefficient of restitution between A and B, (iii) the loss in kinetic energy due to the collision between A and B.

The sphere B strikes C and as a result C receives an impulse of $4mu$. Calculate (iv) the velocities of B and C after their collision, (v) the coefficient of restitution between B and C.   (AEB 1978)

23. A small sphere A, of mass m moving with velocity $2u$ on a smooth horizontal plane, impinges directly on a small sphere B, of equal radius and mass $2m$ moving with velocity u in the same direction on the plane. Given that after impact B moves with velocity $3u/2$, calculate (i) the coefficient of restitution between A and B, (ii) the loss in kinetic energy due to the impact. The sphere B continues to move with velocity $3u/2$ until it hits a vertical wall from which it rebounds and is then brought to rest by a second impact with the approaching sphere A. Calculate (iii) the coefficient of restitution between B and the wall, (iv) the final speed of the sphere.   (AEB 1980)

24. Particles A and B of mass m and $2m$ respectively lie at rest on a smooth horizontal plane. They are projected towards each other both with speed u. Show that, if the coefficient of restitution between the particles is $\frac{3}{4}$, their directions of motion are reversed on impact and find their speeds after impact. Find, also, the loss of kinetic energy during impact. If A subsequently hits a smooth vertical plane normally, show that A and B will collide again only if the coefficient of restitution between A and the vertical plane is greater than $1/8$.   (SU)

25. Two particles A, B of masses M, m respectively are attached to a fixed point O by light inextensible strings of equal length. The particle A is held so that its string is taut and horizontal. It is then released so that it strikes the particle B which was hanging in equilibrium. Prove that if OB just reaches the horizontal then $Me = m$, where e is the coefficient of restitution between the particles.   (O)

26. Two particles, A of mass $2m$ and B of mass m, moving on a smooth horizontal table in opposite directions with speeds $5u$ and $3u$ respectively, collide directly. Find their velocities after the collision in terms of u and the coefficient of restitution e. Show that the magnitude of the impulse exerted by B on A is $16mu(1 + e)/3$. Find the value of e for which the speed of B after the collision is $3u$. Moving at this speed B subsequently collides with a stationary particle C of mass km, and thereafter remains attached to C. Find the velocity of the combined particle and find the range of values of k for which a third collision will occur.   (JMB)

27. Identical beads P and Q are threaded on a smooth circular hoop fixed in a horizontal plane. Initially Q is at rest at a point A of the hoop when P collides with it. Denoting the coefficient of restitution between P and Q by e, find the values of e for which the next collision takes place at A. 			(JMB)

13 Further particle dynamics

13.1 Acceleration as a function of displacement

Let us consider a particle moving along a straight line so that at time t its displacement from a fixed point on the line is s. The velocity v and the acceleration a of the particle at time t are given by:

$$v = \frac{ds}{dt} \quad \text{and} \quad a = \frac{dv}{dt} = \frac{d^2 s}{dt^2}$$

Suppose now that the acceleration a is regarded as a function of the displacement s, then, using the chain rule,

$$a = \frac{dv}{dt} = \frac{dv}{ds} \times \frac{ds}{dt} = \frac{dv}{ds} \times v = v \frac{dv}{ds}$$

$\therefore$ if $a = f(s)$, then
$$v \frac{dv}{ds} = f(s),$$

giving
$$\int v \, dv = \int f(s) \, ds$$

$\therefore$
$$\tfrac{1}{2} v^2 = \int f(s) \, ds$$

i.e.
$$v^2 = 2 \int f(s) \, ds$$

Thus if the acceleration a is a function of the displacement s, the relationship $a = v \dfrac{dv}{ds}$ may be used to obtain an expression for v^2 in terms of s.

Example 1　A particle of mass m moves in a straight line under the action of a force directed towards a fixed point O of the line. The magnitude of the force is $3ms^2$, where

273

s is the displacement of the particle from O at time t. Given that the particle starts from rest at a distance $2a$ from O, find the speed of the particle as it reaches O.

If v is the velocity of the particle at time t, then its acceleration is $v\dfrac{dv}{ds}$ in the direction of the displacement s. Since the force of magnitude $3ms^2$ acts in the opposite direction,

by Newton's second law, $\quad mv\dfrac{dv}{ds} = -3ms^2$

$\therefore \qquad\qquad\qquad v\dfrac{dv}{ds} = -3s^2$

$\therefore \qquad\qquad\qquad \displaystyle\int v\,dv = -\int 3s^2\,ds$

$$\tfrac{1}{2}v^2 = -s^3 + c$$

But $v = 0$ when $s = 2a$,

$\therefore \qquad\qquad\qquad 0 = -8a^3 + c \quad$ i.e. $\quad c = 8a^3$

Thus $\qquad\qquad\qquad v^2 = 2(8a^3 - s^3),$

and when $s = 0$, $\qquad\quad v^2 = 16a^3.$

Hence when the particle reaches O its speed is $4a^{3/2}$.

Example 2 Assuming that the earth is a sphere of radius R, the acceleration due to gravity of an object at a distance x from the centre of the earth is inversely proportional to x^2 when above the earth's surface and equal to g on the surface. Given that an object projected vertically upwards from the earth's surface with speed u rises to a maximum height R above the surface, find u in terms of g and R.

The acceleration of the object is inversely proportional to the square of the displacement x and in the opposite direction,

$\therefore \qquad\qquad\qquad v\dfrac{dv}{dx} = -\dfrac{k}{x^2},$

where v is the velocity and k is constant.
Since the acceleration is $-g$ when $x = R$,

$$-g = -\dfrac{k}{R^2} \quad \text{giving} \quad k = gR^2.$$

$\therefore \qquad\qquad\qquad v\dfrac{dv}{dx} = -\dfrac{gR^2}{x^2}$

$\therefore \qquad\qquad\qquad \displaystyle\int v\,dv = -\int \dfrac{gR^2}{x^2}\,dx$

$$\tfrac{1}{2}v^2 = \dfrac{gR^2}{x} + c$$

Given that $v = 0$ when $x = 2R$,

$$0 = \tfrac{1}{2}gR + c \quad \text{i.e.} \quad c = -\tfrac{1}{2}gR$$

$$\therefore \quad v^2 = \frac{2gR^2}{x} - gR$$

Since $v = u$ when $x = R$, $\quad u^2 = \dfrac{2gR^2}{R} - gR = gR$

Hence $\qquad\qquad\qquad u = \sqrt{(gR)}.$

Exercise 13.1

In questions 1 to 4 a particle moves in a straight line so that after t seconds its displacement from a fixed point on the line is s metres and its velocity is $v\,\mathrm{m\,s^{-1}}$.

1. Given that the acceleration of the particle is $1/(1 + t)\,\mathrm{m\,s^{-2}}$ and that the particle starts from rest, find its speed after 2 seconds.

2. Given that the particle is subject to a retardation of $5e^{-t}\,\mathrm{m\,s^{-2}}$ and that its initial speed is $4\,\mathrm{m\,s^{-1}}$, find the time at which the particle first comes to rest.

3. Given that the acceleration of the particle is $2s\,\mathrm{m\,s^{-2}}$ and that $v = 2$ when $s = 0$, find the speed of the particle when $s = 4$.

4. Given that the particle is subject to a retardation of $2\sin^2 s\,\mathrm{m\,s^{-2}}$ and that $v = 1$ when $s = \pi/4$, find, correct to 3 significant figures, the speed of the particle when $s = \pi/3$.

5. A particle of mass m moving along a straight line is subject to a force $4mx$ acting towards a fixed point O on the line, where x is the displacement of the particle from O. Given that the particle starts from rest at a distance a from O, find the speed of the particle as it passes through O.

6. The acceleration due to gravity of an object at a distance x from the centre of the earth is inversely proportional to x^2 when above the earth's surface and equal to g on the surface. The earth is assumed to be a sphere of radius R. If an object falls from rest at a height $2R$ above the earth's surface, find its speed when it reaches a height R above the surface.

7. A particle of mass m is moving in a straight line under the action of a force $4m/x^3$ directed towards a fixed point O of the line, x being the displacement of the particle from O. Given that initially the particle is at a distance h from O, moving away from O at a speed of $2/h$, find expressions for (a) dx/dt in terms of x, and (b) x in terms of t and h.

8. A particle of mass m is moving in a straight line under the action of a force of magnitude $\tfrac{1}{4}e^{2x}$, where x is the displacement of the particle from a fixed

point O on the line. Initially the particle is at a point A travelling towards O at speed u. Given that the force on the particle acts in the direction of $\overrightarrow{OA}$ and that $OA = \ln(2u)$, find an expression for dx/dt in terms of x. Hence show that

$$x = \ln\left(\frac{2u}{1 + ut}\right).$$

13.2 Acceleration as a function of velocity

We consider again a particle moving in a straight line so that at time t its displacement from a fixed point on the line is s and its velocity is v. If the acceleration of the particle is a function of the velocity, $f(v)$ say, then we may write:

(1) $\dfrac{dv}{dt} = f(v)$, or (2) $v\dfrac{dv}{ds} = f(v)$.

Equation (1) is used when a relationship between velocity and time is required. However, equation (2) may be used to obtain a relationship between velocity and displacement.

Example 1 A particle of mass m is projected vertically upwards from a point O with speed u and after time t its velocity is v. Given that the particle moves under gravity in a medium which exerts a resistance kv per unit mass, where k is a positive constant, find the time taken by the particle to reach its greatest height.

As the particle rises to its highest point the forces acting on it are its weight mg and the resistance mkv, both directed vertically downwards.

Thus, by Newton's second law, $-mg - mkv = m\dfrac{dv}{dt}$

$\therefore$ $\qquad\qquad\qquad -(g + kv) = \dfrac{dv}{dt}$

$$1 = -\frac{1}{(g + kv)}\frac{dv}{dt}$$

$\therefore$ $\qquad\qquad\qquad \displaystyle\int dt = -\int\frac{1}{g + kv}\,dv$

$$t = -\frac{1}{k}\ln(g + kv) + c$$

Since $v = u$ when $t = 0$, $c = \dfrac{1}{k}\ln(g + ku)$

$\therefore$ $\qquad\quad t = -\dfrac{1}{k}\ln(g + kv) + \dfrac{1}{k}\ln(g + ku) = \dfrac{1}{k}\ln\left(\dfrac{g + ku}{g + kv}\right)$

$\therefore$ when $v = 0, t = \dfrac{1}{k}\ln\left(\dfrac{g + ku}{g}\right)$

Hence the time taken by the particle to reach its greatest height is $\dfrac{1}{k}\ln\left(1 + \dfrac{ku}{g}\right)$.

Example 2　A particle of mass m moves in a straight line under the action of a retarding force $mv^4/2k^4$, where k is a positive constant and v is the velocity of the particle. Initially the particle is at a distance k^2 from a fixed point A, travelling away from A at speed k. Find the speed of the particle when its displacement from A is x. Find also the time which elapses before the particle reaches the point B, where $AB = 4k^2$.

Writing the acceleration of the particle in the form $v\,dv/dx$ and using Newton's second law we have:

$$-\frac{mv^4}{2k^4} = mv\frac{dv}{dx}$$

$$\therefore \quad \frac{1}{k^4} = -\frac{2}{v^3}\frac{dv}{dx}$$

$$\therefore \quad \int \frac{1}{k^4}\,dx = \int \left(-\frac{2}{v^3}\right)dv$$

Thus
$$\frac{x}{k^4} = \frac{1}{v^2} + c$$

Since $v = k$ when $x = k^2$, $\quad \dfrac{1}{k^2} = \dfrac{1}{k^2} + c \quad$ i.e. $\quad c = 0$

$$\therefore \quad \frac{x}{k^4} = \frac{1}{v^2}$$

$$v^2 = \frac{k^4}{x}$$

Hence when the displacement of the particle from A is x, its speed is $k^2/\sqrt{x}$.

$\therefore$　if x is the displacement from A at time t,

$$\frac{k^2}{\sqrt{x}} = \frac{dx}{dt}$$

$$\therefore \quad \int k^2\,dt = \int x^{1/2}\,dx$$

$$k^2 t = \tfrac{2}{3}x^{3/2} + C$$

Since $x = k^2$ when $t = 0$, $\quad C = -\tfrac{2}{3}k^3$

$$\therefore \quad k^2 t = \tfrac{2}{3}(x^{3/2} - k^3)$$

Thus when $x = 4k^2$, $\quad k^2 t = \tfrac{2}{3}(8k^3 - k^3) = 14k^3/3$

Hence the time which elapses before the particle reaches B is $14k/3$.

Example 3　A car of mass m moving on a straight horizontal road is subject to a constant resistance R. The engine is working at a constant rate kR. Given that in time t the car accelerates to a speed v from rest, where $v < k$, find an expression for t in terms of m, R, k and v. Find also an expression for the distance x travelled by the car in this time.

If the tractive force exerted by the engine is F when the car is travelling at speed v, then its rate of working $= kR = Fv$,

$$\therefore \qquad F = kR/v$$

Using Newton's second law, the equation of motion is

$$\frac{kR}{v} - R = m\frac{dv}{dt}$$

$$\therefore \qquad R\left(\frac{k-v}{v}\right) = m\frac{dv}{dt} \qquad (1)$$

$$\therefore \qquad \int R\,dt = \int m\left(\frac{v}{k-v}\right)dv$$

$$= \int m\left(\frac{k}{k-v} - 1\right)dv$$

$$\therefore \qquad Rt = m\{-k\ln(k-v) - v\} + c$$

Since $v = 0$ when $t = 0$, $\quad c = mk\ln k$

$$\therefore \qquad Rt = m\{-k\ln(k-v) - v + k\ln k\}$$

Hence

$$t = \frac{m}{R}\left\{k\ln\left(\frac{k}{k-v}\right) - v\right\}$$

Substituting $\dfrac{dv}{dt} = v\dfrac{dv}{dx}$ in equation (1),

$$R\left(\frac{k-v}{v}\right) = mv\frac{dv}{dx}$$

$$\therefore \qquad \int R\,dx = \int m\left(\frac{v^2}{k-v}\right)dv$$

By long division

$$
\begin{array}{r}
-v-k \\
-v+k\overline{)v^2} \\
v^2 - kv \\
\hline
kv \\
kv - k^2 \\
\hline
k^2
\end{array}
$$

$$\frac{v^2}{k-v} = -v - k + \frac{k^2}{k-v}$$

$$\therefore \qquad \int R\,dx = \int m\left\{\frac{k^2}{k-v} - v - k\right\}dv$$

$$\therefore \qquad Rx = m\{-k^2\ln(k-v) - \tfrac{1}{2}v^2 - kv\} + C$$

Since $v = 0$ when $x = 0$, $\quad C = mk^2\ln k$

$$\therefore \qquad Rx = m\{-k^2\ln(k-v) - \tfrac{1}{2}v^2 - kv + k^2\ln k\}$$

Hence

$$x = \frac{m}{R}\left\{k^2\ln\left(\frac{k}{k-v}\right) - \tfrac{1}{2}v^2 - kv\right\}.$$

In certain types of problem it is quicker to use definite integrals rather then indefinite integrals. For instance, if in Example 3 we had been asked to find the time which elapses as the car accelerates from speed $\frac{1}{3}k$ to speed $\frac{2}{3}k$, we could have deduced from equation (1) that:

$$\int_{t_1}^{t_2} R \, dt = \int_{k/3}^{2k/3} m\left(\frac{v}{k-v}\right) dv$$

where $t = t_1$ when $v = \frac{1}{3}k$ and $t = t_2$ when $v = \frac{2}{3}k$

$$\therefore \quad R\int_{t_1}^{t_2} dt = m\int_{k/3}^{2k/3}\left(\frac{k}{k-v} - 1\right) dv$$

$$\therefore \quad R\left[t\right]_{t_1}^{t_2} = m\left[-k\ln(k-v) - v\right]_{k/3}^{2k/3}$$

$$\therefore \quad R(t_2 - t_1) = m(-k\ln\tfrac{1}{3}k - \tfrac{2}{3}k) - m(-k\ln\tfrac{2}{3}k - \tfrac{1}{3}k)$$

$$= mk(\ln\tfrac{2}{3}k - \ln\tfrac{1}{3}k + \tfrac{1}{3} - \tfrac{2}{3})$$

$$= mk(\ln 2 - \tfrac{1}{3})$$

Hence the time taken is $\dfrac{mk}{R}(\ln 2 - \tfrac{1}{3})$.

Exercise 13.2

1. A particle of unit mass, moving in a straight line with speed v at time t, is subject to a retarding force of magnitude $(3 + 2v)$. Given that initially $v = 66$, find the value of t when $v = 6$.

2. A particle travelling in a straight line is subject to a retardation of $(1 + v^2)$, where v is its speed. If the initial speed of the particle is u, find an expression for the distance it travels before coming to rest.

3. A particle is moving in a straight line so that when the displacement of the particle from a fixed point on the line is x, its velocity is v. Given that the acceleration of the particle is $k(1 - v)$, where k is constant and that $x = 0$ when $v = 0$, find an expression for x in terms of v.

4. A particle is projected horizontally from a point O on a horizontal plane with an initial velocity $2a/b$ where a and b are positive constants. The particle is subject to a retardation $a + bv$ where v is the velocity at time t from the commencement of the motion. Show that $bv = a(3e^{-bt} - 1)$ and, using this result or otherwise, find the distance gone by the particle when it comes to instantaneous rest.   (O&C)

5. The retardation of a particle moving in a straight line with speed v is proportional to v^3. The initial speed of the particle is u and s is the displacement of the particle from its initial position at time t. Given that $v = \frac{1}{2}u$ when $s = 2/u$, find an expression for v in terms of u and s. Hence find an expression for t in terms of u and s.

6. Show that the acceleration of an object moving along a straight line may be written as $v\,dv/ds$.

   A vehicle of mass 2500 kg moving on a straight course is subject to a single resisting force in the line of motion of magnitude kv newtons, where v metres per second is the velocity and k is constant. At 100 km/h this force is 2000 N. The vehicle is slowed down from 100 km/h to 50 km/h. Find (i) the distance travelled, (ii) the time taken.   (AEB 1980)

7. A particle falls from rest and, at any moment, it experiences a resistance of size kmv, where m is the mass of the particle, v is its velocity and k is a constant.
   (i) Show that, from the equation of motion we can deduce

$$\int \frac{dv}{g - kv} = \int dt.$$

   (ii) Using this equation, show that the velocity at any time is

$$\frac{g}{k}(1 - e^{-kt}).$$

   (iii) Show that, no matter for how long the particle falls, its velocity never exceeds a certain value. If this value is V, show that k is g/V.   (SU)

8. A particle of mass m moving under gravity is subject to a resistance of magnitude mkv^2, where v is its speed and k is constant. Initially the particle is travelling vertically downwards at speed u, where $u^2 < g/k$. Find the speed of the particle when it has fallen a distance s.

9. A train, when braking, is subject to a retardation of $\left(1 + \dfrac{v}{100}\right)\mathrm{m\,s^{-2}}$, where v is its speed at any time. The brakes are applied when it is travelling at $20\,\mathrm{m\,s^{-1}}$.
   (i) Show that it takes just over 18 seconds to come to rest.
   (ii) Show that it will travel approximately 177 m after the brakes are applied.
   $$\left[\text{It may prove useful to know that } \frac{v}{v + 100} \text{ can be written as } 1 - \frac{100}{v + 100}\right].$$
   (iii) If it then accelerates with acceleration $\left(1 + \dfrac{v^2}{100}\right)\mathrm{m\,s^{-2}}$, find, correct to 3 significant figures, how long it takes to attain a speed of $20\,\mathrm{m\,s^{-1}}$.   (SU)

10. A particle of mass m moves, in the direction of x increasing, along the positive x-axis under the action of two forces. These are (i) a force toward the origin O of magnitude kv, and (ii) a force away from O of magnitude kU^2/v, where k and U are positive constants and v is the speed of the particle at time t. Write down the equation of motion of the particle in the form of a differential equation in v and t, and show that the time taken for the particle to accelerate from speed $\frac{1}{4}U$ to speed $\frac{1}{2}U$ is

$$\frac{m}{2k}\ln\frac{5}{4}.$$

Write the equation of motion in the form of a differential equation in v and x, and hence show that the distance travelled by the particle while it accelerates from speed $\frac{1}{4}U$ to speed $\frac{1}{2}U$ is given by

$$\frac{m}{k} \int_{U/4}^{U/2} \left(\frac{U^2}{U^2 - v^2} - 1 \right) dv.$$

Show that this distance is $\dfrac{mU}{4k} \left(2 \ln \dfrac{9}{5} - 1 \right).$ (C)

11. A particle of mass m moves in a straight line under the action of a retarding force of magnitude $k(4 + v^2)$, where v is the speed of the particle at time t and k is constant. If the initial speed of the particle is u, find an expression of the time taken by the particle to come to rest. Find also an expression, in terms of m, k and u, for the distance travelled in this time.

12. An engine of mass m kilograms, driven by a constant tractive force of P newtons, experiences a resistance which is k times its speed in metres/second. Show that, when moving horizontally from rest, its speed t seconds after the start is $\dfrac{P}{k}(1 - e^{-kt/m})$ metres/second. Hence deduce that it will have travelled mP/ek^2 metres in m/k seconds. What power is being developed by the engine when the time is m/k seconds after the start? (W)

13. A train is pulled along a level track by an engine which exerts a constant pull P newtons at all speeds and the total resistance to motion varies as the square of the speed $v \, \text{m s}^{-1}$. The mass of the engine and train combined is $161\,700\,\text{kg}$, the maximum speed attained is $120\,\text{km h}^{-1}$ and the power then developed is $1078\,\text{kW}$. Show that (a) $P = 32\,340$, (b) $5 \times 10^4 v \dfrac{dv}{ds} = 10^4 - 9v^2$, where s metres is the distance travelled. Hence show that the distance travelled from rest while attaining a speed of $20\,\text{m s}^{-1}$ is about 1240 metres. (C)

14. A train of mass M moves on a straight horizontal track. At speeds less than V the resultant force on the train is constant and equal to P; at speeds not less than V the rate of working of the force is constant and equal to PV. Show that a speed $v(> V)$ is attained from rest in a time $M(V^2 + v^2)/2PV$ and that the distance travelled in this time is $M(V^3 + 2v^3)/6PV$. (W)

15. A car of mass m moving on a level road is subject to a constant resistance R. The engine is working at a constant rate H. Find the time taken for the speed of the car to increase from u to $2u$, where $2Ru < H$. Find also, in terms of m, R, H and u, the distance travelled in this time.

16. A car of mass m moving on a level road is subject to a resisting force kv, where v is the speed of the car at time t and k is constant. When the engine of the car is working at full power S, the car can travel at a steady speed U. Find the

time taken by the car to accelerate under full power from rest to speed V, where $V < U$. Find also the distance travelled in this time. Give both answers in terms of m, S, U and V.

13.3 Simple harmonic motion

Any motion which satisfies a differential equation of the form

$$\ddot{x} = -\omega^2 x$$

where ω is constant, is described as *simple harmonic motion* or **S.H.M.**

For a particle moving in a straight line, the variable x is the displacement of the particle from a fixed point on the line. However, x may also be a displacement measured along a curved path. In the case of circular motion or the rotation of a rigid body x could represent an angle.

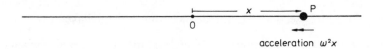

The diagram shows a particle P executing simple harmonic motion along a straight line. If x is the displacement of P from a fixed point O and $\ddot{x} = -\omega^2 x$, then the magnitude of the acceleration of P is a constant multiple of the distance OP. Since when $x > 0, \ddot{x} < 0$ and when $x < 0, \ddot{x} > 0$, the acceleration is always directed towards O. This leads to an alternative definition of simple harmonic motion.

When a particle moves in a straight line with acceleration always directed towards a fixed point of the line and proportional to its distance from that point, the particle is said to be executing simple harmonic motion.

The differential equation $\ddot{x} = -\omega^2 x$, i.e. $\dfrac{d^2x}{dt^2} = -\omega^2 x$, can be solved by expressing the acceleration of the particle in the form $v\, dv/dx$, where v is the velocity at time t, to give:

$$v\frac{dv}{dx} = -\omega^2 x$$

$\therefore$

$$\int 2v\, dv = -\int 2\omega^2 x\, dx$$

$$v^2 = -\omega^2 x^2 + c$$

If $v = 0$ when $x = a$, we find that

$$v^2 = \omega^2(a^2 - x^2) \tag{1}$$

It can be shown that this leads to the general solution:

$$x = a \sin(\omega t + \varepsilon) \tag{2}$$

or the equivalent form:

$$x = A \cos \omega t + B \sin \omega t \tag{3}$$

From equations (1) and (2) we deduce that the particle is oscillating between points A and A', which lie on opposite sides of O at a distance a from O. The point O is called the *centre* or *central point* of the oscillation and a is the *amplitude*.

From equation (1) we see that the particle is momentarily at rest when it reaches A or A', and achieves its maximum speed ωa when passing through O.

Since $\qquad\qquad x = A \cos \omega t + B \sin \omega t$
and $\qquad\qquad v = -A\omega \sin \omega t + B\omega \cos \omega t,$

when ωt is increased to $\omega t + 2\pi$ the same values of x and v are obtained. This means that at times t and $t + 2\pi/\omega$ the particle passes through the same point with the same velocity. Hence $2\pi/\omega$ is the time taken to perform a complete oscillation and is called the *period* of the motion. In particular, $2\pi/\omega$ is the time taken by the particle to move from A to A' and back again to A.

The *frequency*, i.e. the number of complete oscillations per unit time, is $\omega/2\pi$. Summarising the properties of S.H.M. we have:

> $\ddot{x} = -\omega^2 x,$
> $v^2 = \omega^2(a^2 - x^2)$, where a is the amplitude,
> $x = a \sin(\omega t + \varepsilon)$, or
> $x = A \cos \omega t + B \sin \omega t,$
> $T = 2\pi/\omega$, where T is the period of oscillations.

When solving problems involving S.H.M. standard formulae may be quoted without proof. It is usually best to begin be determining a and ω.

Example 1 A particle is performing simple harmonic oscillations between points A and A' which are 6 m apart. When the particle is at a distance $\sqrt{5}$ m from the mid-point O of AA' its speed is 10 m s^{-1}. Find (a) the period of the motion, (b) the maximum speed of the particle, (c) its maximum acceleration.

Let the equation of motion of the particle be

$$\ddot{x} = -\omega^2 x,$$

then
$$v^2 = \omega^2(a^2 - x^2),$$

where x m is the displacement of the particle from O, v m s^{-1} is its speed and a m is the amplitude of the motion.

But $AA' = 6\,\text{m} = 2a\,\text{m}$, which gives $a = 3$

$$\therefore \qquad\qquad v^2 = \omega^2(9 - x^2)$$

Since $v = 10$ when $x = \sqrt{5}$, $100 = \omega^2(9 - 5)$ $\qquad \therefore \quad \omega = 5$

(a) The period of the motion $= \dfrac{2\pi}{\omega}$ seconds $= \dfrac{2\pi}{5}$ seconds.

(b) The speed of the particle is greatest when $x = 0$

$\qquad \therefore \quad$ the maximum speed $= \omega a$ m s$^{-1} = 15$ m s^{-1}.

(c) The acceleration of the particle is greatest when the magnitude of $\omega^2 x$ is greatest,

$\qquad \therefore \quad$ the maximum acceleration $= \omega^2 a$ m s$^{-2} = 75$ m s^{-2}.

In S.H.M. problems involving time we need to find suitable expressions for x and v in terms of t. The forms of these expressions depend on the starting point chosen for the motion. One way of approaching such problems is to write:

$$x = A \cos \omega t + B \sin \omega t, \tag{3}$$
$$v = -A\omega \sin \omega t + B\omega \cos \omega t, \tag{4}$$

then to use any given conditions to determine A and B. We first apply this method to two important special cases.

Case I: $\quad x = a$ when $t = 0$.

Substituting in (3): $\quad a = A$
Since $v = 0$ when $x = a$, from (4): $\quad B = 0$

$$\therefore \qquad \boxed{\;x = a \quad \text{when} \quad t = 0 \;\Rightarrow\; x = a \cos \omega t.\;}$$

Case II: $\quad x = 0$, $v > 0$ when $t = 0$.

Substituting in (3): $\quad 0 = A$
$$\therefore \qquad\qquad\qquad x = B \sin \omega t$$
Since the amplitude of the motion is a and $v > 0$ when $t = 0$, we must have $B = a$.

$$\therefore \qquad \boxed{\;x = 0, v > 0 \quad \text{when} \quad t = 0 \;\Rightarrow\; x = a \sin \omega t.\;}$$

Example 2   A particle moving in a straight line performs simple harmonic oscillations about a point O with amplitude 2 m and maximum speed 1 m s^{-1}. If P

and Q are the two points on the line which lie at a distance $\sqrt{2}$ m from O, find the time taken by the particle to move directly from P to Q.

Let the equation of motion be $\ddot{x} = -\omega^2 x$, then, assuming that $x = a$ when $t = 0$,
$x = a \cos \omega t$.
Since the amplitude of the motion is 2 m, $a = 2$.
The maximum speed of the particle $= \omega a \, \text{m s}^{-1} = 1 \, \text{m s}^{-1}$

$\therefore \qquad \omega = \frac{1}{2}$
Thus $\quad x = 2 \cos \frac{1}{2} t$.

Let P and Q be the points at which $x = \sqrt{2}$ and $x = -\sqrt{2}$ respectively.

For $x = \sqrt{2}$: $\quad \sqrt{2} = 2 \cos \frac{1}{2} t$
i.e. $\qquad \cos \frac{1}{2} t = 1/\sqrt{2}$

$\therefore \quad$ the particle first passes through P when $\frac{1}{2} t = \frac{1}{4}\pi$ i.e. when $t = \frac{1}{2}\pi$.

For $x = -\sqrt{2}$: $\quad -\sqrt{2} = 2 \cos \frac{1}{2} t$
i.e. $\qquad \cos \frac{1}{2} t = -1/\sqrt{2}$

$\therefore \quad$ the particle first passes through Q when $\frac{1}{2} t = \frac{3}{4}\pi$ i.e. when $t = \frac{3}{2}\pi$.
Hence the particle moves directly from P to Q in a time of π seconds.

Example 3 A particle is performing simple harmonic motion about a point O with amplitude 5 m and period $\frac{1}{2}\pi$ seconds. If P is the point at which the speed of the particle is $10 \, \text{m s}^{-1}$, find the time taken by the particle to move directly from O to P.

Let the equation of motion of the particle be $\ddot{x} = -\omega^2 x$, and let $x = a \sin \omega t$, so that the particle is at O when $t = 0$.
Since the amplitude of the motion is 5 m, $a = 5$.

The period of oscillation $= \dfrac{2\pi}{\omega} \text{s} = \dfrac{\pi}{2} \text{s}, \qquad \therefore \quad \omega = 4$.

Thus $x = 5 \sin 4t$ and $v = 20 \cos 4t$.

Substituting $v = 10$: $\quad 10 = 20 \cos 4t$
$\therefore \qquad\qquad\qquad \cos 4t = \frac{1}{2}$

$\therefore \quad$ the particle first passes through P when $4t = \pi/3$. Hence the particle moves directly from O to P in a time of $\pi/12$ seconds.

Example 4 A particle moves on a straight line through a fixed point O so that at time t seconds its displacement from O is x metres and its equation of motion is $\ddot{x} = -9x$. Given that $x = 5$ and $\dot{x} = -6$ when $t = \pi/6$, find the position and speed of the particle when $t = 2\pi/3$.

The general solution of the equation of motion is

$\qquad x = A \cos 3t + B \sin 3t$
$\therefore \quad \dot{x} = -3A \sin 3t + 3B \cos 3t$

Since $x = 5$ and $\dot{x} = -6$ when $t = \pi/6$,

$$5 = A\cos\tfrac{1}{2}\pi + B\sin\tfrac{1}{2}\pi$$

i.e. $\qquad\qquad\qquad 5 = B$

and $\qquad\quad -6 = -3A\sin\tfrac{1}{2}\pi + 3B\cos\tfrac{1}{2}\pi$

i.e. $\qquad\qquad\quad -6 = -3A$

$\therefore\qquad\qquad\qquad A = 2\quad$ and $\quad B = 5$

Thus $\qquad\qquad\quad x = 2\cos 3t + 5\sin 3t,$

$\qquad\qquad\qquad\quad \dot{x} = -6\sin 3t + 15\cos 3t.$

$\therefore\quad$ when $t = 2\pi/3,\ x = 2\cos 2\pi + 5\sin 2\pi = 2$

and $\qquad\qquad\quad \dot{x} = -6\sin 2\pi + 15\cos 2\pi = 15$

i.e. the particle is $2\,\mathrm{m}$ from O moving at $15\,\mathrm{m\,s^{-1}}$.

Exercise 13.3

[Standard formulae may be quoted without proof.]

1.   A particle moves in a straight line with simple harmonic motion of amplitude $2\cdot5\,\mathrm{m}$. If the period of oscillation is π seconds, find the maximum speed of the particle and its maximum acceleration.

2.   A particle moves in a straight line with simple harmonic motion about the point O as centre. The maximum speed of the particle is $6\,\mathrm{m\,s^{-1}}$ and its maximum acceleration is $18\,\mathrm{m\,s^{-2}}$. Find (a) the amplitude of the motion, (b) the period of the motion, (c) the speed of the particle when it is $1\,\mathrm{m}$ from O.

3.   A particle of mass $3\,\mathrm{kg}$ moves in a straight line with simple harmonic motion between two points A and A' which are $15\,\mathrm{m}$ apart. Given that when the particle is at a distance of $3\,\mathrm{m}$ from A its speed is $2\,\mathrm{m\,s^{-1}}$, find the period of the motion. Find also the greatest force exerted on the particle during the motion.

4.   A mass of $10\,\mathrm{kg}$ moves with simple harmonic motion. When it is $2\,\mathrm{m}$ from the centre of the oscillation, the velocity and acceleration of the body are $12\,\mathrm{m\,s^{-1}}$ and $162\,\mathrm{m\,s^{-2}}$ respectively. Calculate (i) the number of oscillations per minute; (ii) the amplitude of the motion; (iii) the force being applied to the body when it is at the extremities of its motion.   (SU)

5.   A particle P moves in a straight line so that its acceleration is always directed towards a point O in its path and is of magnitude proportional to the distance OP. When P is at the point A, where $OA = 1\,\mathrm{m}$, its speed is $3\sqrt{3}\,\mathrm{m/s}$ and when P is at the point B, where $OB = \sqrt{3}\,\mathrm{m}$, its speed is $3\,\mathrm{m/s}$. Calculate the maximum speed attained by P and the maximum value of OP. Show that P takes $\pi/18$ seconds to move directly from A to B. Find, in m/s correct to 2 significant figures, the speed of P one second after it passes O.   (L)

6. A particle, A, is performing simple harmonic oscillations about a point O with amplitude $2\,\mathrm{m}$ and period $12\pi\,\mathrm{s}$. Find the least time from the instant when A passes through O until the instant when (i) its displacement is $1\,\mathrm{m}$, (ii) its velocity is half that at O, (iii) its kinetic energy is half that at O.   (AEB 1978)

7. A particle P is describing simple harmonic motion in the horizontal line $ADCB$, where $AD = DC = \frac{1}{2}CB$. The speed of P as it passes through C is $5\,\mathrm{m/s}$ and P is instantaneously at rest at A and B. Given that P performs 3 complete oscillations per second, calculate (i) the distance AB, (ii) the speed of P as it passes through D, (iii) the distance of P from C at an instant when the acceleration of P is $18\pi\,\mathrm{m/s^2}$, (iv) the time taken by P to go directly from D to A.   (AEB 1978)

8. A particle P moves in a straight line with simple harmonic motion of period 2 seconds and maximum speed $4\,\mathrm{m/s}$. Find the speed of P when it is at the point A which is $2/\pi$ metres from O, the centre of the path. Find also the time taken by P to move directly from O to A. When P is passing through O it strikes and adheres to a stationary particle which is free to move. If each particle is of mass $2\,\mathrm{kg}$, find the kinetic energy lost in the collision.   (L)

9. A particle moves in a straight line so that at time t its displacement from a fixed point on the line is x and its equation of motion is $\ddot{x} = -4x$. Given that $x = 3$ and $\dot{x} = -6$ when $t = \pi/4$, find (a) x in terms of t, (b) the values of x and $\dot{x}$ when $t = 3\pi/4$, (c) the least positive value of t for which $x = 0$.

10. A particle moves in a straight line so that at time t its displacement from a fixed point on the line is x and its equation of motion is $\ddot{x} = -16x$. Given that $x = 3$ and $\dot{x} = 4\sqrt{3}$ when $t = 0$, find (a) x in terms of t, (b) the least positive value of t for which $\dot{x} = 0$, (c) the amplitude of the oscillation.

11. A particle P moves round a circle, diameter AB, with constant angular speed ω. A second particle Q moves along AB so that PQ is always perpendicular to AB, i.e. Q is the projection of P on AB. Show that the motion of Q is simple harmonic.

13.4 Forces producing simple harmonic motion

To show that a given set of forces acting on a particle produce simple harmonic motion we must prove that the equation of motion of the particle can be expressed in the form $\ddot{x} = -\omega^2 x$.

Since the tension in an elastic string is proportional to the extension in the string, it may be possible for a particle attached to an elastic string or a spring to perform simple harmonic motion.

Let us suppose that a light elastic string of natural length l and modulus of elasticity λ has one end fastened to a fixed point O. A particle of mass m is

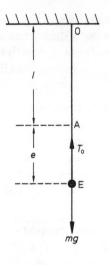

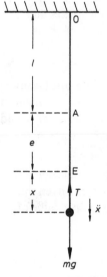

attached to the other end. Let e be the extension in the string and T_0 the tension when the particle hangs in equilibrium at the point E.

By Hooke's law, $\quad T_0 = \dfrac{\lambda e}{l}$

Since the particle is in equilibrium,

$$T_0 - mg = 0$$

$$\therefore \quad \frac{\lambda e}{l} = mg$$

Consider now the forces on the particle when its displacement from E is x vertically downwards.

By Hooke's law, $\quad T = \dfrac{\lambda(x + e)}{l}$

where T is the tension in the string. Applying Newton's second law vertically downwards:

$$mg - T = m\ddot{x}$$

$$\therefore \quad \frac{\lambda e}{l} - \frac{\lambda(x + e)}{l} = m\ddot{x}$$

$$\therefore \quad -\frac{\lambda x}{l} = m\ddot{x}$$

Hence the equation of motion of the particle is $\ddot{x} = -\dfrac{\lambda}{lm}x$. Since this equation is of the form $\ddot{x} = -\omega^2 x$, where $\omega = \sqrt{(\lambda/lm)}$, the particle can perform simple harmonic motion with centre E and period $2\pi\sqrt{(lm/\lambda)}$. The amplitude a of the motion is the maximum distance below E reached by the particle.

Provided that $a < e$ the string will remain taut throughout the motion and complete simple harmonic oscillations will be possible. However, if $a > e$ the particle will perform simple harmonic motion when it is below A, but move freely under gravity when the string becomes slack.

[Note that in the case of a particle suspended from a spring of natural length l, complete S.H.M. involving both extension and compression of the spring is theoretically possible when $a > e$.]

Example 1   A light elastic string of natural length l and modulus mg has one end fastened to a fixed point O. The other end of the string is attached to a particle of mass m which hangs in equilibrium at a point E. Find the distance OE. The particle is now pulled down to a point A at a distance $5l/2$ vertically below O. If at time $t = 0$ the particle is released from rest at A, show that the subsequent motion is simple harmonic and find the speed of the particle as it passes through E. Find also the time at which the particle first passes through the point B which lies at a distance $7l/4$ vertically below O.

When the particle is at E let the tension in the string be T_0 and the extension e.

By Hooke's law: $T_0 = \dfrac{mg \times e}{l}$

But since the particle is in equilibrium, $T_0 = mg$

$\therefore \quad \dfrac{mg \times e}{l} = mg$

$e = l$

Hence $OE = l + e = 2l.$

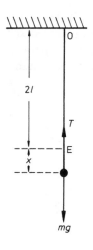

Let T be the tension in the string when the displacement of the particle from E is x vertically downwards.

By Hooke's law: $T = \dfrac{mg(x + l)}{l}$

Applying Newton's second law vertically downwards:

$$mg - T = m\ddot{x}$$

$$\therefore \quad mg - \dfrac{mg(x + l)}{l} = m\ddot{x}$$

$$\therefore \quad \ddot{x} = -\dfrac{g}{l}x$$

Since this equation is of the form $\ddot{x} = -\omega^2 x$, where $\omega = \sqrt{(g/l)}$, the particle performs simple harmonic motion with centre E.

The speed v of the particle is given by the formula

$$v^2 = \omega^2(a^2 - x^2)$$

When the particle is at A, $x = \tfrac{1}{2}l$ and $v = 0$ $\therefore \quad a = \tfrac{1}{2}l$

Hence $v^2 = \dfrac{g}{l}(\tfrac{1}{4}l^2 - x^2).$

$\therefore \quad$ when $x = 0$, $v^2 = \dfrac{g}{l} \times \dfrac{l^2}{4} = \dfrac{gl}{4}$

Hence as the particle passes through E its speed is $\tfrac{1}{2}\sqrt{(gl)}$.

Since $x = \frac{1}{2}l$ and $v = 0$ when $t = 0$,

$$x = \tfrac{1}{2}l\cos\omega t, \quad \text{where} \quad \omega = \sqrt{(g/l)}.$$

When $x = -\frac{1}{4}l$, $-\frac{1}{4}l = \frac{1}{2}l\cos\omega t$

i.e. $\cos\omega t = -\frac{1}{2}$

∴   the particle first passes through B when $\omega t = 2\pi/3$

i.e.   when $t = \dfrac{2\pi}{3}\sqrt{\left(\dfrac{l}{g}\right)}.$

We include the following example as a reminder that many problems involving particles attached to elastic strings can be solved using energy considerations rather than the theory of simple harmonic motion.

Example 2   An elastic string of natural length l and modulus $4mg$ has one end fastened to a fixed point O. The other end of the string is attached to a particle of mass m. If the particle is released from rest at O, find the distance it falls before coming instantaneously to rest at a point A.

Let x be the extension in the string when the particle reaches A. The kinetic energy of the particle is zero when it is released from O and when it comes to rest at A. Since $OA = l + x$, the loss in gravitational potential energy is $mg(l + x)$.
The energy stored in the elastic string as it is stretched to the length $(l + x)$ is $4mgx^2/2l$ i.e. $2mgx^2/l$.
Thus, using the principle of conservation of mechanical energy,

$$\frac{2mgx^2}{l} = mg(l + x)$$

∴ $$2x^2 = l(l + x)$$
$$2x^2 - lx - l^2 = 0$$
$$(x - l)(2x + l) = 0$$

Since $x > 0$, we must have $x = l$.
Hence the particle falls a distance $2l$ before coming to rest.

In the next example we consider oscillations in a horizontal plane.

Example 3   A particle P of mass m lies on a smooth horizontal table and is attached to two fixed points A, B on the table by two elastic strings each of natural length l. The strings AP, PB have moduli $2mg$ and mg respectively and $AB = 5l$. If E is the equilibrium position of the particle, find AE. Given that the particle is released from rest at the point C on AB such that $AC = l$, show that it performs simple harmonic motion, stating the period and the amplitude of the oscillations.

Let T be the tension in both strings when the particle is in equilibrium at E.
If $AE = l + e$, then the extensions in the strings AP and PB are e and $3l - e$
respectively.

By Hooke's law for AP: $T = \dfrac{2mge}{l}$

By Hooke's law for BP: $T = \dfrac{mg(3l - e)}{l}$

$\therefore \quad \dfrac{2mge}{l} = \dfrac{mg(3l - e)}{l}$

$\therefore \quad \begin{aligned} 2e &= 3l - e \\ e &= l \end{aligned}$

Hence $AE = l + e = 2l$.

Suppose now that the displacement of the particle P from E is x, as shown in the
diagram.
Assuming that both strings are taut, i.e. that P lies between the points C and D, the
extension in AP is $(l + x)$ and the extension in PB is $(2l - x)$.
Let T_A and T_B be the tensions in the strings AP and PB respectively, then applying
Hooke's law,

$$T_A = \frac{2mg(l + x)}{l}, \quad T_B = \frac{mg(2l - x)}{l}$$

Using Newton's second law in the direction AB,

$$T_B - T_A = m\ddot{x}$$

$\therefore \quad \dfrac{mg(2l - x)}{l} - \dfrac{2mg(l + x)}{l} = m\ddot{x}$

$$-\frac{3mgx}{l} = m\ddot{x}$$

$\therefore \qquad \ddot{x} = -\dfrac{3g}{l}x$

Thus the equation of motion of the particle is of the form $\ddot{x} = -\omega^2 x$, where
$\omega = \sqrt{(3g/l)}$. Hence when both strings are taut the particle performs simple
harmonic motion with centre E and period $2\pi\sqrt{(l/3g)}$.
Since the particle starts from rest at C, where $CE = l$, the amplitude of the simple
harmonic motion is l.
The diagram shows that complete oscillations of this amplitude are possible with
both strings taut. Thus when the particle is released at C it performs simple
harmonic motion of period $2\pi\sqrt{(l/3g)}$ and amplitude l.

These examples illustrate the fact that in simple harmonic motion the centre of oscillation is an equilibrium position. If a displacement x from this equilibrium position is considered, then the equation of motion is obtained in the standard form

$$\ddot{x} = -\omega^2 x.$$

However, if a displacement from a point which is not an equilibrium position is used, then the simple harmonic motion equation takes the more general form

$$\ddot{x} + \omega^2 x = \text{constant}.$$

Finally, we show that the motion of a *simple pendulum* is approximately simple harmonic. A simple pendulum consists of a particle, known as the "bob", suspended from a fixed point by a light inextensible string. When the particle swings in a vertical plane with the string taut, the bob moves along a circular arc.

It was shown in Chapter 8 that when a particle moves in a circle with variable speed v, then the acceleration of the particle has components v^2/r towards the centre of the circle and dv/dt in the direction of motion. These results can now be used to find the equation of motion of a simple pendulum.

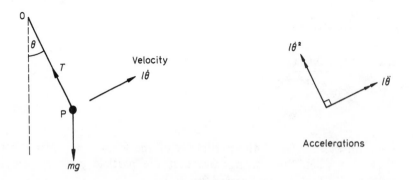

Let the bob of the pendulum be a particle P of mass m and let the length of the string be l. At the instant when the string makes an angle θ with the downward vertical, P is moving perpendicular to the string with velocity $l\dot{\theta}$. Hence the acceleration of P has components $l\dot{\theta}^2$ and $l\ddot{\theta}$ along and perpendicular to the string.

Applying Newton's second law perpendicular to the string,

$$mg \sin \theta = -ml\ddot{\theta}$$

Hence

$$\ddot{\theta} = -\frac{g}{l} \sin \theta$$

However, if θ is small, $\sin \theta \approx \theta$

$$\therefore \qquad \ddot{\theta} \approx -\frac{g}{l} \theta$$

Thus small oscillations of a simple pendulum are approximately simple harmonic.

The period of complete oscillations is $2\pi \sqrt{\dfrac{l}{g}}$.

A pendulum which beats seconds is called a *seconds pendulum*. Such a pendulum swings through its equilibrium position once every second and therefore each complete oscillation takes 2 seconds. Hence the length of a seconds pendulum is found by writing:

$$2\pi \sqrt{\frac{l}{g}} = 2.$$

Exercise 13.4

1. A particle of mass m is attached to one end of a light elastic string of length a and modulus $\frac{3}{2}mg$. The other end of the string is attached to a fixed point O and the particle hangs in equilibrium under gravity at the point E. Find the distance OE. If the particle is a *further* distance x below E show that the resultant force acting on the particle is proportional to x. The particle is pulled down to the point at a distance a below E and released from rest. Show that, in the subsequent motion and while the string is taut, the particle executes Simple Harmonic Motion and that its distance below E at time t after being released is

$$a \cos \left\{ \left(\frac{3g}{2a} \right)^{1/2} t \right\}.$$

(O&C)

2. A light elastic string of natural length l has one end fastened to a fixed point O. The other end of the string is attached to a particle of mass m. When the particle hangs in equilibrium the length of the string is $\frac{7}{4}l$. The particle is displaced from equilibrium so that it moves vertically with the string taut. Show that the motion is simple harmonic with period $\pi\sqrt{(3l/g)}$.

At time $t = 0$ the particle is released from rest at a point A at a distance $\frac{3}{2}l$ vertically below O. Find (i) the depth below O of the lowest point L of the motion, (ii) the time taken to move from A to L, (iii) the depth below O of the particle at time

$$t = \frac{1}{3}\pi \sqrt{\frac{3l}{g}}.$$

(C)

3. A particle of mass m is attached to one end of a light elastic string of natural length l and modulus $2mg$. The other end of the string is fixed at a point A. The

particle rests on a support B vertically below A, with $AB = 5l/4$. Find the tension in the string and the reaction exerted on the particle by the support B. The support B is suddenly removed. Show that the particle will execute simple harmonic motion and find (i) the depth below A of the centre of oscillation, (ii) the period of the motion.

(JMB)

4.   A light elastic spring AB of natural length l has the end A attached to a fixed point and hangs vertically under gravity with a particle of mass m attached at B. The system is set in motion and performs small vertical oscillations. Show that the motion is simple harmonic. The particle of mass m at B is replaced by a particle of mass αm, and it is found that the period of oscillation is doubled. Find the value of α.

(C)

5.   One end of an elastic string of modulus mg and natural length a is attached to a fixed point O. To the other end A are attached two particles P and Q, P having mass $2m$ and Q having mass m. The particles hang down in equilibrium under gravity. If Q falls off, show that P subsequently performs simple harmonic motion and state the period and amplitude of this motion. If on the other hand P falls off, find the distance from O of the highest point reached by Q.

(O&C)

6.   An elastic string of natural length $2a$ and modulus λ has its ends attached to two points A, B on a smooth horizontal table. The distance AB is $4a$ and C is the midpoint of AB. A particle of mass m is attached to the mid-point of the string. The particle is released from rest at D, the mid-point of CB. Denoting by x the displacement of the particle from C, show that the equation of motion of the particle is

$$\frac{d^2x}{dt^2} + \frac{2\lambda}{ma}x = 0.$$

Find the maximum speed of the particle and show that the time taken for the particle to move from D directly to the mid-point of CD is $\dfrac{\pi}{3}\left(\dfrac{ma}{2\lambda}\right)^{1/2}$

(JMB)

7.   A particle P of mass m is attached by two light elastic strings to two fixed points A and B on a smooth horizontal table. Each string is of natural length l and $AB = 4l$. If the strings AP and PB have moduli of elasticity λ and 3λ respectively, find the length of AP when the particle is in equilibrium. If the particle is given a small displacement from the equilibrium position along the line AB, show that while both strings are taut the particle executes simple harmonic motion. Find the period of the oscillations. Given that the string PB just becomes slack in the ensuing motion, find the maximum speed of the particle.

8.   Two fixed points A and B on a smooth horizontal table are at a distance $5l$ apart. A particle of mass m lies between A and B. It is attached to A by means of a light elastic string of modulus mg and natural length l and to B by means of a light elastic string of modulus $2mg$ and natural length $2l$. If O is the point at which the particle would rest in equilibrium, find the distance OA. The particle is projected towards O

from the mid-point of AB with speed u. Show that while both strings remain taut the particle performs simple harmonic motion. Find the period and the amplitude of this motion. Show that the particle will perform complete simple harmonic oscillations if $2u^2 \leqslant 3gl$.

9.   A particle of mass m moving on a smooth horizontal plane is attached to a point O of the plane by an elastic string of natural length l and modulus λ. Initially the particle is at the point A which lies at a distance l from O and is moving away from O at speed u. If the particle first comes to rest at the point B, use energy considerations to find the distance AB. Show that when the particle is moving in the line AB its equation of motion is of the form $\ddot{x} = -\omega^2 x$, where x is its displacement from A. Find the time taken by the particle to move directly from A to B. Find also the further time which elapses before the particle next comes to rest.

10. A particle of mass m is attached to two elastic strings each of natural length a. The first string has modulus $3mg$ and its other end is attached to a fixed point A. The second string has modulus $6mg$ and its other end is attached to a fixed point B which is at a distance $3a$ vertically below A. Show that the particle can rest in equilibrium at a point O between A and B with both strings taut. Find the distance y of O from A. The particle is in motion in the line AB with both strings taut. At time t, the particle is at P where $OP = x$. Prove that $\dfrac{d^2x}{dt^2} = -\dfrac{9g}{a}x$.

The particle is projected vertically upwards from the point at a distance $2a$ below A with speed u. Find the maximum value of u for which the upper string does not become slack in the subsequent motion. For this maximum value of u find the time taken for the particle to travel from O to its highest point.   (O&C)

11. Find, to the nearest millimetre, the length of a seconds pendulum, (a) at Greenwich, where $g \approx 9 \cdot 81$, (b) at the equator, where $g \approx 9 \cdot 78$, (c) at the North Pole, where $g \approx 9 \cdot 83$, (d) on the surface of the moon, where $g \approx 1 \cdot 62$.

12. A musician wishes to use a simple pendulum as a makeshift metronome. Regarding a complete oscillation as two "beats", find, to the nearest centimetre, the length of pendulum required to produce (a) 50 beats per minute, (b) 80 beats per minute, (c) 100 beats per minute, (d) 160 beats per minute. [Take g as $9 \cdot 8\,\mathrm{m\,s^{-2}}$.]

13.5 Motion in a vertical circle

It was established in Chapter 8 that the acceleration of a particle moving in a circle, radius r, with variable speed v has components v^2/r towards the centre of the circle and dv/dt in the direction of motion.

When dealing with motion in a vertical circle we can obtain equations of motion by applying Newton's second law in these two directions. However, it may sometimes be more convenient to use an energy equation.

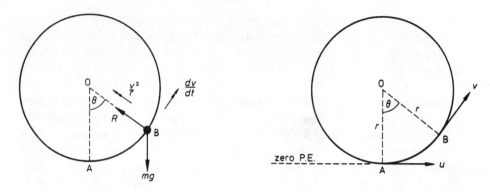

We consider first a small bead of mass m sliding on a smooth circular wire, of centre O and radius r, fixed in a vertical plane. Let u be the speed of the bead as it passes through the lowest point A of the wire and let v be the speed of the bead when it is at a point B such that $\angle AOB = \theta$. Since the wire is smooth the reaction R of the wire on the bead is perpendicular to the wire. Using Newton's second law radially and tangentially,

$$R - mg \cos \theta = m \frac{v^2}{r}$$

$$mg \sin \theta = -m \frac{dv}{dt}$$

The reaction R is perpendicular to the direction of motion and therefore does no work. This means that we can apply the principle of conservation of mechanical energy:

$$\text{(K.E. + P.E.) at } A = \text{(K.E. + P.E.) at } B$$
$$\therefore \qquad \tfrac{1}{2}mu^2 = \tfrac{1}{2}mv^2 + mgr(1 - \cos \theta) \qquad (1)$$

As θ increases the speed of the bead decreases. If the bead comes to rest before it reaches the highest point of the wire it will slide back down the wire and perform oscillations about A. However, if the speed of the bead is greater than zero for all values of θ, it will execute complete circles.

From (1): $v^2 = u^2 - 2gr(1 - \cos \theta)$
$\therefore$ if $v^2 > 0$ for all θ
then $u^2 > 2gr(1 - \cos \theta)$ for all θ

Since the greatest value taken by $(1 - \cos \theta)$ is 2, the condition for performing complete circles is

$$u^2 > 4gr.$$

Example 1   A small ring of mass 0.02 kg is threaded on a smooth circular wire of centre O fixed in a vertical plane. The ring is slightly displaced from rest at the highest point A of the wire. Find the magnitude and direction of the reaction of the wire on the ring when the radius to the ring makes an angle of $45°$ with (a) the upward vertical, (b) the downward vertical.

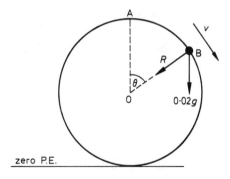

Let $v\,\text{m s}^{-1}$ be the speed of the ring when it is at a point B such that $\angle AOB = \theta$. Let the reaction of the wire on the ring be $R\,\text{N}$ towards O and let the radius of the wire be $r\,\text{m}$.

Using the principle of conservation of mechanical energy,

$$(\text{K.E.} + \text{P.E.}) \text{ at } A = (\text{K.E.} + \text{P.E.}) \text{ at } B$$
$$\therefore \quad 0 + 0 \cdot 02g \times 2r = \tfrac{1}{2} \times 0 \cdot 02 \times v^2 + 0 \cdot 02g \times r(1 + \cos\theta)$$
$$\therefore \quad 4gr = v^2 + 2gr(1 + \cos\theta)$$

Thus $\quad v^2 = 2gr(1 - \cos\theta).$

Applying Newton's second law towards O,

$$R + 0 \cdot 02g \cos\theta = 0 \cdot 02 \times \frac{v^2}{r}$$

$$\therefore \quad R + 0 \cdot 02g \cos\theta = 0 \cdot 02 \times 2g(1 - \cos\theta)$$

Thus $\quad R = 0 \cdot 02g(2 - 3\cos\theta).$

(a) When $\theta = 45°$, $R = 0 \cdot 02 \times 9 \cdot 8 \times (2 - 3\cos 45°) \approx -0 \cdot 024$.
Hence when the radius to the ring makes an angle of $45°$ with the upward vertical the reaction of the wire is $0 \cdot 024\,\text{N}$ *away from O*.

(b) When $\theta = 135°$, $R = 0 \cdot 02 \times 9 \cdot 8 \times (2 - 3\cos 135°) \approx 0 \cdot 808$.
Hence when the radius to the ring makes an angle of $45°$ with the downward vertical the reaction of the wire is $0 \cdot 808\,\text{N}$ *towards O*.

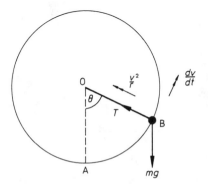

Suppose now that a particle of mass m, suspended from a fixed point O by a light inextensible string of length r, moves in a vertical circle. Let u be the speed of the particle as it passes through its lowest point A and let v be the speed of the particle when it is at a point B such that $\angle AOB = \theta$.

Applying Newton's second law towards O,

$$T - mg\cos\theta = m\frac{v^2}{r} \tag{1}$$

As in the case of a bead sliding on a circular wire, it can also be shown that

$$v^2 = u^2 - 2gr(1 - \cos\theta) \tag{2}$$

$$\therefore \qquad T = \frac{m}{r}\{u^2 - 2gr(1 - \cos\theta)\} + mg\cos\theta$$

i.e. $$T = \frac{mu^2}{r} - 2mg + 3mg\cos\theta \tag{3}$$

Thus when the particle passes through A its speed v and the tension T in the string take their maximum values. As θ increases, both v and T decrease, but the exact nature of the subsequent motion depends on the magnitude of u. We now consider in more detail the following possibilities:
(i) v reaches zero before T,
(ii) T reaches zero before v,
(iii) both v and T are positive for all values of θ.

Case (i):   The particle comes to rest with the string taut.

Substituting $v = 0$ in (1) and (2), then rearranging:

$$T = mg\cos\theta \tag{4}$$
$$2gr - u^2 = 2gr\cos\theta \tag{5}$$

Using (4): $$T > 0 \quad \text{when} \quad v = 0$$
$$\Leftrightarrow \qquad \cos\theta > 0 \quad \text{when} \quad v = 0$$

Hence the particle comes to rest at a point in the lower half of the circle.

Using (5): $$\cos\theta > 0 \quad \text{when} \quad v = 0$$
$$\Leftrightarrow \qquad 2gr - u^2 > 0$$
$$\Leftrightarrow \qquad 2gr > u^2$$

Hence the particle performs oscillations below the level of O with the string taut if and only if $u^2 < 2gr$.

Case (ii):   The string becomes slack while the particle is moving.

Substituting $T = 0$ in (1) and (3), then rearranging:

$$v^2 = -gr\cos\theta \tag{6}$$
$$2gr - u^2 = 3gr\cos\theta \tag{7}$$

Using (6): $$v^2 > 0 \quad \text{when} \quad T = 0$$
$$\Leftrightarrow \qquad -1 < \cos\theta < 0 \quad \text{when} \quad T = 0$$

Hence the string can become slack only at a point in the upper half of the circle.

Using (7): $$-1 < \cos\theta < 0 \qquad \text{when} \quad T = 0$$
$$\Leftrightarrow \quad -3gr < 3gr\cos\theta < 0 \quad \text{when} \quad T = 0$$
$$\Leftrightarrow \quad -3gr < 2gr - u^2 < 0$$
$$\Leftrightarrow \qquad 0 < u^2 - 2gr < 3gr$$
$$\Leftrightarrow \qquad 2gr < u^2 < 5gr$$

Hence the string becomes slack at a point above the level of O if and only if $2gr < u^2 < 5gr$. The particle will then leave its circular path and move freely under gravity until the string is again taut.

Case (iii):   *The particle performs complete circles*

Using (2): $v > 0$ for all θ

               $\Leftrightarrow$ $u^2 > gr(2 - 2\cos\theta)$ for all θ

Using (3): $T > 0$ for all θ

               $\Leftrightarrow$ $u^2 > gr(2 - 3\cos\theta)$ for all θ

Since $\cos\theta$ takes values from -1 to $+1$, both conditions are satisfied if and only if $u^2 > 5gr$. Hence the particle performs complete circles if and only if $u^2 > 5gr$.

Lastly we illustrate, by means of a worked example, a further way in which motion in a vertical circle may arise.

Example 2   A particle of mass m is released from rest at a point A on the outer surface of a smooth fixed sphere of centre O and radius r. Given that OA makes an angle α with the upward vertical, find an expression for the speed at which the particle is travelling when it leaves the surface of the sphere.

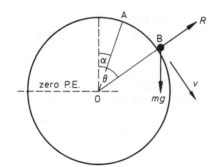

Let v be the speed of the particle when it reaches a point B such that OB makes an angle θ with the upward vertical. Since the sphere is smooth the reaction R of the sphere on the particle acts in the direction OB.

Since the reaction does no work mechanical energy is conserved during the motion,

$\therefore$ (K.E. + P.E.) at A = (K.E. + P.E.) at B

$\therefore$ $0 + mg \times r\cos\alpha = \frac{1}{2}mv^2 + mg \times r\cos\theta.$

i.e. $2gr\cos\alpha = v^2 + 2gr\cos\theta$ (1)

Applying Newton's second law towards O,

$$mg\cos\theta - R = m\frac{v^2}{r} \qquad\qquad (2)$$

The particle will leave the surface of the sphere when R vanishes.
Putting $R = 0$ in equation (2) gives $gr\cos\theta = v^2$

$\therefore$ from (1): $2gr\cos\alpha = v^2 + 2v^2$

i.e. $v^2 = \frac{2}{3}gr\cos\alpha$

Hence the speed at which the particle leaves the surface is $\sqrt{(\frac{2}{3}gr\cos\alpha)}$.

Exercise 13.5

1.   A particle P of mass 2 kg is suspended from a fixed point O by a light inextensible string of length 2·5 m and hangs in equilibrium at a point A. The particle is projected from A with horizontal speed 5 m s^{-1}. Given that when $\angle AOP = \theta$, the speed of the particle is v m s^{-1} and the tension in the string is T N, find expressions for v^2 and T in terms of θ. Hence find the values of v and T when $\theta = 40°$. Find also to the nearest degree, the greatest value attained by θ in the subsequent motion.

2.   A small bead of mass 0·5 kg moves on a smooth circular wire of radius 2 m which is fixed in a vertical plane. When the radius to the bead makes an angle of 60° with the downward vertical the reaction between the bead and the wire is of magnitude 12 N. Find the speed of the bead at this instant and the magnitude of the reaction when the bead passes through the lowest point of the wire.

3.   A particle of mass m is suspended from a fixed point O by a light inextensible string of length a. When the particle is in its lowest position it is given a horizontal speed of $\sqrt{(3ag)}$. If v is the speed of the particle when the string makes an angle θ with the upward vertical, find $\cos \theta$ and an expression for v^2 at the instant when the string becomes slack.

4.   A particle of mass m is placed inside a smooth hollow sphere of radius a. The particle is set in motion at the lowest point of the sphere with speed $\sqrt{(\lambda ag)}$. Show that the particle will perform complete circles if $\lambda > 5$.

5.   A small ring P of mass m is threaded on a smooth circular wire, of centre O and radius r, fixed in a vertical plane. Initially the ring is slightly displaced from the highest point of the wire. Find the magnitude of the force exerted by the ring on the wire when OP makes an angle θ with the upward vertical. Find the range of values of $\cos \theta$ for which this force acts towards O.

6.   A particle of mass m slides down the smooth outside surface of a fixed sphere of radius a. At the top of the sphere its velocity is horizontal and of magnitude u. If θ is the angle that the radius to the particle makes with the upward vertical, show that the reaction between the particle and the sphere is

$$mg(3 \cos \theta - 2) - mu^2/a.$$

Show that the particle, when just displaced from rest at the top, leaves the surface when $\theta = \cos^{-1}\frac{2}{3}$, and find its speed at that instant.   (W)

7.   A light rod OP of length a is free to rotate in a vertical plane about a fixed point O, and a mass m is attached to it at P. Denote by θ the angle between OP and the downward vertical. When $\theta = 0$, P is moving horizontally with speed u. Find the tension in the rod as a function of θ, and show that the value of the function is positive throughout the motion if $u^2 > 5ag$. Find the least value of the tension when $u^2 = 6ag$. Show that, if $u^2 < 2ag$, P remains below the level of O and deduce that, in this case also, the value obtained for the tension is positive throughout the motion.

(JMB)

8.   A particle P is projected horizontally with speed u from the lowest point A of the smooth inside surface of a fixed hollow sphere of internal radius a.
(i)   In the case when $u^2 = ga$ show that P does not leave the surface of the sphere. Show also that, when P has moved halfway along its path from A towards the point at which it first comes to rest, its speed is $\sqrt{\{ga(\sqrt{3} - 1)\}}$.
(ii) Find u^2 in terms of ga in the case when P leaves the surface at a height $3a/2$ above A, and find, in terms of a and g, the speed of P as it leaves the surface.   (JMB)

9.   A particle of mass m, attached to a fixed point O by an inelastic string of length l, is allowed to fall from a point in the horizontal through O at a distance $l \cos \alpha$ from O. Find the speed of the particle when it first begins to move in a circle. In the subsequent motion, show that, when the string first makes an angle θ ($< \frac{1}{2}\pi - \alpha$) with the downward vertical, the speed v of the particle is $\sqrt{\{2gl(\cos \theta - \sin^3 \alpha)\}}$ and the tension in the string is $3mv^2/2l + mg \sin^3 \alpha$. Will the tension vanish during the subsequent motion?   (W)

10.   One end of a light inextensible string of length a is attached to a particle of mass m. The other end is attached to a fixed point O which is at a height $5a/2$ above the horizontal ground. Initially the string is taut and horizontal. The particle is then projected vertically downward with velocity $(2ag)^{\frac{1}{2}}$. When the string has turned through an angle θ ($< \pi$) find the velocity v of the particle and show that the tension in the string is $mg(2 + 3 \sin \theta)$.
(a)   If the string can withstand a tension of at least $5mg$, prove that the string will not break.
(b)   If the string can withstand a tension of at most $7mg/2$, find the values of θ and v when the string breaks. In this case find the time to reach the vertical through O. Hence show that the particle strikes the ground at the point vertically below O.
(O&C)

11.   Two small smooth pegs O and C are fixed at the same level and $OC = a$. A light inextensible string of length $3a$ has one end attached to O and a particle P of mass m hanging at its other end vertically below O. The particle is projected with speed u parallel to OC. Find the speed of P when OP first makes an acute angle θ with the downward vertical and show that the tension in the string is then $mg(3 \cos \theta - 2) + mu^2/3a$. Show that the string will reach a horizontal position if $u^2 \geqslant 6ga$. Given that $u^2 > 6ga$, find the tension when, after the string has struck the peg C, the moving portion CP makes an angle ϕ above the horizontal, and show that P will complete a semicircle with centre C if $u^2 \geqslant 12ga$.   (JMB)

12.

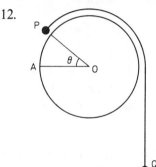

A particle P of mass m is at rest at a point A on the smooth outer surface of a fixed sphere of centre O and radius a, OA being horizontal. The particle is attached to one end of a light inextensible string which is taut and passes over the sphere, its other end carrying a particle Q of mass $2m$ which hangs freely. The string lies in the vertical plane containing OA. The system is released from rest, and after time t the angle POA is θ, as shown in the diagram. Show that, while P remains in contact with the sphere,

$$3a\left(\frac{d\theta}{dt}\right)^2 = 2g(2\theta - \sin\theta).$$

Find the tension in the string and the reaction of the sphere on P in terms of m, g and θ.
(JMB)

Exercise 13.6 (*miscellaneous*)

1. A particle is in motion along a straight line. When at a distance x from a fixed point of the line its velocity is v. Show that its acceleration is $v\,dv/dx$.

The gravitational force per unit mass at a distance $x(> a)$ from the earth's centre is ga^2/x^2, where a is the radius of the earth, and g is constant. A particle is projected vertically upwards from the earth's surface at A with speed u. Show that if $u^2 < 2ag$, the particle rises to a maximum height $au^2/(2ag - u^2)$ above A. What happens if $u^2 > 2ag$?
(O&C)

2. A man pushes a loaded cart of total mass m along a straight horizontal path against a constant resisting force λm. The cart starts from rest, and the man exerts a force, in the direction of the motion, of magnitude $Ke^{-\alpha x}$, where x is the distance moved, α is a positive constant and K is a constant greater than λm. Write down a differential equation, involving x and the speed v, for the motion of the cart (while it continues to move), and hence obtain v in terms of x and the given constants.
(JMB)

3. A particle moves in a straight line in such a manner that when the particle is at the point P, at a distance x from some fixed point O on the line, the only force acting on the particle is in the direction **OP** and has magnitude $m\,\mu\left\{\dfrac{a}{x^3} - \dfrac{1}{x^2}\right\}$, where m is the mass of the particle and μ a positive constant.

If the particle is projected from the point $x = a$ with speed V in the direction **OP** find the set of values to which V must belong if the particle reaches the point $x = 2a$ but does not reach the point $x = 4a$.
(C)

4. A particle moves along the x-axis so that its displacement x from the origin O at time t satisfies the differential equation $\dfrac{d^2x}{dt^2} + 9x - 18 = 0$. Its speed when $t = \pi/12$ is $21/\sqrt{2}$ in the direction of the positive x-axis and its speed when $t = \pi/6$ is 15 in the *opposite* direction. Find x at any time t. What is the greatest distance from O reached by the particle and what is its greatest speed? If the motion starts at $t = 0$, find the time at which the particle first passes through O. [The general solution of the differential equation may be quoted.]
(O&C)

5. A particle is projected vertically upwards under (constant) gravity g from a point A on the earth's surface with an initial speed k. At time t after projection, the

particle is at height x above A and its speed is v; the air resistance is gv/k per unit mass. Show that, before the particle reaches its highest point, $\dfrac{dv}{dt} = -\dfrac{g}{k}(v + k)$, and $v = k(2e^{-gt/k} - 1)$. Hence find the corresponding value of x as a function of t.

(O&C)

6. A bullet of mass 40 g is fired horizontally with velocity 800 m/s into a fixed block of material which exerts a constant resistance, R newtons, which stops it in 0·5 m. Show that $R = 2·56 \times 10^4$ and find the time taken. An identical bullet is fired at the same velocity into a second fixed block which offers a resistance which varies as the square root of the speed of the bullet. The initial value of this resistance is $2·56 \times 10^4$ N. Write down the equation of motion for the bullet and find the time taken to stop it. Explain why the bullet could never be stopped by a material which offered a resistance proportional to the velocity. (AEB 1979)

7. With the usual notation, prove that $\dfrac{dv}{dt} = v\dfrac{dv}{ds}$. A particle P of mass m moves in a straight line and starts from a point O with velocity u. When $OP = x$, where $x \geqslant 0$, the velocity v of P is given by $v = u + \dfrac{x}{T}$, where T is a positive constant. Show that, at any instance, the force acting on P is proportional to v. Given that the velocity of P at the point A is $3u$, calculate (i) the distance OA in terms of u and T, (ii) the time, in terms of T, taken by P to move from O to A, (iii) the work done, in terms of m and u, in moving P from O to A. (AEB 1980)

8. A point P is travelling in the positive direction on the x-axis with acceleration proportional to the square of its speed v. At time $t = 0$ it passes through the origin with speed gT and with acceleration g. Show that $dv/dx = v/(gT^2)$, and hence obtain an expression for v in terms of x, g and T. Prove that, at time t,

$$x = gT^2 \ln\left(\frac{T}{T - t}\right).$$

Sketch the graph of x against t for $0 \leqslant t < T$. (L)

9. A particle is projected vertically upwards with speed u from a point O. The air resistance is proportional to the fourth power of the velocity and is initially equal to the weight of the particle. If v is the speed of the particle when it is at a height z above O, show that $\dfrac{d}{dz}(\tfrac{1}{2}v^2) + g\left(1 + \dfrac{v^4}{u^4}\right) = 0$.

Solve this equation by writing w for v^2 and so prove that the particle is instantaneously at rest when its height above O is $\pi u^2/8g$. (W)

10. A body of mass m falls from rest under gravity through a resisting medium. The resistance is kv^2 per unit mass where k is constant and v is the velocity when the body has fallen a distance x.

(i) Given that u is the limiting value of the velocity, i.e. the velocity for which there would be zero acceleration, establish the differential equation $v\dfrac{dv}{dx} = k(u^2 - v^2)$.

(ii) By solving this differential equation obtain an expression for v in terms of x.

(JMB)

11. A locomotive of mass M works at a constant rate H. Its motion is resisted by a force Mkv, where v is the speed at time t and k is constant. If $c^2 = H/(Mk)$, show that the equation of motion of the locomotive can be written $v\dfrac{dv}{dt} = k(c^2 - v^2)$.

Prove that the locomotive will increase its speed from $\frac{1}{3}c$ to $\frac{1}{2}c$ in time $\{1/(2k)\}\ln(32/27)$, and in this interval of time will travel a distance $\dfrac{c}{2k}\ln(1\cdot5) - \dfrac{c}{6k}$.

(O&C)

12. A car of mass M is driven by an engine working at constant power and the resistance to motion is proportional to the square of the speed. If R is the resistance at full speed V on a horizontal road, prove that the distance covered as the speed increases from v_1 to v_2 is $\dfrac{MV^2}{3R}\log_e\left(\dfrac{V^3 - v_1^3}{V^3 - v_2^3}\right)$.

(O)

13. (a) A particle travelling in a straight line is subject to a retardation of $(v^2 + 25)\,\text{m s}^{-2}$, where $v\,\text{m s}^{-1}$ is its speed at t seconds. If its initial speed is $12\,\text{m s}^{-1}$, show that it travels a distance of $\log_e(13/5)$ metres before coming to rest.

(b) A particle moving with SHM oscillates between points A and B which are $10\,\text{m}$ apart. When it is $1\,\text{m}$ from A, its speed is $16\,\text{m s}^{-1}$. Find (i) the periodic time; (ii) the maximum speed it attains; (iii) the maximum acceleration; (iv) the shortest time it takes to travel from A to C, where AC is $\frac{1}{4}AB$. (SU)

14. A particle moves along a straight line with simple harmonic motion of amplitude $0\cdot5\,\text{m}$ and of period 4 seconds. Find the maximum speed in m/s and the maximum acceleration in m/s^2 of the particle. Find also in m/s the speed of the particle when it is $0\cdot25\,\text{m}$ from its central position. (Answers may be left in terms of π.) Find also the least time which elapses between two instants when the speed of the particle is half its maximum speed.

(L)

15. A particle of mass m moves in simple harmonic motion about O in a straight line, under the action of a restoring force of magnitude proportional to the distance from O. At time $t = 0$ the speed of the particle is zero. After 1 second the speed of the particle is $2\,\text{m s}^{-1}$, after a further second the speed is $2\sqrt{3}\,\text{m s}^{-1}$ and subsequently the particle passes through O for the first time. Show that the speed of particle when it passes through O is $4\,\text{m s}^{-1}$ and find (i) the period and amplitude of the motion, (ii) the time at which the speed of the particle is equal to $2\,\text{m s}^{-1}$ after it first passes through O.

A stationary particle of mass m is placed at O and the moving particle collides and coalesces with this particle. The combined particle moves under the action of the same restoring force as before. Find the period of the subsequent motion and the speed when the displacement is $12/\pi$ m from O. (C)

16. At time t the displacement from the origin of a particle moving along the x-axis under the action of a single force is given by $x = a\cos(\omega t + \alpha)$ where a, ω and α are constants. Find the acceleration of the particle in terms of its displacement from the origin and describe the force acting on the particle. What is the periodic time of this motion?

Two particles, each moving in simple harmonic motion, pass through their centres of oscillation at time $t = 0$. They are next at their greatest distances from their centres at times $t = 2$ s and $t = 3$ s respectively, having been at the same distance from their respective centres at time $t = 1$ s. Show that the amplitudes of their motions are in the ratio $1:\sqrt{2}$. When will the particles next be at their centres, simultaneously? When will the initial conditions next be repeated? (W)

17. A particle moves on a straight line through a fixed point O so that at time t its displacement from O is x and its equation of motion is $\ddot{x} = -\omega^2 x$. If when $t = 0$, $x = d$ and $\dot{x} = u$, show that $x = d\cos\omega t + (u/\omega)\sin\omega t$. Given that the first three times at which the particle passes through the point $x = d$ are $t = 0$, $t = 2$ and $t = 8$, find d in terms of u.

18. A rough horizontal platform moves horizontally in simple harmonic motion. A particle P of mass 2 kg rests on the platform without slipping and is at O, the centre of oscillations when the motion starts; the initial speed of P is $4\,\mathrm{m\,s^{-1}}$. The period of the S.H.M. is 8 s. Find (i) the amplitude of the motion correct to 3 sig. fig., (ii) the distance OP, 1 s after the motion starts, correct to 3 sig. fig., (iii) an expression for the time taken for the particle to be first displaced a distance 1 m from O. Do not evaluate the expression.

Draw a diagram showing the forces acting on P with its acceleration and obtain the maximum frictional force acting on P. Hence give the range of values of the coefficient of friction in order that P should not slip. (SU)

19. The end A of a light elastic string AB, obeying Hooke's law and of natural length 0·5 m, is fixed. When a particle of mass 2 kg is attached to the string at B and hangs freely under gravity, the extension of the string in the equilibrium position is 0·075 m. Calculate, in newtons, the modulus of elasticity of the string. The particle is now pulled down vertically a further 0·1 m and released. Show that, until the string becomes slack, the motion of the particle is simple harmonic. Show that the time that elapses before the particle first passes through the equilibrium position is $(\pi\sqrt{3})/40$ s and find the speed of the particle when it is in this position. [Take g as $10\,\mathrm{m/s^2}$]. (L)

20. One end of a light elastic string of natural length l and modulus λ is attached to a fixed point A, and a small mass m, attached to the other end, hangs in equilibrium at B. A small mass $2m$ is made to adhere to the under side of the first mass, and the combined mass is released from rest at B. Show that the combined mass oscillates

about a point C which is at a depth $l + \dfrac{3mgl}{\lambda}$ below A, and that the equation of motion is

$$\frac{d^2x}{dt^2} = -\frac{\lambda}{3ml}x,$$

where x is the depth below C of the combined mass at time t. Show that the speed of the combined mass when $x = 0$ is $2g\sqrt{(ml/3\lambda)}$. Find the force of adhesion between the masses in terms of m, g, λ and x.   (JMB)

21. A particle P of mass m lies on a smooth horizontal table and is attached to two fixed points A, B on the table by two light elastic strings, each obeying Hooke's law and of natural lengths $2l, 3l$ and of moduli $2mg, mg$, respectively. If $AB = 7l$, show that, when P is in equilibrium, $AP = 5l/2$. The particle P is held at rest at the point C in the line AB, where $AC = 3l$ and C lies between A and B, and is then released. Show that the motion of P is simple harmonic of period $\pi\sqrt{(3l/g)}$. Find the maximum speed of P during the motion.   (O&C)

22. One end of a light elastic string, of natural length $2a$ and modulus $4mg$, is attached to a fixed point A of a smooth horizontal table. A particle of mass m is attached to the other end of the string. The particle is released from rest from a point C of the table, where $AC = 3a$. Show that the particle reaches C again after time $(4 + \pi)\sqrt{(2a/g)}$.   (L)

23. A scale pan of mass m is suspended from a fixed point by an elastic spring, of modulus $2mg$ and natural length l. When the scale pan is hanging at rest, a particle of mass $\frac{1}{2}m$ falls vertically on to the scale pan, striking it with speed $\sqrt{(lg)}$. Find the amplitude of the oscillations which the scale pan starts to make if the particle rebounds, the coefficient of restitution between the particle and the scale pan being $\frac{1}{4}$.   (L)

24. A particle rests on the *outside* of a fixed smooth vertical hoop, of radius a, at its highest point A, and a second particle rests on the *inside* of the hoop at its lowest point B. The particle at A is just disturbed from rest and the particle at B is given a horizontal velocity v such that both particles leave the hoop at the same point P. Show that (i) the radius OP is inclined to the vertical at an angle $\cos^{-1}\frac{2}{3}$, (ii) $v = 2\sqrt{(ag)}$.   (W)

25. A smooth wire in the form of a circle of centre O and radius a is fixed in a vertical plane. Two beads, P of mass $2m$ and Q of mass m, are threaded on to the wire. Initially Q is at rest at A, the lowest point of the wire, and P is held at a point B on the wire, where the angle AOB is $\frac{1}{3}\pi$.

The particle P is then released. Find the speed of P when the angle AOP is θ and P has not yet reached A, and find the reaction then exerted on P by the wire. Show that, when P reaches A, its speed is $\sqrt{(ga)}$. Show that, when the particles collide, the impulse of the reaction between them is of magnitude $\frac{2}{3}m(1 + e)\sqrt{(ga)}$, where e is the coefficient of restitution. In the case when $e = 1/5$ find the height above A which Q subsequently reaches before coming instantaneously to rest. (JMB)

26. A particle is at rest at the lowest point A inside a smooth hollow sphere of radius a. It is projected horizontally with velocity $\sqrt{(7ga/2)}$. Show that it loses contact with the sphere at a height $3a/2$ above A and will next strike the sphere at A. (C)

27.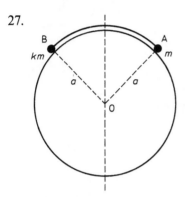

Two particles A and B of masses m and km respectively, where $k < 1$, are joined by a light inextensible string of length $\frac{1}{2}\pi a$. The string is taut and the particles are held, at the same horizontal level, in contact with a fixed smooth cylinder of radius a. The axis of the cylinder is horizontal and the string is in a vertical plane perpendicular to the axis of the cylinder. The system is released from rest. If θ is the angle made with the vertical by the radius OA of the cylinder when the particle A is about to lose contact with the cylinder, show that $(3 + k)\cos\theta + 2k\sin\theta = (1 + k)\sqrt{2}$. (C)

28. Two small equal beads, threaded on a vertical smooth circular wire of radius a, are connected by a light inextensible string of length a. One bead is held at the highest point of the wire with the string taut and is then released. Find the speed of the beads at the instant the string first becomes slack. (O)

29. A particle of mass m is projected horizontally with velocity $\mathbf{u}$ from a point O in a medium producing a resisting force $-mk\dot{\mathbf{r}}$ where k is a positive constant and $\mathbf{r}$ is the position vector of the particle relative to O. The acceleration due to gravity is $\mathbf{g}$. Write down the equation of motion (involving $\ddot{\mathbf{r}}$) and show that at time t

(i) $\dfrac{d}{dt}(\dot{\mathbf{r}}e^{kt}) = (\mathbf{u} + \mathbf{g}t)e^{kt}$,

(ii) $\mathbf{r} = \dfrac{1}{k}(1 - e^{-kt})\mathbf{u} + \dfrac{1}{k^2}(e^{-kt} + kt - 1)\mathbf{g}$.

If k is so small that k^2 may be neglected compared with k, show that approximately $\mathbf{r} = \mathbf{u}t(1 - \frac{1}{2}kt) + \mathbf{g}t^2(\frac{1}{2} - \frac{1}{6}kt)$. (JMB)

14 Probability

14.1 Permutations and combinations

A *permutation* is an arrangement of objects chosen from a given set. In this section we discuss ways of finding the total number of permutations of a set of objects under various conditions. For example, consider the number of ways in which we could arrange four guests in a row of four numbered chairs at a concert.

Any one of the 4 people may sit in the first chair. When the first person is seated, there are 3 people to be considered for the second place. This means that for each of the 4 ways of choosing the first person, there are 3 ways of choosing the second person to be seated. Similarly, in each of these $4 \times 3 = 12$ cases, we are left with 2 ways of choosing the occupant of the third chair. When 3 people are seated, the fourth chair must be filled by the 1 remaining person. Hence the total number of ways of seating the 4 people is $4.3.2.1$, i.e. 24.

Using the letters A, B, C, D to represent the 4 people, these 24 arrangements are as follows:

A B C D	B A C D	C A B D	D A B C
A B D C	B A D C	C A D B	D A C B
A C B D	B C A D	C B A D	D B A C
A C D B	B C D A	C B D A	D B C A
A D B C	B D A C	C D A B	D C A B
A D C B	B D C A	C D B A	D C B A

Since products of the type $4.3.2.1$ frequently arise in this type of work, the *factorial* notation is used. We write $4.3.2.1 = 4!$ which is read 'four factorial' or 'factorial four'. Thus for any positive integer n, $n! = n(n-1)(n-2)...3.2.1$.

The result of the above seating problem can now be generalised.

The number of permutations or arrangements of n different objects is $n!$.

308

Example 1   In how many different ways can 4 people chosen from a set of 6 be seated in a row of four chairs?

There are 6 possible choices for the first chair, then 5 choices for the second, 4 for the third and 3 for the fourth. Hence the total number of ways of seating 4 people out of a set of six is $6.5.4.3$, i.e. 360.
[In factorial notation this number is $6!/2!$]

In general, the number of permutations or arrangements of r different objects chosen from a set of n objects, written $_nP_r$, is given by $_nP_r = \dfrac{n!}{(n-r)!}$.

When $r = n$ this expression becomes $_nP_n = n!/0!$, but as shown above $_nP_n = n!$. Hence, it is convenient to define $0!$ to be 1.

In some problems the order in which objects are arranged is not important. The number of *combinations* of r different objects out of a set of n is the number of different selections, irrespective of order, and is denoted by $_nC_r$, or sometimes $\dbinom{n}{r}$.

Let us suppose that a set of 3 cards is to be dealt from a pack of 52 playing cards. The number of permutations of 3 cards chosen from $52 = 52!/49! = 52.51.50$. However, since any set of 3 cards can be arranged in $3!$ different ways, each set of 3 cards will appear 6 times in the list of all possible arrangements. For instance, the set containing cards X, Y and Z will appear as XYZ, XZY, YXZ, YZX, ZXY and ZYX. Hence the total number of ways of selecting 3 cards $= \dfrac{52!}{3!49!} = \dfrac{52.51.50}{3.2.1} = 22\,100$.

In general, the number of ways of selecting r objects from n unlike objects $= {}_nC_r = \dfrac{n!}{r!(n-r)!}$.

Example 2   A committee of 5 is to be formed from 12 men and 8 women. In how many ways can the committee be chosen so that there are 3 men and 2 women on it?

Number of ways of choosing 3 men from 12

$$= {}_{12}C_3 = \frac{12!}{3!9!} = \frac{12.11.10}{3.2.1} = 220.$$

Number of ways of choosing 2 women from 8

$$= {}_8C_2 = \frac{8!}{2!6!} = \frac{8.7}{2.1} = 28.$$

$\therefore$ the total number of ways of forming the committee

$$= {}_{12}C_3 \times {}_8C_2 = 220 \times 28 = 6160.$$

Exercise 14.1

1. Find the number of ways of arranging 6 different books on a shelf.

2. Find the number of arrangements of 8 items on a shopping list.

3. A lady has 8 house plants. In how many ways can she arrange 6 of them in a line on a window sill?

4. In a competition 6 household products chosen from 10 are to be listed in order of preference. In how many ways can this be done?

5. There are 25 entrants in a gymnastics competition. In how many different ways can the gold, silver and bronze medals be awarded?

6. In how many different ways can 8 books be arranged on a shelf if 2 particular books must be placed next to each other?

7. Three girls and 4 boys are to sit in a row of 7 chairs. If the girls wish to sit in adjacent chairs, how many different arrangements are possible?

8. How many numbers less than 3500 can be formed using one or more of the digits 1, 3, 5, 7, if (a) no digit can be repeated, (b) repetitions are allowed?

9. Verify that $_nC_{n-r} = {_nC_r}$ for the cases
    (a) $n = 8, r = 5$;   (b) $n = 10, r = 2$.

10. In how many ways can
    (a) 4 photographs be chosen from 10 proofs,
    (b) 3 representatives be chosen from 20 students,
    (c) a hand of 5 cards be dealt from a set of 13,
    (d) 11 players be selected from 12 cricketers?

11. Nine people are to go on a journey in cars which can take 2, 3 and 4 passengers respectively. In how many different ways can the party travel, assuming that the seating arrangements inside the cars are not important?

12. In how many ways can a set of 12 unlike objects be divided into (a) 2 sets of 6, (b) 3 sets of 4, (c) 6 sets of 2?

13. A team of 5 students, including a captain and a reserve, is to be selected for a general knowledge contest. In how many ways can the team be chosen from a short list of 12?

14. Find the number of different selections of two letters which can be made from the letters of the word PROBABILITY. How many of these selections do not contain a vowel?

15. Find the number of ways in which 8 books can be distributed to 2 boys, if each boy is to receive at least 2 books.

16. A committee of 6 is to be formed from 13 men and 7 women. In how many ways can the committee be selected .given that (a) it must consist of 4 men and 2 women, (b) it must have at least one member of each sex?

14.2 The language of sets

A *set* is a collection of objects. These objects are the *elements* of the set. A set may be defined either by listing the elements or by describing their properties, e.g. $A = \{2, 4, 7\}$, B is the set of all triangles, $C = \{..., -5, -3, -1, 1, 3, ...\}$ or {odd integers}. Using the colon : to mean 'such that', we may also write $P = \{p : p$ is a prime number}, which is read 'P is the set of all elements p such that p is a prime number'. Whatever form is chosen it must always be possible to decide from the definition whether or not an object belongs to the set.

The statement $x \in S$ means 'x is an element of S' or 'x belongs to S'. Similarly $x \notin S$ means 'x is not an element of the set S'. Thus, for the sets defined above, $2 \in A$ but $2 \notin C$ and $9 \in C$ but $9 \notin P$.

Two sets are *equal* if they contain exactly the same elements, e.g. $\{16, 25, 36, 49, 64, 81\} = \{36, 81, 16, 25, 64, 49\} = $ {two digit squares}. The way in which the elements are listed or described is not important.

Sometimes all the elements of one set are contained in another. If every element of a set A also belongs to a set B, then A is a *subset* of B, written $A \subseteq B$. If A is a subset of B and there is at least one element of B which is not an element of A, then A is a *proper subset* of B and we write $A \subset B$. For instance, if $X = \{a, c\}$, $Y = \{a, c, e\}$ and $Z = \{a, b, c, d\}$, then $X \subset Y$ and $X \subset Z$ but $Y \not\subset Z$. We may also write $Y \supset X$ and $Z \supset X$ using the symbol $\supset$ to mean 'contains as a proper subset'.

Three important properties of the set inclusion relation follow from the definition.

(1) Any set A is a subset of itself, i.e. $A \subseteq A$.

(2) $A \subseteq B$ and $B \subseteq C \Rightarrow A \subseteq C$.

(3) $A \subseteq B$ and $B \subseteq A \Leftrightarrow A = B$.

[Note that if p and q represent statements, then $p \Rightarrow q$ means 'if p then q' or 'p implies q'. The symbol $\Leftarrow$ means 'is implied by'. We write $p \Leftrightarrow q$ meaning 'p implies and is implied by q' when the statements p and q are equivalent.]

All the objects under consideration in any mathematical discussion form a set called the *universal set* (or *universe of discourse*), often denoted by $\mathscr{E}$. For instance, in a geometrical problem the universal set may be a set of points, a set of lines or a set of plane figures. Once a universal set $\mathscr{E}$ has been defined any other set considered must be one of its subsets. Thus for any set A, $A \subseteq \mathscr{E}$.

The set with no elements is called the *null* or *empty set*, written $\varnothing$ or sometimes { }. The empty set $\varnothing$ is considered to be a subset of any set A, i.e. $\varnothing \subseteq A$.

The *complement* of a set A is the set containing all the elements of $\mathscr{E}$ which are not elements of A and is written A'. For instance, if $\mathscr{E} = \{1,2,3,4,5\}$ and $A = \{1,3,5\}$ then $A' = \{2,4\}$. It follows from the definition that for any set A, $(A')' = A$. We also find that $\varnothing' = \mathscr{E}$ and $\mathscr{E}' = \varnothing$.

The *union* of sets A and B, written $A \cup B$, is the set containing all elements which belong to A or B (or both). For instance, if $A = \{1,2,3,4\}$ and $B = \{1,3,5\}$, then $A \cup B = \{1,2,3,4,5\}$.

The *intersection* of sets A and B, written $A \cap B$, is the set containing all elements which belong to both A and B. For instance, if $A = \{2,4,6,8\}$ and $B = \{1,2,3,4\}$, then $A \cap B = \{2,4\}$.

Example 1 If $S = \{x \in \mathbb{R} : 3 \leqslant x \leqslant 5\}$ and $T = \{x \in \mathbb{R} : -1 < x < 4\}$, find $S \cup T$ and $S \cap T$.

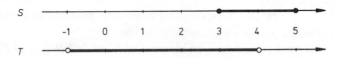

Representing S and T on the real number line we find that
$S \cup T = \{x \in \mathbb{R} : -1 < x \leqslant 5\}$ and $S \cap T = \{x \in \mathbb{R} : 3 \leqslant x < 4\}$.

Venn† *diagrams* are used to represent relationships between sets. The universal set is shown as a rectangle and other sets as regions, often circles, within this rectangle.

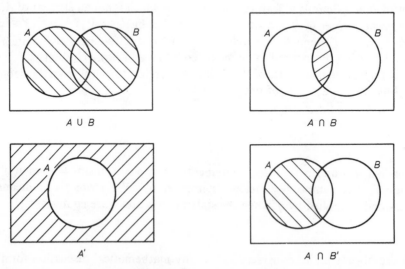

Venn diagrams can be used to demonstrate properties of union and intersection, but such verifications are not regarded as rigorous proofs of the results.

† *Venn, John* (1834–1923) English logician. He developed the theories of probability and mathematical logic. In his *Symbolic Logic* (1881) he improved the diagrammatic methods of earlier writers.

Example 2 Verify using Venn diagrams, the associative law

$$A \cap (B \cap C) = (A \cap B) \cap C.$$

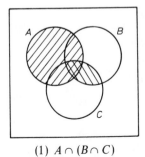

(1) $A \cap (B \cap C)$

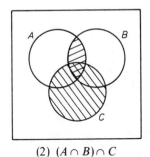

(2) $(A \cap B) \cap C$

In (1) the sets A and $(B \cap C)$ are shaded in different ways, so that the region shaded twice represents $A \cap (B \cap C)$. Similarly in (2) the region shaded twice represents $(A \cap B) \cap C$. Hence, in these diagrams, $A \cap (B \cap C) = (A \cap B) \cap C$.

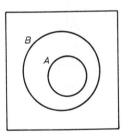

This diagram illustrates the fact that A is a subset of B, i.e. $A \subset B$. We see that in this case $A \cup B = B$ and $A \cap B = A$.

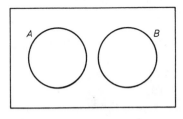

Here the sets A and B have no common elements, i.e. $A \cap B = \emptyset$. Such sets are said to be *disjoint*.

A', the complement of A, contains no elements of A,
∴ A and A' are disjoint and $A \cap A' = \emptyset$.
Since every element of the universal set $\mathscr{E}$ belongs to either A or A', for any set A,
$A \cup A' = \mathscr{E}$.
   Venn diagrams can also be used in problems concerning the numbers of elements in sets. The number of elements in a finite set A is called the *order* or *cardinal number* of the set and is denoted by $n(A)$.

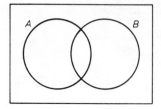

By considering the diagram we see that in the sum $n(A)+n(B)$, the elements of $A \cap B$ have been counted twice.

Hence $\boxed{n(A \cup B) = n(A)+n(B)-n(A \cap B).}$

Example 3 On a shelf of 50 books, there are 37 historical novels and 29 romances, but no other types of book. What conclusion may be drawn from this?

Let H and R be the sets of historical novels and romances respectively, then $n(H) = 37$, $n(R) = 29$ and $n(H \cup R) = 50$.
$$n(H \cup R) = n(H)+n(R)-n(H \cap R)$$
$$50 = 37+29-n(H \cap R)$$
$$\therefore \quad n(H \cap R) = 16.$$
It follows that there are 16 historical romances on the shelf.

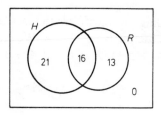

The diagram shows one way of illustrating this result.

Example 4 In a survey of 100 housewives it is found that 65 use brand X and 55 use brand Y washing powder. What can be said about the numbers of housewives using both X and Y.

Let X and Y be the sets of housewives using those brands,
then $$n(X \cup Y) = n(X)+n(Y)-n(X \cap Y)$$
$$= 65+55-n(X \cap Y)$$
$$= 120-n(X \cap Y).$$
As there may be housewives who use neither X nor Y, we may assume only that $n(X \cup Y) \leqslant 100$,
$$\therefore \quad n(X \cap Y) \geqslant 20, \text{ i.e. at least 20 housewives use both } X \text{ and } Y.$$

Karnaugh† *maps* provide a useful alternative to Venn diagrams when dealing with intersecting sets. Karnaugh maps for one set A and for two sets A and B are given below.

---

† Karnaugh maps representing sets are developments of diagrams used to simplify logic circuits in computers and electronic control systems, as described by M. *Karnaugh* in his article *The Map Method for Synthesis of Combinational Logic Circuits* (1953).

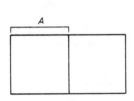

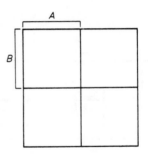

Any set can be represented on a Karnaugh map by shading the appropriate region.

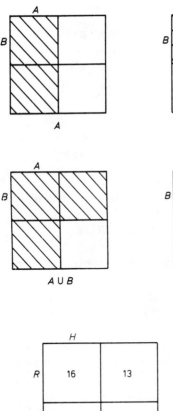

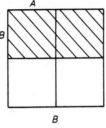

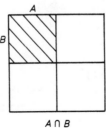

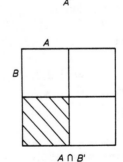

A Karnaugh map could have been used to illustrate the result of Example 3.

The Karnaugh system can be extended to larger numbers of sets. The maps for 3 sets and 4 sets are given here.

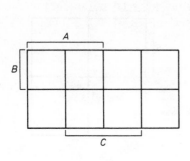
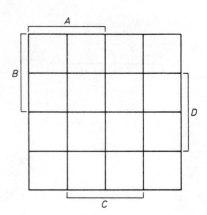

Exercise 14.2

1. If $A = \{x, y, z\}$, $B = \{x, p, q, r\}$, $C = \{x, y, p\}$, list the following sets:
(a) $A \cap B$,
(b) $B \cup C$,
(c) $(A \cup B) \cup C$,
(d) $(A \cup C) \cap B$,
(e) $(A \cap C) \cap B$,
(f) $B \cup (A \cap C)$.

2. Find $P \cup Q$ and $P \cap Q$ in each of the following cases
(a) $P = \{x \in \mathbb{R}: -2 < x < 4\}$, $Q = \{x \in \mathbb{R}: 0 < x < 7\}$,
(b) $P = \{x \in \mathbb{R}: 2 \leqslant x \leqslant 9\}$, $Q = \{x \in \mathbb{R}: x \leqslant 5\}$,
(c) $P = \{x \in \mathbb{R}: |x| < 10\}$, $Q = \{x \in \mathbb{R}: -4 < x < 3\}$,
(d) $P = \{x \in \mathbb{R}: -3 < x < 1\}$, $Q = \{x \in \mathbb{R}: 1 \leqslant x \leqslant 6\}$.

3. If $\mathscr{E} = \{1, 2, 3, 4, 5\}$, $A = \{1, 2, 3\}$, $B = \{5\}$, $C = \{3, 4\}$, list the following sets:
(a) $A \cap B$,
(b) $C \cap A'$,
(c) $(B \cup C) \cap \mathscr{E}$,
(d) $B' \cap C'$,
(e) $A \cup \varnothing$,
(f) $A' \cap (B \cup C)$.

4. If $\mathscr{E} = \{a, b, c, d\}$, $X = \{a, b\}$, $Y = \{b, c\}$, find expressions for the following sets using the symbols X, Y, X', Y', $\cup$ and $\cap$.
(a) $\{c, d\}$,
(b) $\{b\}$,
(c) $\{d\}$,
(d) $\{a, b, d\}$,
(e) $\{a, c, d\}$,
(f) $\{a, c\}$.

5. In each of the following cases draw a Venn diagram showing the universal set $\mathscr{E}$ and three sets A, B and C, then shade the region representing the given set.
(a) $A \cap B \cap C$,
(b) $A' \cap B$,
(c) $B' \cup C$,
(d) $(A \cup B) \cap C'$,
(e) $A \cup (B \cap C')$,
(f) $A' \cap B' \cap C'$.

6. Use Venn diagrams to verify the following:
(a) $A \cap (A \cup B) = A$,
(b) $(A \cap B)' = A' \cup B'$,
(c) $A \cap (B \cup C) = (A \cap B) \cup (A \cap C)$.

7. Draw a Venn diagram to show the relationships between the following sets:
$\mathscr{E} = \{$all triangles$\}$, $P = \{$isosceles triangles$\}$, $Q = \{$equilateral triangles$\}$, $R = \{$right-angled triangles$\}$, $S = \{$acute angled triangles$\}$.

8. Draw a Venn diagram to show the following sets and their non-empty intersections: $\mathscr{E} = \{$positive integers$\}$, $A = \{$even numbers$\}$, $B = \{$multiples of 3$\}$, $C = \{$multiples of 9$\}$, $D = \{$multiples of 12$\}$.

9. Simplify the following expressions, using Venn diagrams if necessary.
(a) $A \cup (A \cap B)$,   (b) $A \cap (A' \cap B)$,
(c) $(A \cap B) \cup (B' \cap A)$,   (d) $(A \cup B') \cap [A \cup (B \cap C)]$.

10. In a survey of 100 children, it is found that 47 have at least one brother, 58 have at least one sister and that 32 children have both. How many of the children have no brothers and sisters?

11. Find an expression for $n(A \cup B \cup C)$ in terms of the numbers of elements in the sets A, B, C and their intersections.

12. Out of 50 people who enrol for evening classes, 30 enrol for Mathematics, 15 for Further Mathematics, 22 for Physics and 8 enrol for none of these subjects. Denoting the sets of students who enrol for Mathematics, Further Mathematics and Physics by M, F and P respectively, what conclusions may be drawn about the values of $n(M \cap F)$, $n(M \cap P)$ and $n(M \cap F \cap P)$?

13. In each of the following cases draw a Karnaugh map for three sets A, B and C, then shade the region representing the given set.
(a) $A \cap B \cap C$,   (b) $A \cap C'$,   (c) $B' \cup C$,
(d) $A' \cap B \cap C'$,   (e) $A \cup (B' \cap C)$,   (f) $(A' \cup B') \cap C'$.

14. Using Karnaugh maps or otherwise, simplify the following expressions.
(a) $A \cap (A \cup B')$,   (b) $(B \cap C) \cup (B \cap C')$,
(c) $(A \cap B \cap C) \cup (A \cap B' \cap C)$,   (d) $(A \cup B \cup C) \cap (A' \cup B \cup C)$.

14.3 Elementary theory of probability

In mathematics probability is the numerical value assigned to the likelihood that a particular event will take place. For instance, if we throw an unbiased die, we have equal chances of scoring any of the numbers 1, 2, 3, 4, 5 and 6. Since there is one chance in six of throwing a 3 the probability of the event occurring is said to be 1/6. Similarly when tossing a coin the probability that it lands heads is considered to be 1/2. This does not, of course, mean that in any two tosses we expect the coin to fall heads once, only that in a long series of tosses the number of heads will be approximately half the total number of throws.

To arrive at a formal definition, consider the set S of all possible *outcomes* of an experiment or *trial*. A set of this kind is sometimes called a *possibility space* or *sample space*. Any *event* A can be represented by the subset A of S, which contains all the outcomes in which the event occurs. If S contains a finite number of *equally likely* outcomes, then the probability $P(A)$ that the event A will occur is given by

$$P(A) = \frac{n(A)}{n(S)}, \quad \text{i.e.} \quad \frac{\text{no. of favourable outcomes}}{\text{no. of possible outcomes}}.$$

If the event A is impossible, then $A = \emptyset$ and $P(A) = 0$. However, if the event A is certain to occur, then $A = S$ and $P(A) = 1$. Otherwise $P(A)$ will take some value between 0 and 1.

[When probabilities are calculated from experimental data, a definition such as the following may be used.

$$\text{Estimated probability} = \frac{\text{no. of successes}}{\text{no. of trials}}.$$

However, this value for the probability could be unreliable unless large numbers of observations are used.]

Example 1   What is the probability of drawing an ace at random from a pack of cards?

Since there are 4 aces in a pack of 52 cards, the probability of drawing an ace is 4/52, i.e. 1/13.

Example 2   If a letter is chosen at random from the word FACETIOUS, what is the probability that it is a vowel?

Since there are 5 vowels out of a total of 9 letters, the probability of choosing a vowel is 5/9.

Returning to the problem of throwing an unbiased die, the probability of throwing a 3 is 1/6, but the probability of not throwing a 3 is 5/6. We notice that the sum of these probabilities is 1. More generally, in a set S of equally likely possible outcomes, if A' denotes the subset of outcomes in which the event A does not occur, then A and A' are called *complementary* events and

$$P(A') = \frac{n(A')}{n(S)} = \frac{n(S) - n(A)}{n(S)} = 1 - \frac{n(A)}{n(S)}$$

$$\therefore \quad \boxed{P(A') = 1 - P(A).}$$

Hence, it seems reasonable to assume that in any sample space, if p is the probability that an event occurs and q is the probability that the event does not occur, then $p + q = 1$.

[Note that the event A' is sometimes referred to as 'not A' and may also be written $\bar{A}$.]

For experiments in which a trial is a throw of two or more dice, we can construct the sample space from the set of outcomes for a single die, $S = \{1, 2, 3, 4, 5, 6\}$. For instance, in the two-dice case, the possible outcomes can be expressed as ordered pairs such as $(1, 3)$, $(4, 6)$ and $(6, 4)$ formed from the elements of S.

A *sample space diagram* can be used to find probabilities as shown in the next example.

Example 3 If two dice are thrown together, what is the probability of the following events?

A: scoring a total of 2 B: scoring a total of 3
C: the same score on both dice D: 3 or more on each die.

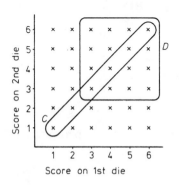

Score on 2nd die

Score on 1st die

The diagram shows that when two dice are thrown, there are 36 possible outcomes. A score of 2 is obtained only when the score on each die is 1

$$\therefore \quad P(A) = \frac{1}{36}.$$

There are two outcomes $(1, 2)$ and $(2; 1)$ which produce a score of 3

$$\therefore \quad P(B) = \frac{2}{36} = \frac{1}{18}.$$

The set of outcomes in which both dice show the same score has 6 elements, as indicated in the diagram

$$\therefore \quad P(C) = \frac{6}{36} = \frac{1}{6}.$$

The diagram also shows that there are 16 outcomes in which both dice show 3 or more

$$\therefore \quad P(D) = \frac{16}{36} = \frac{4}{9}.$$

Example 4 If a coin is spun three times, what is the probability that it lands heads once and tails twice?

[In this case the elements of the sample space may be represented by the paths along a simple *tree diagram*.]

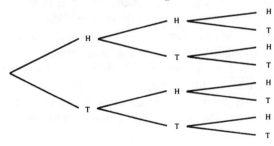

Since the given event occurs in 3 out of 8 equally likely outcomes, i.e. HTT, THT, TTH, the required probability is 3/8.

Let us now consider two different events A and B which may occur in an experiment. The set containing the outcomes in which A or B (or both) occur is the set $A \cup B$, so the probability of event A or event B (or both) is written $P(A \cup B)$. Similarly, the probability that both A and B occur is $P(A \cap B)$.

Example 5   An integer is chosen at random from the set $\{1, 2, 3, \ldots, 14, 15\}$. If A is the event of choosing an even number and B is the event of choosing a multiple of 3, find $P(A \cap B)$, $P(A \cup B)$ and $P(A' \cap B)$.

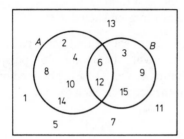

Using the possibility space diagram,

$$P(A \cap B) = \frac{2}{15}$$

$$P(A \cup B) = \frac{10}{15} = \frac{2}{3}$$

$$P(A' \cap B) = \frac{3}{15} = \frac{1}{5}$$

Some problems can be solved using the theory of permutations and combinations.

Example 6   If 4 cards are selected at random from a pack of 52, what is the probability that exactly 3 of them are diamonds?

The number of ways of selecting 3 diamonds from $13 = {}_{13}C_3$.
The number of ways of selecting 1 card from the 39 which are not diamonds $= 39$.
$\therefore$ the number of ways of selecting 4 cards, 3 of which are diamonds $= 39 \times {}_{13}C_3$.
The number of ways of selecting any 4 cards from $52 = {}_{52}C_4$.
Hence the probability that exactly 3 cards out of 4 are diamonds

$$= 39 \times {}_{13}C_3 \div {}_{52}C_4 = 39 \times \frac{13!}{3!10!} \times \frac{4!48!}{52!} \approx 0{\cdot}0412.$$

For a trial in which the possible outcomes are not equally likely, it is more difficult to arrive at a precise definition of the probability of an event. However, the subsets of a sample space S are regarded as events whatever the exact nature of the set S. In all cases $P(A)$, the probability of an event A, is a number or a weighting associated with the subset A. We can consider P to be a *probability mapping* which maps any subset A onto a real number p, where $0 \leqslant p \leqslant 1$. In any experiment the set of events (i.e. the set of subsets of the sample space) to be considered together with the appropriate probability mapping may be referred to as the *probability space*.

Exercise 14.3

In questions 1 to 4 find the probability of events *A, B* and *C*.

1.   A die is thrown. *A*: scoring a four, *B*: scoring an odd number, *C*: scoring four or less.

2.   A card is drawn from a pack. *A*: drawing a red card, *B*: drawing a seven, *C*: drawing a king, a queen or a jack.

3.   Three coins are tossed. *A*: three heads, *B*: at least two tails, *C*: at least one of each.

4.   It rained on exactly two days last week. *A*: it rained on Monday and Tuesday, *B*: it rained on two consecutive days, *C*: it rained on neither Monday nor Tuesday.

5.   For the events in question 1, find
(a) $P(A \cup B)$,   (b) $P(A \cap B)$,   (c) $P(B \cup C)$,   (d) $P(B \cap C')$.

6.   For the events in question 2, find
(a) $P(A \cup B)$,   (b) $P(A' \cap B)$,   (c) $P(B \cap C')$,   (d) $P(A \cap C')$.

7.   An integer is chosen at random from the first 200 positive integers. Find the probability that it is (a) not divisible by 5, (b) a perfect square, (c) divisible by both 5 and 2, (d) divisible by neither 2 nor 7.

8.   Two unbiased dice are thrown. Find the probability that the product of the scores is (a) odd, (b) a multiple of 3, (c) a multiple of 12.

9.   A domino is drawn from a standard set of 28. Find the probability that the sum of its spots is (a) 2, (b) 8, (c) odd, (d) even.

10.   In a cafeteria 80% of the customers order chips and 60% order peas. If 20% of those ordering peas do not want chips, find the probability that a customer chosen at random orders chips but not peas.

11.   The points *A, B, C, D* and *E* are the vertices of a regular pentagon. All possible lines joining pairs of these points are drawn. If two of these lines are chosen at random, that is the probability that their point of intersection is (a) inside the pentagon, (b) one of the points *A, B, C, D, E*.

12.   A box contains 4 discs numbered 1, 2, 2, 3. A disc is drawn from the box then replaced and a second disc is drawn. With the aid of a sample space diagram or otherwise, find the probability that (a) the total score is 6, (b) the total score is 4, (c) the numbers drawn are different, (d) the difference between the two numbers drawn is less than two.

13. A shopper with a keen eye for a bargain has bought a carton of assorted tins without labels. Assuming that the tins came from a large warehouse containing equal numbers of tins of soup, peaches and rice pudding, find the probability that (a) the first tin opened contains soup, (b) the first tin does not contain soup but the second does, (c) none of the first three tins contains soup. [You may find tree diagrams helpful.]

14. Two cards are selected at random without replacement from a set of five numbered 2, 3, 4, 4, 5. With the aid of a diagram or otherwise, find the probability that the numbers on the cards (a) are both even, (b) have a difference of 2, (c) have a sum of 7, (d) have a sum of 8.

15. A bag contains 3 blue beads and 2 red beads. A second bag contains 1 blue bead and 3 red beads. If one bead is drawn from each bag, find the probability that the beads are (a) both blue, (b) one blue and one red.

16. Write down in factorial form the number of different arrangements of the letters of the word EQUILIBRIUM. One of these arrangements is chosen at random. Find the probability that (a) the first two letters of the arrangement are consonants, (b) all the vowels are together.

17. There are 8 dusters in a drawer, 5 orange and 3 pink. If two of the dusters are chosen at random simultaneously, what is the probability that there will be one of each colour.

18. Four balls, two red, one blue and one white, are placed in a bag. The balls are then drawn at random from the bag one at a time and not replaced. Find the probability that (a) the first ball drawn is red, (b) the last ball drawn is white, (c) the red balls are drawn consecutively.

19. A hand of three cards is dealt from a well shuffled pack of 52. Find the probability that the hand contains (a) exactly one ace, (b) three cards of the same suit, (c) no two cards of the same suit.

20. On a plate of 12 assorted cakes, 3 are doughnuts. If 3 cakes are selected at random, find the probabilities that 0, 1, 2, 3 doughnuts are chosen.

21. A bag contains 25 clothes pegs, 15 plastic pegs and 10 wooden pegs. If 4 pegs are taken from the bag at random, find the probability that (a) all 4 are plastic, (b) 2 are plastic and 2 are wooden.

22. Four books are selected at random from a shelf containing 3 cookery books, 5 novels and 2 biographies. Find the probability that the four books (a) are all novels, (b) are 2 novels and 2 cookery books, (c) include at least one biography, (d) include at least one of each type.

14.4 Sum and product laws

If A and B are two different events which may occur in a sample space S, the set theory result

$$n(A \cup B) = n(A) + n(B) - n(A \cap B)$$

discussed in §14.2 can be used to find the probability that A or B (or both) will occur.

$$P(A \cup B) = \frac{n(A \cup B)}{n(S)} = \frac{n(A) + n(B) - n(A \cap B)}{n(S)}$$

$$= \frac{n(A)}{n(S)} + \frac{n(B)}{n(S)} - \frac{n(A \cap B)}{n(S)}$$

$$\therefore \quad \boxed{P(A \cup B) = P(A) + P(B) - P(A \cap B).}$$

This is the *addition law* of probability.

Example 1   A card is drawn at random from a pack. A is the event of drawing an ace and B is the event of drawing a diamond. Find $P(A)$, $P(B)$, $P(A \cap B)$ and deduce $P(A \cup B)$.

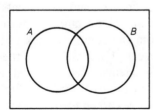

$$P(A) = \frac{4}{52} = \frac{1}{13}, \ P(B) = \frac{13}{52} = \frac{1}{4}.$$

$P(A \cap B)$ is the probability of drawing the ace of diamonds, which is $1/52$.

Hence, using the addition law,

$$P(A \cup B) = P(A) + P(B) - P(A \cap B) = \frac{4}{52} + \frac{13}{52} - \frac{1}{52} = \frac{16}{52} = \frac{4}{13}.$$

Events A and B are said to be *mutually exclusive* if they cannot occur at the same time, i.e. if the sets A and B are disjoint. This means that $A \cap B = \varnothing$ and $P(A \cap B) = 0$, so that for mutually exclusive events the addition law reduces to $P(A \cup B) = P(A) + P(B)$. In particular, if $B = A'$, then $P(A \cup B) = P(A \cup A') = P(S) = 1$, giving the result $1 = P(A) + P(A')$, i.e. $P(A') = 1 - P(A)$, which was obtained in the previous section.

Example 2   A disc is drawn at random from a box containing 12 discs of which 6 are red and 2 are blue. If event A is the choice of a red disc and event B is the choice of a blue disc, find $P(A)$, $P(B)$ and deduce $P(A \cup B)$.

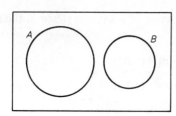

$$P(A) = \frac{6}{12} = \frac{1}{2}, \ P(B) = \frac{2}{12} = \frac{1}{6}$$

Since a disc cannot be both red and blue, the events A and B are mutually exclusive,

$$\therefore \quad P(A \cup B) = P(A) + P(B)$$

$$= \frac{6}{12} + \frac{2}{12} = \frac{8}{12} = \frac{2}{3}.$$

A set of events is said to be *exhaustive* if at least one of them is certain to occur in any trial, e.g. if the events A and B are exhaustive, then $P(A \cup B) = 1$ and the addition law becomes $P(A) + P(B) - P(A \cap B) = 1$. This will reduce to $P(A) + P(B) = 1$, if A and B are also mutually exclusive.

In general, for events A_1, A_2, ..., A_n which are both mutually exclusive and exhaustive

$$P(A_1) + P(A_2) + \ldots + P(A_n) = 1.$$

Two events A and B are said to be *independent* if the occurrence of event A has no effect on the probability of event B. However, if the probability of event B changes when A is known to have occurred then A and B are *dependent* upon one another.

Let us consider a playing card drawn at random from a pack and events A, B and C defined as follows: A: drawing a king, B: drawing a club, C: drawing a black king. The probability of drawing a club from the complete pack is 1/4. If the card drawn is known to be a king, i.e. if event A has occurred, then the probability that the card is a club remains 1/4. Hence events A and B are independent. Since $P(A) = 1/13$, $P(B) = 1/4$ and $P(A \cap B) = 1/52$, we find that $P(A \cap B) = P(A) \cdot P(B)$. However, if the card drawn is known to be a black king, i.e. if event C has occurred, then the probability that the card is a club is now 1/2 rather than 1/4. Hence events B and C are not independent. Since $P(B) = 1/4$, $P(C) = 1/26$ and $P(B \cap C) = 1/52$, in this case $P(B \cap C) \neq P(B) \cdot P(C)$.

This example illustrates the fact that

two events A and B are independent if and only if

$$P(A \cap B) = P(A) \cdot P(B)$$

This is the simplest form of the *multiplication* or *product law*. [The extension to events which are not independent is dealt with in the next section.]

When two dice are thrown, the scores obtained are independent of each other, so the product law may be applied. This provides an alternative approach to Example 3, §14.3.

The probability of throwing 1 on a single die is $\frac{1}{6}$, so the probability of throwing two 1's, i.e. of scoring a total of 2, is $\frac{1}{6} \times \frac{1}{6} = \frac{1}{36}$.

The probabilities of the outcomes $(1,2)$ and $(2,1)$ are both equal to $\frac{1}{6} \times \frac{1}{6} = \frac{1}{36}$. Hence the probability of scoring a total of 3 is $\frac{1}{36} + \frac{1}{36} = \frac{2}{36} = \frac{1}{18}$.

For any score on the 1st die, the probability of the 2nd score being the same is $\frac{1}{6}$. Thus the probability of throwing the same score on both dice is $\frac{1}{6}$.

Since the probability of scoring 3 or more on a single die is $\frac{2}{3}$, the probability of throwing 3 or more on each die is $\frac{2}{3} \times \frac{2}{3} = \frac{4}{9}$.

Example 3 A boy must throw a 6 on a single die to start a game. Find the probability that he succeeds at his third attempt.

The probability of not throwing a 6 in his first turn $= \frac{5}{6}$.

The probability of not throwing a 6 in his second turn $= \frac{5}{6}$.

The probability of throwing a 6 in his third turn $= \frac{1}{6}$.

Hence the probability that he succeeds at his third attempt

$$= \frac{5}{6} \times \frac{5}{6} \times \frac{1}{6} = \frac{25}{216}.$$

Example 4 A card is drawn from a pack and then replaced, the suit being noted. Find the probability that in a sequence of four such trials exactly two diamonds are drawn.

The number of orders in which two diamonds and two other cards may be drawn in the four trials is $\frac{4!}{2!2!}$, i.e. 6.

In each of these 6 cases, the probability of drawing two diamonds and two other cards in the appropriate order is $\left(\frac{1}{4}\right)^2 \left(\frac{3}{4}\right)^2$.

Hence the probability that two diamonds are drawn

$$= 6 \times \frac{3.3}{4.4.4.4} = \frac{27}{128}.$$

Exercise 14.4

1.   If A and B are random events such that $P(A) = 5/12$, $P(B) = 1/3$ and $P(A \cap B) = 1/4$, find $P(A \cup B)$.

2.   In a certain school the probability that a pupil takes part in the annual musical evening is 0.25. The probability that a pupil helps with the school play is 0.1. If the probability of doing both is 0.02, find the probability that a pupil is involved in at least one of these activities.

3.   A butcher observes that the probability that a certain customer buys beef is $\frac{1}{2}$ and the probability that she buys pork is $\frac{1}{3}$. If the probability that this customer buys neither pork nor beef is $\frac{1}{4}$, find the probability that she buys both beef and pork.

In questions 4 and 5 for the given events A, B and C
(i) write down any pairs of events which are (a) mutually exclusive, (b) exhaustive;
(ii) find   (a) $P(A \cap B)$,   (b) $P(A \cup C)$,   (c) $P(B \cap C)$,
            (d) $P(A' \cup C)$,   (e) $P(B \cap C')$,   (f) $P(A' \cup B')$.

4.   A card is drawn at random from a pack of 52. A: drawing a black card, B: drawing a red card, C: drawing a heart.

5.   Two unbiased dice are thrown and the total score recorded. A: a score less than 8, B: a score divisible by 5, C: a score greater than 4.

6.   The events A and B are mutually exclusive. The events A, B and C are exhaustive. If $P(B) = 0.6$ and $P(C) = 0.3$, find the range of possible values of $P(A')$.

In questions 7 and 8, for the given events A, B and C, find $P(A)$, $P(B)$, $P(C)$, $P(A \cap B)$, $P(B \cap C)$, $P(A \cap C)$. Write down any pairs of events which are independent.

7.   A card is drawn at random from a pack of 52. A: drawing a black card, B: drawing the jack of hearts, C: drawing a court card (i.e. jack, queen or king).

8.   A disc is drawn at random from a bag containing discs numbered 1 to 48. A: drawing a multiple of 3, B: drawing a multiple of 4, C: drawing a multiple of 6.

9.   If A and B are two independent events such that $P(A) = 1/4$ and $P(B) = 3/5$, find
(a) $P(A \cap B)$,   (b) $P(A \cup B)$,   (c) $P(A \cap B')$,   (d) $P(A' \cup B')$.

10. A and B are two independent events, such that $P(A \cap B) = 1/3$ and $P(A \cup B) = 9/10$. Given that $P(A) > P(B)$, find $P(A)$ and $P(B)$.

11. If A, B and C are independent random events such that $P(A) = 2/5$, $P(B) = 1/3$, $P(C) = 3/4$, calculate $P(A \cup B \cup C)$ and $P(A' \cup B' \cup C')$.

12. A box contains 5 red balls and 3 blue balls. A second box contains 2 red balls and 3 blue balls. Find the probability that (a) if a ball is drawn at random from each box both will be blue, (b) if two balls are drawn at random from each box all four will be red.

13. A die is biased so that the probability of throwing a six is $\frac{1}{4}$. If the die is thrown twice find the probability of (a) two sixes, (b) at least one six.

14. A man estimates that the probability that he will be early for work is $1/3$, the probability that he will be on time is $1/2$ and the probability that he will be late is $1/6$. Find the probability that in a particular 3-day period he will (a) arrive early every day, (b) never arrive on time, (c) be late at least once.

15. Three unbiased dice are thrown. Find the probability that (a) the score on each die is the same, (b) the total score is 5, (c) the total score is even.

16. Alan and Bob are playing a game which ends when either player is two points ahead of his opponent. If the probability that Alan wins any particular point is $\frac{2}{3}$, find the probabilities that the game ends when the number of points played is (a) 2, (b) 3, (c) 4.

17. Tom and Peter throw a single die in turn. The first player to throw a six wins. If Tom throws first, find the probability that Peter wins on his first, second or third turn. [Give your answer to 3 significant figures.]

18. Cards are drawn at random, with replacement, from a pack of 52. Find the probability that (a) the first two cards drawn are spades, (b) two out of the first three cards drawn are spades, (c) the third card drawn is a club, (d) the fourth card is the first black card to be drawn.

19. A certain committee has 6 members. The probability that any member will attend a particular meeting is $4/5$. Find the probability that the chairman and at least 4 of the 5 other members will attend.

20. An unbiased coin is tossed 5 times. Find the probabilities of (a) 4 heads, (b) 3 heads, (c) at least 2 heads.

21. A bag contains 3 red discs, 4 blue discs and 5 green discs. A trial consists of selecting a disc at random, noting its colour then replacing it. In three such trials, what is the probability of selecting (a) three red discs, (b) two blue discs, (c) one green and two blue discs?

14.5 Conditional probability

The probability of an event B, given that an event A has occurred, is called the *conditional probability* of B upon A, or the probability of B given A, and is written $P(B|A)$. This means that $P(B|A)$ is the probability that B occurs, considering A as sample space.

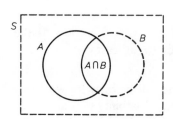

Since the subset of A in which B occurs is $A \cap B$,

$$P(B|A) = \frac{n(A \cap B)}{n(A)} = \frac{n(A \cap B)}{n(S)} \bigg/ \frac{n(A)}{n(S)}$$

$$\therefore \quad \boxed{P(B|A) = \frac{P(A \cap B)}{P(A)}.}$$

The general statement of the product law is obtained by rearranging this result:

$$P(A \cap B) = P(A) . P(B|A).$$

Similarly

$$P(A \cap B) = P(B) . P(A|B).$$

In the case of independent events the probability of B is unaffected by the occurrence of A, so $P(B|A) = P(B)$

$$\therefore \quad P(A \cap B) = P(A) . P(B).$$

Example 1   Two cards are drawn in succession from a pack. What is the probability that they are both diamonds if (a) the first card is replaced before the second is drawn, (b) the first card is not replaced?

(a) Since both cards are drawn from a full pack, in each case the probability of drawing a diamond is $\frac{13}{52}$, i.e. $\frac{1}{4}$

$\therefore$ with replacement the probability of two diamonds is

$$\frac{1}{4} \times \frac{1}{4} = \frac{1}{16}.$$

(b) The probability that the second card is a diamond given that a diamond has already been drawn is $\frac{12}{51} = \frac{4}{17}$,

$\therefore$ without replacement, the probability of two diamonds is

$$\frac{1}{4} \times \frac{4}{17} = \frac{1}{17}.$$

Consider now a trial in which two dice are thrown, where event C is throwing the same score on both dice and event D is throwing 3 or more on each of the dice.

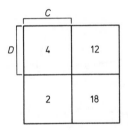

The 36 possible outcomes in the sample space for this trial can be represented in a Karnaugh map for events C and D.

Relationships between probabilities associated with such a trial are often displayed in a *probability tree diagram*.

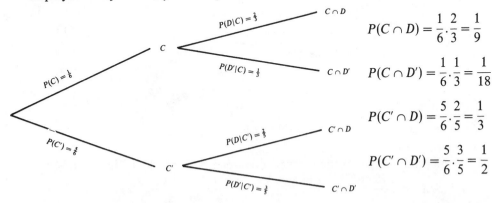

$$P(C \cap D) = \frac{1}{6} \cdot \frac{2}{3} = \frac{1}{9}$$

$$P(C \cap D') = \frac{1}{6} \cdot \frac{1}{3} = \frac{1}{18}$$

$$P(C' \cap D) = \frac{5}{6} \cdot \frac{2}{5} = \frac{1}{3}$$

$$P(C' \cap D') = \frac{5}{6} \cdot \frac{3}{5} = \frac{1}{2}$$

Probabilities can also be recorded in a *contingency table* as shown below. The diagram on the left shows which probabilities should be inserted in each part of the table. The completed table is on the right.

	D	D'	
C	$P(C \cap D)$	$P(C \cap D')$	$P(C)$
C'	$P(C' \cap D)$	$P(C' \cap D')$	$P(C')$
	$P(D)$	$P(D')$	

	D	D'	
C	$\frac{1}{9}$	$\frac{1}{18}$	$\frac{1}{6}$
C'	$\frac{1}{3}$	$\frac{1}{2}$	$\frac{5}{6}$
	$\frac{4}{9}$	$\frac{5}{9}$	1

Both the tree diagram and the contingency table demonstrate that

$$P(C \cap D) + P(C \cap D') + P(C' \cap D) + P(C' \cap D') = P(C) + P(C') = 1.$$

Example 2 A motorist plans a journey and event X is arrival at his destination in less than three hours. He estimates the probabilities of dry weather D, rain R or snow S to be $\frac{1}{3}$, $\frac{1}{2}$ and $\frac{1}{6}$ respectively. The probabilities of event X in these conditions are $\frac{3}{4}$, $\frac{2}{5}$ and $\frac{1}{10}$ respectively. What is the probability that (a) the motorist completes his journey in under 3 hours, (b) if he fails to arrive in less than 3 hours, there was a fall of snow?

(a) On the assumption that events D, R and S are mutually exclusive, the following tree diagram can be constructed.

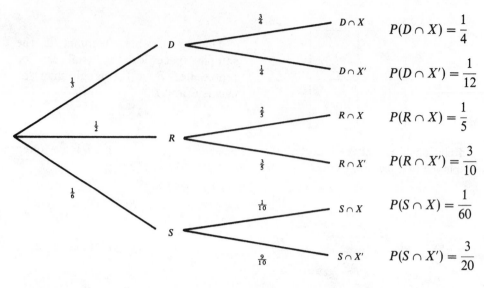

$$P(X) = P(D \cap X) + P(R \cap X) + P(S \cap X) = \frac{1}{4} + \frac{1}{5} + \frac{1}{60} = \frac{7}{15}$$

∴   the probability that the journey is completed in less than 3 hours is 7/15.

(b) $P(S|X') = \dfrac{P(S \cap X')}{P(X')} = \dfrac{P(S \cap X')}{1 - P(X)} = \dfrac{\frac{3}{20}}{1 - \frac{7}{15}} = \dfrac{3}{20} \cdot \dfrac{15}{8} = \dfrac{9}{32}.$

∴   given that the motorist failed to arrive in less than three hours, the probability that it snowed is 9/32.

	D	R	S
X	$\frac{1}{4}$	$\frac{1}{5}$	$\frac{1}{60}$
X'	$\frac{1}{12}$	$\frac{3}{10}$	$\frac{3}{20}$

It is sometimes helpful to display probabilities on a Karnaugh map. We give here the probability map for Example 2. This shows clearly that

$$P(X) = \frac{1}{4} + \frac{1}{5} + \frac{1}{60} = \frac{7}{15}.$$

When finding $P(S|X')$ we consider X' as sample space. Thus, using the lower half of the diagram only,

$$P(S|X') = \frac{3}{20} \Big/ \left(\frac{1}{12} + \frac{3}{10} + \frac{3}{20} \right) = \frac{3}{20} \Big/ \frac{32}{60} = \frac{9}{32}.$$

Exercise 14.5

Questions 1 to 5 concern a trial in which a domino is drawn from a complete set of 28. Event A: it has at least one six on it. Event B: it is a double, i.e. has two identical numbers on it. Event C: the sum of the numbers is six or less.

1.   Find $P(A)$, $P(B)$, $P(C)$.

2.   Find $P(B|A)$, $P(C|A)$, $P(A \cap B)$, $P(A \cap C)$.

3. Find $P(B|C)$, $P(C|B)$, $P(B|C')$, $P(C|B')$.

4. Find $P(B \cap C)$, $P(B \cap C')$, $P(B' \cap C)$.

5. Find $P(A \cap C')$, $P(A' \cap B')$, $P(A' \cap C')$.

Questions 6 to 10 Repeat questions 1 to 5 for a trial in which a card is drawn from a normal pack. Event A: drawing a king or a queen. Event B: drawing a black card. Event C: drawing a heart.

11. A bag contains 4 black discs and 2 white ones. If discs are drawn from the bag one at a time, find the probability that 2 black discs followed by 2 white discs are drawn (a) with replacement, (b) without replacement.

12. A bag contains 10 cards bearing the letters of the word STATISTICS. Find the probability that the first four letters drawn at random from the bag are S, I, T, S in that order (a) with replacement, (b) without replacement.

13. The probability that it will be foggy on a November morning is $\frac{1}{3}$. The probability that Mr. Jones will be late for work when it is foggy is $\frac{1}{2}$. The probability that he will be late if it is not foggy is $\frac{1}{8}$. If on a particular November morning Mr. Jones is late, find the probability that it is foggy.

14. On a day on the summer holidays the probability that Jane will go swimming is 0·6. The probability that both Jane and Karen will go swimming is 0·45. If Jane is seen in the swimming pool what is the probability that Karen also swims that day?

15. The probability that a light bulb has a life of more than 1000 hours is $\frac{1}{2}$ and the probability of a life of more than 2000 hours is $\frac{1}{10}$. What is the probability that a bulb that has already been in use for 1000 hours will last a further 1000 hours?

16. A football star is having injury problems. When he is playing the probability that his team will win is $\frac{3}{4}$, but otherwise it is only $\frac{1}{2}$. The probability that the player will be fit this Saturday is $\frac{1}{3}$. Find the probability that his team will win the match.

17. The probability that it will be sunny tomorrow is 0·25. The probability that Mrs. Brown will go shopping tomorrow is 0·2. The probability that both these events occur is 0·15. Find the probability that (a) neither event occurs, (b) Mrs. Brown goes shopping, given that it is sunny, (c) it is sunny given that Mrs. Brown goes shopping.

18. A bag contains 5 black beads and 3 white beads. A second bag contains 3 black beads and 5 white beads. A bead is drawn at random from the first bag and placed in the second bag. A bead is then drawn at random from the second bag

and placed in the first. Find the probability that each bag now contains (a) 4 black and 4 white beads, (b) the same numbers of each colour as it did initially.

19. A box A contains 3 red balls and 4 black balls. A box B contains 3 red balls and 2 black balls. One box is selected at random and then from that box one ball is selected at random. Find (a) the probability that the ball is red, (b) the probability that the ball came from box A, given that it is red.

20. A member of a slimming club claims that the probability that she will have a chocolate biscuit with her morning coffee is $\frac{1}{6}$ and that on the days that she resists the temptation, the probability that she exceeds her daily calorie allowance is $\frac{1}{5}$. If the probability that she consumes too many calories on any day is $\frac{1}{4}$, find the probability that she does so on a day when she has had a chocolate biscuit. Given that yesterday she kept within her calorie allowance, find the probability that she ate a chocolate biscuit.

Exercise 14.6 (miscellaneous)

1.   How many even five-digit numbers can be formed using the digits 0, 1, 2, 3, 4, 5, 6 (excluding numbers which start with 0) if (a) no digit may be repeated, (b) repetition is allowed?

2.   Find the number of different ways in which the letters of the word ISOSCELES can be arranged. How many of these arrangements (a) begin and end with E, (b) begin with S, (c) end with a vowel?

3.   A man has found 6 records that he likes in a shop, but cannot decide which of them to buy. Assuming that he buys at least one, find the number of different selections he could make.

4.   Six lines are drawn, no two of which are parallel. If no more than two of the lines pass through any one point, find the number of triangles formed.

5.   In how many ways can a group of 9 people attending a conference be split into three sets of 3 people for discussion? Later the same people form new sets of 3. In how many ways can this be done if no two people remain together?

6.   Find the number of ways in which 5 books can be distributed between three people A, B and C if the books are (a) all different, (b) indistinguishable.

7.   Draw a Venn diagram to show the following sets and their non-empty intersections: $\mathscr{E} = \{\text{all quadrilaterals}\}$, $T = \{\text{trapeziums}\}$, $R = \{\text{rectangles}\}$, $P = \{\text{parallelograms}\}$, $K = \{\text{kites, i.e. two pairs of adjacent sides equal}\}$. Describe the elements of the sets $K \cap R$ and $K \cap P$.

8.   Decide whether the following statements are true or false for sets A, B and C, giving brief reasons for your answers.

(a) $A \cap B = A \cup B \Leftrightarrow A = B,$
(b) $A \cup B = A \cup C \Leftrightarrow B = C,$
(c) $A \cap B = A \cap C \Leftrightarrow A = B \cap C,$
(d) $A \cap (B' \cup C') = \emptyset \Leftrightarrow A \subset (B \cup C).$

9. In a certain school half the pupils under 16 years of age are girls, two thirds of the girls in the school are under 16 and a quarter of the pupils are boys of 16 and over. If there are 540 girls in the school, find the total number of pupils.

10. A drawer contains 4 different pairs of socks. Find the probability that (a) if 2 socks are selected at random they will form a pair, (b) if 4 socks are selected at random they will form two pairs.

11. (a) Two dice are thrown together, and the scores added. What is the probability that (i) the total score exceeds 8, (ii) the total score is 9, or the individual scores differ by 1, or both?
(b) A bag contains 3 red balls and 4 black ones. 3 balls are picked out, one at a time and not replaced. What is the probability that there will be 2 red and 1 black in the sample?
(c) A committee of 4 is to be chosen from 6 men and 5 women. One particular man and one particular woman refuse to serve if the other person is on the committee. How many different committees may be formed? (SU)

12. An analysis of the other subjects taken by A-level Mathematics candidates in a certain year showed that 20% of them took Further Mathematics, 50% took Physics and 5% took both Further Mathematics and Physics. A candidate is chosen at random from those who took A-level Mathematics. (i) Calculate the probability that the chosen candidate took neither Further Mathematics nor Physics. (ii) Given that the chosen candidate took at least one of Further Mathematics and Physics, calculate the probability that the candidate took Further Mathematics. (JMB)

13. Two cards are drawn simultaneously from a pack of 52. What is the probability that both are spades if one card is known to be (a) black, (b) red, (c) a spade, (d) a king?

14. An experiment consists of tossing two fair coins one after the other. Let X be the set of events in which the first coin is a head, Y be the set of events in which the second coin is a head and Z be the set of events in which both coins are heads or both coins are tails. Calculate the following probabilities: $p(X)$, $p(Y)$, $p(Z)$, $p(X \cap Z)$, $p(X \cap Y \cap Z)$. (AEB 1977)

15. Three cards are drawn at random without replacement from a pack of ten cards which are numbered from 1 to 10, respectively. Calculate (i) the probability that the numbers drawn consist of two even numbers and one odd number, (ii) the probability that at least one of the numbers drawn is a perfect square greater than 1, (iii) the probability that the smallest number drawn is the 5. (JMB)

16. A disc of diameter 5 cm is tossed at random on to a large sheet of paper ruled with parallel lines 8 cm apart. Assuming the lines to be of negligible thickness, find the probability that the disc lands on a line. If the paper is now ruled with 8 cm squares, find the probability that (a) the disc lands on a line, (b) the disc lands on the intersection of two lines.

17. A pack of 52 cards contains 4 suits each of 13 cards. If 13 cards are taken at random from the pack what is the probability that exactly 10 of them are spades? [You may take $\binom{52}{13} = 6\cdot35 \times 10^{11}$.]   (O&C)

18. A bag contains 5 red, 4 orange and 3 yellow sweets. One after another, three children select and eat one sweet each. When the bag contains n sweets, the probability of any one child choosing any particular sweet is $1/n$. What are the probabilities that (a) they all choose red sweets, (b) at least one orange sweet is chosen, (c) each chooses a different colour, (d) all choose the same colour? [Answers to this question may be left as fractions in their lowest terms.]   (O&C)

19. (a) Two independent events are such that there is a probability of $\frac{1}{6}$ that they will both occur and a probability of $\frac{1}{3}$ that neither will occur. Calculate their individual probabilities of occurring.
(b) A fair cubical die has three of its faces coloured red, two coloured blue and one coloured white. If the die is thrown six times calculate the probabilities that (i) a red face will be uppermost at least once, (ii) a red face will be uppermost exactly three times, (iii) each colour will be uppermost exactly twice.   (W)

20. Four cards are drawn at random from a pack, one at a time with replacement. Find the probability that (a) no heart is drawn, (b) four hearts are drawn, (c) two hearts and two diamonds are drawn (in any order), (d) one card from each suit is drawn.   (L)

21. Two events A and B are such that $P(A) = 0\cdot4$ and $P(A \cup B) = 0\cdot7$. (i) Find the value of $P(A' \cap B)$. (ii) Find the value of $P(B)$ if A and B are mutually exclusive. (iii) Find the value of $P(B)$ if A and B are independent.   (JMB)

22. The following are three of the classical problems in probability.
(a) Compare the probability of a total of 9 with the probability of a total of 10 when three fair dice are tossed once (Galileo and Duke of Tuscany).
(b) Compare the probability of at least one six in 4 tosses of a fair die with the probability of at least one double-six in 24 tosses of two fair dice (Chevalier de Méré).
(c) Compare the probability of at least one six when 6 dice are rolled with the probability of at least two sixes when 12 dice are rolled (Pepys to Newton). Solve each of these problems.   (AEB 1978)

23. (a) From an ordinary pack of 52 cards two are dealt face downwards on a table. What is the probability that (i) the first card dealt is a heart, (ii) the second card dealt is a heart, (iii) both cards are hearts, (iv) at least one card is a heart?

(b) Bag *A* contains 3 white counters and 2 black counters whilst bag *B* contains 2 white and 3 black. One counter is removed from bag *A* and placed in bag *B* without its colour being seen. What is the probability that a counter removed from bag *B* will be white?

(c) A box of 24 eggs is known to contain 4 old and 20 new. If 3 eggs are picked at random determine the probability that (i) 2 are new and the other old, (ii) they are all new. (SU)

24. A hand of 5 cards is drawn from a pack of 52 playing cards. Find the probability of drawing (a) 5 cards of the same suit, (b) a pair plus a triple (e.g. 2 sevens and 3 aces). If a hand consists of 2 aces, a king, a jack and a 4 and a player keeps the pair of aces but discards the other 3 cards and draws 3 more cards from the remaining 47, find the probability of obtaining a pair plus a triple. (L)

25. If *A*, *B* and *C* are exhaustive events, such that *A* cannot occur at the same time as either *B* or *C*, show that
(a) $P(A)+P(B)+P(C) = 1+P(B \cap C)$, (b) $P(A') = P(B \cup C)$.

26. Two cards are drawn without replacement from a pack of playing cards. Using a tree diagram, or otherwise, calculate the probability (a) that both cards are aces, (b) that one (and only one) card is an ace, (c) that the two cards are of different suits. Given that at least one ace is drawn, find the probability that the two cards are of different suits. (L)

27. (a) Two events *A* and *B* are such that $P(A) = \frac{1}{3}$ and $P(B) = \frac{1}{2}$. If *A'* denotes the complement of *A*, calculate $P(A' \cap B)$ in each of the cases when (i) $P(A \cap B) = \frac{1}{8}$, (ii) *A* and *B* are mutually exclusive, (iii) *A* is a subset of *B*.
(b) A Scottish court may give any one of the three verdicts: 'guilty', 'not guilty' and 'not proven'. Of all the cases tried by the court, 70% of the verdicts are 'guilty', 20% are 'not guilty' and 10% are 'not proven'. Suppose that when the court's verdict is 'guilty', 'not guilty' and 'not proven', the probabilities that the accused is really innocent are 0·05, 0·95 and 0·25, respectively. Calculate the probability that an innocent person will be found 'guilty' by the court. (W)

28. Suppose that letters sent by first and second class post have probabilities of being delivered a given number of days after posting according to the following table (weekends are ignored).

Days to delivery	1	2	3
1st class	0·9	0·1	0
2nd class	0·1	0·6	0·3

The secretary of a committee posts a letter to a committee member who replies immediately using the same class of post. What is the probability that four or more days are taken from the secretary posting the letter to receiving the reply if (a) first class, (b) second class post is used? The secretary sends out four letters and each member replies immediately by the same class of post. Assuming the letters move independently, what is the probability that the secretary receives (a) all the replies within three days using first class post, (b) at least two replies within three days using second class post?   (O)

29. In a game, three cubical dice are thrown by a player who attempts to throw the same number on all three. What is the chance of the player (a) throwing the same number on all three, (b) throwing the same number on just two? If the first throw results in just two dice showing the same number, then the third is thrown again. If no two dice show the same number, then all are thrown again. The player then comes to the end of his turn. What is the chance of the player succeeding in throwing three identical numbers in a complete turn? What is the chance that all the numbers are different at the end of a turn?   (O&C)

30. An experiment is performed with a die and two packs of cards. The die is thrown, and if it shows 1, 2, 3 or 4 a card is drawn at random from the first pack, which contains the usual 52 cards; if the score on the die is 5 or 6 a card is drawn from the second pack, which contains only 39 cards, all the clubs having been removed. X denotes the event 'The first pack with 52 cards is used', and Y denotes the event 'The card drawn is a diamond'. Calculate the probabilities (i) $P(X)$, (ii) $P(X \cap Y)$, (iii) $P(Y)$, (iv) $P(Y|X)$, (v) $P(X|Y)$.   (C)

31. Each of two boxes contains ten discs. In one box four of the discs are red, two are white and four are blue; in the other box two are red, three are white and five are blue. One of these two boxes is chosen at random and three discs are drawn at random from it without replacement. Calculate (i) the probability that one disc of each colour will be drawn, (ii) the probability that no white disc will be drawn, (iii) the most probable number of white discs that will be drawn. Given that three blue discs were drawn, calculate the conditional probability that they came from the box that contained four blue discs.   (W)

32. Write down an equation, in terms of probabilities, corresponding to each of the statements (i) the events A and B are independent, (ii) the events A and C are mutually exclusive. The events A, B and C are such that A and B are independent and A and C are mutually exclusive. Given that $P(A) = 0.4$, $P(B) = 0.2$, $P(C) = 0.3$, $P(B \cap C) = 0.1$, calculate $P(A \cup B)$, $P(C|B)$, $P(B|A \cup C)$. Also calculate the probability that one and only one of the events B, C will occur.   (W)

33. A pack of sixteen playing cards consists of the ace, king, queen and jack of each of the four suits, spades, hearts, diamonds and clubs. A man is dealt four cards at random from the pack. (i) Calculate the probability that he has been dealt exactly two aces. (ii) The man is asked whether he has been dealt any aces. He truthfully replies that he has. Calculate the probability that he has been dealt exactly two aces. (iii) By accident the man displays one of his four cards, which is seen to be the ace of spades. Calculate the probability that he has been dealt exactly two aces. Give your answers correct to two significant figures.   (C)

15 Elementary statistics

15.1 Graphical representation of data

Statistics may be described as a subject concerned with the analysis of data obtained from such sources as experiments and surveys. In elementary work this will involve making tables, charts and graphs to present the data as clearly as possible. In more advanced work various numerical measures of the properties of collections of data are studied. These may be used to compare sets of observations, to draw conclusions from information gathered and to make predictions about future events. An important aspect of the subject is measuring the significance of such conclusions and predictions.

We first consider three common ways of presenting information in graphical form. Below are two *pie charts* showing the results of an investigation into which brands of fabric softener housewives use. The charts both show the relative proportions of the different brands used, but the first is quite misleading as it gives no indication that the majority of housewives use no softener at all.

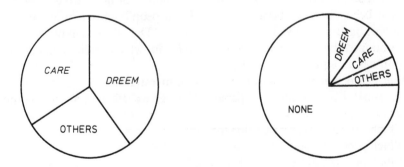

The same results can also be illustrated in the form of a *bar chart* or *block graph*. In both the given charts the vertical scale represents the number of housewives using the products. However, the first diagram exaggerates the lead of 'DREEM' in the market by starting the vertical axis at 60 instead of 0.

337

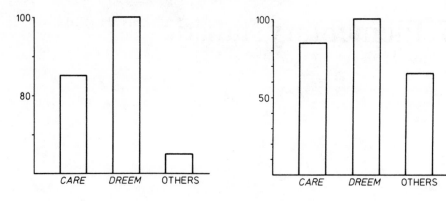

The following *line graphs* both represent the results of 5 successive surveys. This type of graph is used to illustrate a trend or pattern in results. However, in this case either graph on its own could be misleading because although sales of 'DREEM' are rising, its share of the market in fabric softeners is falling.

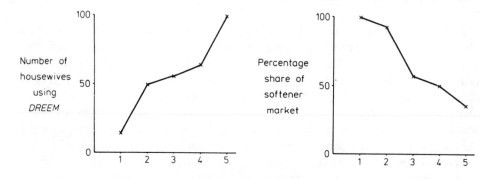

It is clear from these examples that care must be taken when making or interpreting graphs and charts, but it is also important to question the validity of the original data. In this survey a *sample* of 1000 housewives were questioned, but this is only a small proportion of the total *population* of housewives. The results could have been distorted because most of the people chosen belonged to the same income group or lived in the same area. The most reliable results are usually obtained by taking a *random sample*, in which each member of the population has an equal chance of being selected.

Another factor which may affect this type of investigation is the framing of the questions asked. For example, one person might give a different answer to each of the following four questions:

(1) Which product gives best value for money?
(2) Which product do you buy regularly?
(3) Which product did you buy this week?
(4) Which product do you prefer?

A survey based on only one of these questions could give misleading results.

Having considered some of the ways in which statistical information can be misunderstood or even misused, we now examine some more accurate ways of analysing and presenting results.

Example A In a short test given to a set of 15 students the marks were as follows:

$$2 \quad 4 \quad 1 \quad 3 \quad 5 \quad 4 \quad 4 \quad 3 \quad 5 \quad 4 \quad 2 \quad 6 \quad 3 \quad 5 \quad 4$$

Since the test mark, x, of any particular student can take only certain values in the range 1 to 6, it is called a *discrete variable*. For a variable of this type it is helpful to make a table called a *frequency distribution* showing the frequency with which each value occurs. The corresponding diagram is called a *frequency chart*.

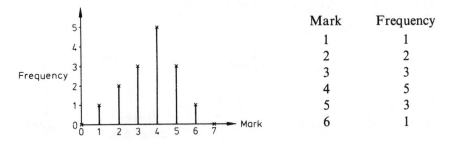

Mark	Frequency
1	1
2	2
3	3
4	5
5	3
6	1

When it is necessary to examine sums of frequencies, such as the number of students who scored 4 marks or less, a *cumulative frequency distribution* may be used. For a discrete variable x the cumulative frequency is the frequency of values *less than or equal to* x. As shown in the *cumulative frequency chart*, for a discrete variable, the cumulative frequency is a *step function*.

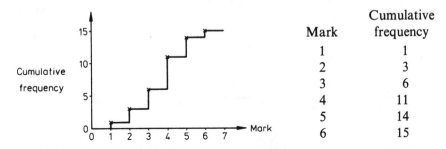

Mark	Cumulative frequency
1	1
2	3
3	6
4	11
5	14
6	15

Example B The table below shows the numbers of children known to have contracted whooping-cough in 1965.

Age	No. of cases (to the nearest 100)
Under 1 year	1400
1–2 years	3300
3–4 years	3500
5–9 years	3900
10–14 years	500

Since the age of a child can take any real value between 0 and 15 years, it is called a *continuous variable*. Because the variable is continuous and because the table gives frequencies for age groups of different sizes, a simple frequency chart similar to the one used in Example A could be misleading. To allow for the various age ranges we draw a *histogram*, in which the *areas* (not the heights) of the columns are proportional to the frequencies.

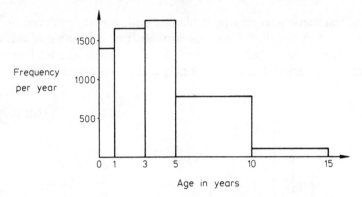

This means that the height of each column represents $\dfrac{\text{frequency}}{\text{column width}}$ (sometimes called *frequency density*). In this case the vertical scale may be taken to represent the number of cases of whooping-cough per one year age group.

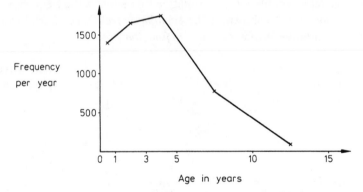

The *frequency polygon* shown here is obtained from the histogram by joining the mid-point of the tops of the columns. As several frequency polygons can be drawn in the same diagram, they are often used for comparing distributions.

For a continuous variable x, it is convenient to regard the cumulative frequency as the frequency of values *less than* x. In this example the cumulative frequency does not move in a series of jumps, but increases gradually throughout the range 0 to 15 years. Thus the values in the cumulative frequency table are used to draw a curve called the *cumulative frequency graph* or *ogive*.

Age	Cumulative frequency
Under 1 year	1400
Under 3 years	4700
Under 5 years	8200
Under 10 years	12 100
Under 15 years	12 600

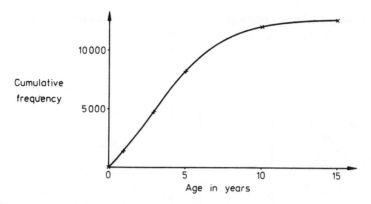

Example C   The table below shows the number of staff meals issued per day in a college refectory over a period of 40 days.

56	50	63	56	58	53	52	71	59	52
45	55	42	62	62	60	57	48	63	68
55	65	50	59	54	54	46	51	73	64
53	50	61	51	58	52	57	67	53	69

In this example the variable is again discrete. However, a frequency table of the type used in Example A would have little meaning as there is a range of 31 from the lowest value 42 to the highest 73. Any pattern in the distribution of observations will be shown more clearly by grouping the numbers. The range could be divided into intervals 40–50, 50–60, 60–70 and 70–80. One difficulty about this choice arises when we come to observations such as 50 which appear in two classes. This could be avoided by choosing intervals such as 40–49, 50–59, ... [In certain circumstances, it may be better to regard 50 as $\frac{1}{2}$ in the 40–50 class and $\frac{1}{2}$ in the 50–60 class.] The other main difficulty is that this grouping produces only 4 classes and will not illustrate the distribution in any detail. From this point of view, the intervals 40–44, 45–49, ... would be better. However, the mid-points of intervals are often used in calculations, so it is convenient if these are round numbers. Thus a reasonable choice in this example is the grouping 38–42, 43–47, ... into intervals of length 5 units with mid-points 40, 45, ... The *class limits* are the lowest and highest observations which could occur in each class, namely 38 and 42, 43 and 47, ... However, the *class boundaries* or *end-points* are taken, in this case, to be 37·5, 42·5, ...

We may now draw up the frequency distribution for the grouped data using *tally marks* as shown below.

No. of meals		Frequency
38–42	I	1
43–47	I I	2
48–52	++++ I I I I	9
53–57	++++ ++++ I	11
58–62	++++ I I I	8
63–67	++++	5
68–72	I I I	3
73–77	I	1

In the histogram of this distribution, since the columns are of equal width, their heights as well as their areas will be proportional to the frequencies.

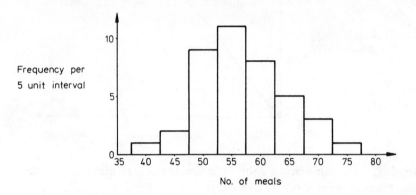

When constructing a frequency polygon it is possible to plot zero frequencies at each end of the diagram to produce a closed polygon.

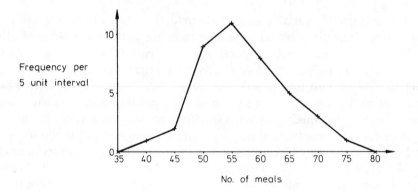

As in Example A the cumulative frequency chart constructed from the original data is a step diagram.

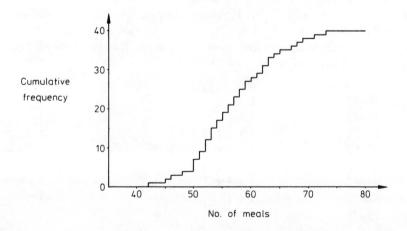

However, a cumulative frequency graph drawn using the grouped frequency distribution will provide a sufficiently good approximation for many purposes. To construct this graph we treat the number of meals as a continuous variable plotting the cumulative frequencies against the corresponding upper class boundaries.

No. of meals less than:	37·5	42·5	47·5	52·5	57·5	62·5	67·5	72·5	77·5
Cumulative frequency	0	1	3	12	23	31	36	39	40

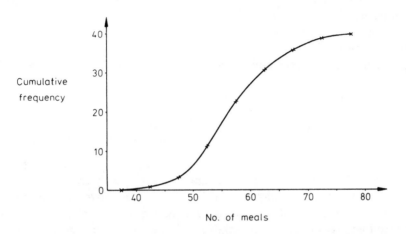

In a similar way we could produce a histogram and a cumulative frequency polygon for the distribution in Example A by regarding it as a grouped distribution with class boundaries 0·5, 1·5, 2·5, ... However, such artificially produced diagrams have very little true meaning.

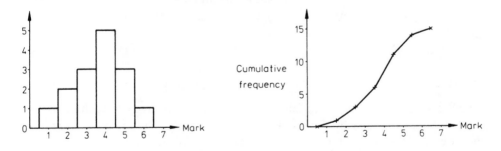

Exercise 15.1

[The data in questions 3 to 8 will be referred to in later exercises.]

1.   Conduct a survey on a suitable topic of your own choice, such as the reading or television viewing habits of a group of students. Consider carefully (a) the questions to be used, (b) the way in which the data is to be recorded, (c) the graphical representation of the data collected. How could such a survey be conducted and the data presented in order to produce distorted or misleading results?

2. The table below shows the sales in two successive years of a particular type of car.

	2-door super	4-door super	4-door de-luxe	estate
1st year	8100	10 800	18 000	3600
2nd year	15 000	21 000	25 000	11 000

(a) Draw two pie charts whose areas allow the total sales for the two years to be compared.
(b) Draw a comparative bar chart, i.e. one in which there are two bars for each model of the car.
(c) Comment briefly on the advantages of the two ways of representing the data.

3. In an experiment the following 20 values of a variable x were recorded.

$$5 \quad 6 \quad 2 \quad 4 \quad 4 \quad 5 \quad 7 \quad 5 \quad 5 \quad 6$$
$$4 \quad 7 \quad 6 \quad 5 \quad 3 \quad 5 \quad 6 \quad 4 \quad 6 \quad 5$$

(a) Given that x is a discrete variable which can take only integral values, draw a frequency distribution chart and a cumulative frequency chart.
(b) Given that x is a continuous variable and that the above values are rounded to the nearest integer, draw a histogram and a cumulative frequency polygon.
(c) Given that x is a continuous variable and that the integral value n is recorded when $n \leqslant x < n+1$, draw a histogram and a cumulative frequency polygon.

4. The table below gives the number of dresses sold each day in a small shop over a 5-week period.

	Monday	Tuesday	Wednesday	Friday	Saturday
Week 1	2	2	4	4	9
Week 2	0	4	7	3	7
Week 3	1	0	3	1	6
Week 4	3	3	2	2	8
Week 5	1	3	5	3	8

Draw a frequency distribution chart and a cumulative frequency chart for the distribution. Comment briefly on other ways of representing the data graphically in order to show any patterns in the distribution more clearly.

5. In an investigation the following 50 values of a variable x were recorded:

$$6 \quad 11 \quad 12 \quad 8 \quad 9 \quad 8 \quad 9 \quad 4 \quad 2 \quad 7$$
$$9 \quad 7 \quad 4 \quad 11 \quad 7 \quad 5 \quad 8 \quad 7 \quad 6 \quad 4$$
$$9 \quad 6 \quad 3 \quad 4 \quad 6 \quad 7 \quad 5 \quad 6 \quad 6 \quad 9$$
$$4 \quad 9 \quad 7 \quad 1 \quad 4 \quad 7 \quad 7 \quad 4 \quad 10 \quad 9$$
$$5 \quad 8 \quad 10 \quad 7 \quad 4 \quad 9 \quad 5 \quad 7 \quad 9 \quad 11$$

Decide whether it would be more appropriate to represent the cumulative frequency distribution by a step diagram or an ogive given that (a) x is a discrete variable which takes only integral values, (b) x is a continuous variable with values rounded to the nearest integer. Draw the appropriate graph in each case.

6.   The length to the nearest minute of a man's journey to work over a period of 40 days are as follows:

57	56	33	56	49	56	44	56	45	58
62	57	42	68	49	44	59	63	50	58
53	58	50	56	60	59	45	51	65	53
50	38	65	43	51	63	56	61	67	61

Construct a suitable grouped frequency table, stating the class boundaries that you have used. Draw the corresponding histogram and cumulative frequency curve. Estimate from your graph the percentage of days on which the journey takes at least 45 minutes.

7.   In a particular year 80 children enter a certain large infants' school. The ages of the children on the day they first attend the school are given in the table below.

Age in years	$4\frac{1}{4}-$	$4\frac{1}{2}-$	$4\frac{3}{4}-$	$5-$	$5\frac{1}{4}-$	$5\frac{1}{2}-$	$6-$	$7-$	$7\frac{3}{4}-$
Frequency	0	10	35	18	7	3	5	2	0

Draw a histogram, a frequency polygon and a cumulative frequency polygon to represent this distribution. Can you account for the entries in the table for children of $5\frac{1}{2}$ years and over? Estimate the probability that a child in the catchment area of this school is under 5 years old when he first attends school, stating any assumptions you have made.

8.   The grouped frequency distribution of the test marks obtained by 150 students is given below.

Class limits	1–5	6–10	11–15	16–20	21–25
Frequency	0	4	12	22	30

Class limits	26–30	31–35	36–40	41–45	Over 45
Frequency	31	24	14	8	5

Draw a histogram to represent the data given that (a) the test was marked out of 50, (b) the test was marked out of 60, (c) the top mark was 54. Construct a cumulative frequency polygon in case (b). Give two reasons why this diagram represents an approximation to the true cumulative frequency distribution. Explain why a cumulative frequency curve may give a better approximation.

15.2 Mode, median and mean

The mode, median and mean of a distribution are all known as measures of *location* (or *central tendency*). For a collection of numerical data, they all indicate the general level or location of the observations by giving an 'average' or central value.

The *mode* is the observation which occurs most frequently. In some cases there are two or more modes.

The *median* is the middle observation when the observations are listed in order of magnitude. If the number of items is even, the average of the middle two is used.

The *mean* of a set of observations is the average or arithmetic mean. For a set of n observations $x_1, x_2, \ldots, x_n$, the mean $\bar{x} = \dfrac{1}{n}(x_1 + x_2 + \ldots + x_n)$. Using the Σ notation, this becomes $\bar{x} = \dfrac{1}{n}\sum_{r=1}^{n} x_r$ or simply $\bar{x} = \dfrac{1}{n}\sum x$.

Of these measures of location, the mean is the one used most frequently, although it can be distorted by extreme values at the ends of a distribution. The median has the advantage that it is not affected in this way.

Example 1   Find the mode, median and mean of the following sets of observations (a) 6, 7, 7, 3, 8, 5, 3, 9; (b) 18, 13, 14, 13, 11, 12, 13, 12, 11.

(a) The distribution has two modes, 3 and 7.

Arranged in order of magnitude the observations are 3, 3, 5, 6, 7, 7, 8, 9. Thus the median is $\frac{1}{2}(6+7) = 6 \cdot 5$. The mean is $\dfrac{1}{8}(6+7+7+3+8+5+3+9) = 6$.

(b) The mode of this distribution is 13.

Arranged in order of magnitude the observations are 11, 11, 12, 12, 13, 13, 13, 14, 18. Thus the median is 13.

The mean is $\dfrac{1}{9}(2.11 + 2.12 + 3.13 + 14 + 18) = 13$.

[Note that arranging a set of observations in order of magnitude is called forming an *array*.]

We now return to Examples A, B and C discussed in the previous section.

Example A   From both the frequency distribution and the frequency chart, it is clear that the mode is 4.

Since there are 15 marks, the median is the 8th mark in order of magnitude. Hence, using the cumulative frequency distribution or the corresponding chart, we find that the median is 4.

When calculating the mean, the total of the marks can be found using the frequency distribution.

Mark (x)	Frequency (f)	fx
1	1	1
2	2	4
3	3	9
4	5	20
5	3	15
6	1	6
	15	55

The formula for the mean can now be expressed as

$$\bar{x} = \frac{1}{n}\sum fx \quad \text{where} \quad n = \sum f.$$

Hence the mean mark $= \dfrac{55}{15} \approx 3\cdot67.$

Example B For grouped data it is not possible to find a true mode, as the values of individual observations are not known. Instead the term *modal class* may be used to describe the interval corresponding to the highest column in the histogram. In this case the modal class is the 3–4 year age group. [Note that this is not the group with the highest number of cases of whooping-cough.]

The median is a value of the variable which has equal numbers of observations above and below it. For grouped data an approximate value of the median can be found either graphically or by calculation. In this example the median is the age below which 6300 whooping-cough cases lie. Thus the median can be estimated from the ogive by reading off the age corresponding to a cumulative frequency of 6300 cases, which is approximately 4 years.

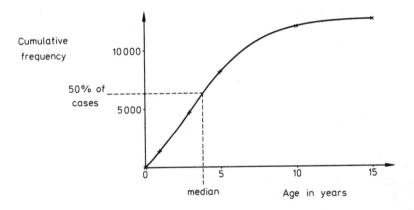

To estimate the median of a grouped frequency distribution by calculation, we assume that the observations in any class are evenly spaced, i.e. that the known points on the ogive can be joined with straight lines. This way of estimating intermediate values of a function is called *linear interpolation*. In this example there are 4700 cases under 3 years old and 8200 under 5 years old, so the median age lies in the 3–4 year class which contains 3500 cases. Since there are a total of 6300 cases below the median, 1600 of the cases in the 3–4 year class must lie below the median and 1900 above it. Thus we assume that the median divides this 2 year interval in the ratio 1600 : 1900

$$\therefore \quad \text{the median} = 3 + \left(\frac{1600}{3500} \times 2\right) \text{years} \approx 3\cdot9 \text{ years.}$$

Finding the median by calculation is equivalent to using a cumulative frequency polygon rather than a curve. This calculated value can also be regarded as the value of the variable at which a vertical line divides the histogram into two equal areas.

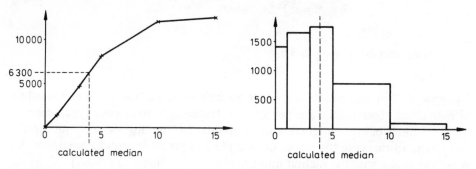

calculated median   calculated median

To find an approximate value for the mean of a grouped frequency distribution, we again assume that observations are evenly spaced. It then follows that the mean of the observations in any one class lies at the mid-point of the class interval. Hence if there are f observations in a class with mid-value x, then the sum of these observations is taken to be fx.

Class	Mid-value (x)	Frequency (f)	fx
Under 1 year	0·5	1400	700
1–2 years	2	3300	6600
3–4 years	4	3500	14 000
5–9 years	7·5	3900	29 250
10–14 years	12·5	500	6250
		$n = 12\,600$	56 800

$$\bar{x} = \frac{1}{n}\sum fx = \frac{56\,800}{12\,600} \approx 4\cdot5$$

Hence the mean age is approximately 4·5 years.

Example C   From the original data this distribution is found to have modes 50, 52 and 53. As these values occur only three times each, this information is probably of little value. The fact that the 53–57 group is the modal class may be more useful.

There are 40 observations, so the median is the average of the 20th and 21st, which is 56. An estimate of the median value can be obtained from the grouped frequency distribution, either graphically or by calculation, using the methods given in Example B. To estimate the median graphically we again use the ogive and obtain an approximate value of 56. To estimate the median by calculation we note, from the cumulative frequency table in §15.1, that 12 values of the variable are less than 52·5 and 23 values are less than 57·5. Since the median lies between the 20th and 21st value, it must be in the 5 unit interval from 52·5 to 57·5, with 8 values below it and 3 above. Assuming that these 11 observations are evenly spaced, the approximate value obtained for the median is $52\cdot5 + \left(\dfrac{8}{11} \times 5\right) \approx 56\cdot1$.

If it is necessary to find the mean from the original data without the aid of a calculator, it helps to use the deviations of the observations from an arbitrary origin. Taking 55 as origin the deviations are:

$$
\begin{array}{rrrrrrrrrr}
1 & -5 & 8 & 1 & 3 & -2 & -3 & 16 & 4 & -3 \\
-10 & 0 & -13 & 7 & 7 & 5 & 2 & -7 & 8 & 13 \\
0 & 10 & -5 & 4 & -1 & -1 & -9 & -4 & 18 & 9 \\
-2 & -5 & 6 & -4 & 3 & -3 & 2 & 12 & -2 & 14
\end{array}
$$

Cancelling equal and opposite numbers, the sum of the deviations reduces to

$$16+8+18+6+12+14 = 74$$

$$\therefore \quad \text{the mean} = 55 + \frac{74}{40} \approx 56 \cdot 9.$$

In this case a good approximation to the value of the mean can be obtained from the grouped data. This estimated value is found to be $56\frac{7}{8}$.

Exercise 15.2

1. Find the mode, median and mean of the following sets of integers
(a) 3, 4, 2, 3, 1, 3, 5, 7, 3, 4,
(b) 24, 38, 8, 13, 25, 3, 29,
(c) 21, 19, 20, 20, 22, 20, 21, 22, 21.

2. If an additional integer 20 is included in each of the lists given in question 1, find the new values of the mode, median and mean in each case.

In questions 3 to 8 use the data given in the corresponding questions in Exercise 15.1.

3. Find the mode, median and mean of the distribution, distinguishing where necessary between cases (a), (b) and (c).

4. Find the mode, median and mean of the distribution. Comment briefly on the usefulness of these measures in this context.

5. Use a frequency distribution table to find the mean of this distribution. Comment on the significance of your answer in cases (a) and (b).

6. (i) State the modal class of the grouped frequency distribution obtained in Exercise 15.1 and use this distribution to estimate the mean of the original data. Use the cumulative frequency curve to obtain a value for the median.
(ii) Form an array of the 40 items of data and write down the mode and the median of the distribution. Use a working origin of 50 to find the mean.
(iii) Comment on your answers to (i) and (ii).

7. (i) Calculate the approximate values of the median and mean of this distribution.

(ii) Assuming that children under $5\frac{1}{2}$ years of age enter a reception class, calculate the median age and the mean age of such children.
(ii) Discuss the significance of your answers.

8.   Use linear interpolation to find the median of this distribution. Estimate the value of the mean in each of the cases (a), (b) and (c).

9.   Construct a flow diagram for a procedure to find the mean of a set of numbers $x_1, x_2, \ldots, x_r$ which occur with frequencies $f_1, f_2, \ldots, f_r$ using a pocket calculator without built-in statistics functions. [Note that unless it is possible to calculate $\sum f$ and $\sum fx$ simultaneously, it will be necessary to input the numbers $f_1, f_2, \ldots, f_r$ twice.]

15.3 Measures of spread

Consider two sets of numbers (i) 1, 13, 15, 20, 21 and (ii) 12, 13, 14, 14, 17. Both have mean 14, but the first is more widely spread than the second. Thus, in addition to measures of location it is useful to have measures of *spread*, sometimes called *dispersion* or *variation*. The simplest of these is the *range*, which is the difference between the highest and the lowest items of data. In the above examples the ranges are (i) 20, (ii) 5. The main disadvantage of the range is that it is often determined by two freak values at the ends of a distribution.

Other measures of spread are obtained using quantities called *percentiles*. Theoretically, the percentiles divide a distribution into 100 equal parts. For instance, the 40th percentile is a value which has 40% of the observations in a distribution on or below it and 60% on or above it. Clearly the 50% percentile is the median. Other percentiles are found by similar methods to those used to find the median in the previous section. The interval between any two percentiles can be used as a measure of spread. Particularly useful in this way are the 25th percentile, referred to as the *first* or *lower quartile* Q_1, and the 75th percentile, the *third* or *upper quartile* Q_3. The *semi-interquartile range* is half the interval between the lower and upper quartiles, i.e. $\frac{1}{2}(Q_3 - Q_1)$. This is a more useful measure than the range because it is not affected by a few untypical values.

We return again to the examples discussed earlier in the chapter.

Example A

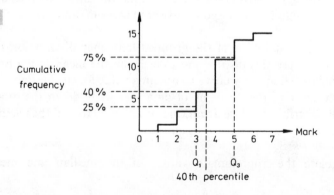

Using the cumulative frequency chart we find that the 40th percentile lies between 3 and 4. We take its value to be 3·5. The lower quartile is 3 and the upper quartile is 5

∴   the semi-interquartile range is $\frac{1}{2}(5-3)$, i.e. 1.

Example B

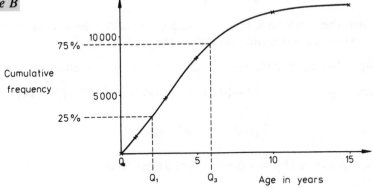

There are a total of 12 600 observations. Hence the lower quartile is the age below which 3150 of the cases occur. From the graph this is approximately 2·1 years. Similarly the upper quartile corresponds to a cumulative frequency of 9450 and is approximately 5·9 years. Hence the semi-interquartile range is $\frac{1}{2}(5·9-2·1)$ years, i.e. 1·9 years.

By calculation the lower quartile is estimated, using the cumulative frequency table, to be

$$1+\left(\frac{\{3150-1400\}}{3300}\times 2\right)\text{ years}\approx 2·1\text{ years.}$$

The upper quartile is $5+\left(\dfrac{\{9450-8200\}}{3900}\times 5\right)\text{ years}\approx 6·6\text{ years.}$

Hence the calculated estimate of the semi-interquartile range is $\frac{1}{2}(6·6-2·1)$ years, i.e. 2·25 years.

[It appears likely that the whooping-cough cases are not spread evenly throughout the 5–9 year age group and that more cases occur in the lower half of the class. Thus it is probable that the estimate of 1·9 years obtained graphically is more accurate than the calculated value of 2·25 years.]

Further measures of spread are obtained by considering the set of *deviations* of the values of a variable x from the mean $\bar{x}$. For a set of n observations the sum of these deviations

$$=\sum(x-\bar{x})=\sum x-n\bar{x}=\sum x-n\left(\frac{1}{n}\sum x\right)=0.$$

Thus the mean deviation is always zero and cannot be used as a measure of spread. However, the *mean absolute deviation*, i.e. $\dfrac{1}{n}\sum|x-\bar{x}|$, is sometimes useful.

The main disadvantage when using this quantity is that moduli are difficult to manipulate algebraically.

The most frequently used measures of dispersion are the *variance*, which is the mean squared deviation, $\operatorname{var}(x) = \dfrac{1}{n}\sum(x-\bar{x})^2$ and the *standard deviation*, which is the square root of the variance $\sqrt{\left\{\dfrac{1}{n}\sum(x-\bar{x})^2\right\}}$.

[Note that the variance is measured in square units, whereas the units of the standard deviation are the same as those of the original data.]

For examples (i) and (ii) considered at the beginning of the section, we have

(i) $\text{variance} = \dfrac{1}{5}\{(1-14)^2+(13-14)^2+(15-14)^2+(20-14)^2+(21-14)^2\}$

$$= \dfrac{1}{5}\{169+1+1+36+49\} = 51\cdot2$$

∴   the variance is 51·2 and the standard deviation is $\sqrt{(51\cdot2)} \approx 7\cdot2$.

(ii) $\text{variance} = \dfrac{1}{5}\{(-2)^2+(-1)^2+0^2+0^2+3^2\} = 2\cdot8$

∴   the variance is 2·8 and the standard deviation is $\sqrt{(2\cdot8)} \approx 1\cdot7$.

To avoid cumbersome calculations with a mean which is not a whole number, we now rearrange the formula for the variance.

$$\operatorname{var}(x) = \dfrac{1}{n}\sum(x-\bar{x})^2 = \dfrac{1}{n}\sum(x^2-2x\bar{x}+\bar{x}^2)$$

$$= \dfrac{1}{n}\sum x^2 - \dfrac{1}{n}\sum 2x\bar{x} + \dfrac{1}{n}\sum\bar{x}^2$$

$$= \dfrac{1}{n}\sum x^2 - 2\bar{x}\cdot\dfrac{1}{n}\sum x + \dfrac{1}{n}\cdot n\bar{x}^2$$

$$= \dfrac{1}{n}\sum x^2 - 2\bar{x}^2 + \bar{x}^2$$

Hence the variance,

$$\boxed{\operatorname{var}(x) = \dfrac{1}{n}\sum x^2 - \bar{x}^2.}$$

When working from a frequency table in which a value x has frequency f we may write:

$$\boxed{\operatorname{var}(x) = \dfrac{1}{n}\sum f(x-\bar{x})^2 = \dfrac{1}{n}\sum fx^2 - \bar{x}^2.}$$

In Example A, assuming that a calculator with built-in statistical data programs is not available, the variance and standard deviation can be obtained in the following way.

Mark (x)	Frequency (f)	fx	fx^2
1	1	1	1
2	2	4	8
3	3	9	27
4	5	20	80
5	3	15	75
6	1	6	36
	15	55	227

$$n = \sum f = 15, \qquad \bar{x} = \frac{1}{n}\sum fx = \frac{55}{15}$$

$$\therefore \ \text{var}(x) = \frac{1}{n}\sum fx^2 - \bar{x}^2 = \frac{1}{15} \times 227 - \left(\frac{55}{15}\right)^2.$$

Hence the variance is 1·69 and the standard deviation is 1·30 (both to 3 s.f.).

The variance of a grouped frequency distribution can be estimated using the formula $\text{var}(x) = \frac{1}{n}\sum fx^2 - \bar{x}^2$ by taking the values of x to be the mid-values in each class.

In Example B the class intervals are quite long, so the estimated variance is likely to differ noticeably from the true value. However, in Example C the class intervals are shorter, so the grouped frequency distribution should give a better value for the variance.

From the original data the variance is found to be approximately 50·7 (measured in 'square meals') and the standard deviation is 7·12 meals. Using the grouped data the estimated variance is 57·1 and the standard deviation 7·56.

Exercise 15.3

1. Find the median, the quartiles and the semi-interquartile range for the following sets of integers.
(a) 8, 3, 5, 7, 11, 9, 7, 6, 7, 5, 8, 11,
(b) 28, 18, 32, 27, 42, 23, 49, 28, 33, 30,
(c) 2, −4, 10, 0, −5, 11, 6, −4; 11.

2. Find the mean, the variance and the standard deviation of the sets of integers given in question 1.

In questions 3 to 8 use the data given in the corresponding questions in Exercise 15.1.

3. Use the appropriate cumulative frequency diagram to find the following in cases (a), (b) and (c):
(i) the 40th and the 70th percentile,
(ii) the semi-interquartile range.

4. Find the variance and standard deviation of the distribution of sales.

5. (i) Use the appropriate cumulative frequency graph to estimate the lower quartile, median and upper quartile of this distribution in cases (a) and (b).
(ii) Use the frequency distribution table to find the standard deviation of the distribution.

6. Find the lower and upper quartiles of this distribution using (i) the original data, (ii) the grouped data and linear interpolation, (iii) an ogive based on the grouped data. Comment on any differences between your answers.

7. (i) Calculate approximate values, to the nearest month, of the 30th and the 65th percentile.
(ii) Estimate the variance of the distribution, stating the units in which your answer is measured.

8. The 150 test marks are to be graded as follows: the top 15% of students, grade I; the next 30%, grade II; the next 35%, grade III; the bottom 20%, grade IV. Use a cumulative frequency polygon to suggest suitable class limits for each grade.

9. Construct a flow diagram for a procedure to find the standard deviation of a set of numbers $x_1, x_2, \ldots, x_r$ which occur with frequencies $f_1, f_2, \ldots, f_r$ using a pocket calculator without built-in statistical functions. [Assume that $n = \sum f$ and $m = \frac{1}{n}\sum fx$ have already been calculated and may be read as data.]

15.4 Change of variable

Suppose we have a distribution of n values of a variable x with mean $\bar{x}$ and standard deviation σ_x. Consider a new variable y, such that $y = ax + b$, where a and b are constants. Let the distribution of the n values of y have mean $\bar{y}$ and standard deviation σ_y, then

$$\bar{y} = \frac{1}{n}\sum y = \frac{1}{n}\sum (ax + b) = \frac{1}{n}\sum ax + \frac{1}{n}\sum b$$

$$= a \cdot \frac{1}{n}\sum x + \frac{1}{n} \cdot nb = a\bar{x} + b$$

$$\text{var}\,(y) = \frac{1}{n}\sum(y-\bar{y})^2 = \frac{1}{n}\sum\{(ax+b)-(a\bar{x}+b)\}^2$$

$$= \frac{1}{n}\sum(ax-a\bar{x})^2 = a^2.\frac{1}{n}\sum(x-\bar{x})^2 = a^2\,\text{var}\,(x).$$

Hence,

> if $\ y = ax+b,\ $ then $\ \bar{y} = a\bar{x}+b\ $ and $\ \text{var}\,(y) = a^2\,\text{var}\,(x).$

Example 1 During an industrial dispute a trade union negotiated a pay increase for its members of £8 a week plus 10%, so that a man earning £x per week received an increase of £$(8+x/10)$ per week. For the original wage distribution the mean was £120 per week and the standard deviation £20 per week. Find the new mean and standard deviation.

Let £y be the new weekly wage of a man originally earning £x per week, then

$$y = x+8 + \frac{x}{10} = \frac{11}{10}x+8$$

$$\therefore \qquad \bar{y} = \frac{11}{10}\bar{x}+8 = \left(\frac{11}{10}\times 120\right)+8 = 140.$$

$$\text{New s.d.} = \frac{11}{10}\times\text{original s.d.} = \frac{11}{10}\times 20 = 22.$$

Hence the new mean weekly wage is £140 and the standard deviation is £22.

A change of variable is sometimes used to simplify the calculation of the mean and standard deviation of a distribution. For instance, if a set of values of a variable x appear to have a mean approximately equal to x_0, then we can take this *assumed mean* as a working origin. If we let $y = x-x_0$, then $\bar{x} = x_0+\bar{y}$ and var $(x) =$ var (y).

Example 2 The weights in kilogrammes of the players selected for a certain Rugby Union football team are 76, 79, 85, 86, 76, 75, 86, 105, 88, 104, 102, 103, 89, 92, 95. Find the mean and standard deviation of the distribution.

If x kg is the weight of a member of the team, let $y = x-90$, then the 15 values of y for the team are $-14,\ -11,\ -5,\ -4,\ -14,\ -15,\ -4,\ 15,\ -2,\ 14,\ 12,\ 13,$ $-1, 2, 5.$

Cancelling equal and opposite values of y,

$$\bar{y} = \frac{1}{15}(-5-4) = -\frac{9}{15} = -0.6.$$

$$\sum y^2 = (-14)^2+(-11)^2+ \ldots +2^2+5^2 = 1563$$

$$\therefore \quad \text{var}\,(y) = \frac{1}{15}\sum y^2 - \bar{y}^2 = \frac{1563}{15} - (0.6)^2 = 103.84$$

$$\therefore \quad \bar{x} = 90+\bar{y} = 89.4 \quad \text{and} \quad \text{var}\,(x) = \text{var}\,(y) = 103.84$$

Hence the mean weight is 89·4 kg and the standard deviation is 10·2 kg.

When using a calculator a change of variable may be used to improve accuracy. For instance, if the values of a variable are given to 5 digits or more, squares of at least 9 digits will be produced in an accurate calculation of the variance. A change to a variable whose values have fewer digits would reduce the truncation and rounding errors generated by a calculator of limited capacity.

In certain situations a change of variable of the form $y = \dfrac{1}{c}(x - x_0)$ is useful.

If $y = \dfrac{1}{c}(x - x_0)$ then $x = x_0 + cy$

$\therefore$ $\bar{x} = x_0 + c\bar{y}$ and $\mathrm{var}(x) = c^2\,\mathrm{var}(y)$.

Applying a transformation of this type to a distribution may be referred to as 'coding' the data. We illustrate the method using the grouped frequency distribution obtained in Example C, §15.1. We take an assumed mean of 55 as the value of x_0 and the class width 5 as the value of c, so that $y = \dfrac{1}{5}(x - 55)$.

Class	Mid-value (x)	y	Frequency (f)	fy	fy^2
38–42	40	-3	1	-3	9
43–47	45	-2	2	-4	8
48–52	50	-1	9	-9	9
53–57	55	0	11	0	0
58–62	60	1	8	8	8
63–67	65	2	5	10	20
68–72	70	3	3	9	27
73–77	75	4	1	4	16
			40	15	97

$$n = \Sigma f = 40, \quad \Sigma fy = 15, \quad \Sigma fy^2 = 97$$

$$\bar{y} = \frac{1}{n}\Sigma fy = \frac{15}{40} = \frac{3}{8}$$

$$\therefore \quad \bar{x} = 55 + 5 \cdot \frac{3}{8} \approx 56 \cdot 9$$

$$\mathrm{var}(y) = \frac{1}{n}\Sigma fy^2 - \bar{y}^2 = \frac{97}{40} - \left(\frac{3}{8}\right)^2$$

$$\therefore \quad \text{s.d. of } x \text{ values} = 5\sigma_y = 5\sqrt{\left(\frac{97}{40} - \frac{9}{64}\right)} \approx 7 \cdot 56.$$

Hence the mean of the distribution is 56·9 and the standard deviation is 7·56.

Exercise 15.4

1. Find the mean, variance and standard deviation of the numbers

$$1, \ 3, \ 3, \ 4, \ 6, \ 6, \ 7, \ 8, \ 8, \ 9.$$

Deduce the mean, variance and standard deviation of the following sets of numbers:

(a) 4, 6, 6, 7, 9, 9, 10, 11, 11, 12,
(b) 4, 12, 12, 16, 24, 24, 28, 32, 32, 36,
(c) 4·1, 4·3, 4·3, 4·4, 4·6, 4·6, 4·7, 4·8, 4·8, 4·9.

2. The mean and standard deviation of a set of mid-day temperatures for the month of June are 23°C and 5°C respectively. Find the mean and standard deviation for the same distribution measured in degrees Fahrenheit.

3. Use a frequency table and an assumed mean of 5 to calculate the mean, variance and standard deviation of the distribution of the discrete variable x given in question 3. Exercise 15.1. Deduce the mean, variance and standard deviation of the variable in case (c).

4. (i) Use an appropriate change of variable to estimate the standard deviation of the data given in question 6, Exercise 15.1 from the grouped frequency table.
(ii) With the aid of a calculator, find the standard deviation of the original distribution.
(iii) Comment on the difference between your answers.

5. Use an appropriate change of variable to find the mean and standard deviation of the distribution given in question 8, Exercise 15.1 assuming that the test is marked out of 60. The marks are to be scaled using the formula $z = ax + b$, where x is the original mark and z the new mark. If the mean and standard deviation of the scaled marks are to be approximately 50 and 15 respectively, find suitable values of a and b correct to 2 significant figures.

6. The variable x_1 represents the mark of a student in an examination. The distribution of marks for a certain group of students has mean $\bar{x}_1$ and standard deviation σ_1. Given that the marks are to be scaled so that the values of the new mark x_2 have mean $\bar{x}_2$ and standard deviation σ_2, prove that

$$x_2 = \bar{x}_2 + \frac{\sigma_2}{\sigma_1}(x_1 - \bar{x}_1).$$

Use this formula to standardise the marks of students A, B and C as given in the table below, taking $\bar{x}_2 = 50$ and $\sigma_2 = 15$. Hence find a combined mark for each student.

Subject	Mean	Standard deviation	A	B	C
Mathematics	60	20	90	96	70
English	45	10	52	46	70

Exercise 15.5 (miscellaneous)

1.   The following table gives an analysis by numbers of employees of the size of UK factories of less than 1000 employees manufacturing clothing and footwear.

Number of employees	11–19	20–24	25–99	100–199	200–499	500–999	Total
Number of factories	1500	800	2300	700	400	100	5800

Calculate as accurately as the data allow the mean and median of this distribution, showing your working. If 90% of the factories have less than N employees, estimate N.   (O & C)

2.   An inspection of 34 aircraft assemblies revealed a number of missing rivets as shown in the following table.

Number of rivets missing	0–2	3–5	6–8	9–11	12–14	15–17	18–20	21–23
Frequency	4	9	11	6	2	1	0	1

Draw a cumulative frequency curve. Use this curve to estimate the median and the quartiles of the distribution.   (O & C)

3.   The distribution of the times taken when a certain task was performed by each of a large number of people was such that its twentieth percentile was 25 minutes, its fortieth percentile was 50 minutes, its sixtieth percentile was 64 minutes and its eightieth percentile was 74 minutes. Use linear interpolation to estimate (i) the median of the distribution, (ii) the upper quartile of the distribution, (iii) the percentage of persons who performed the task in 40 minutes or less.   (JMB)

4.   The weights of a number of school children were measured and the mean weight was found to be 54·1 kg, with standard deviation 3·2 kg. Subsequently it was discovered the weighing machine was reading 0·9 kg under the true weight. How should the mean and standard deviation be revised? Give a clear indication of your reasoning.   (O & C)

5.   A frequency distribution has values $x_1, x_2, \ldots, x_n$ with frequencies $f_1, f_2, \ldots, f_n$ respectively. It has mean $\bar{x}$ and standard deviation σ. Find the mean and standard deviation of the distribution which has values $d_1, d_2, \ldots, d_n$ with frequencies $f_1, f_2, \ldots, f_n$ respectively, where $d_r = \dfrac{x_r - \bar{x}}{\sigma}$.   (AEB 1977)

6.   100 pupils were tested to determine their intelligence quotient (I.Q.), and the results were as follows:

I.Q.	45–	55–	65–	75–	85–	95–	105–	115–	125–134
No. of pupils	1	1	2	6	21	29	24	12	4

All I.Q.s are given to the nearest integer.
(i) Calculate the mean, and the standard deviation.
(ii) Draw a cumulative frequency graph, and estimate how many pupils have I.Q.s within 1 s.d. on either side of the mean. (SU)

7. The haemoglobin levels were measured in a sample of 50 people and the results were as follows, each being correct to 1 place of decimals.

13·5	15·6	16·3	12·3	13·1	14·2	12·4	11·3	14·0	14·6
13·6	14·8	12·7	10·9	11·0	11·4	15·0	10·1	15·4	11·3
10·7	14·6	13·5	15·1	12·1	12·0	14·2	11·4	15·0	13·3
13·2	9·1	16·9	14·2	15·0	13·6	14·8	11·4	14·8	15·7
13·5	13·5	12·9	13·8	13·7	16·2	11·6	13·8	14·2	10·7

(a) Group the data into eight classes, 9·0–9·9, 10·0–10·9, ..., 16·0–16·9.
(b) What are the smallest and largest possible measurements which could be included in the class 9·0–9·9?
(c) Draw a histogram of the grouped data and use it to estimate the median value of the sample, showing your working.
(d) Find the true median of the sample. (SU)

8. A small firm has a total labour force of 267 of whom 250 are craftsmen and the rest managers. The distribution of the weekly pay of all employees is as follows, where, for example, 22·5– means that employees in this group earn at least £22.50, but less than £25.00.

Craftsmen Wages in £	No. of employees	Managers Wages in £	No. of employees
20.0–	29	50.0–	3
22.5–	33	52.5–	9
25.0–	35	55.0–	5
27.5–	40		
30.0–	51		
32.5–	37		
35.0–	25		

Display this information on a block diagram. Calculate (using a working zero of £31.25, or otherwise) the mean pay of (i) the craftsmen, (ii) the managers, (iii) all 267 employees. Comment on these means as they describe the situation in the firm and discuss other measures, such as the median or mode which might be used instead or as well. (SU)

9. The following table gives the maximum temperature in 60 cities on a certain day. Readings are to the nearest degree.

```
72  61  43  54  54  48  59  55  61  50  55  48
30  66  41  55  48  57  61  48  46  61  30  50
66  73  54  48  66  61  45  57  48  70  68  43
52  50  46  64  46  50  50  50  48  37  45  53
64  50  39  32  66  68  41  70  48  73  39  43
```

Gather these measurements into classes at intervals of 5°, starting at 29·5°. From the information in this form construct a cumulative frequency table and draw a graph to display the cumulative frequency. Use this to find the median and semi-interquartile range. For the grouped distribution calculate the mean and standard deviation, explaining what effect the grouping is likely to have had on each.

(AEB 1978)

10. On 1 January 1975 the heights of ten boys, measured in centimetres, were 172·1, 168·6, 174·1, 174·6, 176·1, 167·6, 174·1, 170·1, 172·6, 171·1. Find the mean and standard deviation of these heights. If on 1 January 1976 each boy was 2·5 cm taller, calculate the mean height and variance on that date. If the heights had been measured in inches, find the variance of the heights of the ten boys stating the units in which your answer is given. [Take 2·54 cm = 1 inch.]   (L)

11. For a finite population of size N, the mean of a measurement X is μ_X and the variance σ_X^2 is given by $\sigma_X^2 = \dfrac{1}{N}\sum(X-\mu_X)^2$. If $Y = aX+b$, where a and b are fixed constants, show that $(aN\sigma_X)^2 = N\sum Y^2 - (\sum Y)^2$.
For the finite population given in the table below, calculate the average earnings and the standard deviation of the earnings.

Earnings to nearest £	18–22	23–27	28–32	33–37	38–42
Number of workers	2	2	2	4	5

Earnings to nearest £	43–47	48–52	53–57	58–62	63–67
Number of workers	7	4	7	9	8

(L)

12. The set of positive integers $x_1, x_2, \ldots, x_9$ has a mean of 5 and $\displaystyle\sum_{i=1}^{9}(x_i-5)^2$ = 36. A tenth integer (x_{10}) is added to the set, and the mean and variance of the set of ten integers are denoted by $\bar{x}$ and Var (x) respectively.
(a) Calculate the values of $\bar{x}$ and Var (x) if $x_{10} = 5$.
(b) Calculate the values of $\bar{x}$ and Var (x) if $x_{10} = 9$.
(c) If $0 < x_{10} < 5$ state two inequalities satisfied by $\bar{x}$.
(d) Without doing long calculations, suggest which values for x_{10} would result in Var (x) being greater than 4.

[In this question you should take Var $(x) = \dfrac{1}{10}\displaystyle\sum_{i=1}^{10}(x_i-\bar{x})^2$.]   (L)

13. (i) A distribution, A, contains N_1 observations and has mean and standard deviation μ_1 and σ_1 respectively. A second distribution, B, of N_2 observations has mean and standard deviation μ_2 and σ_2 respectively. The standard deviation of the combined distribution of $N_1 + N_2$ observations is σ. Show that

$$(N_1 + N_2)\sigma^2 = N_1\sigma_1^2 + N_2\sigma_2^2 + \frac{N_1 N_2}{N_1 + N_2}(\mu_1 - \mu_2)^2.$$

(ii) Two teachers A and B each marked 100 exam papers with the following results

Mark	35	36	37	38	39	40	41	42	43	44	45
No. marked by A	4	10	14	18	12	12	10	8	4	5	3
No. marked by B	8	15	16	20	18	5	3	5	2	2	6

The mean mark for A is 39·23 with variance 6·4371. The mean mark for B is 38·51. Calculate the variance of B's marks. It is decided to add 0·72 to each of B's marks to make the mean for his papers the same as for A's. Calculate the mean and variance of the combined set of 200 papers (with B's marks adjusted).

(AEB 1975)

14. The following table gives the frequency distribution of 100 observed values of a random variable x.

x =	1	2	3	4	5	6
Frequency =	12	13	30	20	18	7

(a) Suppose x is the score obtained on a throw of a certain die.
    (i) Calculate the mean and the variance of the observed scores.
    (ii) Use the data to estimate the probability of throwing an even score with this die. Hence estimate the probability that six throws of the die will result in three even and three odd scores.
(b) Suppose, instead, that x is a continuous random variable and that in compiling the above frequency table the observed values were recorded to the nearest integer. Use linear interpolation to estimate the median of the observed values and the proportion of the observed values which exceeded 4·8.

(JMB)

16 Probability distributions

16.1 Discrete probability distributions

The theory of probability is used to set up mathematical models of random experiments or trials. In its simplest form a *probability model* of an experiment consists of a description of the sample space (i.e. the set of possible outcomes) together with estimates of the probabilities associated with the outcomes. Let us consider, for instance, a trial in which a single unbiased die is thrown and the score noted. This can be described as a trial with a sample space containing 6 outcomes each with probability 1/6. We can use this model to make predictions about the behaviour of dice in experiments involving large numbers of such trials. The theory can be tested by comparing these predictions with the observed results of the experiments.

Since the score obtained in any particular throw of a single die cannot be predicted in advance, the trial is said to be *random* and the score obtained is called a *random variable*. In general, the values of a random variable are real numbers assigned to the elements of a sample space. This leads to the following formal definition.

> A random variable X is a function which assigns a real number x to each element s of a sample space S.

A random variable such as the height of students in a class, which may take any real value within a given interval, is said to be *continuous*. A random variable such as the score on a die, which takes only certain specified values, is described as *discrete*.

As we saw in Chapter 14, any subset A of a sample space S is called an event and the probability that event A occurs is denoted by $P(A)$. Thus the probability that the random variable X takes the value x may be written $P(X = x)$. We can now define a probability function on the set of values taken by X.

The probability function p of the discrete random variable X is defined by $p(x) = P(X = x)$, where $0 \leqslant p(x) \leqslant 1$ for all values of x.

The set of values $x_1, x_2, x_3, \ldots$ of a discrete random variable X, together with the corresponding values $p_1, p_2, p_3, \ldots$ of the probability function p, form a *discrete probability distribution*.

Since the sum of the probabilities of all possible outcomes of any experiment must be 1, all discrete probability distributions have the following property.

If a discrete random variable X takes the n values $x_1, x_2, \ldots x_n$ with probabilities $p_1, p_2, \ldots, p_n$ respectively, then $\sum\limits_{r=1}^{n} p_r = 1$.

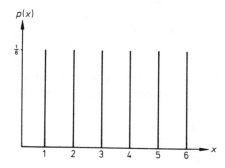

If X represents the score obtained when a single die is thrown, then $p(x) = 1/6$ for $x = 1, 2, 3, 4, 5$ and 6. A distribution such as this, in which all values of the random variable are equally likely, is said to be *rectangular* or *uniform*.

For a trial in which two dice are thrown and the total score noted the sample space S can be regarded as a set of 36 ordered pairs such as $(1, 3)$, $(4, 6)$ and $(6, 4)$. The total score obtained in any throw is a discrete random variable defined on S and takes the values $2, 3, 4, \ldots, 12$. The following diagrams show the sample space and corresponding probability distribution for this two dice trial.

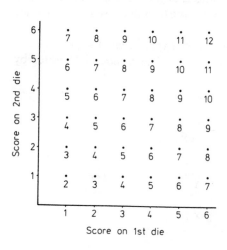

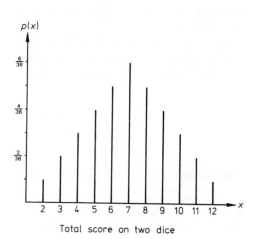

A further type of discrete probability distribution is obtained when a die is thrown repeatedly and the random variable X is the number of throws needed to obtain a six. We then find that

$$p(1) = \frac{1}{6}, p(2) = \frac{5}{6} \times \frac{1}{6}, p(3) = \left(\frac{5}{6}\right)^2 \times \frac{1}{6}, p(4) = \left(\frac{5}{6}\right)^3 \times \frac{1}{6}, \ldots$$

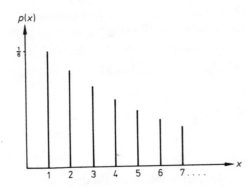

Clearly X may take any one of the infinite set of values $1, 2, 3, 4, \ldots$ Since the corresponding probabilities form a geometric progression, this distribution is described as *geometric*.

In order to discuss the properties of probability distributions in more detail we need to define quantities similar to the measures of location and spread used to describe frequency distributions.

For a frequency distribution in which a set of n observations $x_1, x_2, \ldots, x_n$ occur with frequencies $f_1, f_2, \ldots, f_n$,

$$\text{the mean } \bar{x} = \frac{1}{n}\sum f_r x_r, \text{ where } n = \sum f_r,$$

$$\text{the variance} = \frac{1}{n}\sum f_r(x_r - \bar{x})^2 = \frac{1}{n}\sum f_r x_r^2 - \bar{x}^2$$

If n is fairly large the relative frequency f_r/n is approximately equal to the probability $p(x_r)$. Thus we obtain suitable definitions of the mean and variance of a probability distribution by replacing f_r/n by $p(x_r)$ in the formulae used for frequency distributions.

The mean of a probability distribution is called the *expectation* or *expected value* of the random variable X and is denoted by $E(X)$ or μ. The *variance* is denoted by $\text{Var}(X)$ or σ^2. These quantities are defined as follows:

$$E(X) = \mu = \sum x_r p(x_r)$$
$$\text{Var}(X) = \sigma^2 = \sum (x_r - \mu)^2 p(x_r)$$

The expression for $\text{Var}(X)$ can be rearranged to give:

$$\text{Var}(X) = \sigma^2 = \sum x_r^2 p(x_r) - \mu^2$$

For the two dice trial discussed earlier:

$$E(X) = 2 \cdot \tfrac{1}{36} + 3 \cdot \tfrac{2}{36} + \ldots + 12 \cdot \tfrac{1}{36} = 7$$
$$\text{Var}(X) = 2^2 \cdot \tfrac{1}{36} + 3^2 \cdot \tfrac{2}{36} + \ldots + 12^2 \cdot \tfrac{1}{36} - 7^2 = \tfrac{35}{6} \approx 5 \cdot 83.$$

Example 1 A box contains 10 coloured discs of which 2 are red. A man pays 10 pence to play a game in which discs are drawn one at a time from the box, without replacement, until a red disc is drawn. He will receive 25 pence if the first disc drawn is red, 20 pence if the second disc is red, 5 pence if the third disc is red, but nothing otherwise. Find the man's expected profit or loss in any game.

If the random variable X is the amount in pence received in any game, then X takes the values 25, 20, 5 and 0.

$$p(25) = \tfrac{2}{10} = \tfrac{1}{5}, \; p(20) = \tfrac{8}{10} \times \tfrac{2}{9} = \tfrac{8}{45} \quad \text{and} \quad p(5) = \tfrac{8}{10} \times \tfrac{7}{9} \times \tfrac{2}{8} = \tfrac{7}{45}.$$

∴ the expected value of X

$$= 25 \times p(25) + 20 \times p(20) + 5 \times p(5) + 0 \times p(0)$$
$$= 25 \times \tfrac{1}{5} + 20 \times \tfrac{8}{45} + 5 \times \tfrac{7}{45} + 0 = 9\tfrac{1}{3}$$

Since the man pays 10 pence per game, his expected loss in pence is $\tfrac{2}{3}$.

In the next example we make use of the following results.

$$\sum_{r=1}^{n} r = \tfrac{1}{2}n(n+1), \quad \sum_{r=1}^{n} r^2 = \tfrac{1}{6}n(n+1)(2n+1), \quad \sum_{r=1}^{n} r^3 = \tfrac{1}{4}n^2(n+1)^2.$$

Example 2 The probability distribution of a random variable X is given by

$$P(X = r) = k(n - r) \quad \text{for} \quad r = 1, 2, 3, \ldots, n.$$

Find k in terms of n. Find also the mean and variance of X.

Since X is a discrete random variable, $\sum_{1}^{n} p(r) = 1$.

But $\displaystyle \sum_{1}^{n} p(r) = \sum_{1}^{n} k(n - r) = k \sum_{1}^{n} n - k \sum_{1}^{n} r$

$$= kn^2 - k \cdot \tfrac{1}{2}n(n+1) = \tfrac{1}{2}kn(n-1)$$

Hence $k = 2/n(n - 1)$.

$$E(X) = \sum_{1}^{n} rp(r) = \sum_{1}^{n} kr(n - r)$$

$$= kn \sum_{1}^{n} r - k \sum_{1}^{n} r^2$$

$$= kn \cdot \frac{1}{2}n(n+1) - k \cdot \frac{1}{6}n(n+1)(2n+1)$$

$$= \frac{2}{n(n-1)} \cdot \frac{n(n+1)}{6} \{3n - (2n+1)\} = \frac{1}{3}(n+1)$$

$$\text{Var}(X) = \sum_{1}^{n} r^2 p(r) - \mu^2 = \sum_{1}^{n} k r^2(n-r) - \frac{1}{9}(n+1)^2$$

$$= kn \sum_{1}^{n} r^2 - k \sum_{1}^{n} r^3 - \frac{1}{9}(n+1)^2$$

$$= kn \cdot \frac{1}{6} n(n+1)(2n+1) - k \cdot \frac{1}{4} n^2(n+1)^2 - \frac{1}{9}(n+1)^2$$

$$= \frac{2}{n(n-1)} \cdot \frac{n^2(n+1)}{12} \{2(2n+1) - 3(n+1)\} - \frac{1}{9}(n+1)^2$$

$$= \frac{1}{6} n(n+1) - \frac{1}{9}(n+1)^2$$

$$= \frac{1}{18}(n+1)\{3n - 2(n+1)\} = \frac{1}{18}(n+1)(n-2)$$

Thus the mean and variance of X are $\frac{1}{3}(n+1)$ and $\frac{1}{18}(n+1)(n-2)$ respectively.

Exercise 16.1

1. A student has a week-end job in a warehouse. The probability that he will be given 6 hours work is 1/6, the probability of 9 hours work is 1/3 and the probability of 12 hours work is 1/2. Find the expected number of hours the student will work.

2. A man pays x pence to play a game in which two unbiased dice are rolled. If the total score on the dice is an even number n, then the man receives n pence. Otherwise he receives nothing. Calculate the value of x which makes the game fair.

3. A bag contains one 50p coin, three 20p coins, seven 10p coins and several 5p coins. Given that when one coin is selected at random the expectation is 10p, find the number of 5p coins. Find also the expectation when two coins are selected at random without replacement.

4. Three discs are drawn at random, without replacement from a bag containing three black discs and five red discs. Find (a) the most probable number of black discs drawn, (b) the expected number of black discs drawn.

5. A bag X contains 3 red balls and 6 white balls and a second bag Y contains 5 red balls and 4 white balls. A ball is chosen at random from bag X and placed in bag Y. A ball is then chosen at random from bag Y and placed in bag X. If R is the number of red balls in bag X after these operations, find the probability distribution of R. Hence find the expected value of R.

6. A simple 'fruit machine' has three wheels on which there are pictures of fruit. When 10p is paid into the machine, the wheels spin and then come to rest independently, each showing one fruit. The probabilities that the three wheels show

a lemon are 0·4, 0·2 and 0·1 respectively. The machine pays out 10p for 1 lemon, 30p for 2 lemons and £1·60 for 3 lemons. Find the expected profit or loss per play.

7. In a certain gambling game a player nominates an integer x from 1 to 6 inclusive and he then throws three fair cubical dice. Calculate the probabilities that the number of x's thrown will be 0, 1, 2 and 3. The player pays 5 pence per play of the game and he receives 48 pence if the number of x's thrown is three, 15 pence if the number of x's thrown is two, 5 pence if only one x is thrown and nothing otherwise. Calculate the player's expected gain or loss per play of the game.   (JMB)

8. In a certain snooker match the first man to win 3 frames wins the match. The winner of each frame receives £20 and the winner of the match receives an additional £40. Find the expected cost of the prizes in a match between players A and B if the probability that A wins a frame against B is (a) 0·5, (b) 0·2.

9. A player throws a die whose faces are numbered 1 to 6 inclusive. If the player obtains a six he throws the die a second time, and in this case his score is the sum of 6 and the second number; otherwise his score is the number obtained. The player has no more than two throws. Let X be the random variable denoting the player's score. Write down the probability distribution of X, and determine the mean of X. Show that the probability that the sum of two successive scores is 8 or more is 17/36. Determine the probability that the first of two successive scores is 7 or more, given that their sum is 8 or more.   (C)

10. At a horse show there is a jumping competition in which each horse attempts to clear 4 successive fences, each fence being more difficult than the previous one. A particular horse has probability $(5 - i)/5$ of clearing the ith fence ($i = 1, 2, 3, 4$), independent of its performance over the other fences. (i) Find the probability that the horse clears all four fences. (ii) Find the probability that the horse does not clear any fence. (iii) Determine the expected value of the number of fences that the horse clears.   (C)

11. A disc is drawn from a bag containing 10 discs numbered 0, 1, 2,...9. The random variable X is defined as the square of the number drawn. Find $E(X)$ and $\mathrm{Var}(X)$.

12. A box contains 6 cards all of different colours. A card is drawn at random from the box and its colour noted. If three cards are drawn, with replacement, find the mean and variance of the number of different colours obtained.

13. Let X denote the number of heads obtained when a fair coin is tossed three times. Find the mean and the variance of X. A pack of six cards consists of three cards labelled H and the other three labelled T. Three cards are drawn at random without replacement from the pack. Let Y denote the number of H's obtained. Calculate the probabilities that Y takes the values 0, 1, 2 and 3 respectively. Show that the mean of Y is equal to the mean of X and express the variance of Y as a percentage of the variance of X.   (JMB)

14. In a certain field, each puffball which is growing in one year gives rise to a number, X, of new puffballs in the following year. None of the original puffballs is present in the following year. The probability distribution of the random variable X is as follows:

$$P(X = 0) = P(X = 2) = 0{\cdot}3, P(X = 1) = 0{\cdot}4.$$

Find the probability distribution of Y, the number of puffballs resulting from there being two puffballs in the previous year, and show that the variance of Y is $1{\cdot}2$. Hence, or otherwise, determine the probability distribution of the number, Z, of puffballs present in year 3, given that there was a single puffball present in year 1. Find also the mean and variance of Z.

(C)

15. A cubical die is biased in such a way that the probability of scoring $n(n = 1$ to $6)$ is proportional to n. Determine the mean value and variance of the score obtained in a single throw. What would be the mean and variance if the score showing were doubled?

(O&C)

16. A random variable R takes values $1, 2, \ldots, n$ with equal probabilities. Determine the expectation μ of R and show that the variance σ^2 is given by $12\sigma^2 = n^2 - 1$. Find $P(|R - \mu| > \sigma)$ in the case $n = 100$.

(C)

17. The probability distribution of a random variable R is defined by $P(R = r) = kr$ for $r = 1, 2, \ldots, n$. Find the value of k. Hence find the mean and variance of the distribution.

18. Ten identically shaped discs are in a bag; two of them are black, the rest white. Discs are drawn at random from the bag in turn and NOT replaced. Let X be the number of discs drawn up to AND INCLUDING the first black one. List the values of X and the associated theoretical probabilities. Calculate the mean value of X and its standard deviation. What is the most likely value of X? If instead each disc is replaced before the next is drawn, construct a similar list of values and probabilities and point out the chief differences between the two lists.

(SU)

19. (a) Expand $(1 - x)^{-2}$ in a series of ascending powers of x, giving the first three terms and the term in x^{r-1}.
    (b) A boy is throwing stones at a tin can. The probability of hitting the can with any particular stone is p. Find the probability that the boy first hits the can with the rth stone. If the random variable R is the number of throws needed to hit the can, find the expected value of R in terms of p.

20. A faulty gas-lighter works successfully, on average, once in three attempts. When using it one goes on trying until it does work and the gas lights. What is the probability that the gas lights (i) first time, (ii) second time, (iii) at the fifth attempt? What is the probability that it will not have worked after five attempts? The sellers of the lighter promise that if one is returned, they will pay 25p for each time it fails to work before the gas is lit. What is one's expectation in taking up this offer? What is the probability of getting one's money back (or more) if the original price was £1? If

four people take up this offer, what is the probability that at least two get their money back (or more)? (AEB 1978)

21. An ordinary unbiased cubical die is to be thrown repeatedly. Show that the probability that a score of 6 will occur for the first time on the nth throw with the first $(n-1)$ throws resulting in one odd score and $(n-2)$ even scores (other than 6) is equal to $(n-1)(\frac{1}{4})(\frac{1}{3})^{n-1}$ for $n \geqslant 2$. If the die is to be thrown as many times as it is necessary for a score of 6 to occur, find, using the above result, or otherwise, the probability that only one of the throws will result in an odd score.

[Hint: For $|x| < 1, \sum_{r=0}^{\infty} (r+1)x^r = (1-x)^{-2}$] (JMB)

16.2 The binomial distribution

A *Bernouilli*[†] *trial* is one in which there are two possible outcomes, usually referred to as success and failure. If the probability of success is p and the probability of failure is q, then $p + q = 1$.

If a random variable X represents the number of successes in a sequence of n independent repetitions of a Bernouilli trial, then the resulting probability distribution is called a *binomial distribution*.

Consider, for example, a trial in which an unbiased die is rolled once and success is defined as obtaining a six. In one trial the probability of success is 1/6 and the probability of failure is 5/6. Suppose now that the random variable X is the number of sixes obtained in a sequence of 5 rolls of the die.

Clearly $$P(X = 0) = (\tfrac{5}{6})^5$$

The number of arrangements of a sequence of 4 failures and 1 success = 5.
The probability of each such arrangement = $(\tfrac{5}{6})^4(\tfrac{1}{6})$

$\therefore$ $$P(X = 1) = 5(\tfrac{5}{6})^4(\tfrac{1}{6})$$

The number of arrangements of a sequence of 3 failures and 2 successes = $\frac{5!}{3!2!}$ = 10.
The probability of each such arrangement = $(\tfrac{5}{6})^3(\tfrac{1}{6})^2$

$\therefore$ $$P(X = 2) = 10(\tfrac{5}{6})^3(\tfrac{1}{6})^2$$

Using similar arguments it follows that

$$P(X = 3) = 10(\tfrac{5}{6})^2(\tfrac{1}{6})^3, P(X = 4) = 5(\tfrac{5}{6})(\tfrac{1}{6})^4, P(X = 5) = (\tfrac{1}{6})^5.$$

We see that the probabilities of $0, 1, 2, 3, 4, 5$ sixes in a sequence of 5 rolls of a die are given by the terms in the binomial expansion of $(\tfrac{5}{6} + \tfrac{1}{6})^5$.

To obtain a more general result let us assume that the probability of success in a certain trial is p and that the probability of failure is q, where $q = 1 - p$.

[†] *Bernouilli, Jacques* (1654–1705) Swiss mathematician: one of the members of a large family who were all gifted mathematically. His *Ars Conjectandi* of 1713 contains a considerable quantity of work on probability.

The number of arrangements of a sequence of $(n - r)$ failures and r successes is $\dfrac{n!}{(n - r)!r!}$, written $\dbinom{n}{r}$ or $_nC_r$.

The probability of each such arrangement $= q^{n-r}p^r$.

Hence the probability of r successes in n independent trials is $\dbinom{n}{r}q^{n-r}p^r$.

Thus the probabilities that $r = 0, 1, 2, \ldots, n$ are the terms in the binomial expansion of $(q + p)^n$. This distribution is described as the binomial distribution with *parameters n and p*.

A random variable X is said to have a binomial distribution $B(n, p)$, if

$$P(X = r) = \binom{n}{r}q^{n-r}p^r \quad \text{for} \quad r = 0, 1, 2, \ldots, n,$$

where $0 < p < 1$ and $q = 1 - p$.

This binomial distribution arises when X represents the number of successes in n *independent* trials, each trial having the *constant* probability p of success.

Example 1   A doctor estimates that his treatment of a particular illness is successful in $66\frac{2}{3}\%$ of cases. Find the probability that he will treat successfully exactly 4 out of the 6 patients currently in his care. Find also the probability of success in at least 2 out of the 6 cases.

If X is the number of successes, then X has a binomial distribution with parameters $n = 6$ and $p = \frac{2}{3}$.

$$P(X = 4) = \binom{6}{4}(\tfrac{1}{3})^2(\tfrac{2}{3})^4 = \frac{6!}{2!4!} \times \frac{2^4}{3^6} = \tfrac{80}{243} \approx 0 \cdot 329$$

∴   the probability of success in exactly 4 out of 6 cases is $0 \cdot 329$.

$$P(X = 0) = (\tfrac{1}{3})^6 = \tfrac{1}{729}, \quad P(X = 1) = \binom{6}{1}(\tfrac{1}{3})^5(\tfrac{2}{3}) = \tfrac{4}{243},$$

∴   the probability of at least 2 successes

$$= 1 - \tfrac{1}{729} - \tfrac{4}{243} = \tfrac{716}{729} \approx 0 \cdot 982.$$

If a random variable X has the binomial distribution $B(n, p)$, then

$$\sum_{r=0}^{n} P(X = r) = \sum_{r=0}^{n} \binom{n}{r}q^{n-r}p^r = (q + p)^n = 1.$$

Thus we have verified that for the distribution $B(n, p)$,

$$\sum_{r=0}^{n} p_r = 1, \quad \text{where} \quad p_r = P(X = r).$$

We now obtain the mean and variance of X.

$$E(X) = \sum_{r=0}^{n} r \binom{n}{r} q^{n-r} p^r$$

$$= \sum_{r=0}^{n} \frac{r(n!)}{(n-r)!r!} q^{n-r} p^r$$

$$= \sum_{r=1}^{n} \frac{n!}{(n-r)!(r-1)!} q^{n-r} p^r$$

$$= np \sum_{r=1}^{n} \frac{(n-1)!}{(n-r)!(r-1)!} q^{n-r} p^{r-1} = np(q+p)^{n-1} = np.$$

$$\text{Var}(X) = \sum_{r=0}^{n} r^2 \binom{n}{r} q^{n-r} p^r - \{E(X)\}^2$$

Writing $r^2 = r(r-1) + r$, we obtain:

$$\text{Var}(X) = \sum_{r=0}^{n} \frac{r(r-1)n!}{(n-r)!r!} q^{n-r} p^r + \sum_{r=0}^{n} \frac{r(n!)}{(n-r)!r!} q^{n-r} p^r - n^2 p^2$$

$$= \sum_{r=2}^{n} \frac{n!}{(n-r)!(r-2)!} q^{n-r} p^r + np - n^2 p^2$$

$$= n(n-1)p^2 \sum_{r=2}^{n} \frac{(n-2)!}{(n-r)!(r-2)!} q^{n-r} p^{r-2} + np - n^2 p^2$$

$$= n(n-1)p^2 (q+p)^{n-2} + np - n^2 p^2$$
$$= n(n-1)p^2 + np - n^2 p^2$$
$$= np - np^2 = np(1-p) = npq$$

$\therefore$ | the mean and variance of the binomial distribution $B(n, p)$ are given by

$$\mu = np, \quad \sigma^2 = npq = np(1-p).$$

Example 2 The components produced by a particular machine are tested by taking samples containing 5 components and noting the number of rejects in each. The given table shows the results for 100 samples

Number of rejects (x)	0	1	2	3	4	5
Frequency (f)	10	27	31	20	9	3

(a) Calculate the mean and variance of the number of rejects.
(b) Estimate the probability p that a component selected at random is a reject.

(c) By assuming that the number of rejects in a sample of 5 components has a binomial distribution with parameters $n = 5$ and p, write down the theoretical mean and variance.

(d) Obtain the expected frequency distribution for 100 samples.

(a) $\sum f = 10 + 27 + 31 + 20 + 9 + 3 = 100$

$\sum fx = 0 \times 10 + 1 \times 27 + 2 \times 31 + 3 \times 20 + 4 \times 9 + 5 \times 3 = 200$

$\sum fx^2 = 0^2 \times 10 + 1^2 \times 27 + 2^2 \times 31 + 3^2 \times 20 + 4^2 \times 9 + 5^2 \times 3 = 550$

$\therefore$ the mean $\bar{x} = \dfrac{\sum fx}{\sum f} = \dfrac{200}{100} = 2,$

the variance $= \dfrac{\sum fx^2}{\sum f} - \bar{x}^2 = \dfrac{550}{100} - 2^2 = 1.5.$

(b) Total number of rejects $= \sum fx = 200$
Total number of components $= 5 \times \sum f = 500$
$\therefore$ the probability p that any component is a reject $= \frac{200}{500} = \frac{2}{5}.$

(c) The mean and variance of the binomial distribution with parameters $n = 5$ and $p = 2/5$ are respectively:

$\mu = np = 2,$ $\sigma^2 = np(1 - p) = 1.2.$

(d) $P(\text{no rejects}) = \left(\dfrac{3}{5}\right)^5 \approx 0.08,$

$P(1 \text{ reject}) = \dbinom{5}{1}\left(\dfrac{3}{5}\right)^4\left(\dfrac{2}{5}\right) \approx 0.26,$

$P(2 \text{ rejects}) = \dbinom{5}{2}\left(\dfrac{3}{5}\right)^3\left(\dfrac{2}{5}\right)^2 \approx 0.35,$

$P(3 \text{ rejects}) = \dbinom{5}{3}\left(\dfrac{3}{5}\right)^2\left(\dfrac{2}{5}\right)^3 \approx 0.23,$

$P(4 \text{ rejects}) = \dbinom{5}{4}\left(\dfrac{3}{5}\right)\left(\dfrac{2}{5}\right)^4 \approx 0.08,$

$P(5 \text{ rejects}) = \left(\dfrac{2}{5}\right)^5 \approx 0.01.$

Multiplying these probabilities by 100 gives the expected frequencies in 100 samples (correct to the nearest integer).

Number of rejects	0	1	2	3	4	5
Expected frequency	8	26	35	23	8	1

[Note that because of rounding errors the sum of these expected frequencies is 101. This does not invalidate the results.]

We now consider an alternative way of finding the mean and variance of certain discrete probability distributions including the binomial distribution.

The *probability generating function* (p.g.f.) for the random variable X, which takes the values $0, 1, 2, \ldots, r, \ldots$ with probabilities $p_0, p_1, p_2, \ldots, p_r, \ldots$ is given by

$$G(t) = p_0 + p_1 t + p_2 t^2 + \ldots + p_r t^r + \ldots$$

Thus by using a "dummy" variable t, we are able to write down a single expression $G(t)$ representing a complete probability distribution. We note that since $\sum p_r = 1$, it follows that $G(1) = 1$.

For the binomial distribution with parameters n and p,

$$G(t) = q^n + \binom{n}{1} q^{n-1} pt + \binom{n}{2} q^{n-2} p^2 t^2 + \ldots + \binom{n}{r} q^{n-r} p^r t^r + \ldots$$

$\therefore$ the p.g.f. of the binomial distribution $B(n, p)$ is

$$G(t) = (q + pt)^n, \quad \text{where} \quad q = 1 - p.$$

If $G(t) = p_0 + p_1 t + p_2 t^2 + p_3 t^3 + \ldots + p_r t^r + \ldots$ then, differentiating with respect to t,

$$G'(t) = p_1 + 2p_2 t + 3p_3 t^2 + \ldots + rp_r t^{r-1} + \ldots$$
$$G''(t) = 2p_2 + 3.2p_3 t + \ldots + r(r - 1)p_r t^{r-2} + \ldots$$

$\therefore$
$$G'(1) = p_1 + 2p_2 + 3p_3 + \ldots + rp_r + \ldots = \sum rp_r$$
$$G''(1) = 2p_2 + 3.2p_3 + \ldots + r(r - 1)p_r + \ldots$$
$$= \sum r(r - 1)p_r = \sum r^2 p_r - \sum rp_r$$

Hence $E(X) = \sum rp_r = G'(1)$

and $\text{Var}(X) = \sum r^2 p_r - [E(X)]^2 = G''(1) + G'(1) - [G'(1)]^2$

i.e. for a distribution with p.g.f. $G(t)$

$$\mu = G'(1), \quad \sigma^2 = G''(1) + G'(1) - [G'(1)]^2.$$

For the binomial distribution $B(n, p)$:

$$G(t) = (q + pt)^n$$
$$G'(t) = np(q + pt)^{n-1} \qquad \therefore \quad G'(1) = np$$
$$G''(t) = n(n - 1)p^2(q + pt)^{n-2} \qquad \therefore \quad G''(1) = n(n - 1)p^2$$

Hence $\mu = np$, $\sigma^2 = n(n - 1)p^2 + np - n^2 p^2 = np(1 - p)$.
These results are the same as those obtained earlier by elementary methods.

Exercise 16.2

1. An unbiased die is thrown 9 times. Find the probability of (a) 2 sixes, (b) at least 2 sixes. Find also the mean and variance of the number of sixes thrown.

2. In a large batch of plastic mouldings 25% have faults. If a random sample of 10 mouldings is inspected, find the probability that the sample contains

(a) 3 faulty mouldings, (b) no more than 2 faulty mouldings. Find also the mean and variance of the number of faulty mouldings.

3.   The probability that a certain darts player hits the "treble 20" with one dart is 0·3. Find the probability that the player scores at least one treble 20 with 3 darts. If the probability of scoring at least one treble 20 with n darts is greater than 0·9, find the least possible value of n.

4.   One in eight of the torches assembled by a machine are imperfect. Eight torches are chosen at random. Find the probability that (a) one is imperfect, (b) at least 6 are imperfect. The probability that a box of n torches contains none that are imperfect is less than 0·1. Find the range of possible values of n.

5.   Given that the binomial distribution $B(n, p)$ has mean 9·6 and standard deviation 2·4, find n and p. Hence obtain the probability generating function of the distribution.

6.   Find the probability generating function of a binomial distribution whose mean is 1·8 and whose variance is 0·99. If the random variable X has this binomial distribution, (i) state the greatest possible value that X may take (with non-zero probability), (ii) write down a numerical expression for the probability that a randomly observed value of X will be equal to 3.   (JMB)

7.   A lake contains 1000 fish of species A, 2000 fish of species B and no other fish. Ten fish are taken from the lake at random. Explain why the probabilities of obtaining various numbers of fish of species A in the ten can be very well approximated by a binomial probability distribution, and hence estimate to three significant figures the probability of obtaining 4 fish of species A and six of species B. Estimate also to three significant figures the probability that in a catch of 5 fish altogether there are more fish of species A than there are of species B.   (C)

8.   A manufacturing company sends out invoices to its customers allowing 5% discount to those who settle their accounts within 15 days. In the past, 40% of the customers took advantage of the discount terms. On a particular day the company sent out 10 invoices. Examine critically the appropriateness of the binomial distribution model for this situation, discussing (a) the requirement of constant probability from trial to trial, (b) the independence of trials. Assuming the model to be appropriate, calculate the probability that, of the 10 invoices, less than 2 are settled within 15 days. For days when 10 invoices are sent out, calculate the mean and variance of the distribution of the number of invoices settled within 15 days.
                    (L)

9.   The numbers of males in a sample of 810 litters of 4 cats are recorded in the table below:

No. of males	0	1	2	3	4
No. of litters	156	326	242	74	12

Calculate the mean and variance of the number of males in this sample of litters. Obtain a corresponding table of the above form for a binomial distribution with $p = \frac{1}{3}$.

10. Six dice were thrown together 1000 times. At each throw, the number of ones obtained was noted and the frequency is shown in the table below:

No. of 1's in a single throw	0	1	2	3	4	5	6
No. of throws	370	380	150	90	9	1	0

Calculate the mean and variance of the number of ones obtained in the experiment. Produce a corresponding table of the expected frequencies, to the nearest integer in each case, based on the assumption that the six dice are unbiased and that the 1000 throws are independent. (L)

11. (a) Berg and Korner have a long rivalry in tennis: in the last 25 games, Berg has won 15 times. They start a new series of 8 games. Assuming that the binomial model may be applied, what is the probability that Berg will win at least 6 of these?

(b) Prove that the mean of the binomial distribution is np. A set of 100 pods, each containing 4 peas, was examined to see how many of the peas were good. The following were the results:

No. of good peas in pod	0	1	2	3	4
No. of pods	7	20	35	30	8

(i) What was the probability of getting a good pea? (ii) Calculate the theoretical frequencies of 0, 1, 2, 3, 4 good peas, using the associated theoretical binomial distribution. (SU)

12.

X	frequency
0	36
1	37
2	20
3	5
4	2

The number of wrong numbers (X) obtained in making a set of ten telephone calls is recorded in the given table which records the results obtained in making 100 sets of 10 telephone calls. Assuming that wrong numbers occur randomly, suggest a suitable statistical model to correspond to the making of 10 telephone calls and recording the number of wrong numbers obtained. Using this model estimate the percentage of sets of ten telephone calls in which 2 or more wrong numbers are obtained. What will this percentage be if the chance of getting a wrong number when making a call is doubled? (L)

13. (i) Find the probability of obtaining exactly two sixes in six throws of a single die [You may assume that $(5/6)^5 = 0{\cdot}402$.]

(ii) If two dice are to be thrown together and the sum of their scores is recorded, find the probability that (a) the sum in one throw will be eleven, (b) a score of eleven will occur exactly twice in six throws [assume that $17^4/18^5 = 0.044$], (c) in one throw the score will be less than eight, given that exactly one die shows a four. (L)

14. A crossword puzzle is published in *The Times* each day of the week, except Sunday. A man is able to complete, on average, 8 out of 10 of the crossword puzzles. (i) Find the expected value and the standard deviation of the number of completed crosswords in a given week. (ii) Show that the probability that he will complete at least 5 in a given week is 0.655 (to 3 significant figures). (iii) Given that he completes the puzzle on Monday, find, to three significant figures, the probability that he will complete at least 4 in the rest of the week. (iv) Find, to three significant figures, the probability that, in a period of four weeks, he completes 4 or less in only one of the four weeks. (C)

15. 4 girls and 3 boys plan to meet together on the following Saturday. The probability that each boy will be present is $\frac{2}{3}$ independently of the other boys. Find the probabilities that (a) 0, (b) 1, (c) 2, (d) 3 boys will be present. The probability that each girl will be present is $\frac{1}{2}$ independently of the other girls and of the boys. (e) Find the probability that the number of girls present will equal the number of boys. (f) Find the probability that both sexes will be present. (g) Afterwards it was reported that the gathering had included at least one boy and at least one girl. What is the probability that there were equal numbers of boys and girls in the light of this additional information? (O&C)

16. Each trial of a binomial experiment has a constant probability p of yielding a success. (i) Given that 7 successes occurred in 15 independent trials show that the conditional probability that the first and last trials were successes is $1/5$. (ii) Find the value of p given that in 20 independent trials the probability of exactly 4 successes is twice that of exactly 6 successes. (JMB)

17. The random variable X has the binomial distribution defined by

$$P(X = r) = \binom{n}{r}(1 - p)^{n-r}p^r, \quad r = 0, 1, 2, \ldots, n.$$

Find an expression for $P(X = r)/P(X = r - 1)$. Hence deduce the most likely values of X when (a) $n = 20$, $p = 0.4$, (b) $n = 14$, $p = 0.2$.

18. Cards are drawn at random and with replacement from an ordinary pack of playing cards until three spades have been drawn. Find the probability that the number of draws required is (a) exactly six, (b) at least six. Find an expression for P_n, the probability that exactly n cards have to be drawn to get three spades ($n \geqslant 3$). Hence, or otherwise, find the most likely value (or values) of n. (L)

19. A random variable X has p.g.f. $G(t) = 1/(2 - t)^2$. Find the expressions for (a) $P(X = r)$, (b) $E(X)$, (c) $\text{Var}(X)$.

20. A random variable X is defined as the number of throws of an unbiased die needed to obtain a six. Find the p.g.f. for X and hence determine $E(X)$ and $\text{Var}(X)$.

16.3 Continuous probability distributions

If X is a continuous random variable which may take any real value within some given interval, $0 \leqslant x \leqslant 10$ say, then it is difficult to give a meaning to probabilities such as $P(X = 2)$, $P(X = 7\cdot32054)$, $P(X = 17/39)$. If $P(X = x)$ were non-zero for all values of x, the sum of all such probabilities would be infinite. This means that we must regard the value of $P(X = x)$ as zero. Thus, in order to set up a suitable probability model we clearly need to define a new type of function.

> The *probability density function* (p.d.f.) of the continuous random variable X is a function $f(x)$ such that
>
> $$P(a \leqslant X \leqslant b) = \int_a^b f(x)\,dx.$$

[Since $P(X = a) = P(X = b) = 0$, the values of $P(a < X < b)$, $P(a \leqslant X < b)$ and $P(a < X \leqslant b)$ are also given by this integral.]

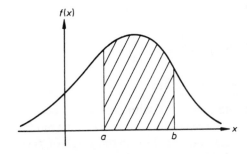

It follows that we can now think of probabilities as areas under the graph of $f(x)$. As probabilities are never negative, $f(x) \geqslant 0$ for all values of x. Since the sum of the probabilities of all possible outcomes of an experiment is 1, the total area under the graph must be 1.

i.e. $\displaystyle \int_{-\infty}^{\infty} f(x)\,dx = 1.$

For a discrete random variable X, $E(X) = \mu = \sum x p(x)$ and $\mathrm{Var}(X) = \sigma^2 = \sum (x - \mu)^2 p(x) = \sum x^2 p(x) - \mu^2$. To obtain similar formulae for the mean and variance of a continuous random variable X, let us consider the probability that the value of X lies between x and $x + \delta x$. Provided that δx is small, this probability is given approximately by $f(x)\delta x$. Thus we let

$$E(X) = \lim_{\delta x \to 0} \sum x f(x) \delta x = \int_{-\infty}^{\infty} x f(x)\,dx.$$

Applying similar arguments to the variance, we have:

> For a continuous random variable X,
>
> $$E(X) = \mu = \int_{-\infty}^{\infty} x f(x)\,dx$$
>
> $$\mathrm{Var}(X) = \sigma^2 = \int_{-\infty}^{\infty} (x - \mu)^2 f(x)\,dx = \int_{-\infty}^{\infty} x^2 f(x)\,dx - \mu^2.$$

One of the simplest types of continuous probability distribution is the *rectangular* or *uniform* distribution. A continuous random variable X is said to be *uniformly distributed* over the interval a to b if $f(x)$ has a constant non-zero value for $a \leqslant x \leqslant b$ and is zero otherwise.

Example 1 Find the mean and variance of the continuous random variable X which is uniformly distributed over the interval from 0 to 3.

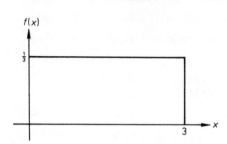

Since the total area under the graph of the probability density function $f(x)$ must be 1,

$$f(x) = \tfrac{1}{3} \quad \text{for} \quad 0 \leqslant x \leqslant 3$$
$$f(x) = 0 \quad \text{otherwise.}$$

$$\therefore \quad E(X) = \int_0^3 x \times \frac{1}{3}\,dx = \left[\frac{1}{6}x^2\right]_0^3 = \frac{3}{2}$$

$$\text{Var}(X) = \int_0^3 x^2 \times \frac{1}{3}\,dx - \left(\frac{3}{2}\right)^2 = \left[\frac{1}{9}x^3\right]_0^3 - \frac{9}{4} = 3 - \frac{9}{4} = \frac{3}{4}$$

Hence the mean of the distribution is $1\frac{1}{2}$ and the variance is $\frac{3}{4}$.

A *mode* or *modal value* of a continuous random variable X with probability density function $f(x)$ is a value of x for which $f(x)$ takes a maximum value. Thus the modes of a distribution are the x-coordinates of the maximum points on the graph of $f(x)$.

The *median* of a continuous random variable X with probability density function $f(x)$ is the value m such that $\displaystyle\int_{-\infty}^{m} f(x)\,dx = 0 \cdot 5$.

Example 2 A continuous random variable X has probability density function $f(x) = kx(9 - x^2)$ for $0 \leqslant x \leqslant 3$ and $f(x) = 0$ otherwise. Find (a) the value of k, (b) the mean, (c) the mode, (d) the median.

(a) $\displaystyle\int_0^3 f(x)\,dx = k\int_0^3 (9x - x^3)\,dx = k\left[\frac{9x^2}{2} - \frac{x^4}{4}\right]_0^3 = \frac{81k}{4}$

Since the total area under the graph of $f(x)$ must be 1, $k = 4/81$.

(b) $\displaystyle E(X) = \int_0^3 xf(x)\,dx = \frac{4}{81}\int_0^3 (9x^2 - x^4)\,dx$

$$= \frac{4}{81}\left[3x^3 - \frac{x^5}{5}\right]_0^3 = 4\left(1 - \frac{3}{5}\right) = \frac{8}{5}$$

Hence the mean of the distribution is $1 \cdot 6$.

(c)

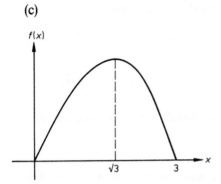

$$f(x) = \tfrac{4}{81}(9x - x^3),$$

$$f'(x) = \tfrac{4}{81}(9 - 3x^2) = \frac{4}{27}(3 - x^2)$$

∴   in   the   interval $0 \leqslant x \leqslant 3$, $f'(x) = 0$ when $x = \sqrt{3}$.
The sketch shows that this gives a maximum value of $f(x)$.

Hence the mode of the distribution is 1·73 (to 3 s.f.)

(d) If m is the median, $\displaystyle\int_0^m f(x)\,dx = \tfrac{1}{2}$

$$\therefore \quad \frac{4}{81}\int_0^m (9x - x^3)\,dx = \frac{4}{81}\left[\frac{9x^2}{2} - \frac{x^4}{4}\right]_0^m = \frac{1}{81}(18m^2 - m^4) = \frac{1}{2}$$

$$36m^2 - 2m^4 = 81$$
$$2m^4 - 36m^2 + 81 = 0$$

$$\therefore \quad m^2 = \frac{36 \pm \sqrt{(36^2 - 8.81)}}{4} = \frac{36 \pm 18\sqrt{(4 - 2)}}{4} = 9 \pm \frac{9}{2}\sqrt{2}$$

Since $0 < m < 3$, we must have $m^2 = 9 - \dfrac{9}{2}\sqrt{2}$

$$\therefore \quad m = \sqrt{\left\{9 - \frac{9}{2}\sqrt{2}\right\}} \approx 1\cdot 62$$

Hence the median of the distribution is 1·62 (to 3 s.f.).

Another function used when modelling continuous probability distributions is defined as follows:

The *cumulative distribution function* (c.d.f.) of the continuous random variable X is the function $F(x)$ such that

$$F(x) = P(X \leqslant x).$$

If X has probability density function $f(x)$, then

$$F(t) = P(X \leqslant t) = \int_{-\infty}^{t} f(x)\,dx.$$

It follows that: $F'(x) = f(x).$

Example 3   A random variable X has cumulative distribution function

$$F(x) = \begin{cases} 0 & \text{for } x \leqslant 0 \\ \frac{1}{6}x^2 & \text{for } 0 \leqslant x \leqslant 2 \\ -2 + 2x - \frac{1}{3}x^2 & \text{for } 2 \leqslant x \leqslant 3 \\ 1 & \text{for } x \geqslant 3. \end{cases}$$

Find (a) $P(X \leqslant 1\cdot5)$, (b) the median, (c) the probability density function $f(x)$.

(a) $P(X \leqslant 1\cdot5) = F(1\cdot5) = \frac{1}{6}(1\cdot5)^2 = 0.375$.
(b) The median is the value m such that $F(m) = \frac{1}{2}$.
Since $F(0) = 0$ and $F(2) = \frac{2}{3}$, m lies in the interval from 0 to 2 and thus $F(m) = \frac{1}{6}m^2$.
∴ $\frac{1}{6}m^2 = \frac{1}{2}$ which gives $m = \sqrt{3}$.
Hence the median of the distribution is $1\cdot73$ (to 3 s.f.).
(c) The probability density function $f(x) = F'(x)$.

∴   for $0 \leqslant x \leqslant 2$, $f(x) = \dfrac{d}{dx}(\frac{1}{6}x^2) = \frac{1}{3}x;$

for $2 \leqslant x \leqslant 3$, $f(x) = \dfrac{d}{dx}(-2 + 2x - \frac{1}{3}x^2) = 2 - \frac{2}{3}x;$

otherwise, $f(x) = 0$.

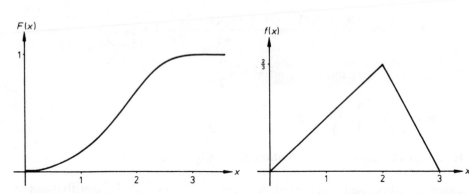

Example 4   A random variable X has probability density function $f(x) = \frac{1}{2}x$ for $0 \leqslant x \leqslant 2$ and $f(x) = 0$ otherwise. Find the cumulative distribution function $F(x)$ of the variable X. Hence find the cumulative distribution function $G(y)$ of the variable $Y = X^2$. Deduce the probability density function $g(y)$.

For $0 \leqslant t \leqslant 2$, $F(t) = \displaystyle\int_0^t \tfrac{1}{2}x\,dx = \left[\tfrac{1}{4}x^2\right]_0^t = \tfrac{1}{4}t^2$.

∴   the cumulative distribution function of X is given by

$F(x) = 0\,(x \leqslant 0), \quad F(x) = \tfrac{1}{4}x^2\,(0 \leqslant x \leqslant 2), \quad F(x) = 1\,(x \geqslant 2)$.
$G(y) = P(Y \leqslant y) = P(X^2 \leqslant y) = P(X \leqslant \sqrt{y}) = F(\sqrt{y})$

∴   the cumulative distribution function of Y is given by

$G'(y) = 0 \, (y \leqslant 0), \quad G(y) = \frac{1}{4}y \, (0 \leqslant y \leqslant 4), \quad G(y) = 1 \, (y \geqslant 4).$

Since $g(y) = G'(y)$, we find that $g(y) = \frac{1}{4} \, (0 \leqslant y \leqslant 4)$ and $g(y) = 0$ otherwise.

[We see that Y is uniformly distributed over the interval from 0 to 4.]

Exercise 16.3

1.   Find the mean and variance of the continuous random variable X which is uniformly distributed over the interval
(a) from 0 to 1,   (b) from 1 to 5,
(c) from 0 to k,   (d) from a to b, where $b > a$.

2.   A continuous random variable X has probability density function

$$f(x) = k(3x^2 - x^3) \quad \text{for} \quad 0 \leqslant x \leqslant 3 \quad \text{and} \quad f(x) = 0 \text{ otherwise.}$$

Find the value of k. Find also the mean, mode and standard deviation of X.

3.   (a) A continuous variable x is distributed at random between the values 2 and 3 and has a probability density function of $6/x^2$. Find the median value of x.
(b) A continuous random variable X takes values between 0 and 1, with a probability density function of $Ax(1 - x)^3$. Find the value of A, and the mean and standard deviation of X.   (SU)

4.   A continuous variable X is distributed at random between two values, $x = 0$ and $x = 2$, and has a probability density function of $ax^2 + bx$. The mean is 1·25. (i) Show that $b = \frac{3}{4}$, and find the value of a. (ii) Find the variance of X. (iii) Verify that the median value of X is approximately 1·3. (iv) Find the mode.   (SU)

5.   The random variable X has a probability density function given by

$$P(x) = \begin{cases} kx(1 - x^2) & (0 \leqslant x \leqslant 1), \\ 0 & \text{elsewhere,} \end{cases}$$

k being a constant. Find the value of k and find also the mean and variance of this distribution. Find the median of the distribution.   (O&C)

6.   The continuous random variable X has probability density function given by

$$f(x) = \begin{cases} k(1 + x^2) & \text{for} \quad -1 \leqslant x \leqslant 1, \\ 0 & \text{otherwise,} \end{cases}$$

where k is a constant. Find the value of k, and determine $E(X)$ and $\text{Var}(X)$. A is the event $X > \frac{1}{2}$; B is the event $X > \frac{3}{4}$. Find (i) $P(B)$, (ii) $P(B|A)$.   (C)

7.   Petrol is delivered to a garage every Monday morning. At this garage the weekly demand for petrol, in thousands of units, is a continuous random variable X distributed with a probability density function of the form

$$f(x) = \begin{cases} ax^2(b - x) & 0 \leqslant x \leqslant 1 \\ 0 & \text{otherwise.} \end{cases}$$

(i) Given that the mean weekly demand is 600 units, determine the values of a and b. (ii) If the storage tanks at this garage are filled to their total capacity of 900 units every Monday morning, what is the probability that in any given week the garage will be unable to meet the demand for petrol?   (AEB 1978)

8.   A continuous random variable X has the probability density function f defined by

$$f(x) = \tfrac{1}{3}cx, \qquad 0 \leqslant x < 3,$$
$$f(x) = c, \qquad 3 \leqslant x \leqslant 4,$$
$$f(x) = 0, \qquad \text{otherwise,}$$

where c is a positive constant. Find (i) the value of c, (ii) the mean of X, (iii) the value, a, for there to be a probability of 0·85 that a randomly observed value of X will exceed a.   (JMB)

9.   A continuous random variable X takes values between 0 and 1 only and its probability density function f is given by $f(x) = kx^2(1 - x)$. Prove that $k = 12$, and find $E(X)$. The cumulative distribution function F is such that $F(x) = P(X \leqslant x)$. Express $F(x)$ in terms of x, and sketch the graph of $y = F(x)$. Verify by calculation that the median of X lies between 0·60 and 0·62.   (C)

10.   The random variable X has the probability density function

$$f(x) = ae^{-ax} \, (0 < x < \infty).$$

Show that the cumulative distribution function of X is $F(x) = 1 - e^{-ax}$. The above distribution, with parameter $a = 0·8$, is proposed as a model for the length of life, in years, of a species of bird. Find the expected frequencies, of a total of 50 birds, that would fall in the class intervals (years) $0-, 1-, 2-, 3-, 4-, 5$ and over.   (O)

11.   A random variable X takes values in the interval $0 < x < 3$ and has probability density function $f(x)$, where

$$f(x) = \begin{cases} ax & (0 < x \leqslant 1), \\ \tfrac{1}{2}a(3 - x) & (1 < x < 3). \end{cases}$$

(i) Find the value of a. (ii) Find the expected value and the standard deviation of X.
(iii) Find the (cumulative) distribution function $F(x)$. (iv) Find $P(|X - 1| < \tfrac{1}{2})$.
          (C)

12. The continuous random variable X has probability density function $f(x)$ defined by

$$f(x) = \begin{cases} c/x^4 & (x < -1) \\ c(2 - x^2) & (-1 \leqslant x \leqslant 1) \\ c/x^4 & (x > 1). \end{cases}$$

(i) Show that $c = \frac{1}{4}$. (ii) Sketch the graph of $f(x)$. (iii) Determine the cumulative distribution function $F(x)$. (iv) Determine the expected value of X and the variance of X. (C)

13. The continuous random variable X has (cumulative) distribution function given by

$$F(x) = \begin{cases} (1 + x)/8 & (-1 \leqslant x \leqslant 0), \\ (1 + 3x)/8 & (0 \leqslant x \leqslant 2), \\ (5 + x)/8 & (2 \leqslant x \leqslant 3), \end{cases}$$

with $F(x) = 0$ for $x < -1$, and $F(x) = 1$ for $x > 3$.
(i)   Sketch the graph of the probability density function $f(x)$.
(ii) Determine the expectation of X and the variance of X.
(iii) Determine $P(3 \leqslant 2X \leqslant 5)$. (C)

14. The length X of an offcut of wooden planking is a random variable which can take any value up to $0.5\,\mathrm{m}$. It is known that the probability of the length being not more than x metres ($0 \leqslant x \leqslant 0.5$) is equal to kx. Determine (i) the value of k, (ii) the probability density function of X, (iii) the expected value of X, (iv) the standard deviation of X (correct to 3 s.f.). (C)

15. The (cumulative) distribution function for a continuous random variable X is given by

$$F(x) = \begin{cases} 0 & \text{for} & x < -2 \\ k(4x - \frac{1}{3}x^3 + \frac{16}{3}) & \text{for} & -2 \leqslant x \leqslant 2, \\ 1 & \text{for} & x > 2. \end{cases}$$

Find (i) the value of k, (ii) $P(-1 < X < 1)$, (iii) the probability density function for X, (iv) the mean and variance of X. (C)

16. A random variable X has probability density function $f(x) = \frac{2}{3}x$ for $1 \leqslant x \leqslant 2$ and $f(x) = 0$ otherwise. Find the cumulative distribution function $F(x)$ of the variable X. Hence find the cumulative distribution function $G(y)$ of the variable $Y = X^{1/2}$. Deduce the probability density function $g(y)$.

17. X is a continuous random variable which is uniformly distributed in the interval $-1 \leqslant x \leqslant 1$. A second random variable Y is given by $Y = X^2$. Show that, if $0 < y < 1$, then $P(Y \leqslant y) = \sqrt{y}$, and deduce the probability density function of Y. Two independent observations of Y are made, and Z denotes the larger of the two observations. By considering the probability that both values of Y are

less than or equal to z, where $0 \leqslant z \leqslant 1$, or otherwise, prove that z is uniformly distributed. Determine the probability density function of W, the smaller of the two values of Y. (C)

18. Write down the probability density function and the cumulative distribution function of a random variable which is uniformly distributed over the interval $[a, b]$.
   A person drives to work, a distance of 12 miles. The time he takes, in minutes, to cover the journey is uniformly distributed over the interval $[20, 30]$. Let V denote the car's average speed in miles per hour on such a journey. Find an expression for $P(V \leqslant v)$, where v is an arbitrary value between 24 and 36. Hence, or otherwise, find (i) the probability density function of V, (ii) the probability that on such a journey the car's average speed will be in excess of 30 m.p.h., (iii) the median average speed for the journey. (W)

19. A continuous random variable X has probability density function defined by

$$f(x) = 2x/a^2 \qquad 0 \leqslant x \leqslant a$$
$$f(x) = 0, \qquad \text{otherwise.}$$

(a) Find the variance of X. (b) Find the cumulative distribution function of X.
(c) If $Y = 1 - (X/a)$, find (i) $P(Y > X)$, (ii) the probability density function of Y. (W)

20. A random variable X has probability density function $f(x) = |x|$ for $-1 \leqslant x \leqslant 1$ and $f(x) = 0$ otherwise. Find the probability density function $g(y)$ of the random variable $Y = X^2$.

16.4 The normal distribution

The *normal distribution* is the most important continuous probability distribution in theoretical statistics. It is found to provide a good probability model for the distributions of many variables such as the heights of people and other measurements of biological characteristics. One of the early uses of the normal distribution was as a model for the distribution of errors in experimental observations.

A continuous random variable X is said to be *normally distributed* with mean μ and variance σ^2 if it has probability density function.

$$f(x) = \frac{1}{\sigma\sqrt{(2\pi)}} e^{-(x-\mu)^2/2\sigma^2} \qquad (\sigma > 0)$$

This distribution is denoted by $N(\mu, \sigma^2)$.

We cannot prove by elementary methods that this is a valid definition of a probability distribution. Clearly $f(x) \geqslant 0$ for all values of x, but for now we must assume that the total area under the graph of $f(x)$ is 1 and that the distribution has mean μ and variance σ^2.

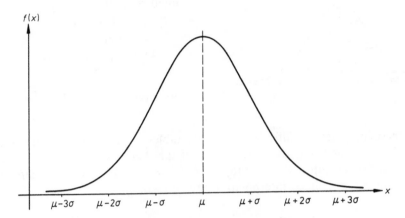

The graph of $f(x)$ is a bell-shaped curve called the *normal curve*. We see that
(1) the curve is symmetrical about the line $x = \mu$;
(2) the x-axis is an asymptote to the curve;
(3) when $x = \mu$, $f(x)$ takes its maximum value $1/\sigma\sqrt{(2\pi)}$ (i.e. $0.4/\sigma$ approximately).
As described in the previous section, the probabilities associated with a continuous random variable X are represented by areas under the graph of the p.d.f. $f(x)$. Thus for the distribution $N(\mu, \sigma^2)$,

$$P(X \leqslant a) = \int_{-\infty}^{a} f(x)\,dx = \int_{-\infty}^{a} \frac{1}{\sigma\sqrt{(2\pi)}} e^{-(x-\mu)^2/2\sigma^2}\,dx.$$

This integral can be simplified by substituting

$$z = \frac{x - \mu}{\sigma} \quad \text{and} \quad dz = \frac{1}{\sigma}dx.$$

Writing $c = \dfrac{a - \mu}{\sigma}$, we have

$$P(X \leqslant a) = P(Z \leqslant c) = \int_{-\infty}^{c} \frac{1}{\sqrt{(2\pi)}} e^{-z^2/2}\,dz.$$

Hence the new random variable $Z = (X - \mu)/\sigma$ has probability density function $\phi(z) = \dfrac{1}{\sqrt{(2\pi)}} e^{-z^2/2}$. We deduce that Z is normally distributed with mean 0 and variance 1. We therefore call Z a *standardised* or *standard* normal variable. To summarise:

If a normal variable X has the distribution $N(\mu, \sigma^2)$ then the random variable $Z = (X - \mu)/\sigma$ has the *standard normal distribution* $N(0, 1)$.

Using this change of variable any problem involving a normal distribution can be restated in terms of the standard distribution $N(0, 1)$.

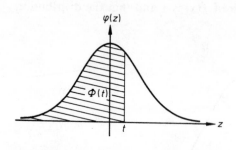

The (cumulative) *distribution function* for the standard normal variable Z is denoted by $\Phi(z)$,

where $\Phi(z) = P(Z \leqslant z)$,

$$\therefore \quad \Phi(t) = \int_{-\infty}^{t} \phi(z)\,dz,$$

where $\phi(z) = \dfrac{1}{\sqrt{(2\pi)}}e^{-z^2/2}$.

Since these integrals are difficult to evaluate, tables of values have been compiled. Table 1, which appears towards the end of this book, gives values of $\Phi(z)$ for $0 \leqslant z \leqslant 4$. For example, $P(Z \leqslant 2\!\cdot\!18) = \Phi(2\!\cdot\!18) = 0\!\cdot\!98537$. If intermediate values of $\Phi(z)$ are required linear interpolation can be used.

Example 1   Use Table 1 to estimate the value of $\Phi(0\!\cdot\!6354)$.

$\Phi(0\!\cdot\!64) - \Phi(0\!\cdot\!63) = 0\!\cdot\!7389 - 0\!\cdot\!7357 = 0\!\cdot\!0032$

$\therefore$ by linear interpolation,

$\Phi(0\!\cdot\!6354) = 0\!\cdot\!7357 + \frac{54}{100} \times 0\!\cdot\!0032 \approx 0\!\cdot\!7374.$

The following diagrams show how the symmetry of the normal distribution can be used to obtain $\Phi(z)$ for negative values of z.

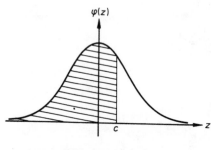

$$P(Z \leqslant c) = \Phi(c)$$

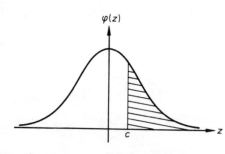

$$P(Z \geqslant c) = 1 - \Phi(c)$$

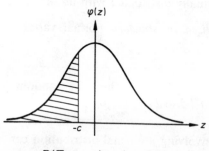

$$P(Z \leqslant -c) = 1 - \Phi(c)$$

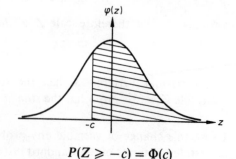

$$P(Z \geqslant -c) = \Phi(c)$$

We may apply these results as follows:

$$P(Z \leqslant -0.72) = 1 - \Phi(0\cdot72) = 1 - 0\cdot7642 = 0.2358$$
$$P(-1\cdot5 \leqslant Z \leqslant -0\cdot5) = P(Z \geqslant -1\cdot5) - P(Z \geqslant -0.5)$$
$$= \Phi(1\cdot5) - \Phi(0\cdot5) = 0\cdot9332 - 0\cdot6915 = 0\cdot2417$$

In the next example we use our knowledge of the standard normal distribution to find probabilities associated with a different normal distribution.

Example 2   Given that a continuous random variable X is normally distributed with mean 20 and variance 16, find $P(15 \leqslant X \leqslant 24)$.

X has mean $\mu = 20$ and standard deviation $\sigma = 4$,
∴   the corresponding standard normal variable is

$$Z = (X - \mu)/\sigma = (X - 20)/4$$

$$P(X \leqslant 24) = P\left(Z \leqslant \frac{24 - 20}{4}\right) = P(Z \leqslant 1) = \Phi(1) = 0\cdot8413$$

$$P(X \leqslant 15) = P\left(Z \leqslant \frac{15 - 20}{4}\right) = P(Z \leqslant -1\cdot25) = 1 - \Phi(1\cdot25) = 0\cdot1056$$

∴ $P(15 \leqslant X \leqslant 24) = 0\cdot8413 - 0\cdot1056 = 0\cdot7357.$

We now demonstrate a different way of using values of the normal distribution function.

Example 3   Given that $\Phi(t) = 0\cdot81$, use Table 1 to estimate the value of t.

$$\Phi(0\cdot87) = 0\cdot8078, \quad \Phi(0\cdot88) = 0\cdot8106,$$
∴   if $\Phi(t) = 0\cdot81$,   then $0\cdot87 < t < 0\cdot88$.
$$\Phi(t) - \Phi(0\cdot87) = 0\cdot0022, \quad \Phi(0\cdot88) - \Phi(0\cdot87) = 0\cdot0028,$$
∴   by linear interpolation, $t = 0\cdot87 + \frac{22}{28} \times 0.01 \approx 0.878$.

For certain values of $\Phi(z)$, the values of z can be obtained directly from Table 2, which gives *percentage points* of the normal distribution $N(0, 1)$. For instance, given that $\Phi(t) = 0\cdot8$, we know that 20% of the distribution lies "to the right" of the value $z = t$. Thus, using Table 2, $t = 0\cdot842$.

Example 4   A random variable X is normally distributed with mean μ and variance σ^2. Given that $P(X < 8) = 0\cdot05$ and $P(X > 15) = 0\cdot1$, find μ and σ^2.

Letting $Z = (X - \mu)/\sigma$ and using tables,
$$0\cdot05 = P(Z > 1\cdot645) = P(Z < -1\cdot645)$$
and $0\cdot1 = P(Z > 1\cdot282)$.

∴ $-1\cdot645 = \dfrac{8 - \mu}{\sigma}$ i.e. $1\cdot645\sigma = \mu - 8$ \hfill (1)

$1\cdot282 = \dfrac{15 - \mu}{\sigma}$ i.e. $1\cdot282\sigma = 15 - \mu$ \hfill (2)

Adding (1) and (2): $2 \cdot 927\sigma = 7$

$$\therefore \quad \sigma = \frac{7}{2 \cdot 927} \quad \text{and} \quad \sigma^2 \approx 5 \cdot 72$$

Substituting in (1): $\mu = 8 + \dfrac{1 \cdot 645 \times 7}{2 \cdot 927} \approx 11 \cdot 9$

The normal distribution arises theoretically as a limit of the binomial distribution, as described in the following theorem:

> If R is a random variable with distribution $B(n, p)$, then the distribution of the variable $T = (R - \mu)/\sigma$, where $\mu = np$ and $\sigma = \sqrt{(npq)}$, tends to $N(0, 1)$ as n tends to infinity.

The proof of this statement is rather difficult, but we can demonstrate the limiting process involved by means of an example. The given set of histograms shows the distribution of the standardised binomial variable T as the value of n increases, but p remains fixed.

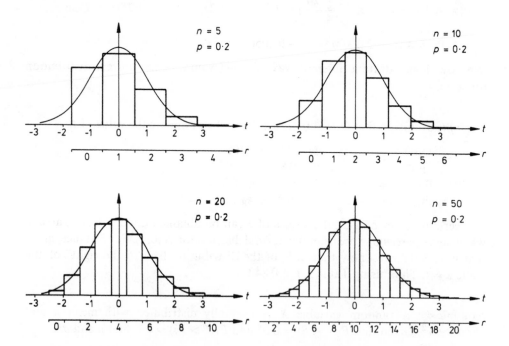

Transforming back to variables with mean $\mu = np$ and variance $\sigma^2 = npq$ we draw the following important conclusion.

> If R is a random variable with distribution $B(n, p)$, then for large n, the distribution of R can be approximated by the normal distribution $N(np, npq)$, where $q = 1 - p$.

This approximation will be close enough for most practical purposes if both np and nq are greater than 5. However, more accurate results will be obtained if both np and nq are greater than 20.

Before considering a numerical example we note that when using the distribution of a continuous variable X as an approximation to the distribution of a discrete variable R, it is necessary to make a *continuity correction*. For instance, if R takes only the integral values $0, 1, 2, \ldots$, then these are assumed to correspond to the intervals $X \leqslant 0 \cdot 5, 0 \cdot 5 \leqslant X \leqslant 1 \cdot 5, 1 \cdot 5 \leqslant X \leqslant 2 \cdot 5, \ldots$.

Let us now suppose that R has a binomial distribution with $n = 50$, $p = 0 \cdot 2$, then R will have mean $\mu = np = 10$ and variance $\sigma^2 = npq = 8$. Thus the corresponding normal variable X also has mean 10 and variance 8. Using $N(10, 8)$ as an approximation to $B(50, 0 \cdot 2)$:

$$P(12 \leqslant R \leqslant 15) = P(11 \cdot 5 \leqslant X \leqslant 15 \cdot 5)$$

$$= P\left(\frac{11 \cdot 5 - 10}{\sqrt{8}} \leqslant \frac{X - 10}{\sqrt{8}} \leqslant \frac{15 \cdot 5 - 10}{\sqrt{8}}\right)$$

$$= P(0 \cdot 5303 \leqslant Z \leqslant 1 \cdot 9445)$$
$$= \Phi(1 \cdot 9445) - \Phi(0 \cdot 5303)$$
$$= 0 \cdot 9741 - 0 \cdot 7020 = 0 \cdot 2721$$

$$\therefore \quad P(12 \leqslant R \leqslant 15) \approx 0 \cdot 27.$$

This turns out to be a fairly good approximation to the true value, which is $0 \cdot 26$ (to 2 d.p.). Even better results are obtained when the value of p is closer to $0 \cdot 5$.

Exercise 16.4

1. Given that X is normally distributed with mean 0 and variance 1, use Table 1 to find
(a) $P(X \leqslant 0 \cdot 3)$,
(b) $P(X \geqslant 1 \cdot 2)$,
(c) $P(X > -2)$,
(d) $P(X \leqslant -2 \cdot 23)$,
(e) $P(0 \cdot 8 \leqslant X \leqslant 1 \cdot 8)$,
(f) $P(-1 \cdot 1 < X < 0 \cdot 5)$.

2. Given that Z is a standardised normal variable, use linear interpolation to find
(a) $P(Z \leqslant 1 \cdot 537)$,
(b) $P(Z < -0.862)$,
(c) $P(Z > -1 \cdot 9035)$,
(d) $P(Z \geqslant 2 \cdot 0067)$,
(e) $P(|Z| \geqslant 1 \cdot 263)$,
(f) $P(|Z + 1| < 0 \cdot 616)$.

3. Given that X is normally distributed with mean 5 and standard deviation 1, find
(a) $P(X < 6 \cdot 7)$,
(b) $P(X \leqslant 4 \cdot 2)$,
(c) $P(3 \cdot 7 < X < 5 \cdot 7)$.

4. Given that X is normally distributed with mean $0 \cdot 2$ and standard deviation $0 \cdot 01$, find
(a) $P(X \geqslant 0 \cdot 205)$,
(b) $P(X > 0 \cdot 198)$,
(c) $P(0 \cdot 199 \leqslant X \leqslant 0 \cdot 201)$.

5. Given that X is normally distributed with mean 12 and variance 1·5, find
(a) $P(X \leqslant 14)$,   (b) $P(X > 9·6)$,   (c) $P(9 \leqslant X \leqslant 10)$.

6. Use Table 1 to estimate the value of t given that
(a) $\Phi(t) = 0·67$,   (b) $\Phi(t) = 0·72$,   (c) $\Phi(t) = 0·19$.

7. Use Table 2 to find the value of t such that
(a) $\Phi(t) = 0·7$,   (b) $\Phi(t) = 0·99$,   (c) $\Phi(t) = 0·9995$.

8. The weights of a large number of cats are normally distributed with mean 1·55 kg and standard deviation 0·2 kg. Find the percentage of cats with weights (a) less than or equal to 1 kg, (b) between 1·2 and 1·3 kg, (c) between 1·5 and 1·75 kg, (d) greater than or equal to 2 kg. (L)

9. The weights of oranges are distributed normally with a mean of 96 g and standard deviation 25 g. For selling purposes, oranges are divided into three grades, I, II and III. Grade I oranges weigh more than 126 g, grade III oranges weigh less than 60 g. All remaining oranges are classed grade II. Calculate the percentage of oranges in each grade. Grade I, II and III oranges sell respectively for 12p, 8p and 4p each. Calculate the expected receipts from the sale of 80 000 oranges. (L)

10. Tests made on 2 types of electric light bulb show the following: Type A, lifetime distributed normally with an average life of 1150 hours and a standard deviation of 30 hours. Type B, long-life bulb, average lifetime of 1900 hours, with standard deviation of 50 hours. (i) What percentage of bulbs of type A could be expected to have a life of more than 1200 hours? (ii) What percentage of type B would you expect to last longer than 1800 hours? (iii) What lifetime limit would you estimate would contain the central 80% of the production of type A? (SU)

11. Batteries for a transistor radio have a mean life under normal usage of 160 hours, with a standard deviation of 30 hours. Assuming the battery life follows a normal distribution, (a) calculate the percentage of batteries which have a life between 150 hours and 180 hours; (b) calculate the range, symmetrical about the mean, within which 75% of the battery lives lie; (c) if a radio takes four of these batteries and requires all of them to be working, calculate the probability that the radio will run for at least 135 hours. (O&C)

12. Adult men in a certain country have heights which are normally distributed with a mean of 1·81 m and a standard deviation of 0.05 m.
(a) Estimate the number of men in a random sample of 100 men whose heights, when measured to the nearest 0·01 m, exceed 1·90 m.
(b) Find the probability that a man selected at random will have a height, when measured to the nearest 0·01 m, less than 1·72 m.
(c) Find the height which is exceeded by 90% of the men. (L)

13. Find the mean and variance of the normally distributed variable X in each of the following cases:

(a) $P(X > 3) = 0.5$, $P(3 < X < 5) = 0.1$.

(b) $P(X > 20) = P(X < 10) = 0.05$.

(c) $P(X < 60) = 0.01$, $P(X > 90) = 0.3$.

(d) $P(X > 10) = 0.1$, $P(9 < X < 10) = 0.2$.

14. A machine is producing curtain rails whose lengths are normally distributed with mean 2.4 m. If 5% of the rails are longer than 2.42 m, find the standard deviation of the distribution. If the machine is adjusted so that 95% of the rails have lengths between 2.38 m and 2.42 m, find the new standard deviation of the distribution.

15. In an examination 30% of the candidates fail and 10% achieve distinction. Last year the pass mark (out of 200) was 84 and the minimum mark required for a distinction was 154. Assuming that the marks of the candidates were normally distributed, estimate the mean mark and the standard deviation. (O&C)

16. A random variable R has the binomial distribution $B(n, p)$. In each of the following cases find both the probability of r successes and the normal approximation to it.

(a) $n = 10$, $p = \frac{1}{2}$, $r = 6$,

(b) $n = 20$, $p = \frac{1}{2}$, $r = 12$,

(c) $n = 50$, $p = \frac{1}{2}$, $r = 30$,

(d) $n = 20$, $p = \frac{1}{4}$· $r = 4$,

(e) $n = 50$, $p = \frac{1}{4}$, $r = 10$,

(f) $n = 100$, $p = \frac{1}{4}$, $r = 20$.

17. Estimate the probability of obtaining more than 60 heads in 100 tosses of an unbiased coin.

18. In a large consignment of peaches 20% of the fruit are bruised. Estimate the probability of fewer than 10 bruised peaches in a box of 60.

19. Tutorial groups, each of 9 students, are picked at random from a large population of which two-thirds are men. (i) What is the probability that a group contains men only? (ii) Calculate the probability that the number of women in a group is either 1, 2, 3, 4 or 5. (iii) Compare this with the probability that a normal variable with the same mean and variance as the distribution appropriate to (ii) should lie between 0.5 and 5.5. (AEB 1979)

20. In a particular community the probability of a man having brown eyes is 2/5. If a random sample of 6 men is to be taken, find the probability that (a) exactly 3 men, (b) at least 3 men will have brown eyes. A second random sample of 100 men is to be taken. Use the normal distribution as an approximation to the binomial distribution, to estimate to 3 decimal places the probabilities that (a) at least half the men have brown eyes and (b) the number of men with brown eyes is between 30 and 45 inclusive. (L)

21. It is known that 30% of an apple crop has been attacked by insects. A random sample of 150 is selected from the crop. Assuming that the distribution of the

number of damaged apples in random samples of 150 may be approximated to by a normal distribution, estimate the probability that (a) more than half the sample is damaged, (b) less than 10% is damaged, (c) the number of damaged apples in the sample lies between 35 and 50, inclusive.

(L)

22. In Urbania selection for the Royal Flying Corps (RFC) is by means of an aptitude test based on a week's intensive military training. It is known that the scores of potential recruits on this test follow a normal distribution with mean 45 and standard deviation 10. (i) What is the probability that a randomly chosen recruit will score between 40 and 60? (ii) What percentage of the recruits is expected to score more than 30? (iii) In a particular year 100 recruits take the test. Assuming that the pass mark is 50, calculate the probability that less than 35 recruits qualify for the RFC.

(AEB 1978)

16.5 The Poisson distribution

The *Poisson*[†] *distribution* was originally derived as a limit of the binomial distribution. It is found to provide a useful model for distributions in which the variable is the number of occurrences of a particular event in a given interval of time or space. Some examples of variables which may have a Poisson distribution are: the number of customers entering a shop in an hour, the number of claims received by an insurance company in a day, the number of flaws in a given length of copper wire, the number of earthworms in a given area of land.

To demonstrate the way in which the Poisson distribution arises as a limit of the binomial distribution, we consider the number of telephone calls received in an hour by a small business. Assuming that the average number of calls received per hour is 4, we can construct a simple binomial model by dividing each hour into 12 five-minute "trials" and taking the probability of a call in any five-minute interval to be 1/3. However, since the firm may receive more than one call in a five-minute period, this model is not entirely satisfactory. It would be better to regard an hour as 60 one-minute trials, taking the probability of a call in any one-minute interval to be 1/15. Remembering the speed with which a modern switchboard can process calls, we should perhaps reduce the time interval to 10 seconds or even to 2 seconds. The given table shows that we are producing a sequence of binomial distributions with increasing numbers of trials but constant mean.

Interval	n	p	Mean	Variance
5 minutes	12	$\frac{1}{3}$	4	$4 \times \frac{2}{3} \approx 2 \cdot 67$
1 minute	60	$\frac{1}{15}$	4	$4 \times \frac{14}{15} \approx 3 \cdot 73$
10 seconds	360	$\frac{1}{90}$	4	$4 \times \frac{89}{90} \approx 3 \cdot 96$
2 seconds	1800	$\frac{1}{450}$	4	$4 \times \frac{449}{450} \approx 3 \cdot 99$

The limit of this sequence is the Poisson distribution with mean and variance 4.

[†]*Poisson, Siméon Denis* (1781–1840) French mathematician. His main contributions were to the theory of electricity and magnetism, but in 1837 he published *Recherches sur la probabilité des jugements*, dealing with probability distributions.

We obtain the general form of the Poisson distribution by considering the limit of the binomial distribution $B(n, p)$ as n tends to infinity in such a way that the mean $\mu = np$ remains constant.

$$P(X = r) = \binom{n}{r} p^r (1 - p)^{n-r}$$

$$= \frac{n(n-1)\ldots(n-r+1)}{r!} \left(\frac{\mu}{n}\right)^r \left(1 - \frac{\mu}{n}\right)^{n-r}$$

$$= \frac{n}{n}\left(\frac{n-1}{n}\right)\ldots\left(\frac{n-r+1}{n}\right)\frac{\mu^r}{r!}\left(1 - \frac{\mu}{n}\right)^n \left(1 - \frac{\mu}{n}\right)^{-r}$$

$$= \left(1 - \frac{1}{n}\right)\ldots\left(1 - \frac{r-1}{n}\right)\frac{\mu^r}{r!}\left(1 - \frac{\mu}{n}\right)^n \Big/ \left(1 - \frac{\mu}{n}\right)^r$$

$$\therefore \quad \lim_{n \to \infty} P(X = r) = \frac{\mu^r}{r!} \lim_{n \to \infty} \left(1 - \frac{\mu}{n}\right)^n$$

It can be shown that

$$\lim_{n \to \infty} \left(1 - \frac{\mu}{n}\right)^n = e^{-\mu}$$

Thus, as $n \to \infty$, $P(X = r) \to \dfrac{\mu^r}{r!} e^{-\mu}$.

This result leads to the following definition:

A discrete random variable X is said to have a Poisson distribution with parameter μ, where $\mu > 0$, if

$$P(X = r) = \frac{\mu^r}{r!} e^{-\mu} \quad \text{for} \quad r = 0, 1, 2, \ldots$$

Considering again the limit of the distribution $B(n, p)$ as $n \to \infty$, we see that if the mean $\mu = np$ remains constant, then $p \to 0$ and the variance $\sigma^2 = np(1 - p)$ tends to μ. This suggests that the Poisson distribution has mean μ and variance μ. These results can proved either directly or by using the appropriate probability generating function. For instance:

$$E(X) = \sum_{r=0}^{\infty} r \left(\frac{\mu^r}{r!} e^{-\mu}\right) = \mu e^{-\mu} \sum_{r=1}^{\infty} \frac{\mu^{r-1}}{(r-1)!}$$

$$= \mu e^{-\mu}\left(1 + \mu + \frac{\mu^2}{2!} + \frac{\mu^3}{3!} + \ldots\right) = \mu e^{-\mu} \times e^{\mu} = \mu.$$

[For other proofs see Exercise 16.5 questions 12 and 13.]

It follows from this discussion that the Poisson distribution is a suitable model for the distribution of the number of events occurring in a specified interval of continuous time or space, provided that

(a) the events occur at random and independently, but may not occur simultaneously;
(b) the expected number of events in any interval is proportional to the size of the interval.

Example 1   A small business receives an average of 4 telephone calls per hour. Use the appropriate Poisson distribution to find the probability that (a) 7 calls are received in a two hour period, (b) up to 3 calls are received in an interval of 30 minutes.

(a) The expected number of calls in 2 hours is 8.

Thus if X is the number of calls received in 2 hours, X has a Poisson distribution with parameter 8

$$\therefore \quad P(X = 7) = \frac{8^7}{7!}e^{-8} \approx 0 \cdot 140.$$

Hence the probability that 7 calls are received in a two hour period is $0 \cdot 140$.

(b) The expected number of calls in 30 minutes is 2.

Thus if Y is the number of calls received in 30 minutes, Y has a Poisson distribution with parameter 2

$$\therefore \quad P(Y \leqslant 3) = P(Y = 0) + P(Y = 1) + P(Y = 2) + P(Y = 3)$$

$$= e^{-2} + 2e^{-2} + \frac{2^2}{2!}e^{-2} + \frac{2^3}{3!}e^{-2}$$

$$= (1 + 2 + 2 + \tfrac{4}{3})e^{-2} \approx 0 \cdot 857.$$

Hence the probability that up to 3 calls are received in 30 minutes is $0 \cdot 857$.

The following diagrams show the Poisson distributions used in Example 1.

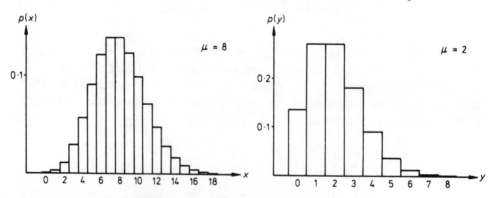

We have seen that the Poisson distribution with parameter $\mu = np$ is a limit of the binomial distribution $B(n, p)$. This means that under certain conditions a Poisson distribution can be used as an approximation to a binomial distribution with the same mean. In practice a Poisson approximation gives fairly accurate results when $n > 50$, $p < 0 \cdot 1$ and $np \leqslant 5$. It may also produce acceptable approximations to binomial distributions which do not satisfy these conditions. However, for a binomial distribution such that both np and $n(1 - p)$ are greater than 5, a normal approximation is usually more appropriate.

It can be shown that as μ tends to infinity, the distribution of the standardised Poisson variable $(X - \mu)/\sqrt{\mu}$ approaches the standard normal distribution $N(0, 1)$. It follows that for large μ, the normal distribution $N(\mu, \mu)$ can be used as an approximation to the Poisson distribution with parameter μ. Fairly good approximations are obtained for $\mu > 5$, but for accurate results it is necessary to have $\mu > 20$.

Exercise 16.5

1. In a school laboratory an average of 8 test-tubes are broken in 20 working days. Find the probability that (a) 5 test-tubes will be broken in the next 10 days; (b) fewer than 2 test-tubes will be broken in the next 3 days.

2. The number of heavy vehicles driving past a certain historic building in an hour is assumed to have a Poisson distribution with mean 3. Find the probability that (a) in the next hour more than 3 heavy vehicles will drive by; (b) in the next two hours fewer than 5 heavy vehicles will drive by.

3. A textile manufacturer estimates that there is an average of 2 faults in every 100 metres of fabric he produces. Find the probability that there is at least 1 fault in a 10-metre length of fabric. Write down an expression for the probability that there is no fault in an n-metre length of fabric. What is the greatest integer n such that this probability is greater than 0·9?

4. The number of plants of a certain species found in one square metre of woodland is assumed to have a Poisson distribution with mean 0·003. Find the probability of observing at least 2 specimens in an area of $400 \, \text{m}^2$. A botanist is more than 99% certain that he will find at least one specimen in an area of $n \, \text{m}^2$. Find the least possible value of the integer n.

In questions 5 to 8 draw up a table showing the values, correct to 3 d.p., of the probabilities $p(0)$, $p(1)$, $p(2)$, ... for (a) the binomial distribution $B(n, p)$; (b) the Poisson distribution with parameter $\mu = np$; (c) the normal approximation to (a); (d) the normal approximation to (b). Comment briefly on your results.

5. $n = 20$, $p = 0·5$.

6. $n = 20$, $p = 0·1$.

7. $n = 50$, $p = 0·1$.

8. $n = 100$, $p = 0·08$.

9. It is found that on average 0·5% of the watches produced by a certain factory are faulty. Estimate the probability that (a) in a batch of 200 watches there are no faulty watches; (b) in a batch of 500 watches more than 2 are faulty.

10. On average 1 out of 50 patients treated with a certain drug suffer side effects. Estimate the probability that (a) if 80 patients take the drug then exactly 2 will have side effects, (b) if 200 patients take the drug then at least 4 will have side effects.

11. In a certain experiment the probability of success in any trial is 0·03. Use appropriate approximations to find the probabilities of (a) at least 2 successes in 50 trials, (b) at least 4 successes in 100 trials, (c) at least 20 successes in 500 trials.

12. Use the identity $r^2 \equiv r(r-1) + r$ to show that

$$\sum_{r=0}^{\infty} \frac{r^2 x^r}{r!} = x^2 e^x + x e^x.$$

Hence show that the Poisson distribution with parameter μ has variance μ.

13. Show that the probability generating function for the Poisson distribution with parameter μ is given by $G(t) = e^{\mu(t-1)}$. Hence show that the distribution has mean μ and variance μ.

14. The number of road accidents at a certain traffic roundabout has been found to follow a Poisson distribution with a mean of 0·8 accidents per week. Calculate, correct to 2 significant figures, the probabilities that (i) there will be at least 2 accidents in a particular week, (ii) there will be exactly 3 accidents in a particular three-week period. After road works have been carried out, the traffic is observed for a period of 8 weeks and in that time only 1 accident occurs. Calculate the probability of at most 1 accident in 8 weeks if the mean is still 0·8 accidents per week. Comment briefly on this result. (C)

15. (a) I recorded the number of phone calls I received over a period of 150 days:

No. of calls	0	1	2	3	4
No. of days	51	54	36	6	3

   (i) Find the average number of calls per day. (ii) Calculate the frequencies of the comparable Poisson distribution.
   (b) A firm selling electrical components packs them in boxes of 60. On average 2% of the components are faulty. What is the chance of getting more than 2 defective components in a box? (Use the Poisson distribution.)   (SU)

16. An aircraft has 116 seats. The airline has found, from long experience, that on average 2·5% of people with tickets for a particular flight do not arrive for that flight. If the airline sells 120 seats for a particular flight, determine, using a suitable approximation, the probability that more than 116 people arrive for that flight. Determine also the probability that there are empty seats on the flight.   (C)

17. A number of different types of fungi are distributed at random in a field. Eighty per cent of these fungi are mushrooms, and the remainder are toadstools. Five per cent of the toadstools are poisonous. A man who cannot distinguish between mushrooms and toadstools, wanders across the field and picks a total of 100 fungi. Determine, correct to 2 significant figures, using approximations, the probability that the man has picked (i) at least 20 toadstools, (ii) exactly two poisonous toadstools.   (C)

18. A new telephone directory is to be published, and before publication takes place the entries have to be checked for misprints and any necessary corrections made. Previous experience suggests that, on average, 0·1% of the entries will require correction, and that entries requiring correction will be randomly distributed. The directory will contain 240 000 entries altogether, printed on 800 pages with 300 entries per page. There are two methods of making corrections: for method A the costs are £C per page containing one entry requiring correction and £$3C$ per page containing two or more entries requiring correction; for method B the costs are £$2C$ per page containing one or more entries requiring correction. Calculate the expected costs of correction for each method.   (C)

19. In a certain office the number of reams of typing paper used per month has a Poisson distribution with mean 25. Estimate the probability that more than 25 reams of paper will be used in the next month. Given that it is more than 95% certain that there is enough paper in the stationery cupboard to last a month, find the minimum number of reams of paper in the cupboard.

20. Show that the variance of a Poisson distribution is equal to the mean. The number of bacteria in 1 ml of inoculum has a Poisson distribution with mean 2·0. If at least 3 bacteria are needed for a dose to be infective, find the probability that a dose of 1 ml will cause infection. Find approximate limits, symmetrical about the mean, between which lies 95% of the distribution of the number of bacteria in 100 ml of inoculum.   (O&C)

16.6 The algebra of expectation and variance

The expectation $E(X)$ and the variance $\text{Var}(X)$ of a random variable X were defined earlier in the chapter.

$$E(X) = \mu = \begin{cases} \sum x_r p(x_r), & \text{for discrete } X \\ \displaystyle\int_{-\infty}^{\infty} x f(x)\, dx, & \text{for continuous } X \end{cases}$$

$$\text{Var}(X) = \sigma^2 = \begin{cases} \sum (x_r - \mu)^2 p(x_r), & \text{for discrete } X \\ \displaystyle\int_{-\infty}^{\infty} (x - \mu)^2 f(x)\, dx, & \text{for continuous } X \end{cases}$$

If a new random variable $g(X)$ is defined in terms of X by a formula such as $g(X) = 2X + 3$ or $g(X) = X^2$, then the expectation of $g(X)$ is given by:

$$E[g(X)] = \begin{cases} \sum g(x_r) p(x_r), & \text{for discrete } X \\ \displaystyle\int_{-\infty}^{\infty} g(x) f(x)\, dx & \text{for continuous } X \end{cases}$$

If X is a discrete variable which takes the values $x_1, x_2, \ldots$ then we can show that this formula for $E[g(X)]$ is consistent with the definition of $E(X)$ by letting $Y = g(X)$.

(i) If Y takes distinct values $y_1 = g(x_1)$, $y_2 = g(x_2), \ldots$, then

$$P(Y = y_r) = P(g(X) = g(x_r)) = P(X = x_r) = p(x_r),$$

$$\therefore \quad E[g(X)] = E(Y) = \sum_{\text{all } r} y_r P(Y = y_r) = \sum_{\text{all } r} g(x_r) p(x_r).$$

(ii) If the values $g(x_1), g(x_2), \ldots$ are not all distinct then we have relationships such as $y_k = g(x_i) = g(x_j) = \ldots$. In these cases

$$P(Y = y_k) = P(X = x_i) + P(X = x_j) + \ldots = p(x_i) + p(x_j) + \ldots$$
$$\therefore \quad y_k P(Y = y_k) = y_k p(x_i) + y_k p(x_j) + \ldots$$
$$= g(x_i) p(x_i) + g(x_j) p(x_j) + \ldots$$

$$\therefore \quad E[g(X)] = E(Y) = \sum_{\text{all } k} y_k P(Y = y_k) = \sum_{\text{all } r} g(x_r) p(x_r).$$

Thus the formula for $E[g(X)]$ is valid for discrete X. We will assume that it is also valid for continuous X.

Example 1   A discrete random variable X takes the values $0, 1, 2, 3$ and $p(0) = 0.1$, $p(1) = p(3) = 0.2$, $p(2) = 0.5$. Find $E(X^2 - X)$.

$$E(X^2 - X) = \sum (x^2 - x) p(x)$$
$$= (0^2 - 0)0.1 + (1^2 - 1)0.2 + (2^2 - 2)0.5 + (3^2 - 3)0.2$$
$$= 0 + 0 + 2 \times 0.5 + 6 \times 0.2 = 2.2.$$

Example 2   Find $E(X^3)$ for the continuous random variable X which has probability density function $f(x) = 2(1 - x)$ for $0 \leqslant x \leqslant 1$ and $f(x) = 0$ otherwise.

$$E(X^3) = \int_0^1 x^3 f(x) \, dx = \int_0^1 x^3 . 2(1 - x) \, dx$$

$$= 2 \int_0^1 (x^3 - x^4) \, dx = 2 \left[\frac{x^4}{4} - \frac{x^5}{5} \right]_0^1 = 2\left(\frac{1}{4} - \frac{1}{5} \right) = 0.1.$$

Two useful properties of expectation follow from the definition of $E[g(X)]$.

> If X is a random variable, discrete or continuous,
> (i) $E(aX + b) = aE(X) + b$, for constants a and b.
> (ii) $E[g(X) + h(X)] = E[g(X)] + E[h(X)]$.

We give here the proof of (i) for discrete X. The remaining proofs are left as an exercise.

$$E(aX + b) = \sum (ax_r + b) p(x_r)$$
$$= \sum \{ ax_r p(x_r) + bp(x_r) \} = a \sum x_r p(x_r) + b \sum p(x_r)$$

But $\sum x_r p(x_r) = E(X)$ and $\sum p(x_r) = 1$

Hence $E(aX + b) = aE(X) + b.$

It is now possible to express the variance of a random variable in terms of expected values:

$$\text{Var}(X) = E[(X - \mu)^2], \quad \text{where} \quad \mu = E(X)$$

Thus, using results (i) and (ii):

$$\text{Var}(X) = E(X^2 - 2\mu X + \mu^2) = E(X^2) - 2\mu E(X) + \mu^2 = E(X^2) - \mu^2$$

i.e.

$$\boxed{\text{Var}(X) = E(X^2) - [E(X)]^2.}$$

Hence if a and b are constants,

$$\begin{aligned}
\text{Var}(aX + b) &= E[(aX + b)^2] - [E(aX + b)]^2 \\
&= E(a^2 X^2 + 2abX + b^2) - [aE(X) + b]^2 \\
&= a^2 E(X^2) + 2abE(X) + b^2 - a^2[E(X)]^2 - 2abE(X) - b^2 \\
&= a^2 E(X^2) - a^2[E(X)]^2 = a^2\{E(X^2) - [E(X)]^2\}
\end{aligned}$$

i.e.

$$\boxed{\text{Var}(aX + b) = a^2 \text{Var}(X)}$$

To develop the theory of expectation further we must now consider the distribution of two discrete random variables X and Y with probability functions $p_X(x)$ and $p_Y(y)$ respectively. Let X take the values $x_1, x_2, \ldots, x_i, \ldots$ and let Y take the values $y_1, y_2, \ldots, y_j, \ldots$

> The *joint probability distribution* of X and Y is the set of all probabilities $p(x_i, y_j)$, where $p(x_i, y_j) = P(X = x_i, Y = y_j)$.

For example if the possible values of X are $0, 1, 2$ and the values of Y are $0, 1, 2, 3$, then the joint distribution will be a set of 12 probabilities, which can be displayed in a two-way table as follows:

X \ Y	0	1	2	3	Total
0	$p(0,0)$	$p(0,1)$	$p(0,2)$	$p(0,3)$	$p_X(0)$
1	$p(1,0)$	$p(1,1)$	$p(1,2)$	$p(1,3)$	$p_X(1)$
2	$p(2,0)$	$p(2,1)$	$p(2,2)$	$p(2,3)$	$p_X(2)$
Total	$p_Y(0)$	$p_Y(1)$	$p_Y(2)$	$p_Y(3)$	1

As indicated in the table, the row totals give the values of $p_X(x)$. For instance

$$p(0,0) + p(0,1) + p(0,2) + p(0,3) = p_X(0).$$

Similarly the column totals are the values of $p_Y(y)$. Since these probabilities appear in the margins, they are called the *marginal distributions* of X and Y. Using this table we could obtain the probability distribution of a random variable such as $X + Y$. We see that $P(X + Y = 0) = p(0,0)$, $P(X + Y = 1) = p(1,0) + p(0,1)$, and so on. However, it is possible to obtain general formulae for the expected values of $X + Y$ and other functions of X and Y.

Taking into account all ordered pairs (x_i, y_j):

$$E(X + Y) = \sum_i \sum_j (x_i + y_j) p(x_i, y_j)$$

$$= \sum_i \left[\sum_j x_i p(x_i, y_j) \right] + \sum_j \left[\sum_i y_j p(x_i, y_j) \right]$$

$$= \sum_i \left[x_i \sum_j p(x_i, y_j) \right] + \sum_j \left[y_j \sum_i p(x_i, y_j) \right]$$

$$= \sum_i x_i p_X(x_i) + \sum_i y_j p_Y(y_j) = E(X) + E(Y).$$

Similar arguments can be used to extend this result to any *linear combination* of random variables.

If X and Y are random variables and a and b are constants, then

$$E(aX + bY) = aE(X) + bE(Y).$$

If $X_1, X_2, \ldots, X_n$ are random variables, then

$$E(X_1 + X_2 + \ldots + X_n) = E(X_1) + E(X_2) + \ldots + E(X_n).$$

[These results are valid for both discrete and continuous variables, but in the continuous case the proofs require integration methods not covered in this course.]

If random variables X and Y are *independent*, then

$$P(X = x_i, Y = y_j) = P(X = x_i) \times P(Y = y_j)$$

i.e.
$$p(x_i, y_j) = p_X(x_i) p_Y(y_j)$$

$$E(XY) = \sum_i \sum_j x_i \, y_j p(x_i, y_j)$$

$$= \sum_i \left[\sum_j x_i y_j p_X(x_i) p_Y(y_j) \right]$$

$$= \sum_i \left[x_i p_X(x_i) \sum_j y_j p_Y(y_j) \right]$$

$$= \left[\sum_i x_i p_X(x_i) \right] \left[\sum_j y_j p_Y(y_j) \right] = E(X) E(Y).$$

$\therefore$

If X and Y are independent random variables, then

$$E(XY) = E(X)E(Y).$$

We are now ready to consider the variance of a linear combination of random variables. In particular:

$$\begin{aligned}
\text{Var}(X + Y) &= E[(X + Y)^2] - [E(X + Y)]^2 \\
&= E(X^2 + 2XY + Y^2) - [E(X) + E(Y)]^2 \\
&= E(X^2) + 2E(XY) + E(Y^2) - [E(X)]^2 - 2E(X)E(Y) - [E(Y)]^2 \\
&= \{E(X^2) - [E(X)]^2\} + 2\{E(XY) - E(X)E(Y)\} \\
&\quad + \{E(Y^2) - [E(Y)]^2\}
\end{aligned}$$

The quantity $E(XY) - E(X)E(Y)$ is called the *covariance* of X and Y, and is denoted by $\text{Cov}(X, Y)$.
Thus, in general:

$$\text{Var}(X + Y) = \text{Var}(X) + 2\,\text{Cov}(X, Y) + \text{Var}(Y).$$

However, if the variables X and Y are independent,

$$\text{Cov}(X, Y) = E(XY) - E(X)E(Y) = 0$$

$$\therefore \quad \text{Var}(X + Y) = \text{Var}(X) + \text{Var}(Y).$$

As before, this basic result can be extended:

If X and Y are independent random variables and a and b are constants, then

$$\text{Var}(aX + bY) = a^2\,\text{Var}(X) + b^2\,\text{Var}(Y).$$

Two important special cases are given by:

$$\text{Var}(X + Y) = \text{Var}(X - Y) = \text{Var}(X) + \text{Var}(Y)$$

If $X_1, X_2, \ldots, X_n$ are independent random variables,

$$\text{Var}(X_1 + X_2 + \ldots + X_n) = \text{Var}(X_1) + \text{Var}(X_2) + \ldots + \text{Var}(X_n).$$

Example 3   In the ice-cream dessert served in a motorway cafeteria, the masses of the portions of ice-cream are distributed about a mean of 80 g with standard deviation 6 g. The fruit topping has mean mass 20 g and standard deviation 4 g. If the cost of 100 g of ice-cream is 5 p and the cost of 100 g of topping is 10 p, find the mean and standard deviation of the cost of a dessert.

Let the random variables X and Y represent the masses in grammes of portions of ice-cream and topping respectively. If Z is the total cost in pence of the dessert, then

$$Z = \tfrac{5}{100}X + \tfrac{10}{100}Y = \tfrac{1}{20}X + \tfrac{1}{10}Y$$

$$\therefore \quad E(Z) = \tfrac{1}{20}E(X) + \tfrac{1}{10}E(Y) = \tfrac{80}{20} + \tfrac{20}{10} = 6,$$

$$\text{Var}(Z) = (\tfrac{1}{20})^2 \, \text{Var}(X) + (\tfrac{1}{10})^2 \, \text{Var}(Y)$$

$$= \frac{6^2}{20^2} + \frac{4^2}{10^2} = \frac{9 + 16}{100} = \frac{1}{4}$$

Hence the cost of a dessert has mean $6\,p$ and standard deviation $\tfrac{1}{2}\,p$.

We now state without proof two important theorems concerning linear combinations of normal random variables.

If X and Y are independent normal random variables with distributions $N(\mu_x, \sigma_x^2)$ and $N(\mu_y, \sigma_y^2)$ respectively, then $Z = aX + bY$, where a and b are constants, is also a normal random variable and has mean $a\mu_x + b\mu_y$, variance $a^2\sigma_x^2 + b^2\sigma_y^2$.

Sums and differences of independent normal variables are of particular interest:

$$Z = X + Y \quad \text{has the distribution} \quad N(\mu_x + \mu_y, \sigma_x^2 + \sigma_y^2),$$
$$Z = X - Y \quad \text{has the distribution} \quad N(\mu_x - \mu_y, \sigma_x^2 + \sigma_y^2).$$

If $X_1, X_2, \ldots, X_n$ are independent observations of a random variable with distribution $N(\mu, \sigma^2)$, then $Z = X_1 + X_2 + \ldots + X_n$ is normally distributed with mean $n\mu$, variance $n\sigma^2$.

Example 4   Brand X beefburgers have masses normally distributed about a mean of $65\,g$ with variance $15\,g^2$. The masses of Brand Y beefburgers are normally distributed with mean $100\,g$, variance $25\,g^2$. Find the probability that the mass of 3 Brand X beefburgers is greater than the mass of 2 Brand Y beefburgers.

[It is tempting to think that what we need to find here is $P(3X - 2Y > 0)$. However, in the expression $3X - 2Y$, $3X$ represents 3 times the mass of one beefburger, not the mass of three beefburgers.]

Let $D = (X_1 + X_2 + X_3) - (Y_1 + Y_2)$, where X_1, X_2, X_3 represent the masses (in grammes) of 3 Brand X beefburgers and Y_1, Y_2 represent the masses of 2 Brand Y beefburgers, then

$$E(D) = E(X_1) + E(X_2) + E(X_3) - E(Y_1) - E(Y_2)$$
$$= 3 \times 65 - 2 \times 100 = -5$$
$$\text{Var}(D) = \text{Var}(X_1) + \text{Var}(X_2) + \text{Var}(X_3) + \text{Var}(Y_1) + \text{Var}(Y_2)$$
$$= 3 \times 15 + 2 \times 25 = 95$$

Letting Z be the standardised normal variable $(D + 5)/\sqrt{95}$,

$$P(D > 0) = P(Z > 5/\sqrt{95})$$
$$= P(Z > 0 \cdot 5130)$$
$$= 1 - \Phi(0 \cdot 5130) = 1 - 0 \cdot 6961 = 0 \cdot 3039$$

$\therefore$ the required probability is approximately $0 \cdot 304$.

Two further results are sometimes useful.

If independent random variables X and Y have distributions $B(m, p)$ and $B(n, p)$, then $X + Y$ has distribution $B(m + n, p)$.

If independent random variables X and Y have Poisson distributions with means λ and μ, then $X + Y$ has a Poisson distribution with mean $\lambda + \mu$.

Methods of proof are indicated in Exercise 16.6 questions 23 and 25.

Exercise 16.6

1. A discrete random variable X takes the values 1, 2, 3, 4, 5 with probabilities $p(1) = p(2) = 0\cdot1, p(3) = 0\cdot15, p(4) = 0\cdot4, p(5) = 0\cdot25$. Find $E(X), E(X^2)$ and $E(1/X)$. Hence find $E(2X^2 - 1)$ and $E[(X + 1)^2/X]$.

2. A discrete random variable X takes the values $-1, 0, 1, 2$ with probabilities $p(-1) = 0\cdot2, p(0) = 0\cdot3, p(1) = 0\cdot4, p(2) = 0\cdot1$. Find $E(X), E(X^2)$ and $E(X^4)$. Hence find $\text{Var}(X)$ and $\text{Var}(X^2)$.

3. A continuous random variable X has probability density function

$$f(x) = \tfrac{1}{2}(3 - x) \text{ for } 1 \leqslant x \leqslant 3 \text{ and } f(x) = 0 \text{ otherwise.}$$

Find $E(X), E(X^2)$ and $E(X^3)$. Hence find $E(3X^3 + 2X)$ and $\text{Var}(X)$.

4. A continuous random variable X has probability density function

$$f(x) = 6x(1 - x) \text{ for } 0 \leqslant x \leqslant 1 \text{ and } f(x) = 0 \text{ otherwise.}$$

Find $E(X), E(X^2)$, and $E(\sqrt{X})$. Hence find $E[X(X - 1)]$ and $\text{Var}(\sqrt{X})$.

5. A random variable X takes the values 5, 8, 4, 7 with equal probability and an independent variable Y takes the values 4, 7, 1 with equal probability. Find the mean and variance of the following:
(a) X (b) Y,   (c) $4X + 3$,   (d) $5 - 2Y$,
(e) $X + Y$,   (f) $X - Y$,   (g) $3X - Y$,   (h) $2X + 3Y$.

6. Independent random variables X and Y are such that $E(X) = 10, \text{Var}(X) = 9$ and $E(Y) = 7, \text{Var}(Y) = 1$. Find (a) the mean and variance of $5X - 3Y + 2$, (b) the values of $E(X^2), E(Y^2)$ and $E(X^2 + Y^2)$.

7. A factory produces nuts with masses distributed about a mean of 5 g with a standard deviation of 0·2 g. These are screwed on to bolts whose masses have mean

20 g and standard deviation 0·1 g. If each bolt is fitted with two nuts, find the mean and standard deviation of the resulting total mass.

8.   In a can containing baked beans and 5 small sausages, the mass of each sausage is distributed about a mean of 20 g with standard deviation 2 g. The mean mass of the baked beans is 100 g with standard deviation 5 g. Find the mean mass of the total contents of a can and the standard deviation.

9.

X \ Y	0	1	2
1	0·06	0·12	0·02
2	0·15	0·3	0·05
3	0·09	0·18	0·03

The given table shows the joint probability distribution of two discrete random variables X and Y.
(a) Use the marginal distributions of X and Y to find $E(X)$, $Var(X)$ and $E(Y)$, $Var(Y)$.

(b) Are there any values of x and y for which

$$P(X = x, Y = y) \neq P(X = x) \times P(Y = y)?$$

Use your answer to determine whether or not X and Y are independent.
(c) Find the distribution of XY i.e. $P(XY = 0)$, $P(XY = 1)$, $P(XY = 2)$,... Hence determine whether or not $E(XY) = E(X)E(Y)$.
(d) Find the distribution of $X + Y$. Hence determine whether or not

$$Var(X + Y) = Var(X) + Var(Y).$$

10.   Repeat question 9 for the following joint distributions.

(i)

X \ Y	0	1	2	3
0	0·03	0·1	0.05	0·02
1	0·05	0	0·25	0·1
2	0·02	0·2	0·1	0·08

(ii)

X \ Y	1	2	3
0	0·05	0·2	0·05
1	0·2	0	0·2
2	0·05	0·2	0·05

11.   A random variable X takes the values 0 and 2 each with probability 0·5. Find $E(X)$, $E(X^2)$, $E(X^3)$, $E(X^4)$. Use the formula $Var(Y) = E(Y^2) - [E(Y)]^2$ to verify that (a) if $Y = 3X - 5$, $Var(Y) = 9 \, Var(X)$,

(b) if $Y = X^2 + X$, $Var(Y) \neq Var(X^2) + Var(X)$.

12.   The daily demand, x kilogrammes, for fresh fish at a certain fishmonger's shop is a continuous random variable with probability density function f, where f is given by $f(x) = (30 - x)/450, 0 \leqslant x \leqslant 30, f(x) = 0$, otherwise. The fishmonger receives a delivery of 20 kg of fresh fish each morning. He makes a profit of 40 pence on each kilogramme of fish sold on the day the fish is delivered; fish left unsold on the day it is

delivered is sold to a fertiliser manufacturer at a loss of 5 pence per kg. Show that on a day when x is less than 20, the fishmonger's profit is $(45x - 100)$ pence and that on a day when x is 20 or more, the fishmonger's profit is £8. Hence determine the fishmonger's expected daily profit from the sale of fresh fish.   (JMB)

13 A sample of four mice is to be chosen at random from a litter of ten mice, of which six are male and four are female. Let X denote the number of male mice in the sample. Calculate the values of $P(X = r)$ for $r = 0, 1, 2, 3, 4$. Hence find the mean and the standard deviation of X. Deduce the mean and the standard deviation of the number of female mice in the sample. Independently of the above, a sample of four mice is to be chosen at random from another litter of ten mice, of which four are male and six are female. Calculate the mean and the standard deviation of the total number of male mice in the combined sample of eight mice.   (W)

14. The joint probability distribution of two discrete random variables X and Y is displayed in the following table, the entries in the body of the table being $P(X = x, Y = y)$.

		x	
	0	1	2
0	0·1	0·1	0
y 1	0·1	0·2	0·1
2	0·1	0·2	0·1

(i) Find $E(X)$ and $E(Y)$. (ii) Determine the distribution of $Z = 2X - Y$ and verify that $E(Z) = 2E(X) - E(Y)$. (iii) Let (X_1, Y_1) and (X_2, Y_2) denote two independent observations of (X, Y). By using the distribution of Z, or otherwise, find the probability that

$$2(X_1 - X_2) = Y_1 - Y_2. \qquad \text{(W)}$$

15. On a piece-work operation a company pays a bonus to any employee who processes in excess of 300 kg of raw material in a day. The daily amounts processed by two employees A and B are independent and normally distributed, the mean and standard deviation of the amounts processed by A being 291 kg and 9 kg, respectively, and of the amounts processed by B being 282 kg and 12 kg, respectively. Calculate, to two significant figures in each case, (i) the proportion of days on which both A and B will earn the bonus, (ii) the probability that the combined daily amount processed by A and B will exceed 600 kg, (iii) the proportion of days on which the amount processed by B will exceed that processed by A.
                    (W)

16. The diameters of axles supplied by a factory have a mean value of 19·92 mm and a standard deviation of 0·05 mm. The inside diameters of bearings supplied by another factory have a mean of 20·04 mm and a standard deviation of 0·03 mm. What is the mean and standard deviation of the random variable defined to be the diameter of a bearing less the diameter of an axle? Assuming that both dimensions are normally distributed, what percentage of axles and bearings taken at random will not fit?   (O&C)

17. The time of arrival of a bus at a bus stop varies in a normal distribution with a mean of 09.00 a.m. and a standard deviation of 2 minutes. Independently a second bus departs from this stop at a time which varies in a normal distribution with a mean of 09.01 a.m. (i.e. one minute past 09.00 a.m.) and a standard deviation of 1 minute. Find the probability that (a) the first bus arrives before the second bus leaves; (b) this happens on 5 given consecutive days.   (O&C)

18. The weight of a large loaf of bread is a normal variable with mean 420 g and standard deviation 30 g. The weight of a small loaf of bread is a normal variable with mean 220 g and standard deviation 10 g. (i) Find the probability that 5 large loaves weigh more than 10 small loaves. (ii) Find the probability that the total weight of 5 large loaves and 10 small loaves lies between 4·25 kg and 4·4 kg.   (C)

19. The mass of a cheese biscuit has a normal distribution with mean 6 g and standard deviation 0·2 g. Determine the probability that (i) a collection of twenty-five cheese biscuits has a mass of more than 149 g, (ii) a collection of thirty cheese biscuits has a mass of less than 180 g, (iii) twenty-five times the mass of a cheese biscuit is less than 149 g. The mass of a ginger biscuit has a normal distribution with mean 10 g and standard deviation 0·3 g. Determine the probability that a collection of seven cheese biscuits has a mass greater than a collection of four ginger biscuits.   (C)

20. Four sprinters A, B, C and D each run 100 m. The times (in seconds) that they take may be regarded as independent observations from a normal distribution with mean 14 and standard deviation 0·2. The athlete E runs 400 m. The time (in seconds) that this athlete takes may be regarded as an observation from a normal distribution with mean 58 and standard deviation 1·0 and is independent of the times of the sprinters. Determine the probability that (i) the time taken by E is less than 3 seconds greater than the sum of the times taken by the four sprinters, (ii) the time taken by E is less than 4 times as great as the time taken by A. For the four sprinters A, B, C and D, find the probability that A is the fastest sprinter of the four. Find also the probability that C and D (in either order) are the two slowest sprinters.   (C)

21. P is a fixed point on the circumference of a circle, centre O, of radius r and Q is a point on the circumference such that $\angle POQ = \theta$, where θ is a random variable with a rectangular distribution in $[0, 2\pi]$. Find the mean and median values for the length of the shorter arc PQ. The length of the chord PQ is X. Find $E(X)$ and show that $\text{Var}(X) = 2r^2(1 - 8/\pi^2)$. Find also $P(X > r\sqrt{3})$.   (C)

22. X and Y are independent random variables with means and variances μ_x, σ_x^2 and μ_y, σ_y^2 respectively, and you may assume that for any such independent variables $E(XY) = E(X)E(Y)$. Find expressions for (i) the expectation of the area of a square of side X, (ii) the expectation and variance of the area of a rectangle of sides X and Y, (iii) the expectation of the volume of a cuboid with a square base of side X and with height Y.   (C)

23. Two independent random variables X and Y have Poisson distributions with means λ and μ respectively. Obtain an expression for $P(X = r, Y = n - r)$. Hence express $P(X + Y = n)$ as the sum of a series. Deduce that $X + Y$ has a Poisson distribution with mean $\lambda + \mu$.

24. Telephone calls reach a secretary independently and at random, internal ones at a mean rate of 2 in any 5 minute period, and external ones at a mean rate of 1 in any 5 minute period. Calculate the probability that there will be more than 2 calls in any period of 2 minutes. (O&C)

25. (a) Verify that if a random variable X has probability generating function $G_X(t)$, then $G_X(t) = E(t^X)$.
   (b) Two independent random variables X and Y have distributions $B(m, p)$ and $B(n, p)$ respectively. Write down expressions for $E(t^X)$ and $E(t^Y)$. Assuming that t^X and t^Y can be regarded as independent random variables, write down $E(t^X \times t^Y)$ and hence find the p.g.f. of the variable $Z = X + Y$. Deduce that Z has the distribution $B(m + n, p)$.

Exercise 16.7 (miscellaneous)

1. A random variable R takes the integer values $1, 2, \ldots, n$ each with probability $1/n$. Find the mean and variance of R. A pack of 15 cards bearing the numbers 1 to 15 is shuffled. Find the probability that the number on the top card is larger than that on the bottom card, giving reasons for your answer. If the sum of these two numbers is S, find (a) the probability that $S \leqslant 4$, (b) the expected value of S. (O&C)

2. The number X of radios sold per week by a certain shop is a binomially distributed random variable with $n = 10$ and $p = 0{\cdot}3$. The number Y of television sets sold per week by the same shop may be 0, 1 or 2 with $P(Y = 0) = 0{\cdot}6$, $P(Y = 1) = 0.3$, $P(Y = 2) = 0{\cdot}1$. The shopkeeper makes a profit of £2 on each radio sold and a profit of £20 on each television set sold. Find the shopkeeper's expected weekly profit from the sale of radios and television sets. (JMB)

3. (a) In a certain manufacturing process, it is known that approximately 10% of the items produced are defective. A quality control scheme is set up, by selecting 20 items out of a large batch, and rejecting the whole batch if 3 or more are defective. Find the probability that the batch is rejected.
   (b) Two boys, John and David, play a game with a die. The die will be thrown 4 times. David will give John £x if there is an odd number of sixes, otherwise John will give David £1. If the game is to be a fair one to both John and David, find the value of x. (SU)

4. The probability of there being X unusable matches in a full box of Surelite matches is given by $P(X = 0) = 8k$, $P(X = 1) = 5k$, $P(X = 2) = P(X = 3) = k$,

$P(X \geqslant 4) = 0$. Determine the constant k and the expectation and variance of X. Two full boxes of Surelite matches are chosen at random and the total number Y of unusable matches is determined. Calculate $P(Y > 4)$, and state the values of the expectation and variance of Y. (C)

5.   Fergus Lightfingers, an educated thief, has broken into a house and has come upon a large safe. Lying upon the table is a bunch of k similar keys, only one of which will open the safe. He considers two possible strategies: (i) randomly select keys, one at a time *without replacement*, until successful; (ii) randomly select keys, one at a time *with replacement*, until successful. Let N, a random variable, be the number of keys including the successful one tried by Fergus in order to open the safe. Derive the probability distribution of N for both strategies. Calculate the expected value of N in each case. Use your statistical judgment in order to select the strategy that Fergus should use. (You may assume that $\sum\limits_{n=1}^{\infty} nx^{n-1} = \dfrac{1}{(1-x)^2}$ for $|x| < 1$.)   (AEB 1978)

6.   A batsman's performance is described by the following probability distribution. For each ball that he receives he has probability $\frac{1}{2}$ of scoring no runs, probability $1/5$ of scoring one run and otherwise he is equally likely to score two runs, four runs, or to be bowled out. In the last case he receives no further balls.
(i)   Determine the probability that the batsman's total score is 0.
(ii) Given that the batsman is not bowled by a particular ball, calculate the expectation of his score from that ball.
(iii) Calculate the expectation of the number of balls that the batsman receives.
(iv) Deduce the expectation of the batsman's total score. (C)

7.   In a series of N independent trials the probability of success in any trial is constant and equal to p. Show that the probability of r successes is given by

$$P(r) = \binom{N}{r} p^r (1 - p)^{N-r}.$$

Find $P(3)$ if $N = 5$ and $p = 0.2$. Write a flow diagram for a program to print values of $P(r)$ if $N = 25$ and $p = 0.4$ for $r = 0(1)25$. (L)

8.   In a certain factory 70% of the microprocessors produced are found to be imperfect and have to be discarded. Find the probability that, in a randomly chosen sample of 5 microprocessors produced, the number of perfect specimens will be (i) 0, (ii) 1, (iii) 2, (iv) 3, (v) 4, (vi) 5. Verify that the probability of more than 3 perfect specimens is less than $1/30$. If a sample of 200 is taken from the same set of microprocessors, find the probability that there are at least 50 perfect specimens. (AEB 1980)

9.   Derive the mean and variance of the binomial distribution. Mass production of miniature hearing aids is a particularly difficult process and so the quality of these products is monitored carefully. Samples of size six are selected regularly and tested for correct operation. The number of defectives in each sample is

recorded. During one particular week 140 samples are taken and the distribution of the number of defectives per sample is given in the following table.

Number of defectives per samples (x)	0	1	2	3	4	5	6
Number of samples with x defectives (f)	27	36	39	22	10	4	2

Find the frequencies of the number of defectives per sample given by a binomial distribution having the same mean and total as the observed distribution.

(AEB 1978)

10. Show that the probability generating function for the binomial distribution arising from n independent trials, in each of which the probability of a success is p, is $(1 - p + pt)^n$. Show that the probability generating function for the number of trials needed to obtain a success is $pt/(1 - t + pt)$, and find the mean and variance of this distribution.

When a gun first fires at a target the probability of a hit is 1/5. Firing continues until the first hit, after which the gun is resighted and the probability of a hit becomes 2/5. Find the probability generating function for the number of shots required to obtain 2 hits and hence find the probability that fewer than 5 shots will be needed.

(O&C)

11. A random variable X takes values in the intervals 0 to 1 and 2 to 3, and has probability density function given by

$$f(x) = \begin{cases} 1 - x & (0 \leqslant x \leqslant 1), \\ x - a & (2 \leqslant x \leqslant 3), \\ 0 & \text{elsewhere.} \end{cases}$$

Determine (i) the value of a, (ii) the expectation, μ, of X, (iii) the variance of X, (iv) the (cumulative) distribution function $F(x)$, (v) the probability that $|X - \mu|$ exceeds 1.

(C)

12. The random variable X is the distance, in metres, that an inexperienced tight-rope walker has moved along a given tight-rope before falling off. It is given that

$$P(X > x) = 1 - x^3/64, \quad 0 \leqslant x \leqslant 4.$$

(i) Show that $E(X) = 3$. (ii) Find the standard deviation, σ, of X. (iii) Show that $P(|X - 3| < \sigma) = \frac{69}{80}\sqrt{\frac{3}{5}}$.

(C)

13. Find the mean and the variance of the distribution whose probability density function f is given by

$$\begin{aligned} f(x) &= x, & 0 \leqslant x < 1, \\ f(x) &= 2 - x, & 1 \leqslant x \leqslant 2, \\ f(x) &= 0, & \text{otherwise.} \end{aligned}$$

A rectangle is constructed with adjacent sides of lengths x cm and $(2 - x)$ cm where x is a random value from the above distribution. Find the probability that the area of the rectangle will exceed 0.75 cm^2. Also find the expected value of the area of the rectangle.   (JMB)

14. The operational lifetime in hundreds of hours of a battery-operated minical-culator may be regarded as a continuous random variable having probability density function

$$f(x) = cx(10 - x), \qquad 5 \leqslant x \leqslant 10,$$
$$f(x) = 0, \qquad\qquad \text{otherwise.}$$

(a) Find the value of c and of the expected operational lifetime of such a mini-calculator.
(b) The purchase price of such a minicalculator is £20 and its running cost (for batteries) amounts to 20 pence per hundred hours operation. Thus, the overall average cost in pence per hundred hours operation of a minicalculator whose operational lifetime is X hundred hours is given by $Y = 20 + (2000/X)$.
(i) Evaluate $E(Y)$, the expected overall average cost per hundred hours. (ii) Find the probability that the overall average cost per hundred hours will exceed £2.70.
                                                                    (W)

15. A random variable X has (cumulative) distribution function

$$F(x) = \begin{cases} 0 & (x \leqslant 0) \\ \tfrac{1}{4}x^2 & (0 \leqslant x \leqslant 1) \\ \alpha x + \beta & (1 \leqslant x \leqslant 2) \\ \tfrac{1}{4}(5 - x)(x - 1) & (2 \leqslant x \leqslant 3) \\ 1 & (3 \leqslant x) \end{cases}$$

Find (i) the values of the constants α and β, (ii) the probability that $1.5 \leqslant X \leqslant 2.5$, (iii) the probability density function $f(x)$. Sketch the graph of $f(x)$, and hence, or otherwise, deduce the mean of X. Determine also the variance of X.   (C)

16. A failure time, X, has density function $\lambda e^{-\lambda x}$ for $x \geqslant 0$, $\lambda > 0$. Find (a) the distribution function; (b) the mean and variance; (c) the median; (d) the time below which it is 95% certain that there will be no failure.   (O)

17. Henri de Lade regularly travels from his home in the suburbs to his office in Paris. He always tries to catch the same train, the 08.05 from his local station. He walks to the station from his home in such a way that his arrival times form a normal distribution with mean 08.00 hours and standard deviation 6 minutes. (i) Assuming that his train always leaves on time, what is the probability that on any given day Henri misses his train? (ii) If Henri visits his office in this way 5 days each week and if his arrival times at the station each day are independent, what is the probability that he misses his train once and only once in a given week?   (AEB 1980)

18. The score, S, gained by an expert rifleman with a single shot, is a random variable with the following probability distribution:

$$P(S = 8) = 0.01, \quad P(S = 9) = 0.29, \quad P(S = 10) = 0.70.$$

(i) Use a normal approximation to determine the probability that the rifleman obtains six or more scores of 8 in a series of 900 independent shots. (ii) Find the expectation and variance of *S*. (iii) Use a normal approximation to determine the probability that the rifleman scores less than 96 with ten independent shots.   (C)

19. The prices of houses on an estate agent's books are approximately normally distributed with a mean price of £18 000. Given that 90% of the houses are priced at less than £30 000, find the standard deviation of the house prices and the percentage of the houses with a price of less than £10 000. Find the mean price and the standard deviation of the prices when the price of each house is increased by (a) £2000, (b) 10%.   (L)

20. The weights of grade *A* oranges are normally distributed with mean 200 g and standard deviation 12 g. Determine, correct to 2 significant figures, the probability that (i) a grade *A* orange weighs more than 190 g but less than 210 g, (ii) a sample of 4 grade *A* oranges weighs more than 820 g. The weights of grade *B* oranges are normally distributed with mean 175 g and standard deviation 9 g. Determine, correct to 2 significant figures, the probability that (iii) a grade *B* orange weighs less than a grade *A* orange, (iv) a sample of 8 grade *B* oranges weighs more than a sample of 7 grade *A* oranges.   (C)

21. Mass-produced right circular cylindrical pipes have internal diameters that are normally distributed with a mean of 10 cm and a standard deviation of 0·4 cm. (i) Find the probability that a randomly chosen pipe will have an internal diameter greater than 10·3 cm. (ii) Find the expected number of pipes in a random sample of 100 pipes that have internal diameters in the range from 9·7 cm to 10·3 cm. (iii) Find the expected value of the internal cross-sectional area of a randomly chosen pipe; give your answer correct to three significant figures. (iv) Mass-produced pistons have diameters that are normally distributed with a mean of 9·9 cm and a standard deviation of 0·3 cm. Find the probability that a randomly selected piston will have a diameter less than the internal diameter of a randomly selected pipe.   (W)

22. Two gauges are used to test the thickness of manufactured metal sheets. Over a long period it is found that 1·25% of the sheets will pass through the smaller gauge of 1·4 mm while 95·4% will pass through the larger gauge of 1·6 mm. Assuming that the distribution of sheet thickness is normal, find its mean and standard deviation. At the next stage of manufacture 2 sheets are clamped together to make a thick plate. Find the mean and the standard deviation of the thickness of these plates. If a plate will pass through a gauge of 3·2 mm but not through one of 2·8 mm, find the probability that both the sheets of which it is composed will pass through the 1·6 mm gauge but not through the 1·4 mm gauge. Find also the size of a gauge which will allow 99·5% of these plates to pass through.   (O&C)

23. Next May, an ornithologist intends to trap one male cuckoo and one female cuckoo. The mass *M* of the male cuckoo may be regarded as being a normal random variable with mean 116 g and standard deviation 16 g. The mass *F* of the female cuckoo may be regarded as being independent of *M* and as being a normal random

variable with mean 106 g and standard deviation 12 g. Determine (i) the probability that the mass of the two birds together will be more than 230 g. (ii) the probability that the mass of the male will be more than the mass of the female. By considering $X = 9M - 16F$, or otherwise, determine the probability that the mass of the female will be less than nine-sixteenths of that of the male. Suppose that one of the two trapped birds escapes. Assuming that the remaining bird will be equally likely to be the male or the female, determine the probability that its mass will be more than 118 g.   (C)

24. (a) The number of accidents notified in a factory per day over a period of 200 days gave rise to the following table:

No. of accidents	0	1	2	3	4	5
No. of days	127	54	14	3	1	1

(i) Calculate the mean number of accidents per day. (ii) Assuming that this situation can be represented by a suitable Poisson distribution, calculate the corresponding frequencies.

(b) Of items produced by a machine, approximately 3% are defective, and these occur at random. What is the probability that, in a sample of 144 items, there will be at least two which are defective?   (SU)

25. Define a Poisson distribution giving the general probability formula; state the relationship between its mean and variance. The distribution of the number of vehicles observed passing under a motorway bridge in 100 successive intervals of 12 seconds, at a time when the traffic flow is 720 vehicles per hour, may be considered to be Poissonian. During how many of the intervals would one expect (i) no cars to have passed? (ii) 2 cars to have passed, (iii) more than 2 cars to have passed? Find the smallest value of N such that the probability of at most N cars in an interval is greater than 0·999.   (AEB 1978)

26. Each play of a one-armed bandit machine has probability 0·04 of yielding a win. It may be assumed that this probability applies independently for each play of the machine. (a) Find the probability that in ten plays of the machine there will be (i) at least two wins, (ii) exactly two wins. (b) For a sequence of n plays of the machine write down an expression for the probability that there will be no win. Hence find the smallest number of plays of the machine for there to be a probability of at least 0·95 of winning at least once. (c) Use an appropriate method to find an approximate value for the probability that there will be six or fewer wins in 80 plays of the machine.   (W)

27. Gnat larvae are distributed at random in pond water so that the number of larvae contained in a random sample of 10 cm³ of pond water may be regarded as a random variable having a Poisson distribution with mean 0·2. Ten independent random samples, each of 10 cm³, of pond water, are taken by a zoologist. Determine (correct to three significant figures) (i) the probability that none of the samples contain larvae, (ii) the probability that one sample contains a single larva and the remainder contain no larvae, (iii) the probability that one sample contains two or

more larvae and the remainder contain no larvae, (iv) the expectation of the total number of larvae contained in the ten samples, (v) the expectation of the number of samples containing no larvae. (C)

28. A prospector for gold examines exactly 800 pans of material every month. The contents of each pan may be assumed to be independent of the others with the probability of a pan containing gold being 0·005 for each pan. The prospector has a good month when 4 or more of the pans that he examines contain gold. Show that, to three significant figures, the probability that a randomly chosen month is a good month is 0·567. Determine the probability that (i) a randomly chosen period of four months contains more than two good months, (ii) a randomly chosen period of 24 months contains more than 12 good months. (C)

29. The number of organic particles suspended in a volume V cm^3 of a certain liquid follows a Poisson distribution with mean 0·1V. (a) Find the probabilities that a sample of 1 cm^3 of the liquid will contain (i) at least one organic particle, (ii) exactly one organic particle. (b) Use an appropriate approximate procedure to find the probability that a sample of 1000 cm^3 of the liquid will contain at least 90 organic particles. (c) The liquid is sold in vials, each vial containing 10 cm^3 of the liquid. The vials are dispatched for sale in boxes, each box containing 100 vials. Find the probability that a vial will contain at least one organic particle. Hence find the mean and the standard deviation of the number of vials per box of 100 vials that contain at least one organic particle. (W)

30. When a number is rounded off to its nearest integer value, the rounding off error X may be regarded as a random variable which is uniformly distributed over the interval $(-\frac{1}{2}, \frac{1}{2})$. Find the variance of X. If n numbers are rounded off to their nearest integer values and then summed, the total error in the sum is given by $Y = X_1 + X_2 + \ldots + X_n$, where $X_1, X_2, \ldots, X_n$ are the individual errors in the n numbers, which may be assumed to be independent and uniformly distributed over $(-\frac{1}{2}, \frac{1}{2})$. Write down the mean and the variance of Y in terms of n. Suppose n is large enough to justify approximating the distribution of Y by a normal distribution. Show that there is a probability in excess of 0·9 that Y will be numerically less than $\frac{1}{2}\sqrt{n}$. Find the largest integer value of n for which there is a probability of at least 0·6 that Y will be numerically less than 1·0. (W)

31. The joint probability function of two discrete random variables X and Y is given by $P(X = r, \ Y = s) = c|r + s|$ for $r = -1, 0, 1$ and $s = -2, -1, 0, 1, 2$,
        $P(X = r, Y = s) = 0$, otherwise.
(a) Show that (i) $c = 0·05$, (ii) $\text{Var}(Y) = 2 + \text{Var}(X)$.
(b) Evaluate $\text{Var}(Y - X)$. (W)

32. A continuous random variable X is distributed with probability density function $f(x) = 3x^{-4}$, $x \geqslant 1$, $f(x) = 0$, otherwise. Find (i) the cumulative distribution function of X, (ii) the mean and the variance of X. The random variable Y is defined by $Y = X^{-1}$. By first finding the cumulative distribution function of Y, or otherwise, determine the probability density function of Y. Verify that $E(X)E(Y)$

and $E(XY)$ are not equal and explain why they have different values in this
particular example. (W)

33. A continuous random variable X has probability density function

$$f(x) = 4x(1 - x^2), \qquad 0 \leqslant x \leqslant 1,$$
$$f(x) = 0, \qquad\qquad \text{otherwise.}$$

(i) Verify that $f(x)$ satisfies the requirements to be a probability density function.
(ii) Find the mean value of X. (iii) Find the cumulative distribution function of X.
(iv) If X denotes the area of a square of side Y find the probability density function
of Y and use it to verify that $E(Y^2) = E(X)$. (W)

34. The probability density function of a continuous random variable X is given by

$$f(x) = \tfrac{2}{3}x, \qquad 1 \leqslant x \leqslant 2,$$
$$f(x) = 0, \qquad \text{otherwise.}$$

(a) Find (i) $E(X^2)$, (ii) $E(X^4)$, (iii) the cumulative distribution function of X.
(b) Suppose X is the length of the side of a square. (i) Find the mean and the
variance of the area of the square. (ii) Show that the area of the square has a
uniform distribution over a certain interval which should be specified. (W)

Formulae for reference

Series

Sum of A.P. $= \frac{1}{2}n\{2a + (n-1)d\}$, sum of G.P. $= \dfrac{a(1-r^n)}{1-r}$

For $|r| < 1$, sum to infinity of G.P. $= a/(1-r)$

$$(a+b)^n = a^n + na^{n-1}b + \frac{n(n-1)}{2!}a^{n-2}b^2 + \cdots + \binom{n}{r}a^{n-r}b^r + \cdots + b^n,$$

where n is a positive integer.

$$\sum_1^n r = \tfrac{1}{2}n(n+1); \quad \sum_1^n r^2 = \tfrac{1}{6}n(n+1)(2n+1); \quad \sum_1^n r^3 = \tfrac{1}{4}n^2(n+1)^2$$

Trigonometry

$$\cos^2\theta + \sin^2\theta = 1; \quad 1 + \tan^2\theta = \sec^2\theta; \quad \cot^2\theta + 1 = \operatorname{cosec}^2\theta.$$

$\sin(A+B) = \sin A \cos B + \cos A \sin B$
$\sin(A-B) = \sin A \cos B - \cos A \sin B$

$\tan(A+B) = \dfrac{\tan A + \tan B}{1 - \tan A \tan B}$

$\cos(A+B) = \cos A \cos B - \sin A \sin B$
$\cos(A-B) = \cos A \cos B + \sin A \sin B$

$\tan(A-B) = \dfrac{\tan A - \tan B}{1 + \tan A \tan B}$

Area of $\triangle ABC = \tfrac{1}{2}bc \sin A$

$$\frac{a}{\sin A} = \frac{b}{\sin B} = \frac{c}{\sin C} = 2R, \quad a^2 = b^2 + c^2 - 2bc \cos A$$

Length of circular arc $= r\theta$, area of sector $= \tfrac{1}{2}r^2\theta$ (θ in radians)

Calculus

$$\frac{d}{dx}(uv) = u\frac{dv}{dx} + v\frac{du}{dx}, \qquad \frac{d}{dx}\left(\frac{u}{v}\right) = \frac{v\dfrac{du}{dx} - u\dfrac{dv}{dx}}{v^2}$$

y	$\sin x$	$\cos x$	$\tan x$	$\cot x$	$\sec x$	$\operatorname{cosec} x$
dy/dx	$\cos x$	$-\sin x$	$\sec^2 x$	$-\operatorname{cosec}^2 x$	$\sec x \tan x$	$-\operatorname{cosec} x \cot x$

$$\int u\frac{dv}{dx}\,dx = uv - \int v\frac{du}{dx}\,dx$$

$$\int e^{kx}\,dx = \frac{1}{k}e^{kx} + c, \qquad \int \frac{dx}{ax + b} = \frac{1}{a}\ln|ax + b| + c,$$

$$\int \frac{dx}{\sqrt{(a^2 - x^2)}} = \sin^{-1}\frac{x}{a} + c, \qquad \int \frac{dx}{a^2 + x^2} = \frac{1}{a}\tan^{-1}\frac{x}{a} + c.$$

Mechanics

Straight line motion with constant acceleration

$$v = u + at; \quad s = ut + \tfrac{1}{2}at^2; \quad s = \tfrac{1}{2}(u + v)t; \quad v^2 = u^2 + 2as.$$

Hooke's law: $T = \dfrac{\lambda}{l}x$; energy stored in string $= \dfrac{\lambda x^2}{2l}$.

Uniform body	Length, area or volume	Centre of mass
Triangular lamina, height h	$\tfrac{1}{2}h \times$ base	$\tfrac{1}{3}h$ from base
Circular arc, radius r, angle at centre 2α	$2r\alpha$	$\dfrac{r\sin\alpha}{\alpha}$ from centre
Sector of circle, radius r, angle at centre 2α	$r^2\alpha$	$\dfrac{2r\sin\alpha}{3\alpha}$ from centre
Solid cone or pyramid, height h	$\tfrac{1}{3}h \times$ base area	$\tfrac{1}{4}h$ from base
Solid hemisphere, radius r	$\tfrac{2}{3}\pi r^3$	$\tfrac{3}{8}r$ from centre
Hemispherical shell, radius r	$2\pi r^2$	$\tfrac{1}{2}r$ from centre

Probability

$$P(A \cup B) = P(A) + P(B) - P(A \cap B), \quad P(A \cap B) = P(A) \times P(B \mid A)$$

$$E(X) = \mu = \begin{cases} \sum x_r p(x_r) & X \text{ discrete} \\ \displaystyle\int_{-\infty}^{\infty} x f(x)\, dx & X \text{ continuous} \end{cases}$$

$$\mathrm{Var}(X) = \sigma^2 = \begin{cases} \sum (x_r - \mu)^2 p(x_r) = \sum x_r^2 p(x_r) - \mu^2, & X \text{ discrete} \\ \displaystyle\int_{-\infty}^{\infty} (x - \mu)^2 f(x)\, dx = \int_{-\infty}^{\infty} x^2 f(x)\, dx - \mu^2, & X \text{ continuous} \end{cases}$$

Binomial distribution $B(n, p)$:

$$P(X = r) = \binom{n}{r} p^r (1 - p)^{n-r} \quad (r = 0, 1, 2, \ldots, n)$$

$$E(X) = np, \quad \mathrm{Var}(X) = np(1 - p)$$

Poisson distribution, parameter μ:

$$P(X = r) = \frac{\mu^r}{r!} e^{-\mu} \quad (r = 0, 1, 2, \ldots)$$

$$E(X) = \mu, \quad \mathrm{Var}(X) = \mu$$

Properties of expectation and variance:

$$E[g(X)] = \begin{cases} \sum g(x_r) p(x_r) & X \text{ discrete} \\ \displaystyle\int_{-\infty}^{\infty} g(x) f(x)\, dx & X \text{ continuous} \end{cases}$$

$$E(aX + b) = aE(X) + b, \qquad E(aX + bY) = aE(X) + bE(Y)$$

$$\mathrm{Var}(X) = E(X^2) - [E(X)]^2, \quad \mathrm{Var}(aX + b) = a^2\, \mathrm{Var}(X)$$

For independent random variables $E(XY) = E(X)E(Y)$ and
$\mathrm{Var}(aX + bY) = a^2\, \mathrm{Var}(X) + b^2\, \mathrm{Var}(Y)$

$$\mathrm{Cov}(X, Y) = E[\{X - E(X)\}\{Y - E(Y)\}] = E(XY) - E(X)E(Y)$$

Statistics

Mean, $\bar{x} = \dfrac{1}{n} \sum x$

Variance, $\mathrm{var}(x) = \dfrac{1}{n} \sum (x - \bar{x})^2 = \dfrac{1}{n} \sum x^2 - \bar{x}^2$

Table 1   The normal distribution function $\Phi(z)$

z	·00	·01	·02	·03	·04	·05	·06	·07	·08	·09
0·0	·5000	·5040	·5080	·5120	·5160	·5199	·5239	·5279	·5319	·5359
01	·5398	·5438	·5478	·5517	·5557	·5596	·5636	·5675	·5714	·5753
0·2	·5793	·5832	·5871	·5910	·5948	·5987	·6026	·6064	·6103	·6141
0·3	·6179	·6217	·6255	·6293	·6331	·6368	·6406	·6443	·6480	·6517
0·4	·6554	·6591	·6628	·6664	·6700	·6736	·6772	·6808	·6844	·6879
0·5	·6915	·6950	·6985	·7019	·7054	·7088	·7123	·7157	·7190	·7224
0·6	·7257	·7291	·7324	·7357	·7389	·7422	·7454	·7486	·7517	·7549
0·7	·7580	·7611	·7642	·7673	·7704	·7734	·7764	·7794	·7823	·7852
0·8	·7881	·7910	·7939	·7967	·7995	·8023	·8051	·8078	·8106	·8133
0·9	·8159	·8186	·8212	·8238	·8264	·8289	·8315	·8340	·8365	·8389
1·0	·8413	·8438	·8461	·8485	·8508	·8531	·8554	·8577	·8599	·8621
1·1	·8643	·8665	·8686	·8708	·8729	·8749	·8770	·8790	·8810	·8830
1·2	·8849	·8869	·8888	·8907	·8925	·8944	·8962	·8980	·8997	·9015
1·3	·9032	·9049	·9066	·9082	·9099	·9115	·9131	·9147	·9162	·9177
1·4	·9192	·9207	·9222	·9236	·9251	·9265	·9279	·9292	·9306	·9319
1·5	·9332	·9345	·9357	·9370	·9382	·9394	·9406	·9418	·9429	·9441
1·6	·9452	·9463	·9474	·9484	·9495	·9505	·9515	·9525	·9535	·9545
1·7	·9554	·9564	·9573	·9582	·9591	·9599	·9608	·9616	·9625	·9633
1·8	·9641	·9649	·9656	·9664	·9671	·9678	·9686	·9693	·9699	·9706
1·9	·9713	·9719	·9726	·9732	·9738	·9744	·9750	·9756	·9761	·9767
2·0	·97725	·97778	·97831	·97882	·97932	·97982	·98030	·98077	·98124	·98169
2·1	·98214	·98257	·98300	·98341	·98382	·98422	·98461	·98500	·98537	·98574
2·2	·98610	·98645	·98679	·98713	·98745	·98778	·98809	·98840	·98870	·98899
2·3	·98928	·98956	·98983	·99010	·99036	·99061	·99086	·99111	·99134	·99158
2·4	·99180	·99202	·99224	·99245	·99266	·99286	·99305	·99324	·99343	·99361
2·5	·99379	·99396	·99413	·99430	·99446	·99461	·99477	·99492	·99506	·99520
2·6	·99534	·99547	·99560	·99573	·99585	·99598	·99609	·99621	·99632	·99643
2·7	·99653	·99664	·99674	·99683	·99693	·99702	·99711	·99720	·99728	·99736
2·8	·99744	·99752	·99760	·99767	·99774	·99781	·99788	·99795	·99801	·99807
2·9	·99813	·99819	·99825	·99831	·99836	·99841	·99846	·99851	·99856	·99861
3·0	·99865	·99869	·99874	·99878	·99882	·99886	·99889	·99893	·99896	·99900

z	3·1	3·2	3·3	3·4	3·5	3·6	3·7	3·8	3·9	4·0
Φ	·99903	·99931	·99952	·99966	·99977	·99984	·99989	·99993	·99995	·99997

Table 2 Percentage points of the normal distribution

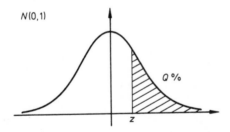

The shaded area represents $Q\%$ of the total distribution.

$$Q(z) = 100P(Z \geq z) = 100\{1 - \Phi(z)\}$$

Q	z	Q	z	Q	z
50	0·000	1·5	2·170	0·2	2·878
40	0·253	1·0	2·326	0·15	2·968
30	0·524	0·9	2·366	0·1	3·090
20	0·842	0·8	2·409	0·05	3·291
10	1·282	0·7	2·457	0·01	3·719
5	1·645	0·6	2·512	0·005	3·891
4	1·751	0·5	2·576	0·001	4·265
3	1·881	0·4	2·652	0·0005	4·417
2·5	1·960	0·3	2·748	0·0001	4·753
2	2·054	0·25	2·807	0·00005	4·892

Answers

Exercise 1.1 (p. 4)

1. (a) **PS**, (b) **AE**, (c) **AB**, (d) **0**, (e) **MR**, (f) **PS**.
2. (a) false, (b) true, (c) true, (d) true, (e) false, (f) true.
3. (a) true, (b) false, (c) true, (d) true, (e) false, (f) false.
4. (a) 3 km E, (b) 10 km N, (c) 1 km N 30° E, (d) 1 km S.
5. (a) $2\sqrt{2}$ km NE, (b) $2\sqrt{2}$ km NE, (c) $2\sqrt{2}$ km SE, (d) $2\sqrt{2}$ km NW.
6. (a) 1 km S 30° E, (b) $\sqrt{3}$ km S, (c) $\sqrt{3}$ km S 60° E, (d) $\sqrt{3}$ km N 60° E.
7. $\mathbf{p}+\mathbf{q}, \mathbf{q}-\mathbf{p}, \frac{1}{2}(\mathbf{p}+\mathbf{q}), \frac{1}{2}(\mathbf{q}-\mathbf{p})$.
8. $-\mathbf{a}, \mathbf{a}-\mathbf{b}, 2\mathbf{b}, 2\mathbf{b}-\mathbf{a}$.   9. $2\mathbf{a}+\mathbf{b}, \mathbf{a}+\mathbf{b}$.

Exercise 1.2 (pp. 7–8)

1. (a) $2\mathbf{b}$, (b) $-3\mathbf{a}$, (c) $2\mathbf{b}-6\mathbf{a}$, (d) $\mathbf{b}-\mathbf{a}$, (e) $\mathbf{a}$, (f) $2\mathbf{b}-\mathbf{a}$.
2. (a) $\mathbf{z}$, (b) $\mathbf{x}$, (c) $-\mathbf{x}$, (d) $\mathbf{z}$, (e) $-\mathbf{x}+\mathbf{z}$, (f) $\mathbf{y}-\mathbf{z}$.
3. (a) $-\mathbf{x}+\mathbf{y}$, (b) $\mathbf{x}+\mathbf{z}$, (c) $-\mathbf{x}+\mathbf{y}-\mathbf{z}$, (d) $2\mathbf{x}-\mathbf{y}$,
   (e) $2\mathbf{x}-\mathbf{y}+2\mathbf{z}$, (f) $-\mathbf{y}+2\mathbf{z}$.
4. (a) $5\mathbf{i}+3\mathbf{j}$, (b) $-\mathbf{i}+6\mathbf{j}$, (c) $-4\mathbf{i}+2\mathbf{j}$, (d) $2\mathbf{i}-\mathbf{j}$,
   (e) $3\mathbf{i}+4\mathbf{j}$, (f) $\mathbf{i}+5\mathbf{j}$.
5. (a) $-4\mathbf{i}+5\mathbf{j}+2\mathbf{k}$, (b) $3\mathbf{j}+2\mathbf{k}$, (c) $\mathbf{i}-\mathbf{j}+\mathbf{k}$, (d) $\mathbf{i}+2\mathbf{j}+3\mathbf{k}$.
6. (a) 13, (b) $\sqrt{5}$, (c) 10, (d) 3, (e) 7, (f) $5\sqrt{3}$.
7. (a) $\dfrac{8}{9}\mathbf{i} - \dfrac{4}{9}\mathbf{j} - \dfrac{1}{9}\mathbf{k}$, (b) $\dfrac{8}{9}\mathbf{i} - \dfrac{4}{9}\mathbf{j} - \dfrac{1}{9}\mathbf{k}$, (c) $-\dfrac{8}{9}\mathbf{i} + \dfrac{4}{9}\mathbf{j} + \dfrac{1}{9}\mathbf{k}$.
8. (a) 5, (b) 3, (c) 6.   9. (a) $\sqrt{29}$, (b) $\sqrt{29}$, (c) 5.
10 (a) $\dfrac{1}{\sqrt{2}}\mathbf{i} - \dfrac{1}{\sqrt{2}}\mathbf{j}$, (b) $-\dfrac{7}{9}\mathbf{i} + \dfrac{4}{9}\mathbf{j} + \dfrac{4}{9}\mathbf{k}$, (c) $\mathbf{i}$.
11. $\mathbf{b}-\mathbf{a}, \mathbf{b}-2\mathbf{a}; 2\mathbf{b}-2\mathbf{a}, 2\mathbf{b}-3\mathbf{a}, \mathbf{b}-2\mathbf{a}$.
12. $\mathbf{a}-\mathbf{b}, \mathbf{c}-\mathbf{b}, \mathbf{a}-2\mathbf{b}+\mathbf{c}; 2\mathbf{a}-3\mathbf{b}+2\mathbf{c}$.
13. (a) 6, $-\frac{1}{3}\mathbf{i}+\frac{2}{3}\mathbf{j}+\frac{2}{3}\mathbf{k}, 2\mathbf{i}-3\mathbf{j}+\mathbf{k}$,
    (b) 22, $\dfrac{6}{11}\mathbf{i} - \dfrac{9}{11}\mathbf{j} - \dfrac{2}{11}\mathbf{k}, -\mathbf{i}+4\mathbf{j}-2\mathbf{k}$,

(c) $\sqrt{10}, \dfrac{3}{\sqrt{10}}\mathbf{j} - \dfrac{1}{\sqrt{10}}\mathbf{k}, \mathbf{i} + \dfrac{1}{2}\mathbf{j} + \dfrac{5}{2}\mathbf{k},$

(d) $3\sqrt{6}, -\dfrac{2}{\sqrt{6}}\mathbf{i} - \dfrac{1}{\sqrt{6}}\mathbf{j} - \dfrac{1}{\sqrt{6}}\mathbf{k}, 2\mathbf{i} + \dfrac{5}{2}\mathbf{j} - \dfrac{1}{2}\mathbf{k}.$

14. 50.

Exercise 1.3 (pp. 8–9)

1. $\mathbf{a}+\mathbf{b}+\mathbf{c}, \mathbf{b}+\mathbf{c}-\mathbf{a}, \mathbf{a}+\mathbf{c}-\mathbf{b}, \mathbf{a}+\mathbf{b}-\mathbf{c}.$

2. (a) $\mathbf{b}-\mathbf{a}$,   (b) $3\mathbf{b}-2\mathbf{a}$,   (c) $3\mathbf{b}-\mathbf{c}$,   (d) $\mathbf{a}-\dfrac{3}{2}\mathbf{b}$,   (e) $-\mathbf{a}-\dfrac{1}{2}\mathbf{b}$,

    (f) $\mathbf{a}+\dfrac{3}{2}\mathbf{b}$.

3. (a) $2\sqrt{6}, 5\sqrt{2}, 20,$ (b) $\frac{2}{3}\mathbf{i}+\frac{1}{3}\mathbf{j}-\frac{2}{3}\mathbf{k}.$

4. (a) $6\sqrt{3},$ (b) $\dfrac{1}{9}\sqrt{3}\mathbf{i} - \dfrac{5}{9}\sqrt{3}\mathbf{j} + \dfrac{1}{9}\sqrt{3}\mathbf{k},$ (c) $-2\mathbf{j}+3\mathbf{k}.$

5. 1, 4.

7. (a) $-\dfrac{1}{\sqrt{2}}\mathbf{i} + \dfrac{1}{\sqrt{2}}\mathbf{j},$ (b) $\dfrac{3}{2}\sqrt{29}.$

8. $\mathbf{a}+k(2\mathbf{b}-\mathbf{a}); 3, 6\mathbf{b}-2\mathbf{a}.$

9. $\frac{1}{3}\mathbf{a}+\frac{1}{3}\mathbf{b}.$

10. $(4, -7, 8)$: 54 sq. units.

Exercise 2.3 (pp. 17–18)

1. (a) 13, 22·6°,   (b) 8·06, 60·3°,   (c) 9·85, 75·3°,
   (d) 14·5, 33°,   (e) 14·1, 37·3°,   (f) 8·86, 17·9°.

2. 133·5°.   3.   14·3 N at 81·4° to **G**.

4. 3·81 N, 15·7 N.   5.   9·43 N, N 12° W.

6. 13·0 N, S 37½° E.   7.   16·8 N, N 57·6° E.

8. (a) 5, N 53·1° E,   (b) 7, E,   (c) 6·71, S 63·4° E,   (d) 7·07, SW.

9. (a) 6,   (b) 17,   (c) 9·95.   10. 15·3 N.

11. $\sqrt{5}.$ 12. $4\sqrt{10}, 6\sqrt{5}.$

Exercise 2.4 (pp. 21–22)

1. (a) 15·3 N, 12·9 N,   (b) 1·46 N, 6·85 N,   (c) 7·05 N, 9·71 N.

2. (a) $-W, N\cos\alpha, T\sin(\alpha + \beta),$ (b) $-W\sin\alpha, 0, T\cos\beta,$
   (c) $W\cos\alpha, -N, -T\sin\beta.$

3. 11·5 N, N 15·5° W.   4.   29·3 N, N 15·8° W.

5. 344·7°.   6.   15·6, 76·6°.

7. 15·2 N, 66·8°.   8.   4·03 N.

9. (a) 48 N, 40 N, 46·2 N,   (b) 14 N, 30 N, 19·2 N,   (c) 134·2 N,
   (d) 20·6 N, 157·4°.

Exercise 2.5 (pp. 27–28)

1. 31·4 N, S 84·6° W.   2. 12·9, 6·39.
3. $5\sqrt{3}$.   4. 6, 8.
5. (a) $20\sqrt{3}$, (b) 20, (c) $10\sqrt{3}$.
6. $3\frac{1}{2}$ N, $12\frac{1}{2}$ N.   7. 1·87 N, 4·41 N.
8. 37·1 N, 19·7 N.
9. (a) $5W$, $5\sqrt{3}W$, (b) $10W/\sqrt{3}$, $10W/\sqrt{3}$.
10. 4·14 N, 43°.   11. $8W$. $6W$.
12. $10\sqrt{3}$ N, $20\sqrt{3}$ N at 30° to vertical.
13. (a) $\sqrt{5}W$, $2\sqrt{2}W$, (b) 63·4°, 45°.
14. $2\sqrt{2}W$, $\sqrt{5}W$, 26·6°.
15. (a) $5\cdot80W$, $4\cdot24W$, $5\cdot02W$, (b) $7\cdot07W$, $5\cdot39W$, $5\cdot39W$.

Exercise 2.6 (pp. 28–30)

1. 69·6°.   2. $\sqrt{10}$, 51·3°.
3. $0 \leqslant \theta \leqslant 36\cdot9°$.   4. $\sqrt{65}$, N 60·3° E.
6. $2\sqrt{5}$ N, $4\sqrt{2}$ N.   7. $5\sqrt{3}$ N.
8. 154·9°.   9. 6·32 N, S 71·6° W.
10. 15·4 N, S 37·6° W.   11. $2\sqrt{5}W$.
12. 12·9 N, 45·2 N.   13. 46·8°, 11·5 N.
15. (a) 25/8 N, (b) 2·62 N.   16. $W/\sqrt{3}$.
19. 16·6 N, 6·50 m.

Exercise 3.1 (pp. 34–35)

1. 13, $25\mathbf{i} + 6\mathbf{j}$.   2. $-2\mathbf{i} + 4\mathbf{j}$.
3. $24\mathbf{i} + 3\mathbf{j} + 12\mathbf{k}$; $8\mathbf{i} + \mathbf{j} + 4\mathbf{k}$, 11.
4. 85 m.   5. $5\mathbf{i} + 8\mathbf{j}$; 7.
6. $-3\mathbf{i} + 6\mathbf{j}$.
7. (a) 13, N 67·4° E, (b) $2\sqrt{10}$, N 71·6° E, (c) $4\sqrt{5}$, S 63·4° E,
    (d) $\sqrt{97}$, S 24° W.
8. (a) $13\cdot6\,\text{m s}^{-1}$, N 45·2° E, (b) 59·7 km/h, S 74·4° E,
    (c) $16\cdot4\,\text{m s}^{-1}$, N 6·6° W, (d) 98·0 km/h, S 48·8° E.
9. (a) $4\cdot18\,\text{m s}^{-1}$, (b) 30 m.
10. 14·6 km/h, N 87° E.

Exercise 3.2 (pp. 37–38)

1. 9·43 km/h from S 58° W.   2. 41·6 km/h, S 70·1° E.
3. 15, 126·9°.   4. $\mathbf{i} - 4\mathbf{j}$, $4\mathbf{i} + 5\mathbf{j}$.
5. 33·1 km/h, S 65° W.   6. $20\sqrt{3}$ km/h, N 60° W.
7. 10·7 km/h from N 37·5° W.   8. 90 km/h.
9. N 73·7° W; 2 min.   10. $2\cdot25\,\text{m s}^{-1}$; at 63·3° to the bank.
11. N 47·3° W; 1 h 30 min.   12. 76·8 km/h; S 64·8° W.

Exercise 3.3 (pp. 41–42)

1. 151·8°, 1 h 47 min.
2. $4\sqrt{3}$ km/h, N 11·4° E, 6 km/h.
3. 28·8 km/h on S 33·7° W; 8·32 km.
4. 5·57 m s^{-1} on 321·1°, 115 s.
5. 25 km/h on S 36·9° E; 60 m.
6. 576 km/h, N 51·3° E; 31·2 km; 10.04, N 38·7° W.
7. $500\sqrt{2}$ km/h, SE; 25·9 km.
8. (ii) $3\mathbf{i} + 4\mathbf{j}$.
9. 3, 500 s; $1000\sqrt{10}$ m.
10. N 73·1° E; 2·9 km.

Exercise 3.4 (pp. 43–45)

1. 203°; 157°; 10·4 knots E.   2. $6\sqrt{3}$ knots, 120°.
3. (i) due north, 100 s, 583 m,   (ii) N 36·9° W, 125 s, 500 m.
4. 95·2 s; 92·3 s; 125 s.   5. 032·8°, 237·2°; 64·4 min.
6. 65 km h^{-1} from N 32·6° E; N 5·8° E, S 54·2° W.
7. 97 min, 69 min, 137 min.   8. 14.36, N 45·2° W; 13.42.
9. N; 26·8 min.
10. (a) 3 m s^{-1},   (b) $\mathbf{i} + 3\mathbf{j}$; $\sqrt{181}$ m s^{-1}.
11. (i) 50 km h^{-1} towards N 73·7° W,   (ii) 112 m,   (iii) 31·36 m, 107·52 m.
12. 42 km/h, S 8·2° E; $13.06\frac{1}{4}$, 8·66 km; 13.25.
13. N 41·4° E, 45 min; N 48·2° E, 7·45 km.
14. 18·0 km/h; 13.12; 4·16 km/h.

Exercise 4.1 (pp. 49–50)

1. (a) $9t^2 - 5$, $18t$,   (b) $4t + 3$, 4.
2. (a) $6t^2 + 7$, $2t^3 + 7t$,   (b) $20 - 10t$, $5 + 20t - 5t^2$,
   (c) $8t^3 - 12t^2 + 4$, $2t^4 - 4t^3 + 4t - 2$.
3. 0, 3; 4.   4. 24; 32 m.
5. 36 m, 9 m s^{-1}.   6. 1 s, 9 s; 16 m s^{-1}.
7. 29, 52 m.   8. -12 m s^{-1}, 16 m; 48 m.
9. (a) $2\frac{1}{2}$,   (b) 5 m.
10. (a) -15 m s^{-1}, -4 m s^{-2},   (b) 0 s, 5 s,   (c) 72 m.
11. (a) $9t - 3t^2$, $\frac{9}{2}t^2 - t^3$,   (b) 27 m.
12. (a) 0 s, 6 s,   (b) 32 m,   (c) 64 m,   (d) 36 m s^{-1}.
13. (a) 1 s, 4 s,   (b) 10 m,   (c) $18\frac{1}{2}$ m,   (d) 7 m s^{-1}.
14. (a) 0 s, $2\frac{1}{4}$ s, 6 s,   (b) $60\frac{3}{4}$ m,   (c) $171\frac{1}{2}$ m,   (d) 90 m s^{-1}.
15. $5\frac{1}{3}$, 10, $14\frac{2}{3}$; 6 m s^{-1}.
16. (a) 27 m,   (b) 16 m s^{-1},   (c) 12 m s^{-2}.

Exercise 4.2 (pp. 54–56)

1. 11, 24.
2. 12, 2.
3. 16, −3.
4. −7, −4.
5. $\frac{1}{2}$, 10.
6. 0, 24.
7. 10, 10 or 15, −10.
8. 1, 60.
9. −2$\frac{1}{2}$, 2.
10. 0, 1$\frac{1}{2}$.
11. $\frac{1}{4}$ km.
12. 1/48.
13. 31$\frac{1}{4}$ m, 5 s.
14. 14 m s^{-1}, 8 m.
15. 5 m s^{-1}, 10 s.
16. 34 m, 20 m s^{-1}.
17. 2$\frac{1}{2}$ m s^{-2}, 1 s.
18. 40 m s^{-1}, 80 m.
19. 1750 m; 48, 100, 32, 45.
20. 30, 28·8 km.
21. 12 min.
22. 2, 10·05.
23. 20.
24. 1 min, 900 m.
25. 3 s, 15 m.
26. 20 m.

Exercise 4.3 (pp. 60–62)

1. 1$\frac{1}{4}$ s; 2$\frac{1}{2}$ s, 53·0 m.
2. 60 m; 35·8 m s^{-1} at 33·2° to horizontal.
3. 50 m; $y = 2x − x^2/50$.
4. 5, 2·5; 30·8 at 54·2° to the horizontal.
5. 20 m s^{-1}, 19·6 m s^{-1}; 44·1 m.
6. 11·2 m s^{-1}; 3·2 m.   8.   4·5 km; 26·6°
9. $y = \dfrac{5}{3}x − \dfrac{49x^2}{90u^2}$; 2·1, 13·5 m.   10. 14, 36·9°.
11. 28; 15° < α < 75°.   12. $6u^2/g$; $2u/g$, $4u/g$.
13. $u/(g \sin \alpha)$.   14. $2V \sin \theta (U + V \cos \theta)/g$.
15. $12V^2/13g$; $2V/(g\sqrt{13})$.
16. $\sqrt{(V^2 − 2gh)}$, $2\sqrt{(V^2 \sin^2 \theta − 2gh)}/g$; 60°.
18. 63·4°, 26·6°; 4 : 5.   19. 81$\frac{2}{3}$; 69·3 m s^{-1}.
20. $2u_2/g$.

Exercise 4.4 (p. 64)

1. (a) $3\mathbf{i} + 6t^2\mathbf{k}$, $12t\mathbf{k}$,   (b) $2t\mathbf{i} + 4t^3\mathbf{j} − 6\mathbf{k}$, $2\mathbf{i} + 12t^2\mathbf{j}$.
2. −3 m s^{-1}, 13 m s^{-1}.
3. $3(t−2)\mathbf{i} + 2(t^2 − 1)\mathbf{j} + t(1 − t^2)\mathbf{k}$.
4. $(3t^2 + 1)\mathbf{i} + \mathbf{j} − 4t\mathbf{k}$, $(t^3 + t)\mathbf{i} + (t + 3)\mathbf{j} − 2t^2\mathbf{k}$.
5. $3\mathbf{i} + (2 − 10t)\mathbf{j}$, $3t\mathbf{i} + (2t − 5t^2)\mathbf{j}$.
6. 31$\frac{1}{4}$ m, 200 m, 5 s.
7. $10\mathbf{i} + (10\sqrt{3} − 10t)\mathbf{j}$, $10t\mathbf{i} + (10\sqrt{3}t − 5t^2)\mathbf{j}$.
8. 48 m, 24 m; 32·0 m s^{-1}.

Exercise 4.5 (pp. 65–67)

1. 25$\frac{11}{27}$ m, 20 m s^{-1}; $t < 2\frac{1}{6}$.
2. 343$\frac{3}{4}$ m; 5 s; 49 m s^{-2}; 108 m s^{-1}.

3. (a) 7,   (b) $2t(35 + 3t - 2t^2)$,   (c) $0 < t < 5$.
6. (i) $b + \frac{1}{2}ft^2 - ut$,   (ii) $b + (V - u)t - V^2/2f$;
    $b - u^2/2f$; car overtakes bus after time $(2fb - V^2)/2f(u - V)$.
7. (a) U/g,   (b) $2U/g$.
8. 18·3 m, 61·6 m, 3·83 s.
9. (i) 40 m,   (ii) 10 m,   (iii) $20 \, \text{m s}^{-1}$ at 45° to horizontal,
    (iv) $2\sqrt{2}$ s; $(20 + 5\sqrt{2}, 8\frac{3}{4})$, $(20 - 5\sqrt{2}, 8\frac{3}{4})$.
10. 40, 45°; 15°.
11. $D^2 \tan^2 \theta - 20D \tan \theta + 20h + D^2 = 0$.
15. $\frac{3}{5}\mathbf{i} - \frac{4}{5}\mathbf{k}$; 2 s, $2\mathbf{j} + 16\mathbf{k}$.
16. 5, 25.

Exercise 5.1 (pp. 71–72)

1. 48 N.   2. $0·2 \, \text{m s}^{-2}$.
3. 12 kg.   4. 40 N.
5. $2\mathbf{i} - 5\mathbf{j}$.   6. $12\mathbf{i} + 4\mathbf{j}$.
7. $6·4 \, \text{m s}^{-2}$ at 17·4° to the 9 N force.
8. 84·9°.   9. $6·25 \, \text{m s}^{-2}$, S 53·1° E.
10. $2·05 \, \text{m s}^{-2}$, N 61·6° W.   11. 1·8 s.
12. 15 N.   13. 10 kg.
14. $10 \, \text{m s}^{-1}$.   15. 8, 540 m.
16. $20 \, \text{m s}^{-1}$; $6\frac{2}{3}$, 10.

Exercise 5.2 (pp. 74–75)

1. (a) 98 N,   (b) 14·7 N,   (c) 2·45 N.
2. $6·2 \, \text{m s}^{-2}$.   3. 62·4 N.
4. (a) 440 N,   (b) 392 N,   (c) 360 N.
5. (a) decelerating at $1·2 \, \text{m s}^{-2}$,   (b) accelerating at $0·8 \, \text{m s}^{-2}$,
    (c) moving with uniform speed.
6. 33·1 N, 280 N.   7. $1·71 \, \text{m s}^{-2}$, 87 N.
8. 5 N, 11·5°.   9. $8·49 \, \text{m s}^{-2}$, 24·5 N.
10. 2·44 s.   11. (a) 8·28 N,   (b) 14·3 N.
12. $2·12 \, \text{m s}^{-2}$, 55·4 N.

Exercise 5.3 (pp. 79–81)

1. (a) $3 \, \text{m s}^{-2}$,   (b) 350 N.
2. (a) 240 N, 80 N,   (b) 2640 N, 880 N.
3. 6000 N, 1200 N, 600 N; $0·25 \, \text{m s}^{-2}$, 7200 N, 3600 N.
4. $4·2 \, \text{m s}^{-2}$, 28 N.   5. $4·9 \, \text{m s}^{-2}$, 44·1 N.
6. $\dfrac{M - m}{M + m}g, \dfrac{2Mm}{M + m}g$.   7. $24mg/5$.
8. $2·45 \, \text{m s}^{-2}$, 8·82 N.
9. 0·392 m; $mg/\sqrt{2} \, \text{N} = 6·93m \, \text{N}$ at 45° to vertical.
10. $3·92 \, \text{m s}^{-2}$, 17·64 N; 30·6 N at 30° to vertical.

11. $m \sin \alpha > M$.   12. 0·5 s.

13. 3·75 m.

14. 0·98 m s^{-2}, 34·3 N; 1·4 m s^{-1}; 1$\frac{1}{6}$ m.

Exercise 5.4 (pp. 83–84)

1. 7·84 m s^{-2}, upwards; 17·64 N.
2. 2·8 m s^{-2}, downwards; 28 N.
3. 6·2 m s^{-2} upwards, 5·8 m s^{-2} downwards; 32 N, 16 N.
4. 1·96 m s^{-2} down, 5·88 m s^{-2} up; 31·4 N, 15·7 N.
5. 1·51 m s^{-2} down, 2·26 m s^{-2} down; 41·5 N, 15·1 N.
6. 1·89 m s^{-2}.   7. 49 $\sin \alpha/(4 + \sin^2 \alpha)$ m s^{-1}.
8. 0·8 m s^{-2} vertically, 3·2 m s^{-2} down plane.

Exercise 5.5 (pp. 84–87)

1. 3·70 kg.   2. 24·1, 242·5°.
3. 1250, 40 s.   4. $10\mathbf{i} + 20\mathbf{j}$, $92\mathbf{i} + 10\mathbf{j}$.
5. 9·16 N.   6. (a) 791 N, (b) 651 N.
7. 2 m s^{-1}; 1980 N, 1960 N, 1920 N.
8. (a) 784 N, 0°, (b) 809 N, 14·3°.
9. $\sqrt{(2gx \sin \alpha)}$.   10. 12·5 m.
11. (a) 2, (b) 56·4°   12. 1071 N, 315 N.
13. 3·15 m.   14. (a) 2$\frac{1}{3}$ m s^{-1}, (b) 1$\frac{13}{15}$ m s^{-1}.
15. 1·70 m s^{-2}, 83·4 N at 25° to the vertical.
16. 47·04 N, 23·52 N; 2·06 m.
17. 30°; mg$\sqrt{3}$ at 30° to vertical; $\dfrac{3}{2}$mg, $\dfrac{1}{4}$g, $\dfrac{3\sqrt{3}}{2}$mg at 30° to vertical.
18. $\dfrac{2}{3}$mg.   19. 48 N, 24 N.
20. 525 N, 11·5°.

Exercise 6.1 (p. 90)

1. (a) 10 N, (b) 0, (c) 5 N.
2. (a) 5 N down plane, (b) 0, (c) 5 N up plane.
3. (a) 3, (b) 12$\sqrt{2}/5 = 3·39$, (c) 4$\sqrt{2} = 5·66$.
4. $\tan 25° = 0·466$.   5. (a) 3·98, (b) 2·45.
6. 0·733 m s^{-2}.   7. 5·75 m s^{-2}.
8. 3·20 m s^{-2}.   9. 0·147.
10. 1·34 m s^{-2}.

Exercise 6.2 (pp. 93–94)

1. 9·8 N, $\frac{1}{4}$.   2. 1·5 s.
3. (a) 6·21 m s^{-2}, (b) 2·79 m s^{-2}.   4. 7·38.

5. (a) $\tan \alpha$, (b) $(g \sin \alpha - a)/g \cos \alpha$.
6. $23 \cdot 04 \, \text{m s}^{-2}, 61 \cdot 0 \, \text{N}$.   7. $36 \cdot 3 \, \text{N}, 0 \cdot 48$.
8. $\mu < 1, 5/13$.   9. $4 \cdot 2 \, \text{m s}^{-2}, 22 \cdot 4 \, \text{N}$.
10. $\frac{2}{3}$; $34 \cdot 6 \, \text{N}$ at $45°$ to horizontal.
11. $1 \cdot 94 \, \text{m s}^{-2}$ up the plane, $39 \cdot 3 \, \text{N}$.
12. (a) $1 \cdot 86 \, \text{m s}^{-2}$ up the plane, (b) $1 \cdot 25 \, \text{m s}^{-2}$ down the plane.

Exercise 6.3 (pp. 95–96)

1. $14°$.   2. (a) $12 \cdot 5 \, \text{N}$, (b) $5 \cdot 47 \, \text{N}$.

3. (a) $\mu \geqslant \frac{1}{3}$, (b) $\mu \geqslant \frac{1}{5}\sqrt{3}$, (c) $\mu \geqslant \frac{1}{7}\sqrt{3}$.

5. $\frac{1}{6}\sqrt{3}$.   6. $2 \cdot 87 \leqslant P \leqslant 4 \cdot 79$.

7. (a) 16, (b) $24\frac{8}{13}$.   8. $M \geqslant 3m$.

Exercise 6.4 (p. 98)

1. (a) 6, (b) $5 \cdot 66$, (c) $9 \cdot 74$.
2. $12 \cdot 5 \, \text{N}, 36 \cdot 9°$.
3. $1 \cdot 94 \, \text{N}$ at $14°$ to horizontal.
4. $W \sin \lambda$ at λ to horizontal.
5. (a) $1 \cdot 20 \, \text{N}$ at $18 \cdot 4°$ to plane, i.e. at $11 \cdot 6°$ above horizontal,
    (b) $4 \cdot 49 \, \text{N}$ at $18 \cdot 4°$ to plane, i.e. at $48 \cdot 4°$ above horizontal.
6. (a) $W \sin (\lambda - \alpha)$ at λ to plane. (b) $W \sin (\lambda + \alpha)$ at λ to plane.

Exercise 6.5 (pp. 101–102)

1. $5 \, \text{N}$.   2. $9 \, \text{N}$.
3. $2 \cdot 4 \, \text{N}$.   4. $1 \cdot 2 \, \text{m}$.
5. $26 \cdot 6°, a(3 + \sqrt{5})$.   6. $6 \cdot 2 \, \text{m s}^{-2}$.
7. $1 \cdot 8 \, \text{m}$.   8. $2 \cdot 5 W/8$.
9. $4 \cdot 8 \, \text{N}$ in $PA, 2 \, \text{N}$ in $PB; 0 \cdot 9 \, \text{m}$.
10. 20.
11. $18 \, \text{N}; 4 \cdot 5 \, \text{cm}, 7 \cdot 5 \, \text{cm}, 12 \, \text{cm}$.
12. $1 \cdot 25 \, \text{m}, 1 \cdot 75 \, \text{m}$.

Exercise 6.6 (pp. 102–106)

1. (a) $140 \, \text{N}$, (b) $135 \, \text{N}$.   2. $\frac{1}{2}W$.
3. (a) $15 \cdot 7$, (b) $7 \cdot 84; 3 \cdot 92 \, \text{m s}^{-2}$.

4. $65, \frac{1}{2}$.   5. (i) $\dfrac{\mu W}{1 + 2\mu^2}$, (ii) $\dfrac{3\mu W}{\sqrt{(1 + 4\mu^2)}}$.

8. $99 \cdot 0, 33 \cdot 0 \, \text{N}$.
9. (a) $4 \cdot 5 \, \text{m s}^{-2}; 42 \, \text{N}, 24 \, \text{N}$, (b) $2 \, \text{m s}^{-2}; 42 \, \text{N}, 24 \, \text{N}$.

11. (a) $\mu < \dfrac{1}{8}$, (b) $\mu < \dfrac{1}{8}$.   12. (ii) $\dfrac{1}{8}g(2-\sqrt{3})$, $\dfrac{1}{8}Mg(6+\sqrt{3})$.

14. $14°$, $2\cdot60\,\mathrm{m\,s^{-2}}$.

15. (a) $0\cdot09\,\mathrm{N}$ at $1\cdot3°$ to horizontal,
    (b) $1\cdot45\,\mathrm{N}$ at $21\cdot3°$ to horizontal.

16. $\lambda(2\sec\theta - 1)$, $W + \lambda(2 - \cos\theta)$, $\lambda(2\tan\theta - \sin\theta)$.

17. (i) $5mg$, $4\sqrt{2}mg$, (ii) $53\cdot1°$, $45°$.

Exercise 7.1 (pp. 109–110)

1. $0, 0, Ps, -Fs$.

2. $-Wx, Px$.

3. $Ws\sin\alpha, 0$; Fs.

4. $Ts, 0$; $Fs, Ws\sin\alpha$.

5. $105\,\mathrm{J}$, $15\,\mathrm{m}$.

6. $-9000\,\mathrm{J}$, $450\,\mathrm{N}$.

7. $45\,\mathrm{kN}$.

8. $770\,\mathrm{N}$.

9. $62\cdot5\,\mathrm{J}$.

10. $300\,\mathrm{J}$; $5/8$.

11. $200\,\mathrm{J}$; 45.

12. $270\,\mathrm{J}$, $180\,\mathrm{J}$; $6\,\mathrm{m\,s^{-1}}$.

Exercise 7.2 (pp. 113–114)

1. $10\cdot5\,\mathrm{m\,s^{-1}}$.

2. (a) $21\cdot6\,\mathrm{m}$ above A,   (b) $40\,\mathrm{m}$ below A.

3. $v^2/2g$.

4. $4\cdot05\,\mathrm{m}$.

5. $5\,\mathrm{m\,s^{-1}}$.

6. $14\,\mathrm{m\,s^{-1}}$.

7. $2\cdot8\,\mathrm{m\,s^{-1}}$.

8. $214\,\mathrm{J}$.

9. $147\,\mathrm{J}$; $7\,\mathrm{m}$.

10. $(M+m)v^2/2(M-m)g$.

11. $1\cdot4\,\mathrm{m\,s^{-1}}$.

12. $10\,\mathrm{m}$.

13. $8\,\mathrm{m}$.

14. (a) $3\cdot5\,\mathrm{m\,s^{-1}}$,   (b) $2\cdot6\,\mathrm{m}$.

15. $19\cdot6\,\mathrm{J}$; $\tfrac{1}{4}$.

Exercise 7.3 (pp. 117–118)

1. (a) $0\cdot2\,\mathrm{J}$,   (b) $5\,\mathrm{J}$.

2. (a) $0\cdot25\,\mathrm{J}$,   (b) $9\,\mathrm{J}$.

3. $2\cdot25\,\mathrm{J}$.

4. $15\,\mathrm{N}$.

5. $7\cdot5\,\mathrm{J}$.

6. $12k, 3ka$.

7. $0\cdot56\,\mathrm{m}$.

8. $2\,\mathrm{m\,s^{-1}}$.

9. $\tfrac{1}{2}\sqrt{(ag)}$.

10. $4\,\mathrm{m}$.

11. $7\,\mathrm{m\,s^{-1}}$.

12. $60\,\mathrm{cm}$; $1\cdot4\,\mathrm{m\,s^{-1}}$.

13. $2\cdot5\,\mathrm{N}$.

14. $1\cdot2\,\mathrm{m}$; (a) $\dfrac{7}{5}\sqrt{3}$,   (b) $0\cdot7\,\mathrm{m}$.

Exercise 7.4 (pp. 121–122)

1. $392\,\mathrm{W}$.

2. $40\,\mathrm{s}$.

3. $400\,\mathrm{W}$.

4. $500\,\mathrm{kg}$.

5. $28\cdot8\,\mathrm{kW}$.

6. $6\cdot8\,\mathrm{kW}$.

7. $335\,\mathrm{W}$.

8. $72\,\mathrm{kN}$.

9. $1\cdot2\,\mathrm{kW}$; $0\cdot1\,\mathrm{m\,s^{-2}}$.

10. (a) 12 kW,　(b) 14·7 kW,　(c) 3 kW.
11. 21 kW.　　　　　　　　　　12. 30 m s^{-1}.
13. (a) 33$\frac{1}{3}$ kW,　(b) 52 kW,　(c) 14$\frac{2}{3}$ kW.
14. 6$\frac{5}{6}$ kN, 13$\frac{1}{3}$ m s^{-1}.
15. (a) 96 km/h,　(b) 36 km/h; 1/6 m/s^2.
16. 0·98 m s^{-2}.　　　　　　　17. 2, 1·4 m/s^2.
18. 20 kW; (i) 6·93 kW,　(ii) 0·201 m s^{-2}.

Exercise 7.5 (pp. 122–127)

1. 1/8.　　　　　　　　　　2. 30/49.
3. 10 N.　　　　　　　　　　4. 53·1°.
5. 68·6 J, 7/12.　　　　　　　6. 2·4 m.
7. 2·8 m s^{-1}.　　　　　　　8. 7 m s^{-1}, 2·4 m.

9. 3, 2·57 m s^{-1}.　　　　　　10. $\frac{3}{2}\sqrt{(ga)}$, 2a.

11. 30 mg/19.
13. (i) 2$\sqrt{(2gb)}$,　(ii) $\sqrt{(10gb)}$,　(iii) 26·6°,　(iv) 4b; $-\frac{1}{2}c$.
14. (i) 2b − l,　(ii) b^2/l.　　　　15. 4·5 × 10^4 N, 450 kW; 24 m s^{-1}.
16. 1800 N, 804$\frac{1}{6}$ N.　　　　　17. 320 kW.
18. 113 kg, 22·3 kW.
19. (i) 19$\frac{7}{11}$ km h^{-1},　(ii) 0·53 m s^{-2}; 60.
20. 500 N, 20 m/s.
21. (a) $(1000H − MVg \sin \alpha)/MV$,　(b) $(1000H + MVg \sin \alpha)/MV$;
　　$1000H/3MVg$, 3V/4.
22. 400 kW, 15 m/s, 20 000 N.　　23. 0·395 m s^{-2}.
24. (i) 0·25 m/s,　(ii) 22·5 m/s; 233$\frac{1}{3}$ m, 15$\frac{5}{9}$ s.
25. 1200 N; 1/40; 10·5 kW.
26. $R + mg \sin \alpha + 2mU^2 \sin \alpha/h$, $2U(R + mg \sin \alpha + 2mU^2 \sin \alpha/h)$,
　　$mgh + 2mU^2 + Rh \operatorname{cosec} \alpha$.

Exercise 8.1 (pp. 130–131)

1. $\frac{3\pi}{2}$ rad s^{-1}, 0·42 m s^{-1}.　　　2. 4 rad s^{-1}.

3. 7·3 × 10^{-5} rad s^{-1}, 470 m s^{-1}.　　4. 2 × 10^{-7} rad s^{-1}, 30 km/s.
5. 57 cm.

6. (a) $\frac{1}{1+t^2}$,　(b) $\frac{6}{9+4t^2}$,　(c) $\frac{2t}{1+t^4}$.

7. (a) $r(\cos \omega t\mathbf{i} + \sin \omega t\mathbf{j})$,　(b) $r(-\sin \omega t\mathbf{i} + \cos \omega t\mathbf{j})$.
8. (a) 2 rad s^{-1}, 6 m s^{-1},　(b) 1 rad s^{-1}, 5 m s^{-1},
　　(c) -2π rad s^{-1}, 2π m s^{-1},　(d) k rad s^{-1}, ak m s^{-1}.
9. $a(\cos \omega t\mathbf{i} + \sin \omega t\mathbf{j})$, $a(-\sin \omega t\mathbf{i} + \cos \omega t\mathbf{j})$,
　　$a\omega(\sin \omega t − \cos \omega t)\mathbf{i} − a\omega(\cos \omega t + \sin \omega t)\mathbf{j}$.

Exercise 8.2 (pp. 133–134)

1. (a) $9\,\mathrm{m\,s^{-2}}$, (b) $4\,\mathrm{m\,s^{-2}}$, (c) $20\,\mathrm{m\,s^{-2}}$, (d) $63\cdot2\,\mathrm{m\,s^{-2}}$.
2. $22\frac{1}{2}\,\mathrm{N}$.   3. $12\,\mathrm{N}$.
4. $375\,\mathrm{N}$, $49\,\mathrm{N}$.   5. $6\,\mathrm{m\,s^{-1}}$.
6. $0\cdot4$.   7. $0\cdot7\,\mathrm{m}$.
8. $1\cdot75\,\mathrm{rad\,s^{-1}}$.

Exercise 8.3 (pp. 137–139)

1. $49\,\mathrm{N}$, $2\cdot8\,\mathrm{m\,s^{-1}}$.   2. $127\cdot4\,\mathrm{N}$, $3\,\mathrm{m}$.
3. $mg\cosec\theta$; $rg\cot\theta$.   4. $2\cdot45\,\mathrm{m}$.
5. $3\cdot15\,\mathrm{m\,s^{-1}}$.   6. $\sqrt{(3ag)}$.
7. $5m(8u^2+9ag)/72a$ in AP, $5m(8u^2-9ag)/72a$ in BP.
8. $17\frac{1}{2}\,\mathrm{m\,s^{-1}}$.   9. $17\cdot7°$.
10. $35\,\mathrm{m\,s^{-1}}$, $5\sqrt{7}\,\mathrm{m\,s^{-1}}$.   11. $7\sqrt{5}\,\mathrm{m\,s^{-1}}$; $12\cdot7°$.

Exercise 8.4 (pp. 139–142)

1. $10\pi/9\,\mathrm{rad\,s^{-1}}$, $0\cdot42\,\mathrm{m\,s^{-1}}$. 2. $25/\pi$, 50.
3. $-6/(5t^2-6t+9)$.   4. $6\,\mathrm{m\,s^{-1}}\,\mathrm{S}\,30°\,\mathrm{W}$.
5. $5/36 \leqslant \mu < 5/9$.   6. $60\,\mathrm{N}$, $75\,\mathrm{N}$.
7. (i) $60°$, (ii) $2mg$, (iii) $\pi\sqrt{(2a/g)}\,\mathrm{s}$.
8. $60°$.   9. (i) $\sqrt{5}$, (ii) $1/6\,\mathrm{N}$.
10. $\frac{1}{2}ma(2\omega^2+\Omega^2)$, $\frac{1}{2}ma(\Omega^2-2\omega^2)$.
11. $\sqrt{\{g(a^2-h^2)/h\}}$.   12. $\frac{2}{3}mg\sqrt{3}$, $m(3u^2-gl\sqrt{3})/3l$.
13. $m(v^2\cos\alpha+gl\sin^2\alpha)/l\sin\alpha$, $m(v^2-gl\cos\alpha)/l$.
14. $36\cdot3°$; $97\cdot8\,\mathrm{m\,s^{-1}}$.   15. $mg(\sqrt{3}-1)$.
16. $\sqrt{(2rg/11)}$ to $\sqrt{(2rg)}$.   17. $\sqrt{(45ag/8)}$.

Exercise 9.1 (pp. 147–149)

1. $-42\,\mathrm{N\,m}$, $14\,\mathrm{N\,m}$, $-21\,\mathrm{N\,m}$, $0\,\mathrm{N\,m}$.
2. $42\,\mathrm{N\,m}$, $-30\,\mathrm{N\,m}$, $-42\,\mathrm{N\,m}$, $30\,\mathrm{N\,m}$, $0\,\mathrm{N\,m}$.
3. $(4+\sqrt{3})\,\mathrm{N\,m}$, $3\sqrt{3}\,\mathrm{N\,m}$, $(2+5\sqrt{3})\,\mathrm{N\,m}$.
4. (a) $6\,\mathrm{N}$, $2\,\mathrm{m}$, (b) $8\,\mathrm{N}$, $3\,\mathrm{m}$.
5. (a) $1\,\mathrm{N}$, $10\,\mathrm{m}$, (b) $1\,\mathrm{N}$, $15\,\mathrm{m}$.
6. $50\,\mathrm{N\,m}$.   7. $F=G=4$.
8. (a) $5\sqrt{2}\,\mathrm{N}$, $4\,\mathrm{m}$, (b) $15\,\mathrm{N}$, $3\,\mathrm{m}$.
9. (a) $4\sqrt{2}\,\mathrm{N}$, $5\,\mathrm{m}$, (b) $6\cdot5\,\mathrm{N}$, $12\,\mathrm{m}$.   10. $6\sqrt{2}\,\mathrm{N}$ along BD.
11. $20\sqrt{3}\,\mathrm{N\,m}$, $10\sqrt{3}\,\mathrm{N\,m}$, $0\,\mathrm{N\,m}$, $0\,\mathrm{N\,m}$, $10\sqrt{3}\,\mathrm{N\,m}$, $20\sqrt{3}\,\mathrm{N\,m}$; $10\,\mathrm{N}$ along CD

Exercise 9.2 (pp. 154–156)

1. $4\,\mathrm{N}$ at $90°$ to AB, $4\,\mathrm{m}$.   2. $2\,\mathrm{N}$ at $90°$ to AB, $5\,\mathrm{m}$.
3. $6\sqrt{3}\,\mathrm{N}$ at $60°$ to AB, $1\,\mathrm{m}$.   4. $6\,\mathrm{N}$ at $60°$ to AB, $2\,\mathrm{m}$.
5. (a) $5P$ at $53\cdot1°$ to AB, (b) $6a$.   6. $3x-7y+7=0$.

7. $2x - 5y + 10 = 0.$ 8.   *a, b.*   9.   *c.*   10. *a, c.*   11. *b, c.*
12. *c.*   13. *c.*   14. *a, c.*   15. *b, c.*   16. *c.*   17. *a.*
18. *b.*   19. *a, c.*   20. 6 N m clockwise; $y = x + 1.$
21. (a) 5, 13,   (b) 2·5, 19·5.   22. $7\sqrt{5}$ N, 1 m; 28 N m in sense *CBA.*
23. (a) 10; 28 N along *AD,*   (b) 18 N, $14\sqrt{3}$ N m in sense *ABC.*
24. (a) 25P, $24y = 7x,$ (b) (i) $S = -18P, T = 15P,$ (ii) $72Pa,$ (iii) clockwise.

Exercise 9.3 (pp. 162–164)

1.   18 cm from *A.*   2.   1·05 m from *P.*   3.   5 cm.   4.   3 cm, 4 cm.
5.   (2, 1).   6. $(3, -\frac{1}{2}).$ 7. $3\mathbf{i} + \mathbf{j}.$ 8. $2\mathbf{i} + 2·5\mathbf{j}.$ 9.   (3, 0).
10. (0·4, 1·6).   11. 10 cm, 3 cm.   12. 10 cm.   13. $1\frac{2}{3}$ cm from *AB.*
14. $6\frac{1}{3}$ cm from *AD,* $4\frac{2}{5}$ cm from *AB.*   15. 11 cm from both *AB* and *AF.*
16. $3\frac{1}{2}$ cm from *AE,* 4 cm from *AB.*   17. 4 cm from *AD,* 3·5 cm from *AB.*
18. 7a/5 above base, 16a/11 above base.

Exercise 9.4 (pp. 170–171)

3. $\dfrac{2a(14 + 3\pi)}{3(8 + \pi)}.$ 4. $\dfrac{2a(26 - 3\pi)}{3(16 - \pi)}.$ 5. $\dfrac{28r}{9\pi}.$

6. $\dfrac{27\sqrt{3}a}{3\sqrt{3} + 4\pi}.$ 7. $\dfrac{11h}{28}.$

8.   (a) $\dfrac{7\sqrt{3}r}{8\pi + 3\sqrt{3}},$ (b) $\dfrac{7\sqrt{3}r}{4\pi - 3\sqrt{3}}.$ 9. $28\pi a^3/3, 12a/7.$ 11. 3r.

Exercise 9.5 (pp. 175–176)

1.   6, 103/15; (9/7, 103/70).   2.   153/4, 414/5; (17/8, 23/5).
3.   ln 2, 7/48; (2 ln 2, 7/24).   4.   1/4, 2/5; (3/8, 3/5).   5.   (20/7, 0).

6.   (3/5, 0).   7.   (0, π/8).   8.   (0, 7/3).   9. $\left(\dfrac{1}{e-1}, \dfrac{e+1}{4}\right).$

10. (1, π/8).   11. (2, 0).   12. (2/3, 0).   13. (2 ln 2, 0).

14. $\left(\dfrac{e^2 - 3}{2(e^2 - 1)}, 0\right).$ 15. (9/7, 0).   16. (0, 14/5).

17. $2\ln 2 - 1, 2\ln 2 - \frac{3}{4}, 2(\ln 2)^2 - 4\ln 2 + 2;$ (1·65, 0·24).

18. 1/6; (1/2, 2/5).

Exercise 9.6 (pp. 176–179)

1. (a) $13P$, $12/5$, (b) $3a$; $12Pa$, sense ABC.   2. $\lambda = 5/2$; $5a/2$; $5a/7$.
3. (c) (i) $3\sqrt{2}$ along AC, $\sqrt{2}$ along BD; $7a$;
   (ii) 7 along AD, $4\sqrt{2}$ along CA, $6\sqrt{2}$ along BD.

4. (a) $4\sqrt{3}P$, $\dfrac{\sqrt{3}}{3}P$; $\dfrac{7\sqrt{3}}{3}P$; (b) $\dfrac{5\sqrt{3}}{3}P$, $\dfrac{\sqrt{3}}{3}P$; $\dfrac{7\sqrt{3}}{3}Pa$ in sense ABC.

5. $p = 11$, $q = 14$; (a) $2\sqrt{19}\,\mathrm{N}$, (b) $12\sqrt{3}\,\mathrm{N\,m}$.
6. (i) $m = 2$, $n = 6$, (iii) $x = 3a\sqrt{3}$; $\sqrt{31}$, $5Pa\sqrt{3}$.
7. $(7a/18, 4a/9)$.
8. $4\cdot8\,\mathrm{cm}$ from OA, $8\cdot8\,\mathrm{cm}$ from OC.
9. $\frac{11}{24}\pi a^3$, $\frac{5}{24}\pi a^3$; $\frac{21}{88}a$, $\frac{27}{40}a$ from centre of hemisphere.

11. $\dfrac{3a}{8}$.   12. $\frac{32}{15}\sqrt{2}$; $\dfrac{8\pi}{5}$.   13. $16/3$; 8π; $(0, 20/3)$.

14. $(0\cdot864, 0\cdot333)$.   15. $4/3$, $104\pi/15$; $(15/13, 0)$.   16. $3\pi a^2$, $(\pi a, 5a/6)$.

Exercise 10.1 (pp. 186–188)

1. $360\,\mathrm{N}$, $2\cdot5\,\mathrm{m}$.   2. $41\,\mathrm{N}$ at A, $33\,\mathrm{N}$ at B.   3. $1\cdot6\,\mathrm{m}$.
4. $0\cdot6\,\mathrm{m}$, $20\,\mathrm{N}$.   5. (a) $1200\,\mathrm{N}$ (b) $3\,\mathrm{m}$.   6. $0\cdot4\,\mathrm{m}$.
7. $5W/8$ at A, $3W/8$ at B.   8. 5.   9. $5a/3$, $5a/2$; $\tan^{-1}10/21 \approx 25\cdot5°$.
10. (a, a); $1/2$.   11. $2/(\pi + 2)$.   12. $1/\pi$.
13. $\tan^{-1}3/4 \approx 36\cdot9°$; $3aW$.   14. $\tan^{-1}11/13 \approx 40\cdot2°$; $26aW/9$.
15. $\sqrt{2}$.   16. $2W/3$.

17. $h + \left(\dfrac{3a^2 - h^2}{8a + 4h}\right)$ from vertex of cone; (a) $17°$, (b) $h = a\sqrt{3}$.

18. $30°$; $1/\sqrt{3}$.   19. $36\cdot9°$.   20. (a) $53\cdot1°$, (b) $26\cdot6°$.

Exercise 10.2 (pp. 195–197)

1. (a) 10, (b) $10\sqrt{5}\,\mathrm{N}$ at $26\cdot6°$ to vertical.

2. $\dfrac{\sqrt{3}}{2}mg$ in AC, $\frac{1}{2}mg$ in BC; $\frac{1}{2}a$.   3. $2\,\mathrm{N}$ at A, $2\sqrt{17}\,\mathrm{N}$ at C.

4. $30\,\mathrm{N}$ at $60°$ to vertical.   5. $45\,\mathrm{cm}$, $16\,\mathrm{N}$.
6. (a) $20\sqrt{3}\,\mathrm{N}$, $90°$, (b) $15\sqrt{5}\,\mathrm{N}$, $63\cdot4°$.   7. $5/6$; $5W/12$, $13W/12$.
8. (a) $W\sqrt{3}$ at both A and C, (b) $2a$.
9. (a) $15\,\mathrm{N}$, (b) $9\,\mathrm{N}$ at $53\cdot1°$ to vertical.   10. $5W$, $75\,\mathrm{cm}$.   11. $\frac{1}{2}$; $30\,\mathrm{cm}$.
12. $5/24$.   13. (a) $\frac{1}{2}mg\cot\alpha$, (b) $\frac{1}{2}\cot\alpha$.
14. $45°$, $\frac{1}{2}W$; half way up, all the way.   15. (a) $30°$, (b) $1/\sqrt{3}$.
17. $1/3$.

Exercise 10.3 (pp. 202–205)

1. (a) 24 N, (b) $12\sqrt{3}$ N, 13 N.
2. (a) 60 N, (b) 48·2 N at 41·6° to horizontal.
3. (a) 15, (b) 47·4 N at 71·6° to horizontal.
4. $4\sqrt{3}$ N perpendicular to rod; $2\sqrt{3}$ N, 10 N.
5. (a) 14 N, 30 N (b) 1·92 m.   6. (a) 4/7, (b) $\tan^{-1}\frac{2}{3} \approx 33\cdot7°$.
7. 5 N, 1/2.   8. 121 N, 17·5 N; 7/48.   9. $\frac{1}{2}\tan\alpha$, $2W\tan\alpha$.
10. $3W/10$, $W/10$; 0·8.   11. 1/5.   12. $8W/15$; $24W/75$, $43W/75$.
13. $(5\sqrt{3})/18$; $(W\sqrt{3})/2$.   14. $5a/3$.   15. $\tan^{-1}(4/3)$; 40, 900 N.
16. 10, 6/17.   17. $W/4$, 1/3.   18. $11W/4$.   19. 5 m.

Exercise 10.4 (pp. 209–211)

1. (a) $5\sqrt{10}$ N, $5\sqrt{5}$ N (b) 21·8°, 45°.   2. $\frac{1}{2}W\sqrt{5}$, 63·4°.
3. $\frac{1}{3}W\sqrt{3}$, $\frac{1}{2}W$.
4. (ii) $W\sqrt{(1+\mu^2)}$ at $\tan^{-1}\mu$ to vertical, (iii) $\mu W = \frac{1}{2}W\cot\theta$.
5. (a) 7/10, (b) $5W/2$, $3W/4$.   6. C; 67·4°.   7. C will slip.
8. (a) $9W/5$, $12W/5$, (b) 3·2°.   9. $\sqrt{3}/2$.   10. $2 - \sqrt{3}$.
11. $\frac{3}{4}W$, $\frac{1}{4}W\tan\alpha$; $1/\sqrt{3}$.
13. (i) $\dfrac{9w}{25}$, (ii) $W + \dfrac{27w}{125}$, (iii) $\dfrac{36w}{125}$.

Exercise 10.5 (pp. 213–215)

1. AB: $\sqrt{3}$ kN tension; BC: $4\sqrt{3}$ kN tension; CD: $2\sqrt{3}$ kN thrust;
   AD: $2\sqrt{3}$ kN thrust; BD: $2\sqrt{3}$ kN tension.
2. AB and BC: 5 kN thrust; BD: no stress; CD: 4 kN tension; AD: 3 kN tension.
3. AB: 2 kN thrust; BC: $2\sqrt{2}$ kN tension; CD: 4 kN tension; AC: $2\sqrt{2}$ kN thrust.
4. AB: 8 kN thrust; BC: $4\sqrt{3}$ kN thrust; CD: $2\sqrt{3}$ kN tension; BD: 4 kN tension.
5. AB: $10\sqrt{2}$ kN thrust; BC: $5\sqrt{2}$ kN thrust; CD: 5 kN tension;
   DE: $5\sqrt{2}$ kN tension; AE: 10 kN tension; BD: 5 kN thrust; BE: 5 kN tension.
6. AB: 4 kN tension; BC: 3 kN thrust; CD: 3 kN thrust; AD: 4 kN tension;
   AC: 15 kN tension.
7. AB: $4\sqrt{3}$ kN tension; BC: $2\sqrt{3}$ kN tension; CD: $4\sqrt{3}$ kN thrust;
   DE: $3\sqrt{3}$ kN thrust; AE: $8\sqrt{3}$ kN thrust; BD: $2\sqrt{3}$ kN tension;
   BE: $2\sqrt{3}$ kN thrust.
8. AB and BC: 6 kN tension; CD and AE: $6\sqrt{3}$ kN thrust; BD and
   BE: $2\sqrt{3}$ kN tension; DE: $4\sqrt{3}$ kN thrust.
9. $P = \frac{1}{3}W\sqrt{2}$; AB: $\frac{2}{3}W$ thrust; BC: $\frac{1}{3}W\sqrt{2}$ tension; CD: $\frac{1}{3}W$ thrust;
   AC: $\frac{2}{3}W\sqrt{2}$ tension; AD: $\frac{2}{3}W$ thrust.
10. (ii) AB: 390 N; BC: 650 N; CD: 150 N; AD: 250 N; AC: $120\sqrt{5}$ N
    (iii) AC and CD.

Exercise 10.6 (pp. 215–222)

2. 4/11; 7:2.   4. $5a/2, 5a/2$; $\tan^{-1}(1/6) \approx 9.5°$; $W/6$.
7. (a) $12\frac{1}{2}$ N; $7\frac{1}{2}$ N in the direction CA,   (b) $6\frac{1}{4}$ N; $6\frac{1}{4}$ N at 53·1° to CA produced;
       8 N acting 0·625 m from A.
8. $\frac{1}{2}W\sqrt{5}$; $7l/12$.
9. (a) 15 N,   (b) 8/3 m,   (c) 42·7 N at 73·7° to the horizontal.
10. (ii) $\frac{1}{4}\sqrt{3}$,   (iii) $24c/7$.   11. 3/46.   12. 3/8, $5l/3$.
14. $\frac{3}{2}mg \cot \alpha$; $mg \cot \alpha$.   15. $\cos^{-1}(2m/M)$.
16. $W(1 - \sin 2\theta)$; 18·4°.
17. $AX = \frac{2}{3}a$, $13W$ at 67·4° to XA; $CY = 11a/12$.
18. (i) $25W/37, 20W/37$,   (iii) 13/40.
20. $(8a/15, 3a/16)$; $128/45 \approx 2.84$.

21. $h + \left(\dfrac{6l^2 - h^2}{4h + 12l}\right)$ from vertex of cone.   22. $\sin^{-1}\left(\dfrac{k + 3}{3k - 24}\right)$.

23. (i) $35\sqrt{2}$ N,   (ii) $5\sqrt{2}$ N.
24. Force at the ground.   25. $\frac{1}{4}Wl\sqrt{3}$.
26. $\frac{1}{2}W/5$; $\frac{1}{2}W, 0$.   27. Slipping at A.
28. (i) $\frac{1}{2}W$,   (ii) $\frac{1}{2}W, W$,   (iv) $\frac{1}{2}$.
29. $2W\sqrt{3}$ along BA; $\frac{1}{3}W\sqrt{3}$, $3W/2$ at A. $\frac{1}{3}W\sqrt{3}$, $\frac{1}{2}W$ at C.
30. $\frac{2}{3}W\sqrt{3}$ between cylinders, $\frac{1}{3}W\sqrt{3}$ at both walls.   31. $1\sqrt{3}$.
32. (i) $35W/4$,   (ii) $0, 5W$ at A; $7W, 5W/4$ at B,   (iii) $21aW/2$.
33. (i) 2400 N,   (ii) 2600 N at 67·4° to vertical,
       (iii) AB: 2400 N; BC: 700 N; CD: $700\sqrt{2}$ N; DE: 1400 N; BD: $700\sqrt{2}$ N;
            BE: $1000\sqrt{2}$ N; rods AB, BC, BD in compression.
34. (i) 14, (ii) AB: $4/\sqrt{3}$ kN tension; BC: $8/\sqrt{3}$ kN thrust; CD: $8/\sqrt{3}$ kN thrust;
       DE: $16/\sqrt{3}$ kN thrust; AE: $2/\sqrt{3}$ kN thrust; BD: $4/\sqrt{3}$ kN tension;
       BE: $4\sqrt{3}$ kN thrust, (iii) 2 kN vertically downwards.

Exercise 11.1 (pp. 227–228)

1. $6\mathbf{i} - 8\mathbf{j}, 4\mathbf{i} + 3\mathbf{j}; 10\mathbf{i} - 5\mathbf{j}$.
2. $3\sqrt{2}$ N, $5\sqrt{2}$ N.   3.   27 N.
4. (a) $\mathbf{r} = (1 + \lambda)\mathbf{i} + (1 + 2\lambda)\mathbf{j}$,   (b) $\mathbf{r} = -2\lambda\mathbf{i} + (5\lambda + 2)\mathbf{j} + (3\lambda - 1)\mathbf{k}$,
       (c) $\mathbf{r} = 3\mathbf{i} - 2\lambda\mathbf{j} + 3\lambda\mathbf{k}$.
5. $\mathbf{r} = (2 + 3\lambda)\mathbf{i} + (\lambda - 1)\mathbf{j} - 2\lambda\mathbf{k}, \mathbf{r} = (9 + \mu)\mathbf{i} - \mu\mathbf{j} + (3\mu - 1)\mathbf{k}; 8\mathbf{i} + \mathbf{j} - 4\mathbf{k}$;
       $\mathbf{r} = (8 + 4t)\mathbf{i} + \mathbf{j} + (t - 4)\mathbf{k}$.
6. 11 N, $\mathbf{r} = (3 + 7\lambda)\mathbf{i} + (5 + 6\lambda)\mathbf{j} + 6\lambda\mathbf{k}$.
7. $3x + y = 26$.
8. $3\sqrt{13}$ N, $\frac{2}{3}$; $2x - 3y + 2 = 0$.
9. (a) $15\mathbf{YX}$, where $BX : XC = 3:2$, $AY : YB = 2:1$,
       (b) $24\mathbf{XY}$, where $AX : XC = 1:3$, $AY : YB = 1:5$,
       (c) $6\mathbf{YX}$, where $AX : XC = 2:1$ and $AY = YB$,
       (d) $21\mathbf{XY}$, where $AX : XC = 1:2$, $AY : YB = 3:4$.

Exercise 11.2 (pp. 231–232)

1. $r_A = (3 + 5t)i + (4 + 2t)j$, $r_B = (5 + 2t)i + (8 + t)j$;
    $AB = (2 - 3t)i + (4 - t)j$; $\sqrt{10}$ m.
2. $4i - 6j$; $(4t - 2)i + (3 - 6t)j$; $t = \frac{1}{2}$.
3. $(2 - 5t)i + (4t - 18)j$; $2\sqrt{41}$ km; $16i + 19j$, $8i + 9j$.
4. $8\cos\omega t i + 8\sin\omega t j$.   5. $i - 2j$, 3 m; 6m s^{-1}.
6. (a) $\pi/4$, (b) $5\pi/4$.   7.   (a) 1/3, (b) 3.
8. (a) $8ti + (9t^2 - 2)j$, $m(8i + 18tj)$,   (b) $-6t^2j + 2tk$, $m(-12tj + 2k)$,
    (c) $(2 - 2t)i + (6\cos 2t)j$, $m\{-2i - (12\sin 2t)j\}$,
    (d) $e^{-t}(1 - t)i - 2j$, $me^{-t}(t - 2)i$.
9. (a) $\sqrt{19}\,\text{m s}^{-1}$, (b) 20i.   10. $12i + 30j$, $18i + 45j$.
11. $40\,\text{m s}^{-1}$, $18i - 35j$.   12. $5i - 3j + 2k$.
13. $2i + 6j$; $9\sqrt{10}$ m.
14. $(16t - 5t^2)j$, $12ti + (25 - 5t^2)j$; 15 m.

Exercise 11.3 (pp. 238–240)

1. $31{\cdot}6°$, $5\,\text{m s}^{-1}$.   2. $\sqrt{41}\,\text{N} \approx 6{\cdot}40\,\text{N}$, $50{\cdot}6°$.
3. (a) 2 N, (b) -3 N, (c) $\sqrt{2}$ N, (d) $-5/3$ N.
4. (a) $8i - 6k$, $3i + 4j + 4k$, (b) $-10j + 24k$, $5i - 12j - 5k$,
    (c) $-6i + 18j - 27k$, $24i + 17j + 6k$, (d) $\frac{2}{3}(4i - 8j + k)$, $\frac{1}{3}(i + 4j + 28k)$.
5. (a) 2 J, (b) 0 J, (c) 21 J, (d) -11 J.
6. (a) $8m$ J, (b) $24m$ J, (c) $360m$ J, (d) 0 J.
7. (a) $4mi$, $4ti - 5k$; $16mt$, (b) $6m(tj - k)$, $3t^2j - 6tk$; $18mt(t^2 + 2)$,
    (c) $-me^{-t}j$, $i + e^{-t}j$; $-me^{-2t}$.
    (d) $-m(\sin tj + 3\cos tk)$, $\cos tj - 3\sin tk$; $4m\sin 2t$.
8. 14 J; $8\,\text{m s}^{-1}$.   9. -114 J; 6; -96 W, -18 W.
10. $t^2i + (1 - 3t)j + k$; 20 J; 31 W.
11. $(4t + 6)i - 2\sin tj + \frac{1}{2}t^2k$, $t^3 + 32t + 48 + 4\sin 2t$.   12. 24 J.

13. $10t^4 + 6t^2 + 2t$; 544 J.   14. $\displaystyle\int_1^2 F.(i - 2\lambda j)d\lambda$; 12.

Exercise 11.4 (pp. 240–242)

1. (i) $26{\cdot}7$ N in the direction of the vector $3i + 13j$; $-36/65$, (ii) $6i + 26j$.
2. $(2T^4 - 2)i + (3T^2 + 3)j$; $94i + 30j$.
3. $6i + 8j$, 6; $6i + 8j + 6(i\cos(\pi t/12) + j\sin(\pi t/12))$; $-\pi^2/24$, $-\pi^2\sqrt{3}/24$;
    $(9 - \sqrt{3}\pi)i + (8 + 3\sqrt{3} + \pi)j$.   4. $1/(1 + \cos\theta)$; towards O.
5. $2/\sqrt{13}$.   6.   (i) $(10 - 2t)i + (5 + 4t)j$, (ii) 14.00 hrs, (iii) $4\sqrt{5}$ km.
7. $(260 - 35t)i - 5\sqrt{3}tj$; 62 km, 19.00 hrs.

8. (a) $v - u$, (b) $p + t(v - u)$; $\left\{p^2 - \dfrac{[p.(u - v)]^2}{|u - v|^2}\right\}^{1/2}$

9. (i) $\mathbf{F} \cdot \mathbf{v}$, (ii) $\int_0^T \mathbf{F} \cdot \mathbf{v}dt$; $-4a\sin 2t\mathbf{i} + 2a\cos 2t\mathbf{j}$,

    $-8ma\cos 2t\mathbf{i} - 4ma\sin 2t\mathbf{j}$; $12ma^2 \sin 4t$; $6ma^2, \frac{1}{4}\pi$.

10. $\frac{1}{2}ma^2(2 - 2\cos\theta)\dot{\theta}^2 + mga(1 + \cos\theta) = 2mga$.

Exercise 12.1 (pp. 248–250)

1. (a) $8\mathbf{i} - 28\mathbf{j}$, (b) $2\mathbf{i} - \frac{2}{3}\mathbf{j} + \mathbf{k}$, (c) 65, (d) 4.
2. (a) $10\mathbf{i} + 6\mathbf{j}$, (b) $2\mathbf{i} - 52\mathbf{j} + 8\mathbf{k}$, (c) $3\mathbf{j}$.
3. (a) 480 N s, (b) 30 000 N s, (c) 12 N s.
4. (a) $12\mathbf{j}$, (b) $-2\mathbf{i} + 6\mathbf{k}$, (c) $-60\mathbf{k}$. 5. 54 N s. 6. 4 N s.
7. 600 N. 8. (a) $16 \cdot 8\,\mathrm{m\,s^{-1}}$, (b) $7 \cdot 2\,\mathrm{m\,s^{-1}}$. 9. $7 \cdot 5\,\mathrm{s}$.
10. $12\mathbf{i} + 15\mathbf{j}$; $2\mathbf{i} + 2 \cdot 5\mathbf{j}$. 11. $8\mathbf{i} + 4\mathbf{j}$; 10 J
12. (a) $14\,\mathrm{m\,s^{-1}}$, 240 J gain, (b) $2\,\mathrm{m\,s^{-1}}$, 48 J loss, (c) $10\,\mathrm{m\,s^{-1}}$, 96 J gain.
13. 2·5 N s. 14. $20\sqrt{3}$ N s. 15. 600 N. 16. $12\,\mathrm{m\,s^{-1}}$.
17. 2 N at 53·1° to horizontal
18. (a) $2\,\mathrm{m\,s^{-1}}, 6\sqrt{3}$ N s, (b) $(4\sqrt{3})/3\,\mathrm{m\,s^{-1}}, 4\sqrt{6}$ N s.
19. $1 \cdot 5\,\mathrm{m\,s^{-1}}$ along AB, $5 \cdot 22\,\mathrm{m\,s^{-1}}$ at 73·3° to AB; 4·5 N s.
20. (a) $2\sqrt{2}\,\mathrm{m\,s^{-1}}, 2\sqrt{2}\,\mathrm{m\,s^{-1}}, 4\,\mathrm{m\,s^{-1}}$, (b) $2\,\mathrm{m\,s^{-1}}, 2\sqrt{3}\,\mathrm{m\,s^{-1}}, 4\,\mathrm{m\,s^{-1}}$.

Exercise 12.2 (pp. 252–253)

1. $5\,\mathrm{m\,s^{-1}}$. 2. $720\,\mathrm{m\,s^{-1}}$. 3. $7 \cdot 5\,\mathrm{m\,s^{-1}}$ towards A; 78·75 J.
4. $2 \cdot 5\,\mathrm{m\,s^{-1}}, 2512 \cdot 5$ J. 5. $5\,\mathrm{m\,s^{-1}}$. 6. $7\,\mathrm{m\,s^{-1}}$. 7. $2\mathbf{i} - 5\mathbf{j}$.
8. $5\mathbf{i} + \frac{5}{2}\mathbf{j}$. 9. 28 J. 10. $3u, 2u$. 11. $6\,\mathrm{m\,s^{-1}}, 26$ kJ.
12. $3 \cdot 5\,\mathrm{m\,s^{-1}}, 2000$ N. 13. $0 \cdot 6\,\mathrm{m\,s^{-1}}, 720$ N s. 14. 30.
15. (a) $14\,\mathrm{m\,s^{-1}}$, (b) $23 \cdot 8\,\mathrm{m\,s^{-1}}$. 16. $u/2g\sin\alpha$.

Exercise 12.3 (pp. 258–260)

1. 4800 N, 5 s. 2. 9000 N, 1/600 s. 3. $2\,\mathrm{m\,s^{-1}}, 25$ m. 4. 1.
5. (a) 70 N s, (b) 77 N s. 6. 10/7 s, $14\sqrt{2}\,\mathrm{m\,s^{-1}}$.
7. $4 \cdot 2\,\mathrm{m\,s^{-1}}, 78\,400$ N. 8. 90 160 N, 1/7 s. 9. 1·25 m.
10. $469\,\mathrm{m\,s^{-1}}$. 11. $h, \frac{1}{4}h$. 12. 0·1 m. 13. $2 \cdot 1\,\mathrm{m\,s^{-1}}, 6 \cdot 3$ N s.
14. $7 \cdot 35\,\mathrm{m\,s^{-1}}, 2\frac{1}{4}$ s. 15. 3 s, $4 \cdot 2\,\mathrm{m\,s^{-1}}$. 16. (a) $\frac{7}{3}h$, (b) $\frac{2}{3}m\sqrt{(\frac{2}{3}gh)}$.
17. $2 \cdot 8\,\mathrm{m\,s^{-1}}, 20 \cdot 6$ J. 18. (i) $\frac{3}{4}mgh$, (ii) $9m^2gh/4M$.
19. (ii) $\frac{12}{5}m\sqrt{(gc)}$, (iii) $\frac{33}{25}c$, (iv) $\frac{12}{5}mgc$.
20. $40\,\mathrm{m\,s^{-1}}, 80$ J; 1200 J; $(d + 14)$ cm; 1, 8000 N.

Exercise 12.4 (pp. 265–267)

1. (a) 2·5 m, (b) 14·7 J, (c) 4·2 N s. 2. $\frac{3}{4}$, 4·05 m. 3. $\frac{2}{3}$.
4. $8\sqrt{5}\,\mathrm{m\,s^{-1}}, 60$ N s. 5. $1/\sqrt{3}$; 45°. 6. 60°.
7. $4\frac{1}{6}\,\mathrm{m\,s^{-1}}$ at 53·1° to horizontal. 8. $2u, 4u$; $18mu^2$. 9. $\frac{1}{2}$.

10. (a) $1\,\mathrm{m\,s^{-1}}$, $4\,\mathrm{m\,s^{-1}}$, same direction.
    (b) $\frac{1}{2}\mathrm{m\,s^{-1}}$, $5\frac{1}{2}\mathrm{m\,s^{-1}}$, opposite directions.
11. $\frac{1}{4}$, $2:3$.　　12. $5\,\mathrm{m\,s^{-1}}$, $-4\,\mathrm{m\,s^{-1}}$, $16\,\mathrm{m\,s^{-1}}$; yes.
13. $u/4$, $3u/16$, $9u/16$; yes.　　14. $2/9$.　　16. $u(1-e)$, u.
17. $\frac{1}{2}\sqrt{(2ag)}$, $\frac{1}{4}\sqrt{(2ag)}$ in same direction.
18. (a) $\frac{1}{3}V(1-2e)$, $\frac{1}{3}V(1+e)$, 0　(b) $\frac{1}{3}V(1-2e)$, $\frac{1}{9}V(1+e)(2-e)$, $\frac{2}{9}V(1+e)^2$.

Exercise 12.5 (pp. 267–272)

1. (i) $9mu$,　(ii) $81mu^2/4$.　　2.　(a) $12\mathbf{i}+4\mathbf{j}$,　(b) $5\mathbf{i}-2\mathbf{j}$,　(c) $32\,\mathrm{J}$.

3. $-\dfrac{mv}{2}\mathbf{i}+\dfrac{mv}{2\sqrt{3}}\mathbf{j}$; $\dfrac{v}{3\sqrt{3}}$ at $30°$ to the x-axis in a clockwise sense.

4. (i) $283\,\mathrm{kg}$,　(ii) $11\,500\,\mathrm{J}$,　(iii) $39\,\mathrm{kW}$,　(iv) $56\,\mathrm{kW}$; $2500\,\mathrm{N}$.
5. (ii) $u/6$, $(u\sqrt{3})/4$; $mu/6$.　　6. $|m_1u_1-m_2u_2|/(m_1+m_2)$.
8. $\frac{1}{2}mgh$, $m(1+\sqrt{2})\sqrt{(gh)}$.　　9. $1\cdot6\,\mathrm{m\,s^{-1}}$, $0\cdot4\,\mathrm{m\,s^{-1}}$; $131\,\mathrm{mm}$, $8\,\mathrm{mm}$.
10. (i) $5\cdot6\,\mathrm{m\,s^{-1}}$,　(ii) $3\cdot2\,\mathrm{m\,s^{-1}}$,　(iii) $13\,440\,\mathrm{J}$,　(iv) $123\cdot9\,\mathrm{kN}$.
11. (i) $\frac{6}{5}m\sqrt{(2ga)}$,　(ii) $\frac{6}{5}mga$,　(iii) $\frac{2}{5}\sqrt{(17ga)}$.
12. $1\cdot96\,\mathrm{m\,s^{-2}}$; $1\cdot12\,\mathrm{m\,s^{-1}}$, $3\cdot36\,\mathrm{N\,s}$.
14. (i) $g/5$, $12mg/5$,　(iii) $9mv/8$,　(iv) $15mv^2/16$,　(v) $1/\sqrt{3}$.
15. $mMu^2/2a(m+M)$.　　16. (b) $16°$,　(c) $5:6$.

17. $\dfrac{u\sin\alpha}{\sin\beta}$; $\frac{1}{2}u\left|\dfrac{\sin(\alpha-\beta)}{\sin\beta}\right|$; $\dfrac{u^2}{g\sqrt{3}}$.

19. (a) $\cot\alpha\tan\beta$,　(b) $u\cos\alpha\sec\beta$,　(c) $mu\sin(\alpha+\beta)\sec\beta$.
20. (a) $\frac{1}{2}mu^2(1-e^2)\cos^2\alpha$,　(b) $u^2e\sin2\alpha/g(1+e)$.
21. $\frac{1}{2}$; $2:7$; $2\,\mathrm{m\,s^{-1}}$, $7\,\mathrm{m\,s^{-1}}$ in opposite directions.
22. (i) u along $\overrightarrow{BA}$,　(ii) $4/5$,　(iii) $3mu^2$,
    (iv) u, $4u/3$ along $\overrightarrow{BC}$,　(v) $1/9$.
23. (i) $\frac{1}{2}$,　(ii) $\frac{1}{4}mu^2$,　(iii) $\frac{2}{3}$,　(iv) u.　　24. $4u/3$, $u/6$; $7mu^2/12$.
26. $\frac{1}{3}(7-8e)u$, $\frac{1}{3}(7+16e)u$ in direction $\overrightarrow{AB}$; $1/8$;
    $3u/(1+k)$, $k>\frac{1}{2}$.

27. $e=1,\frac{1}{3},\frac{1}{5},\frac{1}{7},\ldots,\dfrac{1}{1+2n},\ldots$.

Exercise 13.1 (pp. 275–276)

1. $\ln3\,\mathrm{m\,s^{-1}}$.　　2. $\ln5$ seconds.　　3. $6\,\mathrm{m\,s^{-1}}$.　　4. $0\cdot585\,\mathrm{m\,s^{-1}}$.
5. $2a$.　　6. $\sqrt{(gR/3)}$.　　7. (a) $2/x$,　(b) $\sqrt{(4t+h^2)}$.　　8. $-\frac{1}{2}e^x$.

Exercise 13.2 (pp. 279–282)

1. $\ln3$.　　2. $\frac{1}{2}\ln(1+u^2)$.　　3. $-\dfrac{1}{k}\{v+\ln(1-v)\}$.

4. $\dfrac{a}{b^2}(2 - \ln 3)$.   5. $\dfrac{2u}{2 + su}$; $\dfrac{s^2}{4} + \dfrac{s}{u}$.   6.   (i) 482 m,   (ii) 24·1 s.

8. $\left[\dfrac{g}{k}(1 - e^{-2ks}) + u^2 e^{-2ks}\right]^{1/2}$.   9.   (iii) 11·1 s.

10. $\dfrac{dv}{dt} = \dfrac{k(U^2 - v^2)}{mv}$; $v\dfrac{dv}{dx} = \dfrac{k(U^2 - v^2)}{mv}$.

11. $\dfrac{m}{2k}\tan^{-1}(\tfrac{1}{2}u)$; $\dfrac{m}{2k}\ln(1 + \tfrac{1}{4}u^2)$.   12. $\dfrac{P^2}{k}\left(1 - \dfrac{1}{e}\right)$.

15. $\dfrac{m}{R^2}\left\{H\ln\left(\dfrac{H - Ru}{H - 2Ru}\right) - Ru\right\}$;

$\dfrac{m}{R^3}\left\{H^2\ln\left(\dfrac{H - Ru}{H - 2Ru}\right) - HRu - \tfrac{3}{2}R^2u^2\right\}$.

16. $\dfrac{mU^2}{2S}\ln\left(\dfrac{U^2}{U^2 - V^2}\right)$; $\dfrac{mU^2}{2S}\left\{U\ln\left(\dfrac{U + V}{U - V}\right) - 2V\right\}$.

Exercise 13.3 (pp. 286–287)

1. $5\,\mathrm{m\,s^{-1}}$, $10\,\mathrm{m\,s^{-2}}$.   2.   (a) 2 m, (b) $\tfrac{2}{3}\pi$ s, (c) $3\sqrt{3}\,\mathrm{m\,s^{-1}}$.
3. 6π s; 2·5 N.   4.   (i) $270/\pi$, (ii) $\tfrac{2}{3}\sqrt{13}$ m, (iii) $540\sqrt{13}$ N.
5. $6\,\mathrm{m\,s^{-1}}$, 2 m; $5\cdot9\,\mathrm{m\,s^{-1}}$.   6.   (i) π s, (ii) 2π s, (iii) $3\pi/2$ s.

7.   (i) $\dfrac{5}{3\pi}$ m, (ii) $\tfrac{5}{2}\sqrt{3}\,\mathrm{m\,s^{-1}}$, (iii) $\dfrac{1}{2\pi}$ m, (iv) $\tfrac{1}{18}$ s.

8. $2\sqrt{3}\,\mathrm{m\,s^{-1}}$, 1/6 s; 8 J.
9.   (a) $x = 3\cos 2t + 3\sin 2t$, (b) $-3, 6$, (c) $3\pi/8$.
10.   (a) $x = 3\cos 4t + \sqrt{3}\sin 4t$, (b) $\pi/24$, (c) $2\sqrt{3}$.

Exercise 13.4 (pp. 293–295)

1. $5a/3$.   2.   (i) $2l$, (ii) $\tfrac{1}{2}\pi\sqrt{(3l/g)}$, (iii) $15l/8$.
3. $\tfrac{1}{2}mg$, $\tfrac{1}{2}mg$; (i) $3l/2$, (ii) $\pi(2l/g)^{1/2}$.   4.   4.
5. $2\pi\sqrt{(2a/g)}$, a; $\tfrac{1}{2}a$ above 0.   6. $\sqrt{(2a\lambda/m)}$.

7. $5l/2$, $\pi(lm/\lambda)$, $\sqrt{(\lambda l/m)}$.   8. $2l$; $\pi\sqrt{\left(\dfrac{2l}{g}\right)}$, $\left(\dfrac{2u^2 l + gl^2}{4g}\right)^{1/2}$.

9. $u\sqrt{\left(\dfrac{lm}{\lambda}\right)}$; $\dfrac{\pi}{2}\sqrt{\left(\dfrac{lm}{\lambda}\right)}$; $\pi\sqrt{\left(\dfrac{lm}{\lambda}\right)} + \dfrac{2l}{u}$.   10. $\tfrac{16}{9}a$; $\sqrt{(5ag)}$; $\dfrac{\pi}{6}\sqrt{\left(\dfrac{a}{g}\right)}$.

11.   (a) 994 mm, (b) 991 mm, (c) 996 mm, (d) 164 mm.
12.   (a) 143 cm, (b) 56 cm, (c) 36 cm, (d) 14 cm.

Exercise 13.5 (pp. 300–302)

1. $49\cos\theta - 24$, $58{\cdot}8\cos\theta - 19{\cdot}2$; $3{\cdot}68$, $25{\cdot}8$; $61°$.
2. $6{\cdot}18\,\text{m s}^{-1}$, $19{\cdot}35\,\text{N}$.   3. $\frac{1}{3}, \frac{1}{3}ag$.
5. $mg|3\cos\theta - 2|$; $\frac{2}{3} < \cos\theta < 1$.   6. $\sqrt{(2ag/3)}$.

7. $\dfrac{mu^2}{a} - 2mg + 3mg\cos\theta$; mg.   8.   (ii) $\frac{7}{2}ag$, $\sqrt{(\frac{1}{2}ag)}$.

9. $\cos\alpha\sqrt{(2gl\sin\alpha)}$; no.   10. $\{2ag(1 + \sin\theta)\}^{1/2}$; (b) $\pi/6$, $(3ag)^{1/2}$; $(a/g)^{1/2}$.

11. $\{u^2 - 6ag(1 - \cos\theta)\}^{1/2}$; $\dfrac{mu^2}{2a} - 3mg(1 + \sin\phi)$.

12. $\frac{2}{3}mg(1 + \cos\theta)$, $\frac{1}{3}mg(5\sin\theta - 4\theta)$.

Exercise 13.6 (pp. 302–307)

1.   Particle escapes from the earth.

2. $mv\dfrac{dv}{dx} = Ke^{-ax} - \lambda m$; $\left\{\dfrac{2K}{\alpha m}\left(1 - e^{-ax}\right) - 2\lambda x\right\}^{1/2}$.

3. $\frac{1}{2}(\mu/a)^{1/2} \leqslant V \leqslant \frac{3}{4}(\mu/a)^{1/2}$.

4. $5\cos 3t + 12\sin 3t + 2$; 15, 39; $t \approx 0{\cdot}967$.   5. $\dfrac{2k^2}{g}\left(1 - e^{-gt/k}\right) - kt$.

6. $\frac{1}{800}$ s; $\dfrac{dv}{dt} = -16 \times 10^3(2v)^{1/2}$, $\frac{1}{400}$ s; $v = Ae^{-kt}$, A and k positive constants.

7.   (i) $2uT$,   (ii) $T\ln 3$,   (iii) $4mu^2$.   8. $v = gTe^{-x/gT^2}$

9. $v^2 = u^2\tan\left(\dfrac{\pi}{4} - \dfrac{2gz}{u^2}\right)$.   10.   (ii) $u\sqrt{(1 - e^{-2kx})}$.

13.   (b) (i) $3\pi/8$ s,   (ii) $26\frac{2}{3}\,\text{m s}^{-1}$,   (iii) $142\frac{2}{9}\,\text{m s}^{-2}$,   (iv) $\pi/16$ s.

14. $\dfrac{\pi}{4}\,\text{m/s}$, $\dfrac{\pi^2}{8}\,\text{m/s}^2$; $\dfrac{\pi\sqrt{3}}{8}\,\text{m/s}$, $\frac{2}{3}$ s.

15.   (i) 12 s, $24/\pi$ m,   (ii) $t = 5$; $12\sqrt{2}$ s, $\sqrt{2}\,\text{m s}^{-1}$.
16. $\ddot{x} = -\omega^2 x$, $2\pi/\omega$; $t = 12$ s, $t = 24$ s.   17. $4u/\pi$.

18.   (i) $5{\cdot}09$ m,   (ii) $3{\cdot}60$ m,   (iii) $\dfrac{4}{\pi}\sin^{-1}\left(\dfrac{\pi}{16}\right)$; $2\pi\,\text{N}$, $\mu \geqslant \pi/g$.

19. $\frac{400}{3}\,\text{N}$; $\dfrac{2}{\sqrt{3}}\,\text{m/s}$.   20. $2mg + \dfrac{2\lambda}{3l}x$.   21. $\sqrt{(\frac{1}{3}gl)}$.

23. $\dfrac{5\sqrt{2}}{24}\,l$.   25. $\{ag(2\cos\theta - 1)\}^{1/2}$, $2mg(3\cos\theta - 1)$; $8a/25$.

28. $\sqrt{(3ga/2)}$.   29. $\ddot{\mathbf{r}} = \mathbf{g} - k\dot{\mathbf{r}}$.

Exercise 14.1 (pp. 310–311)

1. 720.   2. 40 320.
3. 20 160.   4. 151 200.
5. 13 800.   6. 10 080.
7. 720.   8. (a) 48.   (b) 180.
10. (a) 210,   (b) 1140,   (c) 1287,   (d) 12.
11. 1260.
12. (a) 462,   (b) 5775,   (c) 10 395.
13. 15 840   14. 38, 16.
15. 238.   16. (a) 15 015,   (b) 37 037.

Exercise 14.2 (pp. 316–317)

1. (a) $\{x\}$,   (b) $\{x, y, p, q, r\}$,   (c) $\{x, y, z, p, q, r\}$,
    (d) $\{x, p\}$,   (e) $\{x\}$,   (f) $\{x, y, p, q, r\}$.
2. (a) $\{x \in \mathbb{R} : -2 < x < 7\}, \{x \in \mathbb{R} : 0 < x < 4\}$,
    (b) $\{x \in \mathbb{R} : x \leqslant 9\}, \{x \in \mathbb{R} : 2 \leqslant x \leqslant 5\}$,
    (c) $\{x \in \mathbb{R} : |x| < 10\}, \{x \in \mathbb{R} : -4 < x < 3\}$,
    (d) $\{x \in \mathbb{R} : -3 < x \leqslant 6\}, \varnothing$.
3. (a) $\varnothing$,   (b) $\{4\}$,   (c) $\{3, 4, 5\}$,   (d) $\{1, 2\}$,   (e) $\{1, 2, 3\}$,   (f) $\{4, 5\}$.
4. (a) X',   (b) $X \cap Y$,   (c) $X' \cap Y'$,   (d) $X \cup Y'$,   (e) $X' \cup Y'$,
    (f) $(X \cup Y) \cap (X' \cup Y')$ or $(X \cap Y') \cup (X' \cap Y)$.
9. (a) A,   (b) $\varnothing$,   (c) A,   (d) A.
10. 27.
11. $n(A) + n(B) + n(C) - n(A \cap B) - n(B \cap C) - n(C \cap A) + n(A \cap B \cap C)$.
12. $n(M \cap F) \geqslant 3, n(M \cap P) \geqslant 10, n(M \cap F \cap P) \leqslant 12$.
14. (a) A,   (b) B,   (c) $A \cap C$,   (d) $B \cup C$.

Exercise 14.3 (pp. 321–322)

1. $\dfrac{1}{6}, \dfrac{1}{2}, \dfrac{2}{3}$.

2. $\dfrac{1}{2}, \dfrac{1}{13}, \dfrac{3}{13}$.

3. $\dfrac{1}{8}, \dfrac{1}{2}, \dfrac{3}{4}$.

4. $\dfrac{1}{21}, \dfrac{2}{7}, \dfrac{10}{21}$.

5. (a) $\dfrac{2}{3}$,   (b) 0,   (c) $\dfrac{5}{6}$,   (d) $\dfrac{1}{6}$.

6. (a) $\dfrac{7}{13}$,   (b) $\dfrac{1}{26}$,   (c) $\dfrac{1}{13}$,   (d) $\dfrac{5}{13}$.

7. (a) 0·8,   (b) 0·07,   (c) 0·1,   (d) 0·43.

8. (a) $\dfrac{1}{4}$,   (b) $\dfrac{5}{9}$,   (c) $\dfrac{7}{36}$.

9. (a) $\dfrac{1}{14}$,   (b) $\dfrac{3}{28}$,   (c) $\dfrac{3}{7}$,   (d) $\dfrac{4}{7}$.

10. 0·32.

11. (a) $\dfrac{1}{9}$,   (b) $\dfrac{2}{3}$.

12. (a) $\dfrac{1}{16}$,   (b) $\dfrac{3}{8}$,   (c) $\dfrac{5}{8}$,   (d) $\dfrac{7}{8}$.

13. (a) $\dfrac{1}{3}$,   (b) $\dfrac{2}{9}$,   (c) $\dfrac{8}{27}$.

14. (a) $\frac{3}{10}$, (b) $\frac{3}{10}$, (c) $\frac{3}{10}$, (d) $\frac{1}{5}$.

15. (a) $\frac{3}{20}$, (b) $\frac{11}{20}$.

16. $\frac{11!}{3!2!}$; (a) $\frac{2}{11}$, (b) $\frac{1}{77}$.

17. $\frac{15}{28}$.

18. (a) $\frac{1}{2}$, (b) $\frac{1}{4}$, (c) $\frac{1}{2}$.

19. (a) 0·204, (b) 0·052, (c) 0·398.

20. $\frac{21}{55}, \frac{27}{55}, \frac{27}{220}, \frac{1}{220}$.

21. (a) 0·108, (b) 0·374.

22. (a) $\frac{1}{42}$, (b) $\frac{1}{7}$, (c) $\frac{2}{3}$, (d) $\frac{1}{2}$.

Exercise 14.4 (pp. 326–327)

1. $\frac{1}{2}$.

2. 0·33.

3. $\frac{1}{12}$.

4. (i) (a) A and B, A and C, (b) A and B;

    (ii) (a) 0, (b) $\frac{3}{4}$, (c) $\frac{1}{4}$, (d) $\frac{1}{2}$, (e) $\frac{1}{4}$, (f) 1.

5. (i) (a) none, (b) A and C;

    (ii) (a) $\frac{1}{9}$, (b) 1, (c) $\frac{7}{36}$, (d) $\frac{5}{6}$, (e) 0, (f) $\frac{8}{9}$.

6. $0·6 \leqslant P(A') \leqslant 0·9$.

7. $\frac{1}{2}, \frac{1}{52}, \frac{3}{13}, 0, \frac{1}{52}, \frac{3}{26}$; A and C.

8. $\frac{1}{3}, \frac{1}{4}, \frac{1}{6}, \frac{1}{12}, \frac{1}{12}, \frac{1}{6}$; A and B.

9. (a) $\frac{3}{20}$, (b) $\frac{7}{10}$, (c) $\frac{1}{10}$, (d) $\frac{17}{20}$.

10. $\frac{5}{6}, \frac{2}{5}$.

11. $\frac{9}{10}, \frac{9}{10}$.

12. (a) $\frac{9}{40}$, (b) $\frac{1}{28}$.

13. (a) $\frac{1}{16}$, (b) $\frac{7}{16}$.

14. (a) $\frac{1}{27}$, (b) $\frac{1}{8}$, (c) $\frac{91}{216}$.

15. (a) $\frac{1}{36}$, (b) $\frac{1}{36}$, (c) $\frac{1}{2}$.

16. (a) $\frac{5}{9}$, (b) 0, (c) $\frac{20}{81}$.

17. 0·302.

18. (a) $\frac{1}{16}$, (b) $\frac{9}{64}$, (c) $\frac{1}{4}$, (d) $\frac{1}{16}$.

19. 0·590.

20. (a) $\dfrac{5}{32}$, (b) $\dfrac{5}{16}$, (c) $\dfrac{13}{16}$.

21. (a) $\dfrac{1}{64}$, (b) $\dfrac{2}{9}$, (c) $\dfrac{5}{36}$.

Exercise 14.5 (pp. 330–332)

1. $\dfrac{1}{4}, \dfrac{1}{4}, \dfrac{4}{7}$.

2. $\dfrac{1}{7}, \dfrac{1}{7}, \dfrac{1}{28}, \dfrac{1}{28}$.

3. $\dfrac{1}{4}, \dfrac{4}{7}, \dfrac{1}{4}, \dfrac{4}{7}$.

4. $\dfrac{1}{7}, \dfrac{3}{28}, \dfrac{3}{7}$.

5. $\dfrac{3}{14}, \dfrac{15}{28}, \dfrac{3}{14}$.

6. $\dfrac{2}{13}, \dfrac{1}{2}, \dfrac{1}{4}$.

7. $\dfrac{1}{2}, \dfrac{1}{4}, \dfrac{1}{13}, \dfrac{1}{26}$.

8. $0, 0, \dfrac{2}{3}, \dfrac{1}{2}$.

9. $0, \dfrac{1}{2}, \dfrac{1}{4}$.

10. $\dfrac{3}{26}, \dfrac{11}{26}, \dfrac{33}{52}$.

11. (a) $\dfrac{4}{81}$, (b) $\dfrac{1}{15}$.

12. (a) $\dfrac{27}{5000}$, (b) $\dfrac{1}{140}$.

13. $\dfrac{2}{3}$.

14. $\dfrac{3}{4}$.

15. $\dfrac{1}{5}$.

16. $\dfrac{7}{12}$.

17. (a) 0·7, (b) 0·6, (c) 0·75.

18. (a) $\dfrac{25}{72}$, (b) $\dfrac{19}{36}$.

19. (a) $\dfrac{18}{35}$, (b) $\dfrac{5}{12}$.

20. $\dfrac{1}{2}, \dfrac{1}{9}$.

Exercise 14.6 (pp. 332–336)

1. (a) 1260, (b) 8232.
2. 30 240; (a) 840, (b) 10 080, (c) 13 440.
3. 63.   4. 20.
5. 280, 36.   6. (a) 243, (b) 21.
7. $K \cap R = \{\text{squares}\}$; $K \cap P = \{\text{rhombuses}\}$.
8. (a) true, (b) false, (c) false, (d) false.

9. 1200.

10. (a) $\dfrac{1}{7}$, (b) $\dfrac{3}{35}$.

11. (a) (i) $\dfrac{5}{18}$, (ii) $\dfrac{1}{3}$, (b) $\dfrac{12}{35}$, (c) 294.

12. (i) $\dfrac{7}{20}$, (ii) $\dfrac{4}{13}$.

13. (a) $\dfrac{6}{77}$, (b) 0, (c) $\dfrac{2}{15}$, (d) $\dfrac{2}{33}$.

14. $\dfrac{1}{2}, \dfrac{1}{2}, \dfrac{1}{2}, \dfrac{1}{4}, \dfrac{1}{4}$.

15. (i) $\dfrac{5}{12}$, (ii) $\dfrac{8}{15}$, (iii) $\dfrac{1}{12}$.

16. $\dfrac{5}{8}$; (a) $\dfrac{55}{64}$, (b) $\dfrac{25\pi}{256}$. 17. $4 \cdot 12 \times 10^{-6}$.

18. (a) $\dfrac{1}{22}$, (b) $\dfrac{41}{55}$, (c) $\dfrac{3}{11}$, (d) $\dfrac{3}{44}$.

19. (a) $\dfrac{1}{3}, \dfrac{1}{2}$, (b) (i) $\dfrac{63}{64}$, (ii) $\dfrac{5}{16}$, (iii) $\dfrac{5}{72}$.

20. (a) $\dfrac{81}{256}$, (b) $\dfrac{1}{256}$, (c) $\dfrac{3}{128}$, (d) $\dfrac{3}{32}$.

21. (i) $0 \cdot 3$, (ii) $0 \cdot 3$, (iii) $0 \cdot 5$.

22. (a) $P(9) = \dfrac{25}{216}$, $P(10) = \dfrac{27}{216}$,

(b) P(at least one six) $= 1 - \left(\dfrac{5}{6}\right)^4 = 0 \cdot 518$;

P(at least one double six) $= 1 - \left(\dfrac{35}{36}\right)^{24} = 0 \cdot 491$.

(c) P(at least one six) $= 1 - \left(\dfrac{5}{6}\right)^6 = 0 \cdot 665$;

P(at least two sixes) $= 1 - \left(\dfrac{5}{6}\right)^{12} - 2\left(\dfrac{5}{6}\right)^{11} = 0 \cdot 619$.

23. (a) (i) $\dfrac{1}{4}$, (ii) $\dfrac{1}{4}$, (iii) $\dfrac{1}{17}$, (iv) $\dfrac{15}{34}$; (b) $\dfrac{13}{30}$;

(c) (i) $\dfrac{95}{253}$, (ii) $\dfrac{285}{506}$.

24. (a) $\dfrac{33}{16\,660}$, (b) $\dfrac{6}{4165}$; $\dfrac{11}{1081}$.

26. (a) $\dfrac{1}{221}$, (b) $\dfrac{32}{221}$, (c) $\dfrac{13}{17}$; $\dfrac{25}{33}$.

27. (a) (i) $\dfrac{3}{8}$, (ii) $\dfrac{1}{2}$, (iii) $\dfrac{1}{6}$; (b) $0 \cdot 14$.

28. (a) $0 \cdot 01$, (b) $0 \cdot 87$; (a) $0 \cdot 9606$, (b) $0 \cdot 0847$.

29. (a) $\dfrac{1}{36}$, (b) $\dfrac{5}{12}$; $\dfrac{73}{648}$, $\dfrac{25}{81}$.

30. (i) $\dfrac{2}{3}$, (ii) $\dfrac{1}{6}$, (iii) $\dfrac{5}{18}$, (iv) $\dfrac{1}{4}$, (v) $\dfrac{3}{5}$.

31. (i) $\dfrac{31}{120}$, (ii) $\dfrac{91}{240}$, (iii) 1; $\dfrac{2}{7}$.

32. (i) $P(A \cap B) = P(A) \cdot P(B)$. (ii) $P(A \cap C) = 0$; $\dfrac{13}{25}, \dfrac{1}{2}, \dfrac{9}{35}$; $\dfrac{3}{10}$.

33. (i) $0 \cdot 22$, (ii) $0 \cdot 30$, (iii) $0 \cdot 44$.

Exercise 15.1 (pp. 343–345)

5. (a) step diagram, (b) ogive.

6.   One possibility is 32·5, 37·5, 42·5, ..., 67·5, 72·5; 88%.
7.   9/14, excluding the 10 late entrants (possibly transfers from schools in other areas).

Exercise 15.2 (pp. 349–350)

1.   (a) 3, 3, $3\frac{1}{2}$.   (b) no mode, 24, 20,   (c) 20 and 21, 21, $20\frac{2}{3}$.
2.   (a) 3, 3, 5,   (b) no mode, 22, 20,   (c) 20, $20\frac{1}{2}$, $20\frac{3}{5}$.
3.   (a) 5, 5, 5,   (b) 5, $5\frac{1}{14}$, 5,   (c) 5, $5\frac{4}{7}$, $5\frac{1}{2}$.
4.   3, 3, 3·64.   5.   6·84.
6.   (i) $52·5 \leqslant x < 57·5$, $54\frac{3}{8}$, 55,   (ii) 56, 56, 54·175.
7.   (i) 4·96, 5·14,   (ii) 4·93, 4·95.
8.   26·6; (a) 27,   (b) 27·2,   (c) 27·1.

Exercise 15.3 (pp. 353–354)

1.   (a) 7; $5\frac{1}{2}$, $8\frac{1}{2}$; $1\frac{1}{2}$,   (b) 29; 27, 33; 3,   (c) 2; −4, 10; 7.
2.   (a) 7·25, 5·19, 2·28,   (b) 31, 71·8, 8·47,   (c) 3, 39·8, 6·31.
3.   (a) (i) 5, 6, (ii) 1;   (b) (i) 4·8, 5·7, (ii) 0·8;
      (c) (i) 5·3, 6·2, (ii) 0·8.
4.   6·31, 2·51.
5.   (i) (a) 5, 7, 9, (b) 4·9, 6·9, 8·8;   (ii) 2·45.
6.   (i) 49·5, 59·5,   (ii) 48·9, 60·3,   (iii) 49, 60.
7.   (i) 4 yrs 10 months, 5 yrs 1 month,   (ii) 46·5 months^2.
8.   I: 38−,   II: 28−37,   III: 19−27,   IV: 0−18.

Exercise 15.4 (p. 357)

1.   5·5, 6·25, 2·5; (a) 8·5, 6·25, 2·5,   (b) 22, 100, 10,
      (c) 4·55, 0·0625, 0·25.
2.   73·4°F, 9°F.   3.   5, 1·5, 1·22; 5·5, 1·5, 1·22.
4.   (i) 7·84,   (ii) 7·98.   5.   27·2, 9·69; 1·5, 9·2.
6.   Mathematics: $72\frac{1}{2}$, 77, $57\frac{1}{2}$; English: $60\frac{1}{2}$, $51\frac{1}{2}$, $87\frac{1}{2}$;
      Combined: 133, $128\frac{1}{2}$, 145.

Exercise 15.5 (pp. 358–361)

1.   86·6, 44·1; 188·1.   2.   6·5; 4·2, 9·0.
3.   (i) 57 min,   (ii) 71·5 min,   (iii) 32%.
4.   mean 55 kg, s.d. 3·2 kg.   5.   0, 1.
6.   (i) 100·7, 14·5,   (ii) 72.
7.   (b) 8·95, 9·95,   (c) 13·53,   (d) 13·55.
8.   (i) £28·87,   (ii) £54·04,   (iii) £30·47.
9.   52°, 7·5°; 53·2°, 10·7°.
10.   172·1 cm, 2·608 cm; 174·6 cm, 6·8 cm^2; 1·054 in^2.
11.   £49, £12·85.
12.   (a) 5, 3·6,   (b) 5·4, 5·04,   (c) $4·5 < \bar{x} < 5·0$,
      (d) $x_{10} \geqslant 8$ or $x_{10} \leqslant 2$.

13. (ii) 6·8299; 39·23, 6·6335.
14. (a) (i) 3·4, 2, (ii) 0·4, 0·276; (b) $3\frac{1}{3}$, 19·6%.

Exercise 16.1 (pp. 366–369)

1. 10.   2. $3\frac{1}{2}$.   3.   14; 20 p.   4.   (a) 1,   (b) 9/8.
5. $p(2) = 2/15$, $p(3) = 8/15$, $p(4) = 1/3$; 3·2.   6.   0·8 p loss.
7. $\frac{125}{216}, \frac{75}{216}, \frac{15}{216}, \frac{1}{216}$; 2 p loss.   8.   (a) £122.50,   (b) £112·672.
9. $p(x) = 1/6$, $x = 1, 2, 3, 4, 5$; $p(6) = 0$; $p(x) = 1/36$, $x = 7, 8, 9, 10, 11, 12$; $4\frac{1}{12}$; 6/17.
10. (i) 24/625,   (ii) 24/625,   (iii) 2.   11.   28·5, 721·05.   12.   2·53, 0·305.
13. $1\frac{1}{2}, \frac{3}{4}; \frac{1}{20}, \frac{9}{20}, \frac{9}{20}, \frac{1}{20}$; 60%.

14.

r	0	1	2	3	4
$P(Y = r)$	0·09	0·24	0·34	0·24	0·09

r	0	1	2	3	4
$P(Z = r)$	0·447	0·232	0·222	0·072	0·027

$E(Z) = 1$, $\text{Var}(Z) = 1·2$.

15. $4\frac{1}{3}, 2\frac{2}{9}; 8\frac{2}{3}, 8\frac{8}{9}$.   16. $\frac{1}{2}(n + 1)$, 0·42.
17. $2/n(n + 1)$; $\frac{1}{3}(2n + 1)$, $\frac{1}{18}(n - 1)(n + 2)$.
18. $x = 1, 2, 3, \ldots, 9$; $p(x) = \frac{9}{45}, \frac{8}{45}, \frac{7}{45}, \ldots, \frac{1}{45}; \frac{11}{3}, \frac{2}{3}\sqrt{11}$; 1;

$$x = 1, 2, 3, \ldots; p(x) = \frac{10 - x}{45}.$$

19. (a) $1 + 2x + 3x^2 + \ldots + rx^{r-1} + \ldots$,   (b) $p(1 - p)^{r-1}$; $1/p$.
20. (i) $\frac{1}{3}$,   (ii) $\frac{2}{9}$,   (iii) $\frac{16}{243}$; $\frac{32}{243}$; 50 p; $\frac{16}{81}$; 0·177.   21.   3/16.

Exercise 16.2 (pp. 373–376)

1. (a) 0·279,   (b) 0·457; 1·5, 1·25.   2.   (a) 0·250,   (b) 0·526; 2·5, 1·875.
3. 0·657; 7.   4.   (a) 0·393,   (b) 0·000 085 2; $n \geqslant 18$.
5. 24, 0·4; $(0·6 + 0·4t)^{24}$.
6. $(0·55 + 0·45t)^4$; (i) 4, (ii) $4(0·55)(0·45)^3$.   7.   0·228, 0·210.
8. 0·0464; 4, 2·4.

9. $\frac{4}{3}, \frac{356}{405}$;

No. of males	0	1	2	3	4
Expected no. of litters	160	320	240	80	10

10. 0·991, 0·977;

No. of ones	0	1	2	3	4	5	6
Expected no. of throws	335	402	201	54	8	1	0

11. (a) 0·315, (b) (i) 0·53, (ii) 5, 22, 37, 28, 8.   12. 26·4%, 62·4%.
13. (i) 0·201; (ii) (a) 0·0556, (b) 0·0367, (c) 0·6.
14. (i) 4·8, 0·98, (iii) 0·737, (iv) 0·388.
15. (a) $\frac{1}{27}$, (b) $\frac{2}{9}$, (c) $\frac{4}{9}$, (d) $\frac{8}{27}$, (e) 0·299, (f) 0·903, (g) 0·328.

16. (ii) 1/5.   17. $\dfrac{(n-r+1)p}{r(1-p)}$; (a) 8, (b) 2, 3.

18. (a) $\dfrac{135}{2048}$; (b) $\dfrac{459}{512}$; $\dbinom{n-1}{2}\left(\dfrac{1}{4}\right)^3\left(\dfrac{3}{4}\right)^{n-3}$; 8, 9.

19. (a) $(r+1)/2^{r+2}$, (b) 2, (c) 4.   20. $t/(6-5t)$; 6, 30.

Exercise 16.3 (pp. 381–384)

1. (a) 1/2, 1/12, (b) 3, 4/3, (c) $k/2, k^2/12$, (d) $(a+b)/2, (b-a)^2/12$.
2. 4/27; 9/5, 2, 3/5.   3. (a) 2·4, (b) 20; 1/3, 0·178.
4. (i) $-3/16$, (ii) 19/80, (iv) 2.   5. 4, 8/15, 11/225; 0·541.
6. 3/8, 0, 2/5; (i) 85/512, (ii) 85/152.   7. (i) 12, 1, (ii) 0·0523.
8. (i) 2/5, (ii) 13/5, (iii) 3/2.
9. 0·6; $F(x) = 0$ for $x \leqslant 0$, $F(x) = 4x^3 - 3x^4$ for $0 \leqslant x \leqslant 1$, $F(x) = 1$ for $x \geqslant 1$.
10. 28, 12, 6, 2, 1, 1.
11. (i) 2/3, (ii) 4/3, $(\sqrt{14})/6$, (iii) $F(x) = 0$ for $x \leqslant 0$, $F(x) = \frac{1}{2}x^2$ for $0 \leqslant x \leqslant 1$, $F(x) = \frac{1}{6}(-3 + 6x - x^2)$ for $1 \leqslant x \leqslant 3$, $F(x) = 1$ for $x \geqslant 3$, (iv) 13/24.
12. (iii) $F(x) = -\frac{1}{12}x^3$ for $x \leqslant -1$, $F(x) = \frac{1}{2} + \frac{1}{4}x - \frac{1}{12}x^3$ for $-1 \leqslant x \leqslant 1$, $F(x) = 1 - \frac{1}{12}x^3$ for $x \geqslant 1$, (iv) $E(X) = 0$, $\text{Var}(X) = 11/15$.
13. (ii) 1, 5/6, (iii) 1/4.
14. (i) $k = 2$, (ii) $f(x) = 2$ for $0 \leqslant x \leqslant 0·5, f(x) = 0$ otherwise, (iii) 0·25, (iv) 0·144.
15. (i) 3/32, (ii) 11/16, (iii) $f(x) = 3(4-x^2)/32$ for $-2 \leqslant x \leqslant 2$, $f(x) = 0$ otherwise, (iv) 0, 4/5.
16. $F(x) = 0$ for $x \leqslant 1$, $F(x) = \frac{1}{3}(x^2 - 1)$ for $1 \leqslant x \leqslant 2$, $F(x) = 1$ for $x \geqslant 2$; $G(y) = 0$ for $y \leqslant 1$, $G(y) = \frac{1}{3}(y^4 - 1)$ for $1 \leqslant y \leqslant \sqrt{2}$, $G(y) = 1$ for $y \geqslant \sqrt{2}$; $g(y) = 4y^3/3$ for $1 \leqslant y \leqslant \sqrt{2}$, $g(y) = 0$ otherwise.
17. $1/(2\sqrt{y})$; $(1/\sqrt{w}) - 1$.
18. $f(x) = 1/(b-a)$ for $a \leqslant x \leqslant b$, $f(x) = 0$ otherwise; $F(x) = 0$ for $x \leqslant a$, $F(x) = (x-a)/(b-a)$ for $a \leqslant x \leqslant b$, $F(x) = 1$ for $x \geqslant b$; $P(V \leqslant v) = 3 - 72/v$; (i) $f(v) = 72/v^2$, (ii) 0·4, (iii) 28·8 m.p.h.
19. (a) $a^2/18$, (b) $F(x) = 0$ for $x \leqslant a$, $F(x) = x^2/a^2$ for $0 \leqslant x \leqslant a$, $F(x) = 1$ for $x \geqslant a$, (c) (i) $1/(a+1)^2$, (ii) $2(1-y)$ for $0 \leqslant y \leqslant 1$, 0 otherwise.
20. $g(y) = 1$ for $0 \leqslant y \leqslant 1$, $g(y) = 0$ otherwise.

Exercise 16.4 (pp. 389–392)

1.   (a) 0·6179,   (b) 0·1151,   (c) 0·97725,   (d) 0·01287,   (e) 0·1760,   (f) 0·5558.
2.   (a) 0·9378,   (b) 0·1944,   (c) 0·9715,   (d) 0·02239,   (e) 0·2065,   (f) 0·2976.
3.   (a) 0·9554,   (b) 0·2119,   (c) 0·6612.
4.   (a) 0·3085,   (b) 0·5793,   (c) 0·0796.
5.   (a) 0·9487,   (b) 0·9750,   (c) 0·04412
6.   (a) 0·44,   (b) 0·583,   (c) −0·878.
7.   (a) 0·524,   (b) 2·326,   (c) 3·291.
8.   (a) 0·3%,   (b) 6·6%,   (c) 44%,   (d) 1·2%.
9.   11·51%, 81%, 7·49%; £6528.64.
10.   (i) 4·8%,   (ii) 97·7%; 1111·5 to 1188·5.
11.   (a) 37·82%,   (b) 125·5 hrs to 194·5 hrs,   (c) 0·405.
12.   (a) 4 men,   (b) 0·0446,   (c) 1·746 m.
13.   (a) 3, 62·3,   (b) 15, 9·24,   (c) 84·5, 111,   (d) 8·31, 1·74.
14.   0·0122, 0·0102.   15.   104, 38·8.
16.   (a) 0·205, 0·205,   (b) 0·120, 0·119,   (c) 0·0419, 0·0416,   (d) 0·190, 0·179,
    (e) 0·0985, 0·0932,   (f) 0·0493, 0·0474.
17.   0·0287.   18.   0·210.   19.   (i) 0·026,   (ii) 0·932,   (iii) 0·923.
20.   (a) 4320/15625;   (b) 7120/15625;   (a) 0·026,   (b) 0·853.
21.   (a) Negligible,   (b) negligible,   (c) 0·806.
22.   (i) 0·648,   (ii) 92·65%,   (iii) 0·654.

Exercise 16.5 (pp. 395–397)

1.   (a) 0·156,   (b) 0·663.   2.   (a) 0·353,   (b) 0·285.
3.   0·181; $e^{-0.02n}$; 5.   4.   0·337; 1536.

5.

r	0	1	2	3	4	5	6	7	8	9	10
(a)				0·001	0·005	0·015	0·037	0·074	0·120	0·160	0·176
(b)			0·002	0·008	0·019	0·038	0·063	0·090	0·113	0·125	0·125
(c)				0·001	0·005	0·015	0·037	0·073	0·119	0·160	0·177
(d)	0·001	0·002	0·005	0·011	0·021	0·036	0·057	0·080	0·103	0·120	0·126

r	11	12	13	14	15	16	17	18	19	20	21
(a)	0·160	0·120	0·074	0·037	0·015	0·005	0·001				
(b)	0·114	0·095	0·073	0·052	0·035	0·022	0·013	0·007	0·004	0·002	0·001
(c)	0·160	0·119	0·073	0·037	0·015	0·005	0·001				
(d)	0·120	0·103	0·080	0·057	0·036	0·021	0·011	0·005	0·002	0·001	

6.

r	0	1	2	3	4	5	6	7	8	9
(a)	0·122	0·270	0·285	0·190	0·090	0·032	0·009	0·002		
(b)	0·135	0·271	0·271	0·180	0·090	0·036	0·012	0·003	0·001	
(c)	0·132	0·223	0·291	0·223	0·101	0·027	0·004			
(d)	0·144	0·217	0·276	0·217	0·106	0·032	0·006	0·001		

7.

r	0	1	2	3	4	5	6	7	8	9
(a)	0·005	0·029	0·078	0·139	0·181	0·185	0·154	0·108	0·064	0·033
(b)	0·007	0·034	0·084	0·140	0·175	0·175	0·146	0·104	0·065	0·036
(c)	0·017	0·033	0·070	0·121	0·167	0·186	0·167	0·121	0·070	0·033
(d)	0·022	0·037	0·073	0·119	0·160	0·177	0·160	0·119	0·073	0·037

r	10	11	12	13
(a)	0·015	0·006	0·002	0·001
(b)	0·018	0·008	0·003	0·001
(c)	0·012	0·004	0·001	
(d)	0·015	0·005	0·001	

8.

r	0	1	2	3	4	5	6	7	8	9
(a)		0·002	0·009	0·025	0·054	0·090	0·123	0·144	0·146	0·129
(b)		0·003	0·011	0·029	0·057	0·092	0·122	0·140	0·140	0·124
(c)	0·003	0·005	0·013	0·027	0·050	0·080	0·112	0·137	0·146	0·137
(d)	0·004	0·007	0·015	0·030	0·052	0·080	0·110	0·132	0·140	0·132

r	10	11	12	13	14	15	16	17	18
(a)	0·102	0·073	0·047	0·028	0·015	0·007	0·003	0·001	0·001
(b)	0·099	0·072	0·048	0·030	0·017	0·009	0·005	0·002	0·001
(c)	0·112	0·080	0·050	0·027	0·013	0·005	0·002	0·001	
(d)	0·110	0·080	0·052	0·030	0·015	0·007	0·003	0·001	

9. (a) 0·368, (b) 0·456.   10. (a) 0·258, (b) 0·567.

11. (a) Poisson approximation: 0·442,
    (b) Poisson approximation: 0·353,
    (c) Normal approximation: 0·119.

14. (i) 0·19, (ii) 0·21, (iii) 0·012.

15. (a) (i) 1·04, (ii) 53, 55, 29, 10, 3; (b) 0·121.

16. 0·647, 0·185.   17. (i) 0·55, (ii) 0·18.

18. £266C, £415C.   19. 0·460; 33.

20. 0·323; 172 to 228.

Exercise 16.6 (pp. 403–407)

1. 3·6, 14·5, 0·35, 28, 5·95.   2. 0·4, 1, 2·2; 0·84, 1·2.

3. $1\frac{2}{3}, 3, 5\frac{4}{9}$; $20\frac{11}{15}, \frac{2}{9}$.

4. $\frac{1}{2}, \frac{3}{10}, \frac{24}{35}$; $-\frac{1}{5}, \frac{73}{2450} \approx 0·0298$.

5. (a) 6, 2·5, (b) 4, 6, (c) 27, 40, (d) −3, 24,
   (e) 10, 8·5, (f) 2, 8·5, (g) 14, 28·5, (h) 24, 64.

6. (a) 31, 234, (b) 109, 50, 159.   7. 30 g, 0·3 g.   8. 200 g, 6·71 g.

9. (a) 2·1, 0·49; 0·8, 0·36, (b) no; independent,

(c)

xy	0	1	2	3	4	6
$p(xy)$	0·3	0·12	0·32	0·18	0·05	0·03

; yes,

(d)

x + y	1	2	3	4	5
$p(x + y)$	0·06	0·27	0·41	0·23	0·03

; yes.

10. (i) (a) 1·2, 0·56; 1·7, 0·81,   (b) all values; not independent,

(c)

xy	0	1	2	3	4	6
$p(xy)$	0·27	0	0·45	0·1	0·1	0·08

; no,

(d)

x + y	0	1	2	3	4	5
$p(x + y)$	0·03	0·15	0·07	0·47	0·2	0·08

; no.

(ii) (a) 1, 0·6; 2, 0·6,   (b) all values, not independent,

(c)

xy	0	1	2	3	4	6
$p(xy)$	0·3	0·2	0·05	0·2	0·2	0·05

; yes,

(d)

x + y	1	2	3	4	5
$p(x + y)$	0·05	0·4	0·1	0·4	0·05

; yes.

11. 1, 2, 4, 8.   12. £3.33.

13. $\frac{1}{210}, \frac{4}{35}, \frac{3}{7}, \frac{8}{21}, \frac{1}{14}$; 2·4, 0·8; 1·6, 0·8; 4, 1·13.

14. (i) 0·9, 1·2,

(ii)

z	−2	−1	0	1	2	3	4
$p(z)$	0·1	0·1	0·3	0·2	0·2	0·1	0

,

(iii) 0·2.

15. (i) 0·011, (ii) 0·036, (iii) 0·27.   16. 0·12 mm, 0·0583 mm; 1·98%

17. (a) 0·673, (b) 0·138.   18. (i) 0·089, (ii) 0·661.

19. (i) 0·841, (ii) 0·500, (iii) 0·421; 0·994.

20. (i) 0·823, (ii) 0·059; 1/4, 1/6.   21. $\frac{1}{2}r\pi, \frac{1}{2}r\pi$; $4r/\pi$; 1/3.

22. (i) $\mu_x^2 + \sigma_x^2$;   (ii) $\mu_x\mu_y$; $\mu_x^2\sigma_y^2 + \mu_y^2\sigma_x^2 + \sigma_x^2\sigma_y^2$;   (iii) $\mu_y(\mu_x^2 + \sigma_x^2)$.

23. $\dfrac{\lambda^r\mu^{n-r}}{r!(n-r)!} e^{-(\lambda+\mu)}$; $\displaystyle\sum_{r=0}^{n} \dfrac{\lambda^r\mu^{n-r}}{r!(n-r)!} e^{-(\lambda+\mu)}$.   24. 0·121.

25.   (b) $(1 - p + pt)^m, (1 - p + pt)^n; (1 - p + pt)^{m+n}$.

Exercise 16.7 (pp. 407–414)

1. $(n + 1)/2, (n^2 - 1)/12; 1/2$; (a) 2/105, (b) 16.

2. £16.   3.   (a) 0·323,   (b) £1$\frac{32}{65}$ ≈ £1.49.
4. 1/15; 2/3, 34/45; 1/75; 4/3, 68/45.

5. (i) $P(N = r) = \dfrac{1}{k}(1 \leqslant r \leqslant k), E(N) = \frac{1}{2}(k + 1),$

   (ii) $P(N = r) = \dfrac{1}{k}\left(\dfrac{k-1}{k}\right)^{r-1} (r \geqslant 1), E(N) = k;$ first strategy.

6. (i) 1/5,   (ii) 8/9,   (iii) 10,   (iv) 8.   7.   0·0512.
8. (i) 0·168,   (ii) 0·360,   (iii) 0·309,   (iv) 0·132,   (v) 0·028,
    (vi) 0·002; 0·947.

9.

No. of defectives	0	1	2	3	4	5	6
Expected frequency	16	42	45	26	8	1	0

10. $\dfrac{1}{p}, \dfrac{1-p}{p^2}; \dfrac{2t^2}{(5-3t)(5-4t)}; \frac{194}{625} = 0.3104.$

11. (i) 2,   (ii) 1$\frac{1}{2}$,   (iii) 1$\frac{5}{12}$,
    (iv) $F(x) = 0$ for $x \leqslant 0$, $F(x) = x - \frac{1}{2}x^2$ for $0 \leqslant x \leqslant 1$, $F(x) = \frac{1}{2}$ for $1 \leqslant x \leqslant 2$,
       $F(x) = \frac{1}{2}x^2 - 2x + \frac{5}{2}$ for $2 \leqslant x \leqslant 3$, $F(x) = 1$ for $x \geqslant 3$,   (v) $\frac{3}{4}$.
12. (ii) $\sqrt{(3/5)}$.   13. 1, 1/6; 3/4; 5/6.
14. (a) 3/250, 6$\frac{7}{8}$, (b) (1) £3.20, (ii) 0·792.
15. (i)   1/2, −1/4,   (ii) 7/16,
    (iii) $f(x) = \frac{1}{2}x$ for $0 \leqslant x \leqslant 1$, $f(x) = \frac{1}{2}$ for $1 \leqslant x \leqslant 2$,
       $f(x) = \frac{3}{2} - \frac{1}{2}x$ for $2 \leqslant x \leqslant 3$, $f(x) = 0$ otherwise; 3/2; 5/12.

16. (a) $1 - e^{-\lambda x}$,   (b) $\dfrac{1}{\lambda}, \dfrac{1}{\lambda^2}$,   (c) $\dfrac{1}{\lambda}\ln 2$ (d) $\dfrac{1}{\lambda}\ln\left(\dfrac{20}{19}\right)$.

17. (i) 0·202,   (ii) 0·410.
18. (i) 0·880,   (ii) 9·69, 0·2339,   (iii) 0·180.
19. £9360, 19·6%; (a) £20 000, £9360; (b) £19 800, £10 296.
20. (i) 0·60,   (ii) 0·20,   (iii) 0·95,   (iv) 0·50.
21. (i) 0·227,   (ii) 54·7,   (iii) 78·7 cm^2,   (iv) 0·579.
22. 1·514 mm, 0·051 mm; 3·028 mm, 0·072 mm; 0·895; 3·214 mm.
23. (i) 0·345,   (ii) 0·692; 0·0033; 0·304.

24. (a) (i) 0·5, (ii)

No. of accidents	0	1	2	3	4	5
Expected no. of days	121	61	15	3	0	0

   (b) Binomial model: 0·932, Poisson approximation: 0·929.
25. (i) 9,   (ii) 26,   (iii) 43; 8.
26. (a) (i) 0·0581, (ii) 0·0519;   (b) (0·96)^n, 74;   (c) 0·955.
27. (i) 0·135,   (ii) 0·271,   (iii) 0·0290,   (iv) 2,   (v) 8·19.
28. (i) 0·419,   (ii) 0·676.
29. (a) (i) 0·0952, (ii) 0·0905;   (b) 0·853;   (c) 0·632; 63·2, 4·82.
30. 1/12; 0, n/12; 16.   31. (b) 2·2.

32. (i) $F(x) = 0$ for $x \leqslant 1$, $F(x) = 1 - x^{-3}$ for $x \geqslant 1$;
     (ii) 3/2, 3/4; p.d.f. of Y: $g(y) = 3y^2$ for $0 \leqslant y \leqslant 1$, $g(y) = 0$ otherwise.

33. (ii) 8/15,
     (iii) $F(x) = 0$ for $x \leqslant 0$, $F(x) = x^2(2 - x^2)$ for $0 \leqslant x \leqslant 1$, $F(x) = 1$ for $x \geqslant 1$;
     (iv) $g(y) = 8y^3(1 - y^4)$ for $0 \leqslant y \leqslant 1$, $g(y) = 0$ otherwise.

34. (a) (i) 5/2, (ii) 7,
         (iii) $F(x) = 0$ for $x \leqslant 1$, $F(x) = \frac{1}{3}(x^2 - 1)$ for $1 \leqslant x \leqslant 2$, $F(x) = 1$ for $x \geqslant 2$;
     (b) (i) 5/2, 3/4, (ii) interval from 1 to 4.

Index